9.90

Evaluation Guide for *Focus on Physical Science*

FOCUS ON PHYSICAL SCIENCE is a textbook that discusses the most modern principles and concepts of physical science. Recent developments and basic ideas in physical science are explained in a vocabulary suited to the abilities of the student. To strengthen the presentation of the textual material with the intent of increasing, foremost, the students' understanding and also their interest in physical science, the authors and editors have included many special features.

To examine examples of the format and the features of FOCUS ON PHYSICAL SCIENCE, please turn to the following pages:

(pp. xvi-1)	A two-page **unit photograph** in color provides a visual introduction to each of the six units.
(p. 20)	A half-page **color photograph**, a **brief paragraph**, and a **goal statement** introduce each chapter.
(pp. 47-48)	**Activities** immediately reinforce scientific principles. Laboratory materials are inexpensive and readily available. Activity segments are effective without being overwhelming. **Drawings** accompany many of the activities to help the student in preparing laboratory materials.
(pp. 121-122)	**Tables** may be read by holding the text in the natural reading position. They appear in the text where they are relevant to the material being presented.
(pp. 138-139)	Important **questions** printed in the margins are useful in guiding students' thinking while reading and reviewing.
(pp. 208-210)	Clearly labeled **line drawings** help students to understand principles of physical science and their applications.
(pp. 256-259)	**Photographs, maps, diagrams,** and **graphs,** most in full color, help students visualize ideas presented in the accompanying text.
(pp. 315-316)	**New terms** are presented in boldface or italic type, defined after their first appearance, and often spelled phonetically.
(pp. 319, 343, 367)	**FOCUS PAGES, People • Careers • Frontiers,** present new developments in physical science and current information on career possibilities in physical science. These are newspaperlike pages with two or three articles per page. Eighteen of these pages are placed throughout the text.
(pp. 371-372)	Meaningful **captions** help students to read with understanding.
(pp. 390, 443)	**Problems** are presented within the context of the material to encourage students to observe, gather data, and search for cause and effect relationships.
(pp. 475-479)	A summary of **main ideas,** a variety of **questions,** suggestions for **interesting reading,** and further **investigations** appear at the end of each chapter.
(pp. 482-487)	**Appendices.**
(pp. 490-499)	**Glossary** with pronunciation key on each page.
(pp. 502-508)	**Index.**

FOCUS ON Physical Science

TEACHER'S ANNOTATED EDITION

Charles H. Heimler
California State University
Northridge, California

Jack Price
San Diego City Schools
San Diego, California

Charles E. Merrill Publishing Co.
A Bell & Howell Company
Columbus, Ohio
Toronto London Sydney

ISBN 0-675-06721-9

Published by
Charles E. Merrill Publishing Co.
A Bell & Howell Company
Columbus, Ohio 43216

Copyright © 1977, 1974, 1969 by BELL & HOWELL
All rights reserved. No part of this book may be reproduced in any form, electronic or mechanical, including photocopy, recording, or any information storage or retrieval system, without permission in writing from the publisher.

Printed in the United States.

Contents

Introduction 5T
Planning the Course 8T
Activity Planning Guide 9T
Adaptability to Differences in
    Student Performance Abilities 13T
Evaluation, Activity-Centered,
    and Laboratory Programs 14T
Careers Related to Physical Science 14T
Performance Objectives 15T
Laboratory Equipment 24T
Preparation of Solutions 27T
Teaching Aids 28T

Unit One 31T

    Chapter 1 . . . . 31T
    Chapter 2 . . . . 33T
    Chapter 3 . . . . 37T
    Chapter 4 . . . . 40T

Unit Two 43T

    Chapter 1 . . . . 43T
    Chapter 2 . . . . 45T
    Chapter 3 . . . . 48T

Unit Three 53T

    Chapter 1 . . . . 53T
    Chapter 2 . . . . 56T
    Chapter 3 . . . . 60T

Unit Four..65T
    Chapter 1.......................................65T
    Chapter 2.......................................69T
    Chapter 3.......................................72T

Unit Five..75T
    Chapter 1.......................................75T
    Chapter 2.......................................77T
    Chapter 3.......................................79T
    Chapter 4.......................................82T

Unit Six...85T
    Chapter 1.......................................85T
    Chapter 2.......................................87T
    Chapter 3.......................................89T
    Chapter 4.......................................91T

Introduction

Text Design

Focus on Physical Science, Third Edition, is designed in six units or modules which are divided into 21 chapters. Each chapter is divided into numbered sections. The units organize the text into major areas of study, and the chapters and sections subdivide the units into specific topics for study. These divisions and subdivisions aid the teacher in planning lessons and in assigning classwork and homework. In addition, they provide for flexibility and adaptation to local school and individual classroom needs. The organization of the text makes it particularly useful in situations where individualized instruction, flexible scheduling, and modules of instruction are employed.

Focus on Physical Science is a readable, enjoyable text. The reading level is low and the interest level is high. Other features include

- A color photo and thought-provoking paragraph at the beginning of each chapter relate the chapter to the student's world.
- A goal statement at the beginning of each chapter lets the student know what he or she can expect to learn from the chapter.
- Questions within each chapter serve as a preview of the chapter or a review of the sections just read.
- Single-text column allows for reading ease.
- Photos, illustrations, tables, graphs, activities and special career pages extend the student's understanding of text material.

Chapter-end materials include a summary, *Main Ideas*; a list of new words, *Vocabulary*; chapter-end questions, *Study Questions*; suggestions for deeper study, *Investigations*; and sources for further reading, *Suggested Readings*. *Appendices* include a table of measurement and temperature units, a table of international atomic masses, and a table of valences. A *Glossary* at the back of the book aids student comprehension by providing a brief definition and a pronunciation guide for boldfaced and italicized words.

Module Design

Each of the six units is also available as a separate, soft-cover module. Each of these modules has its own table of contents, glossary, and index. To facilitate use of the teacher's annotated edition with the modules, special page references and annotations are provided in the teacher's edition. In the solutions manual, the text page reference is followed immediately by the corresponding module page reference in parentheses. The module page number is followed by the letter M. Also, the student text has both consecutive page numbers and module page numbers.

Basic Themes

Several unifying themes pervade *Focus on Physical Science*. These themes serve as a conceptual framework for the physical science content.

1. Studies of physical phenomena lead to knowledge about the physical laws of the universe. Observation and experimentation are the bases of the scientific reasoning which leads to logical conclusions.
2. Physical science is a study of the classification, structure, patterns, and changes in matter, and the relationship between matter and energy. Physical laws explain the relationship between matter and energy.
3. All matter has definite structure. Elements have predictable physical and chemical properties related to their atomic structure.
4. Some changes in matter are related to physical and chemical properties. The major phases and the changes in phase of matter are directly related to temperature and pressure variables.
5. Force, work, and motion are related to the physical laws which govern the universe.
6. Properties of matter are affected by the gain or loss of heat, the kinetic energy of molecules.
7. Many technological developments utilize the wave properties of heat, light, and sound.
8. The effective use of electrical and nuclear energy is directly linked to human resourcefulness.

Also pervading the text are examples of the methods of science. Important topics are treated historically and logically. Classic experiments leading to the development of major principles are discussed and analyzed in chronological fashion. In this way, the student learns to appreciate the manner in which a scientist accumulates and organizes knowledge about the world.

Chapter Opening Material

Each chapter opens with a photograph representing the general theme of the chapter. The photograph is accompanied by a short, thought-provoking paragraph designed to stimulate student interest in the material to be presented and also to increase student awareness of interrelationships in the total environment as well as of his or her own role in it. In the margin at the beginning of each chapter is a statement of goals. This statement gives the overall purpose for studying the chapter.

Problems and Activities

Problems are inserted as a quick test of understanding of new concepts. Each student should solve each problem on an individual basis. Solutions should be demonstrated and discussed. This will clarify concepts and guard against vague acceptance of statements without definite application of new ideas.

Activities are designed to emphasize and clarify new concepts and to teach laboratory techniques. Many activities are open-ended. They provide for the use and development of problem-solving skills. Other activities reinforce or supplement already learned concepts. Experiments provide opportunities to use *controls* within a laboratory experience.

Activities are presented where they apply rather than in a separate laboratory manual. Materials required are inexpensive and readily available. Lists of necessary equipment for individual chapters precede the discussion of each chapter in this Teacher's Guide. A complete list of equipment needed for all activities in the book appears on pp. 24T-27T.

The **Activity Planning Guide,** pp. 9T-13T, provides useful information on how to use each activity. Activities essential to an understanding of physical science are listed under "Necessary." The methods for using each activity are suggested in the remaining columns. The columns "By All Students" and "By Small Group" indicate whether students should perform activities individually or in small groups. The few activities especially suited to demonstrations should be done by an able student unless otherwise directed in the chart.

Students should be shown how to record activities and demonstrations in their notebooks. One method of recording is to organize the activity under these headings: Problem, Procedure, Observations, Conclusions. When the activity is carried out by the teacher or a few students at the lecture-demonstration table, you may wish to develop a statement of the problem through class discussion. The procedure for the activity may be stated for the students, allowing them to record their own observations and conclusions.

Emphasis should be placed on student participation and involvement. Although laboratory situations are desirable, they are not mandatory. Most of the activities can be done in the classroom. Each activity teaches an important concept without elaborate equipment. The laboratory segments are effective without being overwhelming or time-consuming.

Safety

Demonstrate general safety procedures for laboratory work at the beginning of each semester. These procedures should be reviewed at frequent intervals. Familiarize yourself and your students with emergency and first aid procedures. Post fire drill regulations and a chart of emergency procedures in a prominent place in the classroom.

Require that all students wear safety glasses when conducting activities and experiments. Demonstrate the parts and proper use of the Bunsen burner, as well as other laboratory equipment.

Specific safety precautions necessary for individual activities are given in the activity itself and in teacher annotations. Note these precautions and explain them to the students. Student laboratory work must always be supervised. Encourage students to develop serious attitudes toward laboratory methods.

In addition to these general procedures of safety, a list of safety regulations should be given to each student. The following list provides some of the necessary rules of laboratory safety.

Safety Regulations for Science Students
1. Perform *only* those laboratory experiments and activities for which you have received instructions and permission.
2. Be familiar with the locations of the fire extinguishers, fire blanket, and fire alarm box. Be able to operate them correctly should an emergency requiring their use arise.

3. All persons performing and observing science activities must wear approved eye-protective goggles.
4. Never carry hot equipment or dangerous chemicals near other people.
5. Report any personal injury that occurs in the classroom to the teacher *at once*.
6. Only teachers and laboratory assistants shall have access to the stockroom.
7. Long sleeves should be rolled up above the wrist. Coats and sweaters should be removed. Long hair should be confined during an activity, especially when an open flame is nearby.
8. When using chemicals, keep your hands away from your face, eyes, and body. Wash hands thoroughly at the conclusion of a laboratory activity.
9. When heating test tubes, do not look down into the tube while heating it, or point it in the direction of another person.
10. When collecting gas by water displacement, remove the delivery tube from the generating flask prior to removing the heat so that water will not be forced back into the system.
11. Always provide a towel to cover any apparatus used to generate gases.
12. Always test for odor of chemicals by wafting your hand over the container and sniffing cautiously.
13. Never taste chemicals or drink from a beaker.
14. To cut small diameter tubing, use a file or tubing cutter to make a deep scratch. Then wrap the tubing in a paper towel before bending the glass away from your thumbs. Fire polish all ends using a wing tip on a Bunsen burner.
15. When bending glass, allow time for the glass to cool before handling.
16. Never pour reagents back into bottles, exchange bottle stoppers, or lay stoppers on the table.
17. Put all solid waste in receptacles provided by your teacher.
18. When diluting acids, *always pour acids into water,* never the reverse. Combine the liquids slowly while stirring the mixture.
19. Handle squeeze bottles and medicine droppers with extreme care to prevent squirting or spilling.
20. In removing an electrical plug from its socket, pull the plug, not the electrical cord.
21. Notify your teacher when you recognize hazardous conditions or materials in the classroom.

Figures and Tables

Photographs, drawings, graphs, and tables aid in clarifying scientific principles and concepts. Many activities are accompanied by an illustration of the procedure and equipment to be employed. Photographs and drawings help the student to visualize scientific principles and concepts and show practical applications of scientific principles. You may wish to review and analyze a photograph and its caption as a means of introducing a new topic or stimulating class discussion. Graphs and tables show how data is organized in a meaningful way.

Vocabulary

Scientific words and terms appear in either boldface type or italic type where they are defined. Phonetic pronunciations of new scientific words appear directly after the words are introduced. Many definitions and pronunciations are repeated in the *Glossary*.

Questions in the Margins

Questions in the margins near the related text material assist the student by identifying the major principles and concepts, and by serving as a guide to reading and study. In assigning a section for study, you may wish to read these questions to the class or have students read them silently in order to clarify the nature and purpose of the assignment. Questions in the margins provide motivation as well as an opportunity for students to check their learning as they proceed through the assignment. Questions and problems in a given section make excellent written assignments. Oral review of the questions following each assignment makes an excellent summary and helps you to identify points which may require additional explanation.

Mathematics

Selected mathematics concepts from the junior high school curriculum are integrated into the text. This integration provides meaningful illustrations of practical applications of mathematics in science. It also makes mathematics more relevant and interesting for the student. Also, the use of selected mathematics concepts in science reinforces learning.

Calculations for working each kind of physical science problem are presented in step-by-step detail. To provide for individual differences, the problems following each explanation vary in difficulty. You may choose to use only easy problems with students who have less skill in mathematics.

All problems dealing with chemical composition and chemical change involve the concept of ratio or proportion. This topic is covered in the upper elementary and junior high school mathematics curriculum. In teaching quantitative chemical concepts, you may wish to review ratio and proportion. Point out to students the frequency with which this type of calculation is used in chemical change problems.

Chapter-End Material

The five sections at the end of each chapter are *Main Ideas, Vocabulary, Study Questions, Investigations,* and *Interesting Reading.* *Main Ideas* summarize major principles and concepts and serve as a quick review of material presented in the chapter. Discussion of the *Main Ideas* in class provides a good chapter summary. Ask the students to identify two or three examples or illustrations for each principle or concept listed under *Main Ideas*. Use the *Vocabulary* to emphasize concepts and to review students' use of new words. Use the *Study Questions* at the end of the chapter for student self-study, review, or testing. Correction of wrong answers to the *Study Questions* is an effective learning technique.

Inclusion of science investigations and supplementary reading lists gives an "open-ended" aspect to the material in each chapter and further enhances the flexibility of *Focus on Physical Science*. *Investigations* which extend beyond the textbook presentations encourage the able student to develop his knowledge and interest in science. Particular *Investigations* are valuable as projects for science fairs. Supplementary books correlated with topics in the text are listed under *Interesting Reading*. These supplementary readings offer opportunities for students having special interests to find suitable references in science topics. The lists are excellent guides for the purchase of science books for the school library.

Careers • People • Frontiers

Focus on Physical Science features eighteen newspaperlike pages scattered throughout the text. These pages feature articles and photographs on current physical science topics. Each page has two or three articles related to careers, people, or frontiers. Career articles introduce students to various physical science related career opportunities. People articles describe the work of specific persons involved in physical science related activities. They add interest to physical science and give additional information about careers. Frontier articles describe recent developments and illustrate the relevance of physical science to the student. The general subject matter of each page is related to the content of the chapter in which the page is located.

Planning the Course

Focus on Physical Science may be used in a full-year course of two semesters covering the text material, activities and experiments, problems, and chapter-end material. Through the selection of specific units or modules, chapters, and sections which conform to the local course of study, this text may also be used in a one-semester physical science course.

Focus on Physical Science lends itself to a variety of teaching methods—activity-centered, demonstration, group reading of text material, lecture, reporting on an activity or experiment, class discussion of a science current event, reviewing a homework assignment, viewing a film or filmstrip. Different methods serve to reinforce each other and, thereby, may increase student achievement.

Focus on Physical Science is a one-year course in the fundamentals of physical science. However, the text is designed so that the material may be delimited to meet the needs of individual teachers and classes. Some examples are given below.

Two-Semester, One-Year Course in Physical Science

Semester I: Units One through Three
Semester II: Units Four through Six

One-Semester Course in Physical Science

Unit	Chapter	Sections	Title
One	1	all	Physical Science
	2	all	Force and Work
	3	all	Moving Bodies
Two	1	all	Classification of Matter
	2	all	Atoms and Compounds
Three	1	all	Periodic Table
Four	2	2:1-2:6	Chemical Reactions
Five	1	1:1-1:3	Heat Energy
	3	3:1-3:3	Waves
	4	4:1-4:4	Optics
Six	1	all	Electricity

Three-Quarter, One-Year Course in Physical Science

Quarter 1: Units One and Two
Quarter 2: Units Three and Four
Quarter 3: Units Five and Six
These Quarter courses may be used in any order.

Activity Planning Guide

The following table is designed to show which activities are most essential to an understanding of physical science. The column headed "Necessary" indicates that these activities are recommended for all students. Those activities which have been starred suggest that teacher supervision is especially advisable. The next two columns indicate whether these activities should be undertaken by each student or by students in small groups.

The column headed "Optional/Independent" lists activities suitable for advanced or supplemental study. Those activities suitable only for demonstration are listed under "Demonstration." After careful analysis of the demonstration activities, you may wish to conduct an activity either as a teacher demonstration or a student-teacher demonstration. The last two columns, "Written Report" and "Class Discussion," suggest the needed follow-up.

Unit/Chapter/Page	Necessary	By All Students	By Small Group	Optional/Independent	Demonstration	Written Report	Class Discussion
Unit One, Chapter 1							
p. 4	X	X					X
p. 8	X	X					X
p. 10	X	X				X	
p. 11	X		X			X	
p. 13	X	X				X	
p. 14	X	X					X
p. 15 *			X or	X		X	
Unit One, Chapter 2							
p. 26	X	X					X
p. 27	X	X				X	
p. 28			X			X	
p. 31 *	X	X or					X
p. 33	X	X	X			X	
p. 40 *			X or	X			X
Unit One, Chapter 3							
p. 47 *	X	X					X
p. 48 *	X		X			X	
p. 54	X		X			X	
p. 66					X		X
Unit One, Chapter 4							
p. 73	X	X					X

* Teacher supervision advisable

Unit/Chapter/Page	Necessary	By All Students	By Small Group	Optional/Independent	Demonstration	Written Report	Class Discussion
p. 73	X	X				X	
p. 74	X	X					X
p. 78	X	X					X
p. 78	X						X
p. 80	X		X			X	
p. 81 *			X or	X		X	
p. 85				X		X	
p. 86	X	X					X
p. 88	X						X
p. 88	X		X				X
p. 88 *				X		X	
Unit Two, Chapter 1							
p. 99 (3M) *	X	X					X
p. 102 (6M) *	X	X					
p. 103 (7M) *			X or	X		X	
p. 103 (7M) *	X	X					X
p. 105 (9M) *	X	X				X	
p. 105 (9M)	X	X				X	
p. 106 (10M) *	X	X				X	
p. 111 (15M) *	X	X					X
p. 111 (15M) *			X or	X or	X		X
p. 112 (16M) *			X or	X			
p. 113 (17M) *	X	X				X	
p. 114 (18M) *				X		X	
Unit Two, Chapter 2							
p. 122 (26M)	X	X					X
p. 123 (27M)	X	X					X
p. 131 (35M)					X	X	
Unit Two, Chapter 3							
p. 137 (41M)	X	X				X	
p. 138 (42M)	X	X				X	
p. 138 (42M)	X	X				X	
p. 140 (44M)	X	X					
p. 140 (44M)	X	X					X
p. 141 (45M) *					X		X
p. 143 (47M)			X or	X		X	
p. 143 (47M)	X	X					X
p. 144 (48M)				X		X	
p. 146 (50M) *	X	X					X
p. 147 (51M)	X	X				X	
p. 147 (51M)	X	X				X	
p. 150 (54M)					X		X
p. 152 (56M)	X	X				X	
p. 152 (56M)	X	X				X	
p. 154 (58M) *			X or	X or	X		
Unit Three, Chapter 1							
p. 163 (3M)	X	X					X
p. 164 (4M) *	X	X				X	
p. 175 (15M)	X	X			X	X	

* Teacher supervision advisable

Unit/Chapter/Page	Necessary	By All Students	By Small Group	Optional/ Independent	Demonstration	Written Report	Class Discussion
Unit Three, Chapter 2							
p. 184 (24M)	X	X				X	
p. 184 (24M)			X or	X			
p. 186 (26M)	X	X				X	
p. 187 (27M) *			X or	X or	X	X	
p. 189 (29M) *			X or	X		X	
p. 193 (33M) *			X or	X or	X	X	
p. 198 (38M) *	X	X				X	
Unit Three, Chapter 3							
p. 211 (51M)	X	X					
p. 212 (52M) *			X or	X	X	X	
p. 213 (53M)	X	X					
p. 214 (54M)	X	X				X	
p. 217 (57M) *			X or	X	X	X	
p. 218 (58M) *	X	X				X	X
Unit Four, Chapter 1							
p. 227 (3M)	X	X				X	
p. 228 (4M)	X	X				X	
p. 229 (5M) *			X or	X or	X	X	
p. 231 (7M)	X	X					X
p. 233 (9M)	X	X					X
p. 236 (12M) *			X or	X or	X	X	X
p. 238 (14M)	X	X				X	X
p. 239 (15M)			X or	X		X	
p. 240 (16M) *			X or	X or	X		X
p. 241 (17M) *	X	X					X
p. 242 (18M)	X	X				X	
p. 243 (19M) *			X or	X		X	
p. 243 (19M)			X or	X or	X	X	
p. 244 (20M)	X	X				X	X
p. 245 (21M)	X	X				X	X
Unit Four, Chapter 2							
p. 251 (27M) *	X	X				X	
p. 251 (27M) *			X or	X		X	
p. 255 (31M) *			X or	X or	X	X	
p. 256 (32M) *	X	X				X	X
p. 258 (34M) *	X	X				X	X
p. 260 (36M) *			X or	X or	X	X	X
p. 261 (37M) *			X	or	X	X	X
p. 262 (38M) *			X	or	X	X	X
Unit Four, Chapter 3							
p. 272 (48M) *	X	X				X	X
p. 274 (50M) *	X	X				X	X
p. 275 (51M)	X	X				X	X
p. 276 (52M)	X	X				X	X
p. 277 (53M)			X or	X		X	
p. 280 (56M)	X	X				X	
p. 282 (58M) *	X	X					X
Unit Five, Chapter 1							
p. 291 (3M)	X	X					X

* Teacher supervision advisable

Unit/Chapter/Page	Necessary	By All Students	By Small Group	Optional/Independent	Demonstration	Written Report	Class Discussion
p. 292 (4M)	X	X					X
p. 293 (5M)	X	X					X
p. 293 (5M)	X	X				X	
p. 294 (6M)			X or	X		X	
p. 295 (7M)	X	X				X	
p. 296 (8M)	X	X				X	
p. 297 (9M)				X or	X	X	X
p. 298 (10M)			X or	X or	X		X
p. 301 (13M)	X	X					X
p. 301 (13M)	X	X				X	
p. 303 (15M) *			X		X		X
p. 305 (17M) *			X or	X or	X	X	
Unit Five, Chapter 2							
p. 311 (23M)	X	X				X	
p. 312 (24M)	X	X				X	
p. 315 (27M)		X	X or	X or	X		X
p. 317 (29M)				X		X	
p. 317 (29M)	X	X				X	
p. 318 (30M)	X	X				X	
p. 320 (32M) *	X	X					X
Unit Five, Chapter 3							
p. 333 (45M)	X	X					X
p. 335 (47M)	X	X					X
p. 336 (48M)	X	X or	X			X	
p. 338 (50M)	X	X or	X				X
p. 338 (50M)			X	or	X		X
p. 340 (52M)			X or	X or	X		X
p. 341 (53M)	X	X					X
p. 342 (54M)	X	X or	X			X	
p. 344 (56M)			X or	X or	X	X	
p. 347 (59M)	X	X					X
p. 347 (59M)	X	X	X	or	X		X
p. 348 (60M)	X				X		X
p. 350 (62M)	X				X		X
Unit Five, Chapter 4							
p. 360 (72M)	X		X				X
p. 361 (73M) *	X		X	or	X		
p. 362 (74M) *	X		X	or	X		
p. 363 (75M)	X	X					X
p. 365 (77M)			X or	X or	X		
p. 366 (78M)			X or	X or	X	X or	X
p. 368 (80M)				X or	X		
p. 373 (85M)	X				X		
p. 376 (88M)	X	X					X
p. 379 (91M)				X or	X	X	
p. 379 (91M)				X or	X	X	
Unit Six, Chapter 1							
p. 387 (3M)	X	X					X
p. 389 (5M)	X	X					X
p. 390 (6M)			X or	X or	X		

* Teacher supervision advisable

Unit/Chapter/Page	Necessary	By All Students	By Small Group	Optional Independent	Demonstration	Written Report	Class Discussion
p. 391 (7M)	X		X	or	X	X	
p. 392 (8M)	X		X	or	X	X	
p. 394 (10M)	X		X	or	X	X	
p. 396 (12M) *			X	or X or	X		
p. 398 (14M) *			X	or X		X	
p. 400 (16M)			X	or X		X	
p. 401 (17M)	X	X					X
p. 401 (17M)	X	X					X
p. 402 (18M)			X	or X			X
p. 403 (19M)	X		X	or	X		X
p. 406 (22M)	X		X	or	X	X	
Unit Six, Chapter 2							
p. 414 (30M)	X	X or	X				X
p. 414 (30M)			X	or X		X	
p. 415 (31M)			X	or X		X	
p. 419 (35M)				X or	X		X
p. 422 (38M) *					X		X
Unit Six, Chapter 3							
p. 437 (53M) *					X		X
p. 446 (62M)	X	X				X	X
p. 451 (67M) *				X or	X	X	
Unit Six, Chapter 4							
p. 464 (80M)	X		X				X

* Teacher supervision advisable

Adaptability to Differences in Student Performance Abilities

Focus on Physical Science is designed for maximum utilization by teachers preferring either a conventional approach with some laboratory and/or demonstration experiences, or an activity-centered approach using a discovery method of learning. The text, as well as the program supplements—*Focus on Physical Science: Activity-Centered Program, Teacher's Guide; Physical Science: A Learning Strategy for the Laboratory;* and *Physical Science Skillcards*—provide many opportunities for flexibility.

Focus on Physical Science is also adaptable to meet the needs of students with different performance abilities. There are often many levels of performance within a single class or among several classes. Many students are able to meet performance objectives easily, while there are those functioning either above or below this level. To help teachers plan appropriate and meaningful learning experiences for students with a wide range of ability levels, many alternatives and aids are included within the teacher's edition.

Specific teaching suggestions are included throughout each chapter of the teacher's annotated edition. Each annotation is designed to facilitate teacher planning. The Teacher's Guide offers many helpful methods of organizing the course for a variety of student abilities. The **Activity Planning Guide,** pages 9T-13T, is a tool which may be used to plan a year's course for students functioning at varied performance levels. This course plan indicates the essential laboratory experiences. The headings "Necessary," "By All Students," and "By Small Group" identify the key experiences in each chapter. These activities should be undertaken by *all* students. The activities which have been starred indicate that teacher supervision is especially advisable for safety reasons or for additional help. The activities listed under "Optional/Independent" offer opportunities for the more able student to study independently.

The supplementary programs also offer many alternatives to the teacher in planning for several ability levels. For students requiring a more advanced course of study, independent enrichment exercises are recommended. Many of the experiments and activities in *Focus on Physical Science: Activity-Centered Program, Teacher's Guide* are suitable for use as independent enrichment exercises. Selected materials in *Physical Science: A Learning Strategy for the Laboratory* and *Physical Science Skillcards* can also be used independently. Encouragement should be given to capable students to engage in these supplementary activities, as well as the investigations at the end of each chapter.

The supplementary programs may also be used by students functioning at lower performance levels. These students may require additional study in selected areas and/or reinforcement of previously introduced concepts. With frequent evaluation of the less able student's progress, a teacher may determine the areas in which additional attention is needed. Under teacher supervision, pre-selected activities and puzzles in *Physical Science: A Learning Strategy for the Laboratory* and *Physical Science Skillcards* may be used. Activities from *Focus on Physical Science: Activity-Centered Program, Teacher's Guide* may also be selected. These activities, when used in conjunction with the text, offer many opportunities to the less able student.

Evaluation, Activity-Centered, and Laboratory Programs

For assessing student progress, an *Evaluation Program* has been prepared to accompany *Focus on Physical Science*. The program consists of spirit duplicating masters for chapter tests. Each test includes questions and problems of varying difficulty focused on different levels of learning. The tests can be used not only for assessments but also as learning tools to help students improve their knowledge of physical science.

The *Physical Science: Activity-Centered Program, Teacher's Guide* aids the teaching of physical science in classrooms lacking adequate science facilities. Detailed instructions are given for carrying out activities and experiments.

Physical Science: A Learning Strategy for the Laboratory is a learning-through-doing program of experiments and activities designed to reinforce important concepts. The investigations are written for ease of understanding, and extensive illustrations show the student what to do.

The *Physical Science Skillcards* offer supplementary activities for those students needing additional reinforcement of learned concepts or independent enrichment.

Careers Related to Physical Science

Most students are affected by principles of physical science in their daily lives. Everywhere they look, they will find some principle at work. For this reason, student interest in physical science is often derived from the world around them. Physical science has a wide appeal because many hobbies are related to this field. Amateur radio, electronics, sewing, model building, and photography are a few examples.

Many occupations are also related to physical science. For instance, the production of steel and other building materials provides a livelihood for many people throughout the world. Technology within this field constantly improves methods and even creates new jobs.

Engineering is one of the major occupations in this field. Engineers are employed by industry, federal, state, and city government, health institutions, and the military. There are many divisions of engineering. State and city government agencies often employ civil engineers to plan and help construct major roadways and other projects. Telephone companies employ electrical engineers in a variety of capacities. They are often involved in planning improved telephone service, as well as maintaining equipment. Industrial engineers work for large and small industries in management and planning positions.

Other careers utilizing the principles of physical science include X-ray technicians, computer programmers, electricians, TV repair persons, radio technicians, physicists, and teachers. These are only a few of the occupations within the physical science field.

All of these jobs require some type of training. For example, an X-ray technician needs technical training given by a technical college or a hospital training program. A physicist completes at least four years of college majoring in physics. Often advanced degrees in physics, master's and/or doctorate, are required by many employers. Many other occupations require a vocational school training and/or an apprenticeship.

Physical science careers are diverse and require a variety of training programs. Students may be interested in many of these careers. Guest speakers and/or displays on various careers could be scheduled throughout the year to help familiarize the students with career possibilities.

Performance Objectives

What Is a Performance Objective?

Pick up almost any book on science education and you'll find reasons for teaching science:
> "For students to acquire habits of critical thinking. . . ."
> "To instill an appreciation for their natural environment. . . ."
> "To learn scientific terms, concepts, and principles. . . ."
> "So that students will sustain and enhance their natural curiosity. . . ."

This list could go on and on, and no doubt you could add your own reasons as to why you teach science in your classroom. Statements of what science teaching intends to accomplish are no doubt valid and justifiable. The question is: How do you know that you are succeeding in achieving the goals of science education?
> What would you look for if students really were thinking critically?
> What would students be doing if they are appreciating their natural environment?
> How could you tell whether or not a student has learned a scientific term, concept, or principle?
> How would you know if your teaching enhanced or extinguished a student's natural curiosity?

Therein lies the value of performance objectives—the behaviors which you, the teacher, can observe and which seem to indicate that students are actually achieving the lofty goals of science education.

For example, let's take the first one: "For students to acquire habits of critical thinking. . . ." Now what can you think of that students might do if they are thinking critically? Here are some behaviors which you might observe:
> Students ask questions related to the topic being discussed.
> They gather data or share evidence which supports their answers.
> They question or express doubt about the theories posed by others.
> They suggest alternate solutions to a problem.
> They reject their ideas when the evidence they gather does not support their theories.

Perhaps you could think of other behaviors which would indicate that students are thinking critically. This list is not exhaustive by any means. It only serves as an example of what you might look for if you were accomplishing that goal.

Let's try another one: "To learn scientific terms, concepts, and principles. . . ." How could students demonstrate to you that they have learned something? For example, when discussing the concepts of gravity and force does the student use the terms weight and mass correctly? If so, you might think that the student has learned them.

Or, when asked to define them orally, does the student say something like: "Weight is a measure of the pull of gravity on a body. Mass is the amount of material in a body." If so, you might agree that the student learned the terms correctly.

Or, when asked to demonstrate how to measure the mass and weight of a body, the student would use a pan balance to measure mass and a spring balance to measure weight. If the student can demonstrate this, even without saying one word, you might conclude that he or she has learned these terms.

Or, when presented with the units of mass and weight and asked to identify each, the student does so correctly.

Or, given the definitions of the two words, the student matches the words with the correct definition.

An unlimited number of behaviors could be cited which indicate a student has learned something. Basically, **a performance objective is a description of the behavior you might observe if a student is achieving an educational goal.**

What Is a Good Performance Objective?

Statements of performance objectives can usually be divided into three distinct parts. First is a **description of the conditions under which the desired behavior will be observed.** Here are some examples which describe the condition:

"When presented with atomic models of chlorine, sodium, and hydrogen. . . ."
"When asked to list the parts of a nuclear reactor. . . ."
"When presented wtih the materials suggested on page. . . ."
"After having read and discussed. . . ."
"In groups of five students, given a sextant and graph paper. . . ."

A good performance objective includes a condition which tells what causes, stimulates, or motivates the student to perform the behaviors or under what circumstances those behaviors will be performed.

The second part of a well-stated performance objective is a **clear description of exactly what behavior you're looking for.** A good performance objective would avoid using such terms as "know about," "appreciate," or "sense the relationship between." Rather, a good performance objective will include terms which describe what you could observe students doing if they do "know about" or "appreciate." It's almost impossible to observe a student "appreciating," but you can gather some evidence that the student is appreciating science if he or she is:

reading science books instead of comic books.
staying in a free period or coming to class early to manipulate science materials.
requesting that you repeat a science demonstration or wanting to do it alone.
expressing to you a liking for science.

In other words, **a good performance objective uses verbs which express some type of observable action.** Here are some examples of action verbs which describe observable behaviors:

states orally	manipulates
matches	measures
distinguishes between	expresses
	watches
constructs	states hypotheses
identifies	recalls
lists	

The third part of a well-stated performance objective is **a description of some level of performance or criteria which may help you to know if the student or class has performed to the degree which you hoped for.**

For example, if you were teaching students to use a ruler, would you want all of your class to be able to accurately measure the perimeter of a desk or table? Would you feel satisfied if 90% of your class could perform this skill? 80%? 50%? Would you be happy if just one student did it? Obviously, this level of performance would vary for each class, each student, each teacher, and each task. In some classrooms, a teacher might think that all students should be able to measure accurately. In other classrooms, a teacher would be elated if even a few students could measure accurately.

What do we mean by accurately? Would you be satisfied if students could measure the table to the nearest centimeter? Half-centimeter? Millimeter? More accurately than that? Just how accurately would be acceptable? Here then, is another aspect of a level of performance: A well-stated performance objective might also include some description of **how precise, how accurate, how well** the behavior should be performed in order for you to know that the student has really achieved the objective.

Another kind of a criterion measure or performance level which might be included in a performance objective is a statement of **how often or how many times** a student must perform the behavior in order to demonstrate that he or she has learned something. For example, if the student measured the tabletop with a ruler accurately just one time, would you conclude that he or she has learned how to measure? What if you asked a student to measure five objects with a ruler, and you were looking for ability to measure them correctly to the nearest centimeter? Would you be satisfied if the student measured four of them correctly? Three out of five? Or would you only be satisfied if the student measured all five of them correctly?

Again, this decision will have to be made on the basis of what you know about the student's ability, and the task at hand. For some students, you'd be happy if they could do it just once; for other students, you might expect perfection four out of five trials.

Now let's put all these parts together and see what a well-stated performance objective looks like:

Conditions
(tell you how to plan and organize your class and what materials you'll need)

Working in groups of five students, when presented with a sextant, graph paper, and instructions,

Performance
(tells you what behaviors of students to look for)

Students will measure a flagpole by triangulation. Students will correctly use the sextant. Students will evaluate the performance of each of the other members of the group as they use the method of indirect measurement.

Criterion Measure
(tells you how many of the students or to what degree the objective should be achieved)

Of all the students, 85% will achieve 100% of the above objectives.

Why Should You Use Performance Objectives?

A performance objective cannot and should not tell you how to teach. Your teaching strategy is a product of your own creativity as a professional teacher, your knowledge of science and teaching methodology, suggestions from teacher's guides and textbooks, and immediate clues from your students. A performance objective is only a suggested outcome of what students will be able to do after or during your teaching.

Planning instruction is one use of a performance objective. It can help you decide what materials, classroom conditions, grouping, and teaching strategies you must acquire or develop prior to meeting with your students. This description of conditions is part of the well-stated objective. It helps you think through what you, the teacher, must do to cause the desired behavior to happen.

Another use of a performance objective is to help you **gather and provide evidence** that students in your class are learning. It allows you to become **accountable for time and energy** you spend teaching science. It means, however, that you have to evaluate and keep records of student progress. Some suggestions for record keeping are given on page 21T. If you do keep such records, then, you or anyone else—parent, teacher, administrator, or supervisor—could observe and evaluate your teaching of science. If anyone were to ask you how you know your students are learning something, you could provide them with some performance evidence that the goals of your science program were being achieved. Of course, students may not exhibit the desired behaviors. If they don't, you have a basis for examining your own teaching, the instructional materials, the classroom, and the school environment and changing them to make them more conducive to learning. But you wouldn't know what changes to make unless you knew what performance outcomes you desired. Part of the well-stated performance objective describes the performance. A precise description tells you what behaviors you should be able to observe if students are achieving the goals of science.

Diagnosing a student's abilities is another use of performance objectives. When you can observe and evaluate certain behaviors, it is easier to determine what a student is capable of doing, or what has been accomplished in the past, and what has yet to be mastered. It more clearly defines the boundaries between what the student knows and what he doesn't know. With this information, you can provide a better individualized learning situation for each student. If the students already have demonstrated to you that, for example, they can distinguish between physical and chemical changes around them, why dwell on that? Go on to another objective. Or, perhaps some of your students can do this while others cannot. If it is an important goal, then you'll need to provide some individual or small group activities for some of your students while others might be pursuing other goals. An effective teacher will provide for these individual differences. It is the criterion measure part of the well-stated performance objective that allows you to diagnose which students have accomplished the objective and to what degree they have achieved it.

In addition, performing objectives are helpful because they **tune students in** to what it is you're trying to achieve. When it is apparent to students what it is you are trying to accomplish, when it is clear to all what is meant by successful completion, then students may use their energies to achieve the objective rather than try to "psych-out" what the teacher wants them to do. Many teachers have found that when they share with students what objectives are sought (if they are reasonable), much of the teaching job is accomplished. Most students will accept the challenge rather than try to "play games" with the teacher.

Where Do Performance Objectives Come From?

Statements of performance objectives come in many forms, and no given number of them constitute a science curriculum. You could never say that students, having achieved the objectives contained in this textbook, will then "know" science. The performance objectives for each school, class, group of students, or individual student will vary according to the students, the teacher, the resources available in the learning environment, and the task at hand.

Books are available which contain performance objectives for science. Several are listed in the bibliography. There is even an Instructional Objectives Exchange to which you can subscribe.* It is difficult for teachers in New York or Washington or Los Angeles to write adequate performance objectives for teachers to use with their students in Centerville, Garden City, or Westberg. Even school districts which employ science curriculum specialists cannot decide what objectives are appropriate for you and your students in your situation with the materials and resources you have available.

Ultimately, the task of selecting, composing and evaluating performance objectives is up to you. You should draw upon the performance objectives in this guide and upon other sources or other people who could help you. Students are good, if not the best, sources of performance objectives. When they can express to you their questions, their interests, and their goals, then you can cooperatively decide what objectives shall be reached. The objectives in this guide and any other list of performance objectives provides a basis for selecting what is appropriate for your students. Select from these lists, objectives from other teachers and consultants, and create some of your own. **The ultimate decision of what to teach is yours; the decision of what to learn is the student's.**

Any performance objective for teaching science should be based upon one or more of the goals of science education. You should be able to say that the reason you're working to accomplish this particular objective is because it's one step or one part of a long range goal of science education. For example, if one of the goals of science education is to develop the student's ability to utilize some of the methods and processes by which problems are solved scientifically, then one of the purposes of a lesson might be to develop an understanding of what an experiment is. If a student does understand what an experiment is:

When asked to define an experiment, the student will state that it is a test or way of proving some theory or principle.

When asked what to do to find out if warm air rises, the student will describe what to do and use the term "experiment" in the description.

When asked for examples of experiments which have been conducted so far this semester, the student will cite at least three.

Specific performance objectives such as the above are only examples of one small part of that large, broader goal for science education. However, each performance objective should be consistent with one or more of those goals so that you can justify what you are teaching, and so that you can see students progress toward that goal.

How Do You Use the Performance Objectives in This Teacher's Guide?

Performance objectives are listed for each chapter of *Focus on Physical Science, Third Edition*. They are related to four broad goals of science education.

A 1. **Attitudes:** To develop students' attitudes of curiosity, of wonderment about and involvement with phenomena in their natural environment; to develop an appreciation for the contributions of science to daily living; and to develop the

---

*Information and a catalog of objective collections can be obtained from: Instructional Objectives Exchange, Center for the Study of Evaluation, Graduate School of Education, University of California, Los Angeles, California 90024.

value and inclinations toward solving problems in a scientific manner.

P 2. **Processes:** To develop those intellectual processes of inquiry by which scientific problems and phenomena are explained, predicted and/or controlled.

K 3. **Knowledge:** To develop knowledge of facts, terminology, concepts, generalizations and principles which help the students confront and interpret their environment.

S 4. **Skills:** To develop the student's ability to handle, construct and manipulate materials and equipment in a productive and safe manner, and to develop an ability to measure, organize and communicate scientific information.

Next to each performance objective you will find one or more of the following capital letters: **A, P, K, S.** They indicate the goal on which the objective is based—**A**ttitudes, **P**rocesses, **K**nowledge, **S**kills. Designed to help you see a consistency between the specific objectives and the goals of science education, it may serve to help you keep in mind a balance between each of these four goals since they are all of equal priority.

1. The statements of performance objectives which are identified as **"A"**—developing Attitude goals—are behaviors which you might observe as students increase their enjoyment of science activities, and as they demonstrate an interest in the scientific objects and events in their environment. You will find such statements as:

Students will request that the demonstration be repeated.

Students will volunteer to conduct the activity at home.

Students will request the use of the science equipment during free periods.

When given a choice between having a free period or working at a science activity, students choose the science activity.

Students will volunteer to do research and report their findings in class.

As you can see, few of these behaviors are prompted by the teacher. They are voluntary behaviors which indicate an affinity for, an inclination toward, and a preference for science. You will find suggested attitudinal behaviors throughout the list and particularly at the end of each unit or chapter when students go beyond the information presented in the text.

2. The statements of performance objectives which are identified as **"P"**—developing Process goals—are behaviors which you might observe as students use the thinking processes of analyzing, experimenting, applying, hypothesizing, theorizing, comparing and contrasting, classifying, observing, etc. You will find such statements as:

When presented with various objects, students will compare and contrast their similarities and differences and place them in groups of metallic and nonmetallic.

Given data on the solubility of various substances in water, students will predict the solubility of these substances in another solvent.

Given pictures of various types of levers, students will identify the fulcrum, resistance and effort arms, and group them in one of three classes.

3. The statements of performance objectives which are identified as **"K"**—developing Knowledge goals—are behaviors which you might observe as students demonstrate they have gained an understanding and use of certain terms, concepts, and generalizations of science. You will find such statements as:

When asked, students will define the term "weight" correctly.

Students will explain the reason why objects fall toward the earth by using the term gravity, gravitational pull, or force of gravity.

Students will describe inertia.

Students will describe the possible effects of thermal pollution on large cities.

Generally, a knowledge objective is one which calls upon students to recall or explain information, concepts, or principles which they learned in the past or which have been presented in the text and other materials.

4. The statements of performance objectives which are identified as **"S"**—developing Skills goals—are behaviors which you might observe as students gain skill in using scientific equipment correctly, and organizing, recording or reporting information accurately. Some examples of such statements are:

Students will diagram the relationship between gravity and distance from the earth's core.

Using a stopwatch, students will count the number of swings a pendulum makes in one minute.

While observing the demonstration, students will record their observations in their notebooks.

Using a ball and chalk, students will measure the angles of reflection and incidence as the ball is bounced against the wall.

In the Teacher's Guide that follows, each unit of the text begins with the purpose and a statement of the goals of the unit. The unit is then divided into chapters. A specific statement of the goal for each chapter is given. A goal statement is also given at the beginning of each chapter in the student's text. Following the goal statement in the Teacher's Guide, the specific performance objectives for each section of the chapter are listed. There may be several objectives in each section. Each objective is numbered to correspond to that section of the chapter. For example, 2:5 is Chapter 2, section 5. From these objectives you should be able to determine and plan for the achievement of the objectives for each section of a chapter.

Remember, **these performance objectives are not meant to be all inclusive.** You should supplement them with objectives from other sources and with those you create yourself.

As you examine these objectives, you will find many of them include a description of the conditions. Feel free to alter these conditions according to your own classroom situation. For example, the objectives may state a condition: "When presented with three types of magnets: bar, horseshoe and cylindrical. . . ." You may not have these types of magnets in your classroom. Change the statement of conditions to reflect those particular materials you have available. Another example. "When asked to state . . . ." Maybe you'd prefer your students to write or to demonstrate a certain response. Make adjustments as required.

You will also find that the criterion or level of performance for each objective is not included. The intent was to create guidelines and not to state levels of expectancies for you. Only you can decide if 100% or only 50% of your students should be able to accomplish each task. You will need to develop and insert these criterion levels for your own students based upon your knowledge of their abilities, your materials, and your own situation.

How Do You Know You've Achieved Your Objectives?

When you try to find out if students have learned anything, you probably give some form of written test—true-false, completion, matching, or essay type of examination. All of these forms of evaluation are important in determining whether or not students have achieved their objectives. Other evaluation materials are available to accompany the Merrill Science Programs.

DISCOVERING SCIENCE Evaluation Program, Learning Through Testing, Levels 3–6

PRINCIPLES OF SCIENCE, Book One (Third Edition), Spirit Duplicating Evaluation Program

PRINCIPLES OF SCIENCE, Book Two (Third Edition), Spirit Duplicating Evaluation Program

FOCUS ON LIFE SCIENCE (Third Edition), Spirit Duplicating Evaluation Program

FOCUS ON EARTH SCIENCE (Third Edition), Spirit Duplicating Evaluation Program

FOCUS ON PHYSICAL SCIENCE (Third Edition), Spirit Duplicating Evaluation Program

Some of the performance objectives in this Teacher's Guide do not lend themselves to a written evaluation. It is very difficult to assess through written tests the degree to which students are developing attitudes toward science. Therefore, some other ways of evaluating the achievement of your objectives may be necessary.

Personal observation is probably the best way to evaluate student growth toward the goals of science education. But if you have a large class or are in a departmentalized system, personal observation becomes an overwhelming task. If there were a quick way of recording your observations of student behavior to indicate the achievement of an objective, the task might be easier.

Performance checklists molded to your needs can be used to collect evidence of the achievement of your objectives. **Caution:** Don't try to observe all students performing all the behaviors at once. Select several students to observe at one time; the next day, observe several more. Record your observations soon after or during the lesson.

In the simple performance checklist given below, enter the performance objectives by number or by statement for each section. Then, as you observe your students, mark the square which corresponds to the student and the objective he or she performs.

Date: January 9
Page: 40-45
Topic: Controlling Sound Waves

OBJECTIVE	Linda	Bill	Mike D.	Sarah	Gina
1. Uses term "reflected" correctly	✓	✓		✓	
2. Compares materials which absorb/ reflect sound	✓	✓	✓	✓	
3. Describes function of megaphone			✓	✓	
4. Suggests ways to soundproof building					
5.					

Another type of checklist may help you to record attitudinal objectives. You might keep one of these for each student, and record growth as the student demonstrates some of the behaviors which indicate to you that he or she is developing a positive attitude toward science. It would be impossible to keep a daily record; however, you could complete it five or six times a year. Just before sending out report cards is a good time.

STUDENT: Jamie Barnes
Date: January 9   Observation period: 2nd 6 weeks

BEHAVIOR	Never	Sometimes	Always
1. Expresses a liking for science		✓	
2. Requests to use science materials		✓	
3. Reads science books		✓	
4. Does activities at home			
5. Volunteers to bring in equipment			✓
6. Asks questions beyond the text material			✓
7. Volunteers to do research	✓		

Another way of eliciting students' attitudes is through opinion surveys. These are helpful in determining how students feel about themselves, the subject, your teaching strategies, their own learning style, and the materials of instruction. Following is only a sample of the type of questions which you might use to construct an opinion survey:

OPINION SURVEY   Name *Bush, Sarah*

Chapter *Waves*   Date *March 11, 1977*

1. While studying this chapter, I found it most difficult to: (Check the three answers which best describe your feelings)

    _____ understand the diagrams
    _____ do the experiments suggested
    _____ understand the new vocabulary
    _____ express my opinion
    _____ understand the written assignments
    _____ discuss my misunderstandings with the teacher

2. Which do you enjoy doing most? (Check three answers)

    _____ performing experiments
    _____ reading the textbook
    _____ answering the questions at the end of the chapter
    _____ asking questions of the teacher
    _____ listening to the teacher
    _____ listening to the opinions of other students
    _____ doing research on my own in the library
    _____ watching films
    _____ experimenting on my own
    _____ other (describe)

3. I have learned the most about the chapter from:

    _____ watching films
    _____ doing my own experiments
    _____ listening to the discussion
    _____ asking questions about something that interests me
    _____ listening to the teacher explain
    _____ reading the text
    _____ reading other supplementary materials
    _____ participating in class discussions
    _____ participating in small group discussions

Recording group behavior allows you to estimate the number of students who have completed each activity, and the time you've spent on each. This information might indicate whether you should spend more time with the whole class or with individual students. It also gives you a record of how much time you've spent teaching science during the year.

| Unit __4__ | | | No. of students in class __28__ | |
| Chapter __1__ | | | Topic __Solutions__ | |
Page	Dates	Activity	Number of students completing	Time spent
228	2/1 – 2/3	Gaseous solution	25	40 minutes
239	2/11 – 2/12	Solubility of table salt	23	50 minutes

These performance checklists are merely suggestions intended to supplement the many other forms of evaluation with which you may be familiar. All are intended to help you answer the question: "How do you know you're achieving the goals of science education?"

Bibliography

Bloom, Benjamin, Hastings, J. Thomas, and Madaus, George, *Handbook on Formative and Summative Evaluation of Student Learning.* McGraw-Hill Book Co., New York, 1971.

Bloom, Benjamin and others, *Taxonomy of Educational Objectives, Handbook I: Cognitive Domain.* David McKay, New York, 1956.

California State Department of Education, *Science Framework for California Public Schools.* Sacramento, Calif., 1970.

Costa, Arthur, Lowery, Lawrence, and Strasser, Ben, *Strategies for Science Instruction: A Personal Workshop.* Rapid Printers, Inc., Hayward, Calif., 1972.

Eiss, Albert F., and Harbeck, Mary B., *Behavioral Objectives in the Affective Domain.* National Science Teachers Association, National Education Association, Washington, D.C., 1969.

Kibler, Robert J., et al., *Objectives for Instruction and Evaluation.* Allyn and Bacon, Inc., Boston, Mass., 1974.

Krathwohl, D. R., Bloom, Benjamin, and Masia, Bertram R., *Taxonomy of Educational Objectives, Handbook II: Affective Domain.* David McKay, New York, 1956.

Mager, Robert, *Preparing Instructional Objectives.* Fearon Publishers, Inc., Palo Alto, Calif., 1962.

Picard, Anthony, and Sund, Robert, *Behavioral Objectives and Evaluational Measures for Science and Mathematics.* Charles E. Merrill Publishing Co., Columbus, Ohio, 1971.

Plowman, Paul, *Behavioral Objectives in Science.* Science Research Associates, Chicago, 1969.

Popham, W. James, and Baker, Eva L., *Establishing Instructional Goals.* Prentice-Hall, Inc., Englewood Cliffs, N.J., 1970.

Walbesser, Henry H., *Constructing Behavioral Objectives.* Bureau of Educational Research and Field Services, University of Maryland, College Park, Md., 1970.

Laboratory Equipment

Required for One Demonstration of Each Activity

A complete list of equipment for the entire course is given below for your convenience in ordering equipment for the entire school year. The activities are designed so that very simple apparatus can be used. Use materials that are available locally where or whenever possible.

aluminum foil—1 box
aluminum sheet, 2 mm thick—0.2 m^2
ammeter, D.C., 0–5 amp—1
asbestos pad—2
balances
    beam—1
    pan—1
balls
    hollow rubber—1
    basketball—1
    Ping-Pong—several
    small, metal—1
    small, rubber—1
    iron with ring—1
    styrofoam for models—several
balloons, various sizes—several
bath, ice—1
beakers
    400 ml—2
    250 ml—6
    150 ml—6
bell—1
bimetallic strip (with wooden handle)—1
bottles
    pint (glass with screwcap)—4
    quart—1
brick—1
Bunsen burner—1
buret, 25 ml—1
buret clamp—1
calorimeter, laboratory (styrofoam cups)—1
candles—several
cans
    #2½—1
    #1—1
    same size and makeup—several
card, playing or index—5
cardboard—several pieces
    mailing tubes (that will slide in each other)—3
    shoeboxes—2
cathode-ray tube—1
cellophane, red and blue—several pieces
cement, rubber—1 bottle
chalk—several pieces

clamp
    tubing—2
    flasks—4
clay, modeling—1 pkg
coins—several
collection bottles—4
comb—1
concave lens—2
condensing tube—1
convex lens—2
corks, assorted sizes—several
cotton, absorbent—1 pkg
Crooke's tube and high voltage source—1
crucible and cover—1
cups
    china—1
    paper—12
    styrofoam—12
deflagrating spoon—1
diffraction gratings—several
diodes and triodes, used—several
dowels, 0.5 cm—several
distilling flasks—2
dry cells
    used—several
    battery 6 V—3
    battery 1.5 V—6
dye, vegetable (ink)—5 types
electric bell—1
electric drill (to make holes in wooden top of homemade calorimeter)—1
electric hot plate—1
electrolysis apparatus (Hoffman)—1
electroscope—1
electrostatic machine (van de Graff generator)—1
evaporating dishes—3
file, triangular—1
filter paper—1 pkg
fingerbowls—2
flashlight (any light source)—1
flasks
    distilling—2
    Erlenmeyer 500 ml—1
    400 ml—3
    250 ml—4

forceps—1
funnel
   glass—1
   dropping—1
galvanometer—1
Geiger counter—1
glass
   jars, with and without lid—2
   8 oz tumblers—2
   block of, 0.5 to 1.5 cm thick—1
   plates, 5 cm × 5 cm—6
   prism, 60° × 60° × 60°—1
         45° × 45° × 90°—1
glass rods
   static—2
   stirring—1
glass slides, microscope—1 box
glass wool—1 pkg
graduated cylinders
   10 ml—2
   25 ml—2
   50 ml—2
   250 ml—2
graph paper, centimeter, ruled—100 sheets
hacksaw blade—1
hammer—1
hanger, wire—2
hydrometer, straw—1
knife—1
labels—1 pkg
lead sinkers (or other small, dense objects)—several
lenses
   convex—several
   concave, different focal lengths—several
light meter (or camera with light meter)—1
litmus, red and blue—1 vial each
magnets, of varying strength—several
magnifying glass—1
marbles, various sizes—30
marking pens—several
masking tape—1 roll
masses, for balance—several
medicine droppers—4
metal, pieces of Al, Fe, Cu of same mass—3
metal rods (with ball end for making electroscope)—2
meter sticks—2
metronome (if available)—1
microlamps (electric bulb that can be connected to circuit)—3
microscope, binocular—1

mirrors
   plane, small—2
   curved, metal—1
   magnifying—1
mortar and pestle—1
mouse traps—8
nails, iron, assorted sizes—several
needle, knitting (metal)—1
paint, black (black shoe polish)—1 small can
pans
   flat clear glass—2
   oblong metal—1
paper
   white—several sheets
   colored—several sheets
paper towels—2 pkg
paper clips—1 pkg
pencils—2
pins, straight—1 pkg
pipe cleaners—several
plastic bags, various sizes—several
plastic pans—2
plastic static rods (ebonite rods)—2
pneumatic trough—1
polarizing filters (old sunglasses)—2
prisms—2
projector, overhead—1
protractor—1
pulleys
   movable, double sheave—1
   single sheave—3
radiation source (watch with radium dial)—1
razor blades, single edge—1 pkg
resonator box—1
refrigerator—1
rheostat or resistance box—1
ring stand and ring—2
ring-stand clamps, assorted sizes—several
rope—1 piece
rubber bands—1 pkg
rubber sheeting, 5 cm × 5 cm—2 pieces
ruler, foot and metric—2
safety apron—several
safety glasses—several
safety gloves—several
sandpaper, sheets—several
scale, bathroom—1
scales, spring—3
scissors—1 pr
screwdriver, small, large—2
screw eyes—several
silk cloth—1 piece
silk thread—1 spool

sink (large, deep container)—1
slinky coil spring—1
shot (steel ball bearings)—25
solder, liquid or cold—1 tube
spatula—2
splints, wooden—1 pkg
springs—2
steam boiler—1
steel wool—1 pkg
stones, small (mineral samples)—several
stoppers, rubber 2-hole, 1-hole, no-hole, assorted sizes—several
straws, soda—1 pkg
string, strong cord—1 ball
switches—2
table—1
tape measure—1
test tubes, various sizes, some Pyrex—3 doz
test tube brush—1
test tube clamps—3
test tube racks—2
textile samples—several
theromometers, Celsius—4
thermostat (from old gas hot water heater)—1
thimble (or other small common object)—1
thread spools (to make pulleys)—6
timer (watch with second hand)—1
tongs, metal—1
toothpicks (pipe cleaners)—1 pkg
towel—1
tubes
    glass 1 in. × 18 in.—1
    thistle—1
    U-shaped—1
tubing, glass, assorted diameters—several meters
tubing, rubber
    flexible—several meters
    thick-walled—1 meter
tuning forks
    assorted frequencies—several
    same frequency as resonator box—1
tweezers—1
universal pH paper—1 box
vacuum bottle, pint size—1
vacuum pump—1
voltmeter, D.C., 0-10V—1
washers, metal—several
watch glasses (large)—several
whistles (inexpensive)—2
wire
    fine iron—1 m
    copper—10 m
    insulated bell—10 m
wire gauze—1
wire loop with handle—1
wood
    blocks of various sizes—several
    stick, 1 m—1
    plywood board, 60 cm^2—1
    smooth plank—1
    board, 15 cm × 4 cm—2
    circular piece (top for calorimeter)—1
wool cloth—1 piece
zinc plate, 5 cm × 5 cm—1

Chemicals

The approximate amounts needed for four classes of students. Most reagents are more economical to buy in larger lots rather than in the smaller amounts listed.

acetic acid, 99.5%—0.5 ℓ
alcohol
    ethyl, 95%—1 ℓ
    isopropyl—0.5 ℓ
alum—250 g
aluminum potassium sulfate—250 g
ammonia—0.25 ℓ
ammonium chloride—125 g
antimony (III) chloride—125 g
ascorbic acid—0.5 ℓ
aspirin—several
banana—1
barium chloride—125 g
bread—several slices
bromine water—0.5 ℓ
cadmium nitrate—125 g
calcium metal—125 g
calcium carbide—125 g
calcium chloride—125 g
calcium oxide—450 g
carbon tetrachloride—0.5 ℓ
carrot—1
chlorine water—0.5 ℓ
copper, strip—12 strips
copper (II) sulfate, crystals—250 g
corn kernels—100
cream of tartar—1 box
detergent, liquid—1 bottle
dry ice—25 g

Epsom salts (MgSO$_4$·7 H$_2$O)—25 g
ether—0.25 ℓ
ethylene glycol—0.25 ℓ
formalin (formaldehyde)—0.5 ℓ
gelatin—1 pkg
graphite (pencil lead)—10 g
hydrochloric acid, 38%—1 ℓ
hydrogen peroxide (H$_2$O$_2$), 3%—0.5 ℓ
hydrogen sulfide (H$_2$S)—125 g
ice
indophenol—0.5 ℓ
iodine solution—125 g
iodine crystals—125 g
iron filings—450 g
iron, steel wool—1 box
iron sulfate (FeSO$_4$)—125 g
lead
   strip—12 strips
   thin sheet—0.1 m^2
lemon juice—0.5 ℓ
soda lime (CaO and NaOH)—125 g
lithium chloride—125 g
lithium carbonate—125 g
magnesium
   metal—50 g
   wire—0.5 m
manganese dioxide (MnO$_2$)—125 g
matches—1 pkg
mica—several pieces
milk—0.25 ℓ
mineral oil—0.5 ℓ
naphtha (lighter fluid)—1 can
nickel sulfate—125 g
petroleum jelly—1 jar
phenol—125 g
phenolphthalein—125 g
platinum or nichrome wire—1 small roll
potassium, metal—125 g
potassium bromate—125 g
potassium bromide—125 g
potassium chlorate—125 g
potassium chloride—125 g

potassium iodide—125 g
potassium permanganate—125 g
potassium sulfate—125 g
potato—1
Rochelle salt crystals—450 g
sand—1 kg
silver nitrate (AgNO$_3$)—125 g
soap
   liquid—0.25 ℓ
   solid—1 bar
soda pop—1 bottle
sodium, metal—125 g
sodium acetate—125 g
soda water—0.5 ℓ
sodium bicarbonate—1 box
sodium carbonate—125 g
sodium chloride (table salt, uniodized)—1 kg
sodium dichromate dihydrate—125 g
sodium hydroxide, pellets—450 g
sodium hypochlorite (commercial bleaching solution)—1 bottle
sodium nitrate—125 g
sodium peroxide—600 g
sodium sulfate—125 g
sodium thiosulfate (hypo)—450 g
starch, liquid solution—0.5 ℓ
strontium chloride—125 g
sucrose, table sugar—1 kg
sulfur (roll)—450 g
sulfuric acid
   concentrated 96%—1 ℓ
   dilute—1 ℓ
vegetable oil—0.5 ℓ
vinegar, white—0.5 ℓ
water—as needed
   tap
   distilled
wax (paraffin)—1 box
zinc
   strip—12 strips
   mossy—450 g
zinc sulfate—125 g

Preparation of Solutions

This list gives directions for the preparation of various reagent solutions. Volumes are in milliters (ml), masses are in grams (g). Use distilled water for the preparation of solutions.

Acetic acid, 0.5M: 28.5 ml of 17M HC$_2$H$_3$O$_2$ per liter of solution

Ammonium hydroxide (dilute), 3M: 200 ml of concentrated NH$_4$OH per liter

Antimony (III) chloride, 0.167M: 38 g SbCl$_3$ per liter

Barium chloride, 0.1M: 24.4 g BaCl$_2$·2 H$_2$O per liter

Bromine water: Use commercial solution.

Cadmium nitrate, 0.25M: 77 g Cd(NO$_3$)$_2$ · 4 H$_2$O per liter

Calcium hydroxide, 0.02M: Make a saturated solution of CaO; use some excess, then filter. Protect the solution from air.

Chlorine water (saturated): Bubble Cl$_2$ (g) from a cylinder of compressed Cl$_2$ into distilled water. Or, to 150 ml of 5% NaClO (commercial bleaching solution), add water and about 35 ml of 6M HCl as needed to give the characteristic greenish-yellow color of chlorine, and dilute to 1 liter.

Copper sulfate, 0.5M: 124.8 g CuSO$_4$ · 5 H$_2$O per liter

Hydrochloric acid, 6M: Mix equal volumes of 12M (concentrated) HCl and water.

Hydrochloric acid (dilute), 3M: 258 ml concentrated HCl per liter

Hydrochloric acid, 0.1M: 8.55 ml concentrated HCl per liter

Hydrogen sulfide water: Generate H$_2$S gas by adding dilute HCl in a gas generation apparatus. Bubble the gas in distilled water for at least 5 minutes. Use a 250-ml wide mouth jar about half-filled with distilled water.

Iodine solution, 0.05M: Dissolve 12.7 g I$_2$ and 53 g KI in 250 ml water. After complete solution, dilute to 1 liter

Indophenol, 0.1% solution: Dissolve 1 g of indophenol in 1000 ml water

Iron (II) sulfate, 0.5M: Dissolve 139 g of FeSO$_4$ · 7 H$_2$O in water containing 10 ml of concentrated H$_2$SO$_4$. Dilute to 1 liter. Solution does not keep well.

Lead nitrate, 0.1M: 33.1 g Pb(NO$_3$)$_2$ per liter

Limewater (*see Calcium hydroxide*)

Mercury (II) chloride, 0.25M: 68 g HgCl$_2$ per liter

Nickel sulfate, 0.25M: 66 g NiSO$_4$ · 6 H$_2$O per liter

Nitric acid (dilute), 3M: 195 ml HNO$_3$ per liter

Phenolphthalein: 1 g phenolphthalein (solid) per 100 ml 50% ethanol

Potassium bromide, 0.5M: 60 g KBr per liter

Potassium iodide, 0.5M: 83 g KI per liter

Potassium permanganate, 0.02M: 3.16 g KMnO$_4$ per liter

Silver nitrate, 0.1M: 17.0 g AgNO$_3$ per liter

Sodium chloride, 0.1M: 5.85 g NaCl per liter

Sodium hydroxide (dilute), 3M: 126 g NaOH per liter

Sodium hydroxide 0.1M: 4 g NaOH per liter

Sodium hypochlorite, 5%: Use commercial 5% NaClO bleaching solution.

Sodium nitrate, 0.1M: 8.5 g NaNO$_3$ per liter

Sodium thiosulfate, 1M: 248 g Na$_2$S$_2$O$_3$ per liter

Starch solution: This starch solution will keep for long periods of time. Mix 250 ml saturated NaCl solution (filtered), 40 ml glacial acetic acid, 10 ml water, 2 g starch. Bring slowly to a boil and boil for 2 minutes.

Sulfuric acid (dilute), 3M: 167 ml concentrated H$_2$SO$_4$ per liter

Sulfuric acid, 0.25M: 14.0 ml concentrated H$_2$SO$_4$ per liter

Zinc sulfate, 0.25M: 72 g ZnSO$_4$ · 7 H$_2$O per liter

Teaching Aids

Films and Filmstrips

Reviews of new science films providing information useful in selecting films for physical science are available in *Science Books and Films*. It is published quarterly by the American Association for the Advancement of Science, 1515 Massachusetts Avenue, N.W., Washington, D. C. 20005.

Catalogs listing films and filmstrips for purchase or rental may be obtained from the following distributors. (Most filmstrips are not distributed on a rental basis.)

Some of the larger companies maintain branch offices in various regions of the country. In requisitioning films, it is desirable to locate a branch office or nearby film library when one is available. Films must be ordered months in advance, with alternate choice of dates for their use. Therefore, it is advisable to order films for specific units of study at least three months in advance of the time you wish to use them.

You should preview films and filmstrips before they are shown to the class. Often a class will benefit most if a film is viewed twice—the first time to overview the material and the second time to identify specific principles and concepts. Also, the teaching value of a film may be increased if students are given a list of five to ten questions covering the main ideas in the film. Students should be directed to answer the questions on the basis of what they have learned from the film. This technique increases student attention and retention.

Distributors

United States

Almanac Films, Inc., 915 Broadway, New York, New York 10010

Alturas Films, P.O. Box 940, Stanford, California 94305

American Film Registry, 24 East 8th Street, Chicago, Illinois 60415

Arco Film Productions, 580 Fifth Avenue, New York, New York 10032

Associated Films, Inc., 79 East Adams Street, Chicago, Illinois 60003

Association Films, Inc., 866 Third Avenue, New York, New York 10022

Athena Films, Inc., 165 West 45th Street, New York, New York 10019

Audio Film Center, 34 MacQuesten Parkway South, Mt. Vernon, New York 10550

Audio Productions, Inc., 630 Ninth Avenue, New York, New York 10036

AVI Associates, Inc., 825 Third Avenue, New York, New York 10022

Bailey Films, Inc., 6509 De Longpre Avenue, Hollywood, California 90028

Stanley Bowmar Co., 4 Broadway, Valhalla, New York 10595

Brandon Films, Inc., 34 MacQuesten Parkway South, Mt. Vernon, New York 10550

Bray Studios, Inc., 630 Ninth Avenue, New York, New York 10036

Colonial Films, 752 Spring Street N. W., Atlanta, Georgia 30308

Contemporary Films, Inc., 330 West 42nd Street, New York, New York 10036

Coronet Films, 65 East South Water Street, Chicago, Illinois 60601

William Cox Enterprises, 2900 South Sawtelle Boulevard, Los Angeles, California 90024

Walt Disney Productions, 800 Sonora Avenue, Glendale, California 91201

Ealing Productions, Inc., Chapel Bridge Park, 55 Chapel Street, Newton, Massachusetts

Eastman Kodak Co., Audio-Visual Service, 343 State Street, Rochester, New York 14604

Educational Film Library Association, Inc., 19 West 60th Street, New York, New York 10023

Encyclopaedia Britannica Films, Inc., 425 North Michigan Avenue, Chicago, Illinois 60611

Farm Film Foundation, 1425 H Street N.W., Washington, D.C. 20005

Films of the Nation Distributors, Inc., 5113 16th Avenue, Brooklyn, New York 11204

Filmstrip House, 432 Park Avenue S, New York, New York 10016

Film Strip of the Month Club, Inc., 353 4th Avenue, New York, New York 10010

Gateway Productions, Inc., Bureau of Audio-Visual Services, Univ. of Arizona, Tucson, Arizona 85721

Golden Key Productions, Inc., Film Distributors, 1921 Hillhurst Avenue, Hollywood, California 90027

Handel Film Corporation, 8730 Sunset Boulevard, Los Angeles, California 90069

Harcourt Brace Jovanovich, Inc., 750 Third Avenue, New York, New York 10017

Harper & Row Publishers, Inc., School Department, 2500 Crawford Avenue, Evanston, Illinois 60201

Heidenkamp Nature Pictures, 538 Glen Arden Drive, Pittsburgh, Pennsylvania 15208

Hubbard Scientific Company, P.O. Box 105, Northbrook, Illinois 60062

Huyck Corp., 200 East 42nd Street, New York, New York 10017

Ideal Pictures Corp., 3910 Harlem Road, Buffalo, New York 14226

Indiana University Films, Audio-Visual Center, Bloomington, Indiana 47401

Institutional Cinema Service, Inc., 915 Broadway, New York, New York 10010

Instructional Films, Inc., 1150 Wilmette Avenue, Wilmette, Illinois 60091

International Film Bureau, Inc., 332 South Michigan Avenue, Chicago, Illinois 60604

International Film Foundation, Inc., Suite 916, 475 Fifth Avenue, New York, New York 10017

Jam Handy Organization, 2821 East Grand Boulevard, Detroit, Michigan 48211

Learning Corporation of America, 711 Fifth Avenue, New York, New York 10022

Library Films, Inc., 25 West 45th Street, New York, New York 10019

McGraw-Hill Publishing Co., 330 West 42nd Street, New York, New York 10036

Modern Talking Picture Service, Inc., 1145 North McCadden Pl., Los Angeles, California 90038

National Film Board of Canada, Suite 819, 680 Fifth Avenue, New York, New York 10019

Ohio Bell Telephone Company, 35 East Gay Street, Columbus, Ohio 43215

Samuel Orleans and Associates, Inc., 211 West Cumberland Avenue, Knoxville, Tennessee 37915

Photolab, Inc., 3825 Georgia Avenue N, Washington, D.C., 20011

Prism Productions, Inc., 220 East 23rd Street, New York, New York 10010

Society for Visual Education, Inc., 1345 Diversey Parkway, Chicago, Illinois 60614

Sterling-Movies, U.S.A., Inc., 241 East 34th Street, New York, New York 10016

Teaching Films Custodians, Inc., 25 West 43rd Street, New York, New York 10036

Time-Life Films, 43 West 16th Street, New York, New York 10011

United World Films, Inc., 1445 Park Avenue, New York, New York 10029

Venard Organization, P.O. Box 1332, Peoria, Illinois 61601

Visual Education Consultants, P.O. Box 52, Madison, Wisconsin 53701

Visual Sciences, P.O. Box 599RB, Suffern, New York 10901

Ward's Natural Science Establishment, P.O. Box 1712, Rochester, New York 14603

Wilner Films and Slides, P.O. Box 231, Cathedral Station, New York, New York 10025

Young America Films, Inc., 18 East 41st Street, New York, New York 10017

U.S. Government Agencies

NASA, National Audio Visual Center, Washington, D.C. 20409

National Aeronautics and Space Administration, Washington, D.C. 20546

Energy Research and Development Administration, Washington, D.C. 20545

U.S. Department of Agriculture, Washington, D.C. 20250

Canada

Audio-Visual Supply Co., Toronto General Trusts Building, Winnipeg, Manitoba

Canadian Film Institute, 142 Sparks Street, Ottawa, Ontario

General Films Limited, 1534 13th Avenue, Regina, Saskatchewan

Radio-Cinema, 5011 Verdun Avenue, Montreal, Quebec

Suppliers

Equipment and materials needed for the activities and experiments in *Focus on Physical Science* are inexpensive and readily available. Most supplies can be gathered from local stores and other local suppliers. In addition to local suppliers, teachers may wish to obtain supplementary supplies from other sources. The following list of suppliers readily provide scientific materials to schools and school systems.

Central Scientific Company, 2600 S. Kostner Avenue, Chicago, Illinois 60623

Sargent-Welch Scientific Company, 7300 North Linder Avenue, Skokie, Illinois 60076

Science Kit, Inc., 777 East Park Drive, Tonawanda, New York 14150

The Stansi Educational Materials Division—Fisher Scientific Company, 1231 North Honore Street, Chicago, Illinois 60622

Macalaster Scientific Company, Rte. 111 & Everett Turnpike, Nashua, New Hampshire 03060

Frey Scientific Company, 465 S. Diamond Street, Mansfield, Ohio 44903

La Pine Scientific Company, 6001 S. Knox Avenue, Chicago, Illinois 60629

V W R Scientific, Box 3200, Rincon Annex, San Francisco, California 94119

Unit One   Measurement and Motion

Goals: Students will gain an understanding of the methods of science, the use of measurement in science and in everyday life, as well as applications of measurement in the study of forces and motion. They will gain an understanding of work, forces, and the laws of motion.

Unit One, Chapter 1
Physical Science

PERFORMANCE OBJECTIVES
Goal: Students will gain an understanding of the nature and the methods of science.
Objectives: Upon completion of the reading and activities and when asked to diagram, demonstrate, or respond either orally or on a written test, students will:

1:1-2	K	differentiate between science and technology.
1:3	K	list the methods used by scientists in developing and testing scientific knowledge.
1:3	S/P	conduct an experiment to demonstrate some methods of science.
1:4	K	define the role of a control in experimentation.
1:5	K	differentiate between theory and law.
1:6	K	define physical science.
1:7	P	explain the importance of measurements in science.
1:7-10	K	compare units of measure in the metric system and English system.
1:8-10	S	measure specified bodies with recommended measuring instruments.
1:11	S/K	conduct an activity to demonstrate a method of indirect measurement.
	S/A	When conducting activities and experiments, students will use laboratory materials and equipment in the prescribed manner.
		Upon completion of the reading and activities, students will exhibit an interest in science by:
	A	reading unassigned literature related to ideas presented in the chapter.
	A/S	voluntarily measuring a number of objects with different measuring instruments.
	A/S	volunteering to design and conduct a demonstration for the class.
	A/S	volunteering to help maintain and care for laboratory equipment.

EQUIPMENT FOR ACTIVITIES
balloons
beam balance
cardboard box
flasks (600 ml), 2
graduated cylinders, 25 and 50 ml
hot plate
ice
masking tape
metal washer
metric-English ruler
meter stick, yardstick
protractor
soda straw
string
test tubes (different sizes)

Page 4. Problem
1. Answers will vary. Examples are:
   (a) Solar cells for heating and cooking by sun
   (b) Chemical precipitation to recycle wastes
   (c) Nuclear reactor to desalinate seawater
   (d) Seismograph to find new sources of energy

Page 4. Activity
Place an interesting object in a box and seal it. Show the box to the students and give them three clues to its contents. Have the students ask questions that have a "yes" or "no" answer. Then have the students shake the box or manipulate it and make observations.

Page 7. Problems
2. Problem: Do pigeons use their ears to guide them home?
   Procedure: Cover the ears of pigeons, let them fly home.
   Observations: No pigeons arrived home.

Conclusion: Pigeons use their ears to guide them.
3. Problem: Does air expand when it is heated?
Procedure: Attach balloon to glass tubing, place tube and balloon in flask, heat flask. Put flask on ice.
Observation: Balloon expands when flask on hot plate; contracts when flask on ice.
Conclusion: Balloon in heated flask expands.

Page 8. Experiment
Before students proceed with the steps of the experiment, make sure they have recorded the "problem" and outlined the "procedure."

Page 8. Problems
4. The group not given the drug.
5. Answers will vary. Example: Mask the ears of half of the birds; leave half without ear masks.

Page 12. Problem
6. $\dfrac{55 \text{ km}}{1 \text{ hr}} \mid \dfrac{1 \text{ mi}}{1.61 \text{ km}} = 34$ mi/hr
34 mi/hr is less than speed limit

Page 13. Activity
You may wish to have students compare metric units of mass or weight with English units of mass or weight. Display a spring balance. Students may wish to use it in making a comparison with a beam (pan) balance.

Page 13. Problems
7. Answers will vary. Example:
$5.3g + 10.4g + 6.5g + 19g + 25g =$
$\dfrac{66.2 \text{ g}}{} \mid \dfrac{1 \text{ kg}}{1000 \text{ g}} = 0.066$ kg
8. Answers will vary. Example:
$\dfrac{120 \text{ lb}}{} \mid \dfrac{1 \text{ kg}}{2.2 \text{ lb}} = 54.5$ kg
9. Volume = 10 cm × 10 cm × 5 cm = 500 cm³
Water density = 1 g/cm³
$D = \dfrac{m}{V}$, m = DV
m = (1 g/cm³)(500 cm³) = 500 g

Page 14. Activity
Students may want to compare a liter with a gallon or make additional comparisons between the metric and English units of volume measurement.

Page 15. Activity
Students will need much help with this activity. You might introduce it by discussing scale drawings and maps. Sample scale drawing:

If the angle is taken from a ground position 10 m from the pole, and the angle is 35°, the pole will be about 7 m high.

Pages 16-18. Study Questions
A. *True or False*
1. True 2. False (Product and process of science are not both the same.) 3. False (A hypothesis may be true.) 4. True 5. False (The control in an experiment is not the same as a conclusion.) 6. False (A scientific law can be disproved.) 7. True 8. True 9. False (A meter stick and a yardstick do not have the same length.) 10. False (The gram is the metric unit of mass.)

B. *Multiple Choice*
1. 100 2. 1/100 3. 10 4. 1/1000 5. 1000 6. 1000 7. 2.2 8. 1 9. 1 ml 10. 1000

C. *Completion*
1. length 2. 10 m 3. scale drawing 4. technology 5. liter 6. 15 g 7. 4 ml 8. ten 9. volume 10. law

D. *How and Why*
1. Answers will vary. Examples are ruler, thermometer, graduated cylinder, balance, sextant; centimeters, degrees, milliliters, grams, angles
2. Physical Science is the study of matter and energy.
3. Answers will vary. Examples are: Observation: carefully noting changes under

controlled conditions; making and testing hypotheses: trying to test for all possible exceptions to hypothesis; stating theories that explain known facts.
4. Science includes the body of knowledge and the methods. Technology includes application of science to inventions and processes.
5. Answers will vary. Examples are: decimal system is easier to calculate; universal system for whole world.
6. Yes, $\dfrac{50 \text{ mi/hr} \times 1.61 \text{ km}}{1 \text{ mi}} = 80$ km/hr
Speedometer reads 80 km/hr
7. $\dfrac{250 \text{ ml} \times 1 \text{ }\ell}{1000 \text{ ml}} = 0.25 \text{ }\ell$
1000 ml = 1 ℓ
5000 ml = 5 ℓ
8. Mass is measured on a beam balance, volume is measured either by linear measurement or in graduated cylinder.
9. Measure a known distance from object. Measure angle (vertical) to top of object. Make a scale drawing. Read height from drawing.
10. 0.55 m, 5.5 m, 5.5 m

Page 18. Investigations
1. Other objects may be substituted.
2. Some students might like to make a scale model of buildings in one city block using their measurements.
3. The use of metric units in the United States is optional. Many manufacturers label their products in both English and metric units. Students should include examples of the use of metric units in their reports.

Unit One, Chapter 2
Force and Work

PERFORMANCE OBJECTIVES
Goal: Students will gain an understanding of forces, work, simple machines, mechanical advantage, and power.
Objectives: Upon completion of the reading and activities and when asked to diagram, demonstrate, or respond either orally or on a written test, students will:

2:1	P	compare and contrast force and resistance.
2:2	P	explain how work is related to force and distance.
2:2	P	compare and contrast the unit of force in the English system and the unit of force in the metric system.
2:3-11	K	list the six simple machines and indicate examples of each.
2:4	P	compare and contrast ideal mechanical advantage and actual mechanical advantage.
2:5-11	S/P	conduct activities to demonstrate how machines make work easier.
2:6-11	P	explain how the ideal mechanical advantage of the six simple machines can be calculated.
2:12	P	relate the efficiency of a machine to work input and work output.
2:13	P	explain the relationships of power, work, horsepower, and watt.
	S/A	When conducting activities, students will use laboratory materials and equipment in the prescribed manner.

Upon completion of the reading and activities, students will exhibit an interest in science by:

A	reading unassigned literature related to ideas presented in the chapter.
A/S	volunteering to develop and conduct a demonstration for the class.
A	relating ideas presented in this chapter to things which happen in everyday life.

EQUIPMENT FOR ACTIVITIES
bathroom scale
board
brick
masses, 200 g
       100 g
       2 equal
       2 unequal
       0.5 lb
pulley, 1 movable
       1 fixed
       2 fixed in tandem
ring stand
ruler
scissors

spring scales, 2
string
watch
wood, triangular block

Page 21. Problems
1. A student's arms could lift or push it if the desk is not bolted down. If the desk is bolted down, it would require a jack to lift it or a very large push or pull by many students.
2. The forces of muscles pulling on the bones inside body limbs move your body parts.
3. Sit on a chair, place hands on the chair, and push down.

Page 23. Problems
4. $W = FD$
   $W = 15 \text{ lb} \times 2 \text{ ft}$
   $W = 30 \text{ ft-lb}$
5. $W = FD$
   $W = 3 \text{ lb} \times 2 \text{ ft}$
   $W = 6 \text{ ft-lb}$
6. Lifting the suitcase might take more work. The distance component in each case is the same but the force needed to overcome gravity is probably more than the force needed to overcome inertia.
7. $W = FD$
   $W = 40 \text{ nt} \times 4 \text{ m}$
   $W = 160 \text{ nt-m}$

Page 24. Problem
8. (a) force used to move pedals converted into larger force of the wheel pushing on the road
   (b) oar acts as a lever to push boat
   (c) the needle acts as a wedge, great gain in speed
   (d) elevator uses pulleys to reduce force needed to lift objects
   (e) block and tackle sets several pulleys in tandem to distribute force
   (f) crowbar acts as a lever

Page 25. Problem
9. A.M.A. It takes friction into account.

Page 26. Problem
10. First Class Lever
    effort/fulcrum/resistance
    Second Class Lever
    effort/resistance/fulcrum
    Third Class Lever
    resistance/effort/fulcrum

Page 26. Activity
Use this activity to illustrate the types of levers and the properties of each type. Refer to Figure 2-9 for the types of levers. In Part 1 the second class lever is considered. The fulcrum is under the book at the point that the ruler touches the table. In Part 2, the pivot point is at the edge of the table. Since the fulcrum is between the effort arm and the resistance arm, this is a first class lever like a crowbar. In Part 3, the third class lever is presented. The effort force lies between the resistance and the fulcrum.

The second class lever has the highest M.A. and makes the task the easiest. The third class has the lowest M.A.

Page 27. Activity
This activity is designed to enable students to have a practical experience with levers and more fully understand how to balance levers.

The 100-g mass must be moved farther from the fulcrum to balance the 200-g mass. The smaller the mass, the farther the distance from the fulcrum.

Page 29. Problems
11. $F_R \times D_R = F_E \times D_E$
    $100 \text{ lb} \times 4 \text{ ft} = F_E \times 5 \text{ ft}$
    $F_E = \dfrac{400 \text{ ft-lb}}{5 \text{ ft}} = 80 \text{ lb}$
12. $F_R \times D_R = F_E \times D_E$
    $100 \text{ lb} \times 3 \text{ ft} = 75 \text{ lb} \times D_E$
    $300 \text{ ft-lb} = 75 \text{ lb} \times D_E$
    $D_E = 4 \text{ ft}$
13. $\text{I.M.A.} = \dfrac{\text{Effort Arm}}{\text{Resistance Arm}}$
    $\text{I.M.A.} = \dfrac{5m}{2m}$
    $\text{I.M.A.} = 2.5$
14. $\text{I.M.A.} = \dfrac{\text{Effort Arm}}{\text{Resistance Arm}}$
    $\text{I.M.A.} = \dfrac{0.8m}{0.2m}$
    $\text{I.M.A.} = 4$

Page 31. Activity
In Part 1 each spring scale should register ¼ lb. In Part 2 when the single movable pulley is used, the force on the spring scale

should still be ¼ lb. The movable pulley has a mechanical advantage of 2. When the fixed pulley and movable pulley are used as in Figure 2-20c the mechanical advantage is increased to 3. In Figure 2-20d the force needed to lift the weight will be 1/6 lb (M.A. = 3) since only three support ropes involve the movable pulley. The addition of the third pulley allows for a change in the direction of the force. The addition of support ropes increases the mechanical advantage. Try to keep the length of the string as equal as possible for all setups for the sake of experimental control. The students might want to measure the distance the effort and resistance forces move to reinforce the idea of mechanical advantage.

Page 31. Problem
15.

Pulleys	Effort Force	Distance	Resistance Force
Set A	10 lb	2 ft	20 lb
Set B	10 lb	3 ft	50 lb
Set C	5 lb	20 ft	20 lb

Resistance Distance	Support Ropes	I.M.A.
1 ft	2	2
0.6 ft	5	5
5 ft	4	4

Page 32. Problem
16. Answers given by students will vary. Automobile, lawnmower, bicycle, wagon, eggbeater are examples.

Page 33. Problems
17. roads to higher elevations, stairs from one floor of house to another, loading ramps, ramps over curbs, boards to load trucks, trailer hitches for transporting cars
18. Rather than lifting an object straight up, the force needed to overcome gravity changes direction and is spread over a distance. The overall force required is greater but the average force/unit time is less.

Page 34. Problem
19. knife, razor blade, hatchet, ice pick, wood planer, chisel

Page 37. Problems
20. $D_E = 6$ m
$F_E = 100$ nt
$D_R = 2$ m
$F_R = 200$ nt

21. $W_i = F_E \times D_E$
$W_i = 100$ nt $\times$ 6 m
$W_i = 600$ nt-m
$W_o = F_R \times D_R$
$W_o = 200$ nt $\times$ 2 m
$W_o = 400$ nt-m

22. % Efficiency $= \dfrac{\text{Work output}}{\text{Work input}} \times 100\%$

% $E = \dfrac{W_o}{W_i} \times 100$

% $E = \dfrac{400 \text{ nt-m}}{600 \text{ nt-m}} \times 100$

% $E = 66.7\%$

Page 40. Problems
23. $P = \dfrac{W}{t}$

$P = \dfrac{2000 \text{ ft-lb}}{4 \text{ sec}}$

$P = 500$ ft-lb/sec

$P(\text{hp}) = \dfrac{500 \text{ ft-lb/sec}}{550 \text{ ft-lb/sec}}$

$P = 0.91$ hp

24. $P = \dfrac{W}{t}$

$P = \dfrac{3000 \text{ ft-lb}}{60 \text{ sec}} \times \dfrac{1 \text{ hp}}{550 \text{ ft-lb/sec}}$

$P = 50$ ft-lb/sec $\times \dfrac{1 \text{ hp}}{550 \text{ ft-lb/sec}}$

$P = 0.09$ hp

25. $W = FD$
$W = 40{,}000$ lb $\times$ 100 ft
$W = 4{,}000{,}000$ ft-lb

$P = \dfrac{4{,}000{,}000 \text{ ft-lb}}{120 \text{ sec}} \times \dfrac{1 \text{ hp}}{550 \text{ ft-lb/sec}}$

$P = 60.7$ hp

Page 41. Problem
26. lowest (a), (b), (d), (c), (f), (e), highest

Pages 42-44. Study Questions
A. True or False
1. True 2. False (A pulley is an example

of a simple machine.) 3. False (The M.A. of a machine is not always greater than one.) 4. True 5. False (An eggbeater is an example of a compound machine.) 6. False (Newton is the metric unit of force.) 7. False (The efficiency of a machine is calculated by dividing work output by work input.) 8. True 9. False (One horsepower is 550 ft-lb of work per second.) 10. True

B. Multiple Choice
1. force 2. work 3. lever 4. two or more
5. 1 6. greater than 7. Fulcrum 8. 2
9. equal 10. spring scale

C. Completion
1. friction 2. four 3. four 4. lever 5. output, input 6. lubricants 7. time 8. 550
9. power 10. efficiency

D. How and Why
1. $W = F \times D$
   $W = 25 \text{ nt} \times 10 \text{ m}$
   $W = 250 \text{ nt-m}$
2.

	Fulcrum	F_R	F_E
(a) oar	oarlock	blade	handle
(b) pliers	bolt	jaws	handles
(c) wheelbarrow	axle	box	handles

3. Effort force will move 5 in.

mechanical advantage of five

4. They all make work easier by changing the direction, size, or distance through which a force moves.

5. typewriter—lever
car—wheel and axle, lever, screw
record player—wheel and axle
can opener—wedge
lawn mower—wheel and axle
tape dispenser—wheel and axle

6. $\% E = \dfrac{W_o}{W_i} \times 100$

   $\% E = \dfrac{200 \text{ nt-m}}{250 \text{ nt-m}} \times 100$

   $\% E = 80\%$

7. $F_E \times D_E = F_R \times D_R$
   $F_E \times 1 \text{ ft} = 50 \text{ lb} \times 10 \text{ ft}$
   $F_E = \dfrac{500 \text{ ft-lb}}{1 \text{ ft}}$
   $F_E = 500 \text{ lb}$

8. $P = \dfrac{W}{t}$

   $P = \dfrac{24{,}750 \text{ ft-lb}}{180 \text{ sec}}$

   $P = 137 \dfrac{\text{ft-lb}}{\text{sec}}$

   $hp = \dfrac{137 \dfrac{\text{ft-lb}}{\text{sec}}}{550 \dfrac{\text{ft-lb}}{\text{sec}}}$

   $hp = \tfrac{1}{4}$

9. Since power is work per unit time, the more powerful engine (1 hp) will be able to do the work twice as fast.

10. $W = F \times D$
    $W = 175 \text{ lb} \times 16 \text{ ft}$
    $W = 2800 \text{ ft-lb}$

Pages 44-45. Investigations
1. Tuning the engine means making sure the engine's ignition system fires the spark plugs at the correct time. Contact points, distributor, rotor, and spark plugs are checked.
2. Sample set up:

3. Find out about the r.p.m. "power bands" of different motorcycles.
4. Try to build a model of an early "perpetual motion" machine.
5. You may wish to compare these to five years earlier. Information can be obtained from manuals published by car manufacturers.

Unit One, Chapter 3
Moving Bodies

PERFORMANCE OBJECTIVES
Goal: Students will gain an understanding of the differences between weight and mass, speed and velocity, and relationships between forces and motion.

Objectives: Upon completion of the reading and activities and when asked to diagram, demonstrate, or respond either orally or on a written test, students will:

3:1	P/K	compare and contrast the meanings of weight and mass.
3:1	S/P	conduct activities to demonstrate the difference between mass and weight.
3:2	P	state Newton's law of gravitation and explain how it can be used to predict what an object will weigh at a particular altitude.
3:3	P	compare and contrast the meanings of constant speed and average speed.
3:4-5	P	compare and contrast the meanings of acceleration and deceleration.
3:6	K	define vector.
3:6	S/P	conduct an activity to illustrate the parallelogram method for determining a resultant force.
3:7	P	compare and contrast the meanings of velocity and speed.
3:7	P/S	solve assigned problems which require the use of vectors to determine the velocity of a body.
	S/A	When conducting activities, students will use laboratory materials and equipment in the prescribed manner.

Upon completion of the reading and activities, students will exhibit an interest in science by:

A	reading unassigned literature related to ideas presented in the chapter.
A/S	volunteering to develop and conduct a demonstration for the class.
A	relating ideas presented in this chapter to things which happen in everyday life.

EQUIPMENT FOR ACTIVITIES
beaker, 400 ml
board, 2 m × 15 cm plywood, 60 cm²
cardboard
clamp
lead sinker
marble
masses, metric, 3 (100 g, 250 g, 500 g)
meter stick
pan balance
paper clips
paper cup
pen, pencil
ring stand
rubber band
ruler
screw eyes, 2
spring
spring scales, 2
stopwatch
string
thimble
washers, 10

Page 48. Problem
1. As submarine submerges it takes on water to reduce its buoyancy. To surface it forces water out of the ballast tank with compressed air. It decreases in weight and floats to the surface.

Page 51. Problem
2. (a) decrease weight to one fourth
(b) $\frac{1}{9}$ of surface weight

Page 53. Problems
3. $v = \dfrac{d}{t}$

$v = \dfrac{100 \text{ m}}{50 \text{ sec}}$

$v = 2 \text{ m/sec}$

4. $v = \dfrac{d}{t}$

$\dfrac{50 \text{ m}}{\text{sec}} = \dfrac{d}{600 \text{ sec}}$

$$d = \frac{50 \text{ m}}{\text{sec}} \times 600 \text{ sec} = 30{,}000 \text{ m}$$

5. train
6. The speed of car in Figure 3-12 is constant but the speed of the car in Figure 3-13 changes. Since each speed shown is maintained for the same time, average speed may be computed by finding the arithmetic average of the speeds shown in the graph.

average speed =
$$\frac{(30 + 20 + 40 + 10 + 20) \text{ km}}{5 \text{ hr}} = \frac{120 \text{ km}}{5 \text{ hr}} = 24 \text{ km/hr}$$

Page 54. Problems

7. $v = \frac{d}{t}$

   $v = \frac{4800 \text{ km}}{6 \text{ hr}}$

   $v = 800$ km/hr

8. $v = \frac{d}{t}$

   $v = \frac{1000 \text{ m}}{5 \text{ sec}}$

   $v = 200$ m/sec

Page 54. Activity

The marble does not have a constant speed. It is accelerating due to the force of gravity. Therefore, the results will be average speed over the entire run not the actual speed of any moment.

Page 56. Problem

9. $a = \frac{v_2 - v_1}{t}$

   $a = \frac{585 - 450 \text{ km/hr}}{15 \text{ sec}}$

   $a = \frac{135 \text{ km/hr}}{15 \text{ sec}}$

   $a = 9$ km/hr/sec

Page 57. Problems

10. $a = \frac{v_2 - v_1}{t}$

    $a = \frac{400 \text{ km/hr} - 500 \text{ km/hr}}{20 \text{ sec}}$

    $a = \frac{-100 \text{ km/hr}}{20 \text{ sec}}$

    $a = -5$ km/hr/sec

11. $a = \frac{v_2 - v_1}{t}$

    $a = \frac{130 \text{ km/hr} - 260 \text{ km/hr}}{10 \text{ sec}}$

    $a = \frac{-130 \text{ km/hr}}{10 \text{ sec}}$

    $a = -13$ km/hr/sec

12. Passenger car and drag race car—forces produced by the engine and the tires against the road.
    Jet plane—reaction forces produced by jet engines, force of gravity if the plane falls a short distance in a low pressure pocket.

13. Passenger car—forces produced by brake drums against the wheels and road against the wheels. Drag race car—same as for passenger car or, if the racer is equipped with a drag chute which is released at the end of the run, the force of air against the drag chute.
    Jet plane—force of air against the airplane, force produced by reversing the engines just after landing. The engines produce a force opposite to the direction the plane is moving. Brakes and the ground produce forces against the wheels which stop the plane after landing.

Page 62. Problems

14. If 1 cm = 5 nt, then 3 cm = 15 nt.
15. If 1 cm = 10 nt, then 8 cm = 80 nt.

Page 63. Problem

16.

Page 64. Problem

17.

Page 66. Problem

18. Answers will vary depending on accuracy of drawing. The students may be inter-

ested to note that the larger the scale of the parallelogram the greater the accuracy of the calculation when the same method and tools are used. Pythagorean Theorem can be used: c² = a² + b²

Resultant = 360 nt

Page 66. Demonstration
You may wish to demonstrate the entire activity or have students do selected parts. Knowledge of your students' ability will be helpful in determining how this activity will be used.

Page 67. Problem
19. Scale 1 cm = 5 km/hr
Resultant = 21 km/hr
Answers will vary according to accuracy.
Using Pythagorean Theorem:
c² = a² + b²
c² = (20)² + 5²
c² = 425 km²
c = 20.6 km

Pages 68-70. Study Questions
A. True or False
1. True 2. True 3. True 4. True 5. False (Gravity is a force.) 6. True 7. True 8. True 9. False (Speed is not a vector quantity.) 10. False (The kilometer/hour is a unit of speed.)

B. Multiple Choice
1. newton 2. 30 km/hr 3. $v = \dfrac{d}{t}$ 4. loses velocity 5. 15 km/min/sec 6. vector 7. add 8. draw a parallelogram 9. kilograms 10. North pole

C. Completion
1. velocity 2. direction 3. 180 lb 4. zero 5. direction 6. accelerated 7. newton (nt) 8. force 9. deceleration 10. negative

D. How and Why
1. $v = \dfrac{d}{t} = \dfrac{120 \text{ km}}{2 \text{ hr}} \bigg| \dfrac{1 \text{ hr}}{60 \text{ min}} = 1 \text{ km/min}$

2. $a = \dfrac{v_2 - v_1}{t} = \dfrac{50 \text{ km/hr} - 10 \text{ km/hr}}{6 \text{ sec}} =$ 6.7 km/hr/sec

3. $v = at = \dfrac{1 \text{ m}}{\text{sec/sec}} \bigg| \dfrac{6 \text{ sec}}{} = 6 \text{ m/sec}$

4. $v = \dfrac{v_1 + v_2}{2} = \dfrac{0 \text{ m/sec} + 6 \text{ m/sec}}{2} =$ 3 m/sec

5. $d = vt = \dfrac{3 \text{ m}}{\text{sec}} \bigg| \dfrac{6 \text{ sec}}{} = 18 \text{ m}$

6. (a) 23 km/hr (b) 2 km/hr (c) 2 min to 2.7 min (d) 0.5 min to 2 min, 2.7 min to 4.2 min and 4.8 min to 5 min

7. $t = \dfrac{v}{a} = \dfrac{30 \text{ m/sec}}{6 \text{ m/sec/sec}} = 5 \text{ sec}$
$v = \dfrac{v_1 + v_2}{2} = \dfrac{30 \text{ m/sec} + 0 \text{ m/sec}}{2} =$ 15 m/sec
$d = vt = \dfrac{15 \text{ m}}{\text{sec}} \bigg| \dfrac{5 \text{ sec}}{} = 75 \text{ m}$

8. Winds affect the velocity and direction of the airplane's flight. Headwinds decrease velocity with respect to the ground and tailwinds increase the velocity. Crosswinds may force an airplane off a direct course and must be compensated for in air navigation.

9. No. The forward push of air by the fan (action force) is equal to the opposing reaction force of the air against the fan. The blast of air pushes forward against the sail and the fan pushes backward

against the boat. Since action and reaction forces are equal and opposite, the boat does not move.
10. A hammer's weight is the force of gravity acting on the hammer. For example, a 0.5 lb hammer exerts 0.5 lb of force when lying at rest. When a hammer is swung to strike a nail, it is accelerated; both the force of gravity and the force of the arm accelerate it. This force, which is larger than the hammer's weight, is exerted against the nail.

Page 71. Investigations
1. A flight instructor at a local airport will probably have information and might be willing to talk to the class.
2. A sailboat can sail against the wind if there is a resultant force vector opposite the wind direction.
3. An airline company, as well as books on flight, are good sources of information.

Unit One, Chapter 4
Laws of Motion

PERFORMANCE OBJECTIVES
Goal: Students will gain an understanding of Newton's laws, the effects of gravity on motion, projectile motion, motion in curves, and momentum.
Objectives: Upon completion of the reading and activities and when asked to diagram, demonstrate, or respond either orally or on a written test, students will:

4:1-3	K	state Newton's three laws of motion and give examples of each.
4:1-3	S/P	conduct activities to demonstrate Newton's three laws of motion.
4:4	S/P	conduct an activity to demonstrate the effects of gravity on falling bodies.
4:4	P	compare and contrast the effects of gravity on falling bodies and bodies thrown vertically upward.
4:5	S/P	conduct an activity to illustrate how the velocity of a projectile changes during its flight.
4:6	P/K	compare and contrast centrifugal force and centripetal force.
4:7	K	indicate the relationships among mass, velocity, and momentum.
4:7	K	explain conservation of momentum.
	S/A	When conducting activities, students will use laboratory materials and equipment in the prescribed manner.

Upon completion of the reading and activities, students will exhibit an interest in science by:

A	reading unassigned literature related to ideas presented in the chapter.
A	relating ideas presented in the chapter to things which happen in everyday life.
A/S	calculating the momentum of various moving bodies and explaining the results to the class.
A	requesting permission to perform demonstrations to the class.

EQUIPMENT FOR ACTIVITIES
aluminum foil
ball, rubber
   Ping-Pong
   metal
balloon
boards, 15 cm × 4 m, 2
coins, 2
dry cell, 6 V
electric bell
glass, 8 oz tumbler
hammer
metronome
nails
paper, 8 × 15 cm card
   graph
protractor
rulers, metric
solder, liquid
spring scales, 3
stick (60-cm)
stopper, rubber
string
tube, plastic 2 cm × 15 cm
washers, 9
wire, bell
wire hanger

Page 74. Problem
1. slot car—wheels against track; sailboat—wind on sails; girl in bus—motion of bus. Speed and direction of each of these mov-

ing bodies is directly proportional to the size and direction of the forces involved.

Page 75. Problems
2. car—tires against road; arrow—snap of the bow after it is stretched and released; jet airplane—hot gases escaping from engine; roller skates—push of skate against the sidewalk or floor.
3. rocket—atmosphere when a rocket enters the earth's atmosphere, gravity and Earth when a rocket falls back to the ground; submarine—water against the hull, rudder pushing against water when course is changed, gravity when submarine submerges, buoyant force of the water; surfboard—wave against board, beach against board at end of ride, gravity in a wipe out; car—road against tires; bowling ball—force of floor on a spinning ball will cause it to curve, backstop stops ball at end of alley.
4. Gravity is involved when a rocket falls back to Earth, a submarine submerges, a surfboard wipes out; by shifting his weight a rider controls surfboard. In each case gravity forces the body toward the earth.
5. Seat belts hold the passenger in the seat if the car stops suddenly and prevents him or her from being thrown forward and possibly injured. Also, the seat belt may prevent injury by holding a passenger in the seat during an accident.

Page 77. Problems
6. A fly. A fly has less mass; therefore less inertia. Its wings can create more force per unit of body mass.
7. The moving van needs more force to stop than a sports car at the same speed. The moving van has more mass; therefore, for the same deceleration, it will need more force.
8. Pedaling a bicycle hard to make it go faster; jumping up out of a chair; throwing a ball. Other examples may be given by students.
9. In each case a force causes a body to accelerate.

Page 78. Problems
10. Your weight, a force, down on the earth.
11. Upward force of the floor on your feet.
12. Recoil, the sharp backward movement of the cannon, is the reaction force that fires the shell out of the barrel.

Page 80. Problems
13. Action force of pencil against paper is opposed by the reaction force of paper against pencil.
14. The rocket engine and balloon would have the same motion if there was no gravity. The balloon and rocket would continue in a path out to space. The motions would be faster since there would be no opposing friction force due to air resistance.
15. (a) Newton's third law—action and reaction forces
    (b) Newton's first law—inertia
    (c) Newton's second law—greater force, greater distance
    (d) Newton's first law—inertia
    (e) Newton's first or third law—depending on frame of reference

Page 83. Problem
16. $v = gt = \dfrac{9.8 \text{ m}}{\text{sec}^2} \cdot \dfrac{2 \text{ sec}}{1} = 19.6 \text{ m/sec}$

Page 84. Problems
17. $d = \frac{1}{2} gt^2$ $\quad d = \dfrac{1}{2} \cdot \dfrac{9.8 \text{ m}}{\text{sec}^2} \cdot \dfrac{9 \text{ sec}^2}{1}$
    $d = 44.1 \text{ m}$
18. $d = \frac{1}{2} gt^2$
    $d = \dfrac{1}{2} \cdot \dfrac{9.8 \text{ m}}{\text{sec}^2} \cdot \dfrac{1 \text{ sec}^2}{1}$
    $d = 4.9 \text{ m}$

Page 89. Problems
19. Due to inertia the car tends to keep moving in a straight line rather than rounding the curve. Ice decreases the friction between the tires and the road (centripetal force).
20. Inertia tends to cause it to go off in a straight line instead of curving in a circle; your hand must keep pulling inward.
21. More of the car's weight is centered over the wheels. This increases the centripetal force and makes it less likely for the car to slide off the road.

Page 90. Problems
22. billiard ball has more momentum because it has more mass
23. The momentum of the tennis ball is equal to the momentum of the golf ball because both have the same mass and velocity.

Pages 93-94. Study Questions

A. True or False
1. True 2. True 3. False (It takes greater force to accelerate a golf ball than a baseball from rest to a speed of 16 m/sec.) 4. True 5. False (Action-reaction forces make a rotary sprinkler spin.) 6. False (A hypothesis is not always correct.) 7. True 8. False (To hit a distant target, a bow is aimed above the target.) 9. True 10. True

B. Multiple Choice
1. balance 2. more 3. action-reaction 4. bowling ball 5. proportional to 6. educated guess 7. 9.8 m/sec² 8. parabola 9. inertia 10. centrifugal

C. Completion
1. Centripetal 2. newton, pound 3. gravity 4. reaction 5. vertical 6. terminal velocity 7. increases 8. acceleration 9. zero 10. forces opposing motion

D. How and Why
1. Pendulum swinging back and forth. Coasting automobile. Trying to move a heavy boulder. Other examples given by students. Passenger in an automobile thrown forward when car stops suddenly and passenger hits dashboard. Other examples given by students.
2. (a) 1st—inertia
   (b) 3rd—action and reaction forces
   (c) 2nd—deceleration
   (d) 3rd—action and reaction
3. $v = gt = 9.8 \text{ m/sec}^2 \times 3 \text{ sec} = 29.4 \text{ m/sec}$
4. Drop the stone off the bridge and time the seconds it falls. Use the formula $d = \frac{1}{2} gt^2$
5. $t = v/\text{-}g = \dfrac{9.8 \text{ m/sec}}{9.8 \text{ m/sec}^2} = 1 \text{ sec}$
6. The resultant of the horizontal and vertical motion is a parabola.
7. The force of gravity pulls the arrow toward the ground while it is moving forward. An arrow aimed above the mark would land on target.
8. The momentum of an object varies directly with its mass and speed. A bowling ball has more momentum than a tennis ball when both are at the same speed. A tennis ball at 5 cm/sec has less momentum than one at 50 cm/sec.
9. The centripetal force causes large particles to move to the bottom of the test tubes in the centrifuge. (See page 89.)
10. A falling sheet of open paper has more air resistance than a crumpled sheet of paper. Therefore, a crumpled sheet of paper falls faster.

Page 95. Investigations
1. Model plane kits supply information on parts and their functions.
2. A report on space scientists Goddard or von Braun might be of interest to students.
3. Many books on flight explain the forces involved in changing speed and direction. Many motor car manufacturers can provide this information.

Unit Two Properties of Matter

Goal: Students will gain an understanding of the nature of matter.

Unit Two, Chapter 1
Classification of Matter

PERFORMANCE OBJECTIVES
Goal: Students will gain an understanding of the ways in which matter is classified and the differences between physical and chemical changes.
Objectives: Upon completion of the reading and activities and when asked to diagram, demonstrate, or respond either orally or on a written test, students will:

1:1	K	define matter.
1:1	S	conduct an activity to demonstrate that no two pieces of matter can occupy the same place at the same time.
1:2-4	P	distinguish between elements, compounds, and mixtures.
1:4	S/P	conduct an activity to separate a mixture of salt and sand.
1:4	S/P	conduct an activity to demonstrate how iodine can be separated from a mixture by sublimation.
1:4	S/P	conduct an activity to demonstrate how water can be purified by evaporation and condensation.
1:5-6	P	contrast the physical properties of objects with the chemical properties of objects.
1:5	S	calculate the density of an object given dimensions and mass.
1:5	S/P	conduct an activity to determine the freezing point of water.
1:7-8	P	contrast physical changes with chemical changes.
1:8	S/P	conduct an activity to demonstrate the difference between a mixture of iron and sulfur and a compound of iron and sulfur (iron sulfide).
1:8	S/P	conduct an activity to demonstrate a chemical change in the production of hydrogen and to determine if hydrogen has been produced.
1:8	S/P	conduct an activity to demonstrate methods of making physical separations.
1:8	S/P	conduct an activity to demonstrate distillation.
1:8	S/P	conduct an activity to demonstrate some characteristics of a chemical change.
	S/A	When conducting activities, students will use laboratory materials and equipment in the prescribed manner.

Upon completion of the reading and activities, students will exhibit an interest in science by:

A	reading unassigned literature related to ideas presented in the chapter.
A/S	voluntarily helping to maintain and care for laboratory materials and equipment.

EQUIPMENT FOR ACTIVITIES
Equipment
asbestos pad
balance, pan
beaker (400-ml)
block of wood, rectangular
Bunsen burner
condensing tube
distilling flask
filter paper
flask (400-ml)
flask, distilling
funnel (glass)
glass tubing (10-cm, 45-cm)
graduated cylinder (25-ml)
hammer
magnet
milk bottle
mineral oil
plastic bag
ring stand and ring
rubber 2-hole stopper (to fit milk bottle)
rubber 1-hole stopper (to fit test tube)
  (to fit distilling flask)
rubber tube pinch clamp
rubber tubing (15-cm)
safety glasses
safety apron, gloves
soft glass test tubes
stone

string
test tubes
thermometers (Celsius), 2
towel
watch glass (large)
wire gauge square

Reagents
alcohol (ethyl)
aluminum squares
hydrochloric acid (dilute)
ice cubes
ice, crushed
iodine crystals
iron filings
mineral oil
sand
sugar
sulfur (powdered)
table salt
water
zinc (mossy)

Page 100 (4M). Problems
1. oxygen, carbon, magnesium, mercury, silver, sodium, chlorine, iron
2. (a) iron (b) carbon (c) mercury (d) oxygen (e) chlorine

Page 101 (5M). Problems
3. nitrogen, hydrogen—1:3
4. N_2O
5. carbon, hydrogen, oxygen
   iron, oxygen
   sodium, hydrogen, carbon, oxygen
   hydrogen, oxygen

Page 102 (6M). Problem
6. use magnet to attract iron filings or dissolve salt in water

Page 103 (7M). Problem
7. (a) distillation (b) filtration

Page 105 (9M). Problems
8. Answers will vary. For example, aluminum—aircraft, low density
   balsam wood—models, low density
   lead—fishing sinkers, high density
   cast iron—engine blocks, high density
   styrofoam—packing material, low density
9. Oil is more dense than water. This can be observed by combining the two liquids.

Page 106 (10M). Problem
10. (a) coal and snow—color, melting point, density
    (b) strawberry ice cream and vanilla ice cream—color, taste
    (c) soda pop and water—taste, density
    (d) lead and aluminum—density
    (e) salt and sugar—taste
    (f) baseball and football—shape

Page 108 (12M). Problems
11. Substances that burn: paper, wood, sulfur, hydrogen, most manufactured fibers, cotton, etc.
12. Burning is a chemical property since it depends upon uniting with another substance, usually O_2.

Page 112 (16M). Problems
13. Chemical changes: (b) burning sulfur (d) baking a cake
14. Physical changes: (a) opening an envelope (c) paneling a room
15. Separation of:
    (a) sulfur-sand; carbon disulfide (CS_2) or carbon tetrachloride (CCl_4)
    (b) iodine-iron; heat or magnet
    (c) salt-iodine; heat or alcohol
    (d) sand-sugar; water and filter
16. A chemical change, electrolysis, separates water to H_2 and O_2.

Page 113 (17M). Problems
17. Separations in the activity were physical (distillation of liquid).
18. The water in the condenser cools the vapor so that it condenses.

Page 114 (18M). Problems
19. The HCl was evaporated to show that it did *not* produce the crystals.
20. Aluminum dissolves in HCl; a new compound is formed (white crystals); H_2 gas is formed; test tube becomes warm.
21. Aluminum chloride is formed:
    $2\,Al + 6\,HCl \rightarrow AlCl_3 + 3\,H_2\,(g)$

Pages 115-117 (19M-21M). Study Questions
A. True or False
1. True 2. False (Ideas are not matter because they have no mass.) 3. False (Making ice cubes is a physical change.) 4. True 5. False (Sodium chloride is a compound.) 6.

False (The composition of a mixture varies.) 7. False (Elements in compounds can be separated by chemical means.) 8. False (Mixtures can be separated by physical means.) 9. True 10. True

B. Multiple Choice
1. mixture 2. compound 3. Burning 4. Water 5. Burning 6. solid 7. gas 8. temperature 9. Rusting 10. element

C. Completion
1. mixture 2. physical 3. temperature, pressure 4. physical 5. chemical 6. low 7. physical 8. Density 9. chemical 10. taste

D. How and Why
1. Chemical properties of water: relatively stable, oxidizes metals, a product of a neutralization reaction, forms many crystal hydrates.
   Physical properties: density = 1g/cm³, MP = 0°C, BP = 100°C, specific heat = 1 cal/g-C°, highly polar molecules, ice is less dense than water, colorless, odorless, tasteless.
2. If a liquid turns blue while you are absent, it does not necessarily mean that a chemical change has taken place.
3. Physical—shape, color, taste, floats in water.
   Chemical—inside turns brown when exposed to air.
4. Physical (and chemical).
5. It can be demonstrated that helium will displace a liquid, therefore it has mass.
6. A mixture is not the same throughout, can be separated by physical means, and has no definite proportion of components. A compound is same composition throughout, is decomposed by chemical means, and has definite proportion by weight.
7. Mixtures—air, soil, concrete, lemonade
   Compounds—water, sugar, salt, ammonia
8. Seat covers should have: strength, resilience, color, durability, little static producing ability.
9. Evaporate a small amount of the liquid. If a residue remains, it is salt water.
10. Using a distilling flask and condenser, the liquid with the lower boiling point (if it is sufficiently different) will boil off first. See Activity on page 113 (17M).

Page 117 (21M). Investigations
1. Some properties that might be tested are density, hardness, color and luster.
2. There is usually enough information on the container of antifreeze to provide data for this investigation.
3. Results will vary depending on the kind of oil and concentration of salt solutions. Be sure you have a thermometer with a wide enough range. The oil will become *very* hot (about 400° F).
4. A Brinell test calculates the hardness of materials (especially metals) by forcing hardened steel balls against the sample at a specified pressure.

Unit Two, Chapter 2
Atoms and Compounds

PERFORMANCE OBJECTIVES
Goal: Students will gain an understanding of the nature of ionic and covalent bonds in terms of the atomic theory and electron structure.
Objectives: Upon completion of the reading and activities and when asked to diagram, demonstrate, or respond either orally or on a written test, students will:

2:1	K	state the atomic theory and define atom.
2:2	K	define and list the characteristics of electrons, protons, and neutrons.
2:3	P	discuss the value of models in explaining scientific ideas.
2:3	P	compare and contrast the Bohr model of the atom with the electron cloud model of the atom.
2:3	K	define isotope.
2:4	K	explain electron energy levels or shells.
2:5	P	compare the properties of an element with the properties of a compound.
2:6	P	differentiate between ionic and covalent bonding.
2:6	S/K	explain ionic bonding between sodium and chlorine.
2:6	S/K	explain covalent bonding between chlorine and hydrogen.

2:7	K	define valence and list the valences of some common elements.
2:7	K	write the chemical formulas for a given list of combinations of elements.
2:8-9	P	compare and contrast binary compounds with compounds containing polyatomic ions.
2:9	S/P	determine the percent of oxygen in potassium chlorate in a teacher demonstration.
	S/A	When conducting activities, students will use laboratory materials and equipment in the prescribed manner.

Upon completion of the reading and activities, students will exhibit an interest in science by:

	A	reading unassigned literature related to the ideas presented in the chapter.
	A/S	volunteering to construct models of atoms and molecules.

EQUIPMENT FOR ACTIVITIES
Bunsen burner
gumdrops
laboratory balance
potassium chlorate (powdered)
safety glasses
test tube (Pyrex)
test tube clamp
toothpicks

Page 121 (25M). Problem
1. Each additional neutron increases the mass of an atom by one a.m.u.

Page 124 (28M). Problems
2. (a) HCl—1 hydrogen, 1 chlorine
   (b) Na$_2$O—2 sodium, 1 oxygen
   (c) KOH—1 potassium, 1 oxygen, 1 hydrogen
   (d) H$_2$SO$_4$—2 hydrogen, 1 sulfur, 4 oxygen
   (e) F$_2$—2 fluorine
   (f) Fe$_2$S$_3$—2 iron (III), 3 sulfur
   (g) Br$_2$—2 bromine
   (h) NH$_3$—1 nitrogen (III), 3 hydrogen
3. Compounds: (a) HCl (b) Na$_2$O (c) KOH (d) H$_2$SO$_4$ (f) Fe$_2$S$_3$ (h) NH$_3$
   Elements: (e) F$_2$ (g) Br$_2$
4. Symbols indicate the kind of atoms in the substance. The subscripts indicate the ratio of the atoms.

Page 125 (29M). Problem
5. Na—silvery metal reacts violently with water
   Cl—yellowish-green gas, highly corrosive
   NaCl—white solid used in cooking as a seasoning

Page 126 (30M). Problem
6. H$_2$O

Page 127 (31M). Problem
7. (a) sodium bromide, NaBr
   (b) potassium iodide, KI
   (c) hydrogen bromide, HBr
   (d) hydrogen sulfide, H$_2$S
   (e) magnesium fluoride, MgF$_2$
   (f) calcium chloride, CaCl$_2$
   (g) lithium sulfide, Li$_2$S
   (h) aluminum chloride, AlCl$_3$
   (i) copper (II) sulfide, CuS

Page 128 (32M). Problems
8. (a) NaCl, sodium chloride
   (b) CuBr, copper (I) bromide
   (c) BaS, barium sulfide
   (d) MgO, magnesium oxide
   (e) KI, potassium iodide
   (f) MgBr$_2$, magnesium bromide
   (g) CaS, calcium sulfide
   (h) CuO, copper (II) oxide
   (i) FeCl$_3$, iron (III) chloride
   (j) FeO, iron (II) oxide
9. (a) calcium bromide, CaBr$_2$
   (b) potassium oxide, K$_2$O
   (c) aluminum chloride, AlCl$_3$
   (d) iron (III) iodide, FeI$_3$
   (e) copper (I) sulfide, Cu$_2$S
   (f) lithium fluoride, LiF
   (g) sodium bromide, NaBr
   (h) copper (II) chloride, CuCl$_2$

Page 131 (35M). Problems
10. (a) sodium nitrate, NaNO$_3$
    (b) silver sulfate, Ag$_2$SO$_4$
    (c) iron (II) chloride, FeCl$_2$
    (d) potassium phosphate, K$_3$PO$_4$
    (e) copper (II) iodide, CuI$_2$
11. (a) Na$_2$SO$_4$, sodium sulfate
    (b) (NH$_4$)$_3$PO$_4$, ammonium phosphate
    (c) FeO, iron (II) oxide
    (d) AgNO$_3$, silver nitrate
    (e) KBr, potassium bromide
12. In Problem 10:
    (a) 1 sodium, 1 nitrogen, 3 oxygen

(b) 2 silver, 1 sulfur, 4 oxygen
(c) 1 iron, 2 chlorine
(d) 3 potassium, 1 phosphorus, 4 oxygen
(e) 1 copper, 2 iodine
In Problem 11:
(a) 2 sodium, 1 sulfur, 4 oxygen
(b) 3 nitrogen, 12 hydrogen, 1 phosphorus, 4 oxygen
(c) 1 iron, 1 oxygen
(d) 1 silver, 1 nitrogen, 3 oxygen
(e) 1 potassium, 1 bromine

Page 131 (35M). Demonstration

Before you start the demonstration, have the students practice calculating the percentage of composition. Make sure that the students understand each step in the data table and how it relates to the calculations.
Sample data table:
1. Mass of test tube with KClO$_3$ _____ g
2. Mass of empty test tube _____ g
3. Mass of KClO$_3$ (Step 1—Step 2) _____ g
4. Mass of test tube + KClO$_3$ after heat _____ g
5. Mass of oxygen driven off (Step 3—Step 4) _____ g
6. Percent of oxygen in KClO$_3$ _____ %
$= \dfrac{\text{Step 5}}{\text{Step 3}} \Big| 100$

You can calculate the theoretical percentage of oxygen in KClO$_3$:

1 atom K @ 39 a.m.u. = 39 a.m.u.
1 atom Cl @ 35.5 a.m.u. = 35.5 a.m.u.
3 atoms O @ 16 a.m.u. = 48 a.m.u.
Total 122.5 a.m.u.

% oxygen = $\dfrac{\text{a.m.u. oxygen}}{\text{a.m.u. compound}} \Big| 100\%$ =

$\dfrac{48 \text{ a.m.u.}}{122.5 \text{ a.m.u.}} \Big| 100\%$ = 39%

Calculate percent error:
$\dfrac{\text{difference between theoretical value and experimental value}}{\text{theoretical value}} \Big| 100\%$

If students have a large percentage of error, ask them to find some explanation for the large error.

You may also have the students find the percent of water in CuSO$_4$ · 5 H$_2$O or in BaCl$_2$ · 2 H$_2$O. These compounds are a bit safer for the students to use than KClO$_3$. You can also use larger quantities without danger.

Pages 132-134. (36M-38M). Study Questions

A. True or False
1. True 2. True 3. True 4. False (The mass of an electron is many times smaller than the mass of a proton.) 5. True 6. True 7. False (Atoms of the same element have different masses.) 8. True 9. False (Electrons in the outer shell of an atom have great effect upon its chemical properties.) 10. True

B. Multiple Choice
1. Dalton 2. molecule 3. oxygen 4. neutral 5. FeS 6. one ion 7. two 8. proton 9. 2 10. 12

C. Completion
1. 1+ 2. loses 3. three 4. covalent 5. ion 6. isotopes 7. two 8. Ionic 9. positively 10. nucleus

D. How and Why
1. In covalent bonding, electrons are shared by atoms; in ionic bonding, electrons are transferred and atoms are bonded electrostatically.
2. (a) NaCl, sodium chloride (b) NH$_4$NO$_3$, ammonium nitrate (c) Ca$_3$(PO$_4$)$_2$, calcium phosphate
3. (a) potassium sulfate, K$_2$SO$_4$ (b) sulfur dioxide, SO$_2$ (c) mercury (I) sulfide, Hg$_2$S
4. Two electrons from the outer shell of Mg could be transferred to the outer shells of two bromine atoms. The resulting charged particles would bond together by electrostatic attraction.
5. Electrons have negligible mass, negative charge, and orbit the nucleus. Protons are positive and have same mass as neutrons. Neutrons have no charge. Protons and neutrons are found in nucleus.
6. Oxygen has 2 electrons in first shell, 6 in second shell.
7. (1) All matter is made of atoms. (2) Atoms cannot be divided. (3) All atoms of the same element are alike.
    The last two have been modified by experimentation. Atoms can be divided into subatomic particles. Isotopes show that all atoms of the same element are not alike. All atoms of the same element have the same number of protons.
8. The element's valence should be 2+. It would probably give up the two electrons

in the outer shell to form compounds. It would probably exhibit ionic bonding.
9. Magnesium, 1 atom; nitrogen, 2; oxygen, 4.
10. One carbon atom can share two pairs of electrons with one atom of oxygen to form CO or share one pair of electrons with each of two oxygen atoms to form CO_2.

Pages 134-135 (38M-39M). Investigations
1. Chemical formulas for some common substances are found in the *Handbook of Chemistry and Physics*. Examples are: Sodium bicarbonate, $NaHCO_3$; Vinegar, CH_3COOH; Aspirin, $CH_3COOC_6H_4COOH$; Borax, $Na_2B_4O_7$; Cream of Tartar, $KHC_4H_4O_6$; Epsom Salts, $MgSO_4$; Milk of Magnesia, $Mg(OH)_2$; Plaster of Paris, $CaSO_4$; Washing Soda, Na_2CO_3.
2. Some students might be interested in reporting on the life of Lise Meitner, one of the early atomic physicists along with Bohr, Rutherford, and Fermi.
3.

	Shell 1	Shell 2		Total
H	1			1
He	2			2
Li	2	1		3
Be	2	2		4
B	2	2	1	5
C	2	2	2	6
N	2	2	3	7
O	2	2	4	8
F	2	2	5	9
Ne	2	2	6	10

4. Students may want to use other materials such as gumdrops and toothpicks.
5. Some examples are: H_2O, CO_2, SO_2, H_2S, $CaCO_3$, NH_4OH.

Unit Two, Chapter 3
Solids, Liquids, and Gases

PERFORMANCE OBJECTIVES
Goal: Students will gain an understanding of the main characteristics of solids and fluids and factors which cause changes in phase.
Objectives: Upon completion of the reading and activities and when asked to diagram, demonstrate, or respond either orally or on a written test, students will:

3:1	K	name the three common phases of matter.
3:2	K	define solid and list examples of solids.
3:3	K	define crystal and list examples of crystalline substances.
	S/P	conduct an activity to compare crystals of different substances and list similarities and differences for these crystals.
3:3	S/P	examine a mica crystal under the microscope, diagram the crystal's shape, and explain the cleavage pattern.
3:4-5	P	compare types of bonding in crystals including ionic, covalent, and metallic bonding.
3:4	S	observe the growth of macromolecular crystals from a solution of sodium hydroxide, sodium dichromate dihydrate, lithium carbonate, and water.
3:5	P	explain why metals are good conductors of electricity and how this property is related to crystal structure.
3:6	P	compare the formation of crystals from a melt with the formation of crystals from a solution.
3:7	K	define amorphous solid and list examples of amorphous solids.
3:8	K	define liquids and list examples of liquids.
3:8	S/P	conduct an activity to demonstrate that alcohol molecules move into space between water molecules.
3:9-10	P	compare physical characteristics of gases with physical characteristics of liquids.
3:10	K	state and explain Pascal's law.
3:10	S/P	conduct an activity to demonstrate Pascal's law.
3:11-14	K	explain what happens when matter changes phase.
3:11	S/P	conduct an activity to demonstrate that the temperature of water does not change as it boils.
	S/A	When conducting activities, students will use laboratory materials and equipment in the prescribed manner.

Upon completion of the reading and activities, students will exhibit an interest in science by:

A   reading unassigned literature related to ideas presented in the chapter.
A/S   voluntarily building and demonstrating a crystal model.
A/S   voluntarily growing a large alum crystal and bringing it to class.
A   voluntarily visiting a local garage, examining the hydraulic lift, and calculating the force exerted on the small piston when it lifts an automobile.

EQUIPMENT FOR ACTIVITIES
Equipment
- beaker (250-ml)
- BB pellets
- Bunsen burner
- clamp for thermometer
- cloth
- colored paper
- evaporating dishes, 3
- filter paper
- glass jar (covered and uncovered)
- glass slide (microscope)
- glass tubing
- glass U-tube
- graduated cylinder (25-ml and 50-ml)
- graph paper
- hollow rubber ball
- lamp (40-watt) and socket
- magnifying glass
- marbles
- microscope
- pins
- ring stand and ring
- rubber band
- rubber sheeting
- rubber tubing
- shot (ball bearings)
- sink
- styrofoam balls, 6 small, 1 large
- test tube
- thermometers (Celsius), 2
- thistle tube
- thread
- toothpicks
- wire gauze

Reagents
- alcohol (ethyl or isopropyl)
- alum
- copper sulfate
- Epsom salts
- gelatin, unflavored
- ice cubes
- lithium carbonate crystals
- mercury metal
- mica
- nickel sulfate crystals
- potassium bromate
- Rochelle salt crystals
- sodium dichromate dihydrate
- sodium dichromate
- sodium hydroxide (solid)
- sodium nitrate crystals
- sugar
- sulfur
- table salt

Page 138 (42M). Activity
Try to have several microscopes available so that each student has a chance to observe several types of crystal structure.

Compound	Formula	Structure
sodium chloride	NaCl	cubic
Rochelle salt (potassium sodium tartrate)	$KNaC_4H_4O_6 \cdot H_2O$	orthorhombic
alum (potassium ammonium sulfate)	KNH_4SO_4	cubic
nickel sulfate	$NiSO_4 \cdot 7H_2O$	orthorhombic
copper (II) sulfate	$CuSO_4 \cdot 5H_2O$	triclinic
sodium nitrate	$NaNO_3$	orthorhombic

Page 140 (44M). Additional Information: Attractive Forces
Some crystals are held together by van der Waals forces. **Van der Waals forces** are the attraction of the positively charged nucleus of one atom for the electrons of another atom. Van der Waals forces are very weak compared to ionic bonds.

Another force is the **dipole-dipole attraction.** When two atoms form a covalent bond, the shared electrons are not always shared equally. For example, two hydrogen atoms and one oxygen atom form one molecule of water through covalent bonding. Oxygen has eight protons in its nucleus. Hydrogen has one proton. Therefore, oxygen has a greater positive nuclear charge than hydrogen. For this reason, electrons in the water molecule spend more time near the oxygen nucleus than the hydrogen nucleus. Thus, the oxygen end of the molecule has a negative charge. The hydrogen end of the molecule is positively charged; it has an absence of electrons. Since the water molecule has a positive end and a negative end, it is called a **dipole** (two poles).

In effect, a dipole molecule acts like a magnet. It has positive and negative ends like a magnet's north and south poles. In dipole-dipole attraction, the positive end of one molecule attracts the negative end of other molecules. The positive end of the others will attract the negative end of still other molecules, and so on. This produces a crystal that is held together by weak attractive forces. These forces are far weaker than the ionic attraction in a crystal such as sodium chloride.

Crystals formed by van der Waals and dipole forces have some similar properties. They are soft and have low melting points. They do not conduct electricity. Iodine crystals are a good example of crystals formed by van der Waals bonding.

Page 141 (45M). Demonstration

This activity illustrates the formation of a "double compound" (note that Rochelle salt is a "double compound"). Lithium trisodium chromate hexahydrate is formed by the reaction of sodium dichromate dihydrate with lithium carbonate and sodium hydroxide. The crystals of $LiNa_3(CrO_4)_2 \cdot 6H_2O$ are hexagonal and yellow in color.

If crystals fail to form spontaneously, evaporate few drops of the solution and use the residue as seed crystals.

Page 143 (47M). Activity

The structure of sulfur crystals changes with temperature. At room temperature sulfur has rhombic crystals. Above room temperature but below the melting point, it has monoclinic crystals. If cooled very quickly, plastic sulfur can be formed.

Page 144 (48M). Activity

When extra salt is added, the solution becomes supersaturated. By suspending the crystal, crystallization is facilitated. The crystal provides a natural surface for the formation of other crystals. Be sure the beaker is clean and unscratched.

Page 144 (48M). Problems

1. Both melting and dissolving involve increase in disorder of a substance. When a substance melts its molecules become less ordered and move about more because heat was applied. Energy is given off. When a substance dissolves, molecules of solvent interfere with its structure. Energy is usually absorbed.
2. Very little difference. The crystals in both cases resume original structure. In one case space between molecules decreases. In the other, solvent molecules no longer disrupt structure.
3. They have no regular crystalline structure, yet they are solids.

Page 148 (52M). Problem
4. Pressure is decreased.

Page 149 (53M). Problem
5. The air forced into the balloon increases the internal pressure causing the balloon to expand.

Page 150 (54M). Problem
6. Air "gives" when hitting bumps, etc., by compressing. A liquid does not.

Page 150 (54M). Demonstration

Water will spray in all directions so do this experiment outside if possible. The liquid forced into the ball will not compress. The pressure exerted by the water is transmitted equally to all surfaces. Water flows at same speed from each hole.

Page 151 (55M). Problem
7. The air will compress and the brake force will not be transmitted to the brake shoes on the wheels.

Page 152 (56M). Problems
8. Molecules of water move farther apart when freezing.
9. Molecules in the vapor phase move farther apart.

Page 155 (59M). Problems
10. At 1000 mm Hg pressure, BP of H_2O is greater than 100° C.
11. The pressure cooker increases the boiling point of water, and as a result, the tem-

perature inside the cooker is hotter than under normal conditions. Therefore, the food cooks faster.

Page 155 (59M). Additional Information: Liquefication

Generally, in a liquid there are two bond forces acting: dipole-dipole and van der Waals.

The van der Waals forces appear to get larger as more electrons and protons are involved in the substance. This would be expected, since van der Waals attraction occurs between the electrons of one particle and the protons of another. Radon gas is composed of atoms with 86 protons and 86 electrons. Thus, it would more likely be found as a liquid than would helium. Helium has atoms with only two electrons and two protons. In liquids, the molecules with the greater number of electrons should attract each other more strongly and be less likely to change to a gas.

Since dipoles attract each other, liquids whose molecules are dipoles tend to be less likely to form a gas than do similar compounds whose molecules are not dipoles. Dipoles have greater attraction to each other, and additional heat is needed to break these bonds.

Bonding type also has some effect on the melting points of substances which occur as solids at normal temperatures. Molecules of solid methane, for example, are held together only by weak van der Waals forces. Thus, methane crystals have a much lower melting point than sodium chloride crystals (ionic bonds) or diamond (covalent bonds).

In the same manner, elements or compounds which normally are gases are more difficult to liquefy the fewer the number of electrons and protons.

Pages 157-159 (61M-63M). Study Questions
A. True or False
1. False (The molecules of a solid are held together by strong ionic, covalent, or metallic bonds.) 2. True 3. False (Different crystals have different cleavage properties.) 4. True 5. False (Crystals can be formed from a solution.) 6. True 7. True 8. False (The volume of a gas can be decreased by increasing the pressure on the gas in a closed container.) 9. False (If 10 ml of water is mixed with 10 ml of alcohol the total volume of the mixture will be less than 20 ml.) 10. True

B. Multiple Choice
1. brittle 2. electrons 3. electrons 4. sometimes 5. cleavage axis 6. increases 7. hard 8. flow 9. point, axis 10. Iodine

C. Completion
1. low 2. Pascal's 3. gases 4. glass, wax 5. freezing 6. temperature, pressure 7. vapor 8. increases 9. gas 10. 0

D. How and Why
1. Crystals have a definite crystalline structure with specific cleavage axes. Amorphous solids do not and may have a tendency to flow.
2. Generally, crystals are held together by ionic or covalent bonding. (If discussed, van der Waals and dipole-dipole forces could be mentioned.) Metallic bonding results from electrons being shared throughout the entire material.
3. Crystals may be formed from melts or from solution. The substance has a characteristic crystal pattern and the particles of the substance form this pattern through their particular type of bonding.
4. The particles of the two gases can fit between each other and still fill only the container. Since there are now more particles in the container than before, the pressure will increase.
5. The bubble is under greatest pressure at the bottom of the pool. As it rises the pressure decreases and the gas expands causing the bubble to get larger. This is the process which also occurs in boiling liquids.
6. As the temperature on a gas increases, the volume increases. As the pressure on gas increases, the volume decreases.
7. A small force on a small piston produces pressure undiminished through a liquid. This produces a large force on a great area (the hoist).
8. Both liquids and gases take the shape of their containers, they both flow, and they both respond to heat.
9. A diamond has a three-dimensional strong bond while graphite has only a two-dimensional strong bond. "Plates" of graphite can slide over each other.
10. Differences in phases result from relationships of particles of the substance. The farther apart the particles are, the less

effect they have on each other. The kinetic theory states that particles are always in motion. Temperature is a measure of the average kinetic energy. As temperature increases, the motion increases and the particles move farther apart, accounting for different phases.

Page 159 (63M). Investigations
1. Compressor liquefies a gas. The liquid is carried to refrigeration unit where it expands, changing to gas. This change of state takes heat energy from surrounding unit.
2. Synthetic diamonds are made by subjecting carbon (graphite) to great heat and pressure for extended lengths of time.
3. The major crystal types can be found in a geology book.
4. Hydraulic lift uses a reservoir of oil. Compressed air creates force on surface of reservoir. Pressure is transmitted through oil to piston which lifts car.

Unit Three Patterns of Matter

Goal: Students will gain an understanding of elements and their properties through a study of the periodic law.

Unit Three, Chapter 1
Periodic Table

PERFORMANCE OBJECTIVES
Goal: Students will gain an understanding of the location and use of certain information in the periodic table of the elements.

Objectives: Upon completion of the reading and activities and when asked to diagram, demonstrate, or respond either orally or on a written test, the student will:

1:1	K	define atomic mass.
1:1	S/P	conduct an activity with marbles and steel balls to demonstrate the value of using relative mass rather than actual mass when determining mass ratios.
1:2	S/P	conduct an activity to demonstrate how sodium, potassium, calcium, and magnesium might be grouped into two chemical families based upon their observed properties.
1:2-3	P	compare and contrast the periodic table developed by Mendeleev with the periodic table developed by Moseley.
1:3	K	list the meanings of the symbols and numbers contained in a square of the periodic table of the elements.
1:4	K	define isotopes.
1:4	K	list and explain the two methods used to distinguish between isotopes of an element.
1:5	P	explain why the average atomic mass is used when referring to the atomic weight of an element.
1:5	K	differentiate between the atomic mass number of an element and its average atomic mass.
1:6-7	P	compare and contrast the patterns in the periodic table of the elements when reading from left to right in a row and when reading from top to bottom in a column.
1:8	P	predict the chemical activity and probable bond types of some elements based on the position of each in the periodic table.
1:8	S/P	conduct an activity to demonstrate the relative chemical activity of the halogens.
	S/A	When conducting activities, students will use laboratory materials and equipment in the prescribed manner.

Upon completion of the reading and activities, students will exhibit an interest in science by:

A	reading unassigned literature related to ideas presented in the chapter.
A	voluntarily visiting a chemical laboratory and reporting to the class.

EQUIPMENT FOR ACTIVITIES
Equipment
  balance, pan
  beaker
  forceps
  knife
  marbles (about 20)
  steel balls (about 20), ball bearings, or BB shot
  test tube rack
  test tubes

Reagents
  bromine water
  calcium metal
  carbon tetrachloride (CCl_4)
  chlorine water
  iodine solution
  magnesium metal
  potassium bromide solution
  potassium iodide solution
  potassium metal
  sodium chloride solution
  sodium metal

Page 163 (3M). Activity
1. Mass of beaker + bearings, marbles _____g
2. Mass of empty beaker _____g
3. Mass of ball bearings + marbles (Step 1 − Step 2) _____g

4. Mass of ball bearing + beaker _____ g
5. Mass of marbles (Step 1 − Step 4) _____ g
6. Mass of ball bearings (Step 4 − Step 2) _____ g

$$\frac{\text{mass bearings}}{\text{mass marbles}} = \frac{X}{1}$$

X will represent ratio of ball bearing mass to mass of marbles as 1.

Questions:
1. The lightest object is given a mass of 1 because if the heavier were given a mass of 1, the lighter would be less than 1. The activity is, in effect, a way of using a binary compound XY to determine the mass of one element when the mass of the other is known.
2. If the ratio of marbles to ball bearings had been 2:1 rather than 1:1 (XY_2 rather than XY), an adjustment in the ratio would have had to be made.
3. The total mass of one element is of no value if the ratio of number of atoms is not known.

Page 164 (4M). Problem
1. 24 + 28 = 52 a.m.u.

Page 164 (4M). Activity
1. Sodium and potassium are stored in kerosene because they react with moisture in the air.
2. Family groups: Sodium, potassium; magnesium, calcium.
3.

	Chemical properties	Physical properties
Sodium and potassium	So reactive that it has little practical value in pure form. Combines violently with water.	Silvery white metal, soft
Magnesium and calcium	Less reactive than sodium and potassium. Combines readily with oxygen.	Silvery white metal, soft

Page 168 (8M). Problems
2. 74
3. Carbon
4. 11 protons
5. 23 protons and neutrons
6. 11 electrons

Page 170 (10M). Problems
7. Average atomic mass
$$= \frac{90\,(20\text{ a.m.u.}) + 10\,(22\text{ a.m.u.})}{100}$$
$$= \frac{2020\text{ a.m.u.}}{100} = 20.2\text{ a.m.u.}$$

8. If the atomic mass is not a whole number, it has isotopes.
9. F = 18.9984, Cl = 35.453, Br = 79.909, I = 126.9044
10.

	A	Z
Li	7	3
N	14	7
K	39	19

11.

	A	Z
Fe	56	26
Ra	226	88
Al	27	13
Au	197	79
Cu	64	29

Page 172 (12M). Problems
12. Both A and Z increase down a column.
13. Any element has more protons than an element above or to the left of it on the chart.

Page 173 (13M). Problem
14. From left to right, Z and A increase with three exceptions in A.

Page 175 (15M). Demonstrations
1. After shaking KI solution with CCl_4, two layers form (CCl_4, and solution). After shaking with chlorine water, CCl_4 layer turns purple. Cl_2 replaces iodine which dissolves in CCl_4.
2. Bromine water added to KI solution and CCl_4 gives a purple layer. Bromine displaces iodine.
3. After shaking KBr solution with CCl_4, two layers form. When chlorine water is added, the CCl_4 layer becomes reddish-brown in color. Chlorine displaces bromine.
4. After adding iodine solution to KBr and CCl_4, there is no color change in either layer. Iodine does not replace bromine.
5. When iodine is added to NaCl solution and CCl_4, no color change results. Iodine does not replace chlorine.

Pages 176-178 (16M-18M). Study Questions
A. *True or False*
1. True 2. True 3. True 4. False (Men-

deleev's periodic table was arranged according to increasing atomic mass.) 5. False (Atomic number of an element equals the total number of protons or electrons in an element's atom.) 6. False (The letter *A* is used as a symbol for atomic mass.) 7. False (The mass of an electron is so small that it is considered zero.) 8. False (Noble gases are chemically inactive.) 9. True 10. False (Boron is a metalloid.)

B. *Multiple Choice*
1. helium 2. protons 3. Carbon 4. 3
5. neutrons 6. left 7. right 8. magnesium
9. nonmetal 10. 3

C. *Completion*
1. sharing 2. Na_2O, H_2S, etc. 3. Mendeleev
4. IA 5. three 6. cobalt, nickel 7. 26, 30
8. protons, electrons 9. transition 10. greatest

D. *How and Why*
1. The periodic table gives clues to properties of elements. Families of elements tend to have similar properties. The chart also provides in one place, information on *A*, *Z*, electronic configuration, and other useful information.
2. Metals—lithium, sodium, copper, iron, and tin are examples
   Nonmetals—oxygen, nitrogen, fluorine, chlorine, and iodine are examples
3. average atomic mass
$$= \frac{60\ (30\ a.m.u.) + 40\ (32\ a.m.u.)}{100}$$
$$= \frac{3080\ a.m.u.}{100}$$
$$= 30.8\ a.m.u.$$
4.   *Metals*
   1-3 electrons in outer shell
   luster
   malleable or ductile
   conductor
        Nonmetals
   4-8 electrons in outer shell
   no luster
   brittle
   nonconductor
5. Transition metals—iron, cobalt, nickel, copper, and zinc are examples
6. The element has 15 protons, 15 electrons; has isotopes; atomic mass number 33; electron structure, 2, 8, 5 ($1s^2\ 2s^2\ 2p^6\ 3s^2\ 3p^3$); probably a nonmetal.
7. All the differences of metals and nonmetals plus numbers of subatomic particles. Magnesium has 2+ valence, chlorine 1−.
8. The two tables are alike except for the three pairs of elements whose *Z* and *A* are not in the same order: iodine—tellurium, cobalt—nickel, argon—potassium. The noble gases were unknown to Mendeleev and, therefore, were not in his table.
9. Chemically active metals are at the bottom left and chemically active nonmetals are at the top right of the table.
10. Noble gases have complete outer shells and do not take on or share electrons easily. Neon and helium are two examples.

Page 178 (18M). Investigations
1. Helium was discovered first in the spectrum of the sun. Its name is derived from the Greek word, *Helios,* sun. Helium was not actually isolated from Earth's atmosphere until several years later.
2. The rare earth elements are very difficult to isolate. The element Lanthanum was named after the Greek word meaning hidden. Rare earth elements are hardly ever found in the free state because they combine easily with other elements.
3. In 1863, John Newlands, an English chemist, found that, if he arranged the elements in order of their increasing atomic weights, there appeared to be a repetition of similar properties every eight elements.

    One of the earliest attempts at classification of elements was by John Dobereiner, a German chemist, in 1817. Dobereiner observed that the properties of the three metals calcium, barium, and strontium were very similar and that the atomic weight of strontium was about midway between those of calcium and barium. He found other groups of three elements that reacted similarly.
4. Mendeleev arranged the elements in a table according to their atomic masses. Moseley developed the table on the basis of the atomic weights of elements. There were several developments which led up to Moseley's periodic table. Ernest Marsden and Hans Geiger found the solution to the problem of the out of order elements. Students may wish to research into this development, as well as others in this field.

Page 179 (19M). Additional Activity

Provide students with the empty chart and the clues. Have them use the information below to put elements in their proper position on the periodic chart.

Periodic Chart for Mars and Its 30 Known Elements*

Can you place the elements in their proper place in the outline? Remember, natural laws are believed to be the same for the whole universe. (Symbols and elements used are, of course, fictitious.)

	+1	+2	+3	+4	−3	−2	−1	
1	A							B
2	C	D	E	F	G	N	I	L
3	‡	Z	Y	H	M	O	K	J
4	Q	⌀	R	T	S	U	V	W
5	X	P	♀	⊞	(Undiscovered at this time.)

Elements List

A	K	U
B	L	V
C	M	W
D	N	X
E	O	Y
F	P	Z
G	Q	⌀
H	R	♀
I	S	⊞
J	T	‡

1. The most metallic element: X
2. The most nonmetallic element: I
3. Inert gases are B, L, W, J. B is lightest, W is the heaviest, L is in period 2.
4. Their lightest element of all is A.

*Material used with permission of the San Diego Unified School District, San Diego, Calif.

5. All the following elements have three shells and the number of electrons listed in the outermost shell—‡-1, Z-2, Y-3, H-4, M-5, O-6, K-7
6. Element H has 14 protons
7. G has 7 electrons
8. C has an atomic weight of 5 and forms the compound CI
9. Q has only 1 electron in its outer shell but has 4 shells
10. The E family is made up of the elements E, Y, R, ♀ (in order of increasing weight)
11. ⊞ is the heaviest of all atoms and is radioactive
12. P is in period V and has a 2+ oxidation state
13. D is in period II and has the formula DI_2 for a salt
14. F is like our element carbon and is in the same family as H, T and ⊞
15. Their solvent like our most important liquid has the formula A_2N
16. Here are a few compounds based on the Martian chart—AV, ⌀I_2, DU, FA_4, ⌀U, ⌀$_3S_2$
17. Now every space should be filled. Can you give each element its proper atomic number?

Unit Three, Chapter 2
Families of Elements

PERFORMANCE OBJECTIVES
Goal: Students will gain an understanding of the properties of chemical families.
Objectives: Upon completion of the reading and activities and when asked to diagram, demonstrate, or respond either orally or on a written test, students will:

2:1	K	list the elements in the halogen family and indicate the characteristics of each.
2:1	K	define electrolysis.
2:1	S/P	conduct an activity to devise a test for starch
2:1	S/P	conduct an activity to test various foods for starch.
2:2	K	list the elements in the oxygen

2:2	K	family and indicate the characteristics of each element.
2:2	K	define allotropes and list examples.
2:2	S/P	conduct an activity to demonstrate that there is free oxygen in the atmosphere and that approximately 20% of air by volume is free oxygen.
2:2	S/P	conduct an activity to demonstrate how oxygen can be produced in the laboratory and to test some of the chemical properties of oxygen.
2:2	S/P	conduct an activity to demonstrate a method of determining the identity of sulfides of some metals.
2:2	K	define photoconductivity and indicate two elements which are good photoconductors.
2:3	K	list the elements in the nitrogen family and indicate the characteristics of each element.
2:3	S/P	conduct an activity to demonstrate a test for the nitrate ion.
2:3	K	state the law of multiple proportions and list examples of this law.
2:4	K	list the alkali metals and indicate the characteristics of each alkali metal.
2:4	K/A	explain the importance of knowing the spectrum of an element.
2:4	S/P	conduct an activity to demonstrate the identification of some elements on the basis of their characteristic flame tests.
2:5	K	list the alkaline earth metals and describe the characteristics of each alkaline earth element.
2:6	K	list the elements in the noble gas family and describe the characteristics of these elements.
	S/A	When conducting activities, students will use laboratory materials and equipment in the prescribed manner.

Upon completion of the reading and activities, students will exhibit an interest in science by:

A   reading unassigned literature related to ideas presented in the chapter.

A   voluntarily visiting a plant which produces chemicals commercially and reporting to the class.

EQUIPMENT FOR ACTIVITIES

Equipment
   Bunsen burner
   collection bottles
   deflagrating spoon
   dropping funnel (or medicine dropper)
   flat pan
   glass plates
   graduated cylinder, 25 ml
   labels
   piece of cork
   platinum (nichrome) wire
   pneumatic trough
   ring stand
   rubber tubing
   test tubes (glass and large, Pyrex)
   test tube clamp
   test tube rack
   tongs
   wing tip for Bunsen burner
   wood splints

Reagents
   alcohol (ethyl)
   antimony (II) chloride solution
   banana
   barium chloride
   bread
   cadmium nitrate solution
   calcium chloride
   carbon tetrachloride
   carrot
   copper chloride
   copper (II) sulfate solution
   distilled water
   hydrogen sulfide (H_2S) solution
   iodine crystals
   iodine solution
   iron sulfate solution
   liquid starch solution
   lithium chloride
   manganese dioxide
   mineral oil
   potassium chlorate
   potassium chloride
   potassium nitrate
   potato
   sodium chloride
   sodium nitrate
   sodium peroxide

steel wool
strontium chloride
sulfur
sulfuric acid (concentrated)
zinc sulfate solution

Page 182 (22M). Problem
1. Halogens easily gain electrons.

Page 183 (23M). Additional Experiment
A demonstration of the relative activities of the halogens is their ability to bleach litmus paper. Place a piece of red litmus and blue litmus in a test tube. Add 5 ml of bromine water. Repeat the procedure separately with chlorine water and iodine solution. The chlorine bleaches readily; bromine, somewhat; iodine not at all.

Page 183 (23M). Additional Experiment
Steel wool appears to "burn" in chlorine gas. This experiment should be done as demonstration under a hood. Prepare chlorine gas by adding one-half teaspoon of bleaching powder to a bottle. Add 2 ml of concentrated sulfuric acid. Cover with glass plate. Hold a small piece of steel wool with metal tongs and heat in a Bunsen burner flame until it glows red. Remove the cover from the bottle and quickly thrust the steel wool into the chlorine gas. The steel wool is rapidly oxidized forming $FeCl_3$.

Page 184 (24M). Activity
Some of the properties of iodine are demonstrated in this activity. Have the students set up the test tubes as described. Then have them make an identical set of test tubes filled with distilled water. Add a crystal of iodine to each of the test tubes (alcohol, water, mineral oil), but add the crystal to only one of the test tubes of distilled water. Iodine dissolves readily in alcohol.

Add starch solution to all of the test tubes. The starch will turn blue in any of the tubes in which the iodine dissolved. The blue color results from a complex ion formed by reaction of the starch with the iodine. Try some other solvents such as benzene, or other organic solvents.

Page 185 (25M). Problems
2. F_2, Cl_2, Br_2, I_2
3. each has 7 electrons in outer shell
4. F—preparation of freon; Cl—pool disinfectant; Br—preparation of bromides for photography; I—antiseptic, prevention of goiter

Page 186 (26M). Activity
The steel wool will react more quickly with oxygen if it is rinsed in alcohol or vinegar to remove the rust-preventive coating and then dried.

The iron reacts with the oxygen forming rust.

$$4 Fe + 3 O_2 \rightarrow 2 Fe_2O_3$$

The water level rises because the molecules of oxygen were removed from the atmosphere inside the graduated cylinder and reduced the pressure.

Page 187 (27M). Activity
The production of oxygen by water displacement using sodium peroxide and water. If the reaction is too slow, gentle heat may be added. If heat is added, students should be sure to remove the delivery tube from the water as soon as the heat is removed. Otherwise the water will be siphoned back into the flask and the rapid cooling may break it.

The glowing splint will burst into flame in the atmosphere of pure oxygen. The steel wool will oxidize very rapidly, and the sulfur will burn with a blue flame.

burning of wood   *cellulose* $(C_6H_{12}O_6)n + nO_2 \rightarrow nCO_2 + nH_2O$
oxidation of iron $4 Fe + 3 O_2 \rightarrow 2 Fe_2O_3$
burning of sulfur $S + O_2 \rightarrow SO_2$

Page 189 (29M). Activity
One of the tests for metallic ions in qualitative analysis is the reaction of the metallic ions

with hydrogen sulfide. The metallic sulfides have characteristic colors (Table 2-3, p. 189, 29 M).

If students perform this activity, have the reagents in dropper bottles to avoid spilling. Only a very small amount of each is needed for the reaction.

Ions			Precipitate	Color
2 Ag^+	+	S^{2-} →	Ag_2S	(black)
Cd^{2+}	+	S^{2-} →	CdS	(yellow)
Pb^{2+}	+	S^{2-} →	PbS	(black)
Zn^{2+}	+	S^{2-} →	ZnS	(white)
2 Sb^{3+}	+	$3S^{2-}$ →	Sb_2S_3	(orange)
Cu^{2+}	+	S^{2-} →	CuS	(black)

Page 190 (30M). Problems
5. Bleach, insecticide, drugs, rubber, fertilizers
6. Each has 6 electrons in the outer shell.
7. All have the same numbers of electrons in their outer shell.

Page 193 (33M). Activity
Test for nitrate ion. When Fe^{2+} and NO_3^- ions are in solution, they form a brown compound $(FeNO)^{2+}$ complex at the interface between the solution (upper layer in test tube) and concentrated sulfuric acid. If nitrate ions are not present, no brown ring (no iron complex) will form.
3 Fe^{2+} + NO_3^- + $4H^+$ → 3 Fe^{3+} + NO + 2 H_2O
Fe^{2+} + NO → $(FeNO)^{2+}$ brown

Page 195 (35M). Problems
8. Examples: use low phosphate detergents, be conservative with fertilizers
9. Examples: fertilizers, antibiotics, alloys, plant and animal growth, typesetting, matches
10. Five
11. covalent

Page 198 (38M). Activity
The flame test is a common method of qualitative analysis. When heated to incandescence, elements give off characteristic spectra. The light occurs because electrons excited by heat emit light of definite energies as they return to lower energy levels. If a pure solution of the compound is heated, the spectra can be used to identify component cations. Be sure to warn students to clean wire (and burner) between samples. Compare color of unknowns with knowns (or with photos on p. 197, 37 M).

Page 198 (38M). Problems
12. one
13. They combine very readily (explosively) with oxygen or water vapor in the air.

Page 200 (40M). Problems
14. Components of bones and teeth, health care, plaster and cement products are examples.
15. two
16. $BeCl_2$, $MgCl_2$, $CaCl_2$, $SrCl_2$, $BaCl_2$, $RaCl_2$

Page 201 (41M). Problems
17. 8 (2 for helium)
18. First energy shell only has positions for two electrons.

Pages 202-204 (42M-44M). Study Questions
A. *True or False*
1. True 2. False (Under normal room temperature and pressure, all of the halogen elements form diatomic molecules.) 3. False (Uncombined fluoride is not found free in nature.) 4. True 5. False (At room temperature and pressure iodine is a gray crystalline solid.) 6. True 7. True 8. True 9. True 10. False (The low melting point of bismuth makes it suitable for use in automatic sprinkler systems used for fire prevention.)

B. *Multiple Choice*
1. Sodium 2. selenium 3. 7 4. covalent and ionic 5. ice cream 6. nitrogen 7. Bismuth 8. oxygen 9. nitrogen 10. Helium

C. *Completion*
1. diatomic 2. multiple proportions 3. light 4. oxygen 5. air 6. distillation 7. flame 8. bismuth 9. selenium 10. bones, teeth

D. *How and Why*
1. Those elements grouped in the same column in the periodic table are called a family. They exhibit similar properties—oxygen family.
2. ammonia, NH_3; urea, N_2H_4CO; nitric acid, HNO_3 are examples
3. Binary compounds of the nitrogen family form covalent bonds whereas binary compounds of alkali metals and halogens form ionic bonds.
4. You can distinguish between metallic and nonmetallic members of a family of elements by their properties. Generally the elements with the higher atomic numbers will be more metallic.

5. Sulfur and oxygen differ in atomic structure (number of protons, electrons, neutrons); physical state (solid versus gas); melting and boiling points; color; allotropic forms.
6. Law of Multiple Proportions: Two or more elements may unite to form more than one compound. The combining masses will be in the ratio of whole numbers. The law of definite proportions states that all compounds have a definite proportion by weight. Even though two elements may combine in two or more ways to form compounds, each of the compounds will always have the same proportions of elements. (N_2O, NO_2 are examples.)
7. Allotropes are different molecular forms of the same element whereas isotopes are forms of the same element which differ in the number of neutrons in the nucleus.
8. Answers will vary. Noble gases do not combine easily with other elements. The first of the noble gases had been found as had the first of other families, thus giving a starting place.
9. A diatomic gas is one in which the molecular form contains two atoms: Cl_2, chlorine; O_2, oxygen; N_2, nitrogen.
10. (a) (1) boron nitride (2) iron (III) oxide (3) magnesium chloride (4) carbon disulfide (5) lithium hydride
    (b) 1, 2, 4, 5 are covalent because of the number of electrons in the outer shell. They have a tendency to share rather than gain or lose electrons. 3 ionic—magnesium is likely to give up two electrons.

Page 204 (44M). Investigations
1. Pesticides: Chlorine, hydrocarbons
   Fertilizer: Phosphorus, nitrogen, potassium
2. Answers will vary depending on brands of products.
3. Answers will vary. Chlorine is most common.

Unit Three, Chapter 3
Carbon and Its Compounds

PERFORMANCE OBJECTIVES
Goal: Students will gain an understanding of the reasons for the large number of carbon compounds.

Objectives: Upon completion of the reading and activities and when asked to diagram, demonstrate, or respond either orally or on a written test, students will:

3:1	K	explain the different ways carbon atoms can bond with each other.
3:2	P/A	explain why the structural formulas of carbon compounds are important.
3:3	K	explain what isomers are and diagram examples.
3:4-5	P	compare and contrast saturated hydrocarbons and unsaturated hydrocarbons.
3:4	S/P	conduct an activity to demonstrate a method of producing methane gas and testing its properties.
3:4	S/P	conduct an activity to demonstrate a paper chromatography method of separating chemical compounds.
3:5	S/P	conduct an activity to demonstrate a method of producing acetylene gas and testing its properties.
3:6	S/P	conduct an activity to test the properties of both natural and synthetic fibers.
3:7	K	list some ring compounds of carbon, some substituted hydrocarbons, and some common alcohols and their uses.
	S/A	When conducting activities, students will use laboratory materials and equipment in the prescribed manner.

Upon completion of the reading and activities, students will exhibit an interest in science by:

A	reading unassigned literature related to ideas presented in the chapter.
A	voluntarily tracing the history of the discovery of an organic compound and its uses and report findings to the class.

EQUIPMENT FOR ACTIVITIES
Equipment
beaker (250-ml)
Bunsen burner
collection bottles
filter paper

flask (250-ml)
forceps
glass jar with lid (small)
glass plates (square)
glass tubing
marking pens (felt tip)
medicine dropper
mortar and pestle
paper towel strips
pipe cleaners or toothpicks
pneumatic trough
ring stand and clamps
rubber stoppers (assorted)
rubber tubing
styrofoam balls
tape
test tubes (small, glass; large, Pyrex)
water bath
wood splints

Reagents
acetic acid
alcohol (ethyl)
bromine water
calcium carbide
food coloring (various colors)
formalin (formaldehyde)
limewater (freshly made)
phenol
potassium permanganate solution
soda lime (CaO and NaOH mixture)
sodium acetate (solid)
sodium hydroxide (solid and solution)
sulfuric acid (concentrated)
textile materials

Page 211 (51M). Problem
1. Yes, two have carbon atoms with more than two other carbon atoms attached.

Page 211 (51M.) Activity
The seven isomers of $C_5H_{11}Cl$ are

[structural formulas]

(The remaining bonds are filled by hydrogen atoms.)

Page 211 (51M). Problems
2. The four isomers of C_4H_9Cl are

[structural formulas]

(The remaining bonds are filled by hydrogen atoms.)

3. A structural formula for CH_3CH_2CHO is

[structural formula]

Page 212 (52M). Problem
4. Each carbon has two atoms of hydrogen except for the two end carbons. Therefore, there will always be twice as many hydrogens as carbons plus two. A general formula would be C_2H_{2n+2}.

Page 212 (52M). Activity
You may wish to use this activity, the preparation of methane gas, as a demonstration. If the students perform the activity, observe the following safety precautions:

1. Keep the gas collection bottles away from open flames.
2. Maintain proper ventilation or use the fume hood.
3. Wear safety glasses.

Have the students note the physical properties of the gas—color, odor, and density. Store the bottles of gas upside down because the gas is lighter than air.

Methane burns with a blue flame, and limewater turns milky indicating that carbon dioxide is a product. The equation for the burning of methane in air:

$$CH_4 + 2\ O_2 \rightarrow CO_2 + 2\ H_2O$$

The bromine water remains red in the presence of methane because methane is a saturated hydrocarbon and is therefore rather unreactive. Potassium permanganate is a strong oxidizing agent but is not reduced by methane.

Page 214 (54M). Problem
5. (a) gas
   (b) solid
   (c) liquid
   (d) gas
   (e) liquid

Page 216 (56M). Problem
6.

[Structural formulas of two alkynes with hydrogen atoms shown]

Page 217 (57M). Activity
Before performing this activity, review the results of the activity with methane. Observe the same safety precautions as with the preparation of methane—acetylene is more reactive than methane. Acetylene is an unsaturated hydrocarbon and is more reactive than the saturated methane. Acetylene bleaches red bromine water and reduces purple $KMnO_4$ solution. Be careful with the $KMnO_4$ solution as it can stain the hands and clothing.

Page 218 (58M). Additional Activity
Perform this activity as a demonstration since the reagents are very caustic. Use eye and clothing protection.

Mix 50 g of phenol and 80 g of formalin in a beaker. Heat the beaker in a pan of water until the crystals melt. Add ½ g of solid sodium hydroxide and heat gently. If needed, add a small amount of solid sodium hydroxide to thicken the mixture.

The reaction of phenol, C_6H_5OH, wtih formalin, CH_2O, is one of the oldest known methods of preparing thermosetting synthetic polymer. The NaOH is a catalyst. The resin that is formed is known as Bakelite and is a three-dimensional polymer with structure:

[Structural formula of Bakelite polymer]

Page 219 (59M). Additional Problem
Have students draw a structural formula for cyclopentane. Its simple molecular formula is C_5H_{10}. The structural formula is

[Structural formula of cyclopentane ring]

Page 219 (59M). Additional Activity
This activity can be done readily by all students. Mix 3 ml of acetic acid and 2 ml of ethyl alcohol in a test tube. Add 3 drops of concentrated sulfuric acid. Heat gently. Do not sniff the odor directly but waft the vapor toward your nose with your hand. The organic compound you have prepared is called an ester. Repeat the procedure with amyl alcohol instead of ethyl alcohol. Esters are formed

from organic acids and alcohols. The other product of the reaction is water. The esterification proceeds faster if the water is removed. This is the purpose of the concentrated H_2SO_4.

$$CH_3COOH + CH_3CH_2OH \xrightarrow{\text{conc.}\ H_2SO_4}$$
acetic acid   ethyl alcohol

$$CH_3COOCH_2CH_3 + H_2O$$
ethyl acetate   water

$$CH_3COOH + CH_3CH_2COH(CH_3)_2 \xrightarrow{\text{conc.}\ H_2SO_4}$$
acetic acid   amyl alcohol

$$CH_3COOC(CH_3)_2\ CH_2CH_3 + H_2O$$
amyl acetate   water

Ethyl acetate has the odor of apples, amyl acetate has the odor of bananas. Esters are known by their characteristic odors:

ethyl butanoate	peach
methyl butanoate	pineapple
octyl ethanoate	orange
pentyl butanoate	apricot
pentyl ethanoate	pear

A. True or False
1. False (Carbon is in the IVA column of the periodic table.) 2. False (A carbon atom has 4 electrons in its outer shell.) 3. True 4. False (A saturated hydrocarbon has carbon atoms joined by single bonds.) 5. True 6. True 7. False (Propane is a member of the alkane series.) 8. True 9. False (Cooking oil is an unsaturated hydrocarbon.) 10. False (A substituted hydrocarbon contains atoms of hydrogen and carbon and other elements.)

B. Multiple Choice
1. carbon 2. 4 3. no known limit of 4. OH 5. polymer 6. alkane 7. unsaturated 8. alkyne 9. polymer 10. graphic

C. Completion
1. structural 2. covalent 3. triple 4. substituted 5. fractionation 6. polymers 7. saturated 8. Answers will vary: neoprene, rubber, vinyl, rubber are examples 9. methane 10. gases, liquids

D. How and Why
1.
```
    H
    ..
H : C : H
    ..
    H
```

2. Isomers are compounds with the same formulas but different structures. Isotopes are elements with the same number of protons but different numbers of neutrons.

3. Carbon bonds with other carbon atoms to form long chains, carbon atoms can form double bonds with other atoms, carbon can form ring compounds.

4. Benzene and cyclohexane are similar in that both have six carbon atoms formed into a ring. However, cyclohexane has the formula C_6H_{12}, whereas benzene is C_6H_6; benzene has three double bonds and cyclohexane is saturated.

5. Answers will vary.

```
    H              H   H
    |              |   |
H—C—H          H—C = C—H
    |
    H
```

6. methane   ethene
   CH_4, C_2H_6, C_3H_8, C_2H_2

7.
$$C_5H_{10}$$

```
      H   H H  H
      |   | |  |
   H—C—C=C—C—C—H
      |   | |  |
      H   H H  H
```

or

(ring structure of cyclopentane)

C_2H_5OH C_2H_3OH

```
  H H                     H H
  | |                     | |
H—C—C—OH              H—C=C—OH
  | |
  H H
```

8. Polymers are very large molecules formed from the combination of molecules of many compounds. Examples of organic compounds are acetylene, isoprene, ethylene.

9. The name of the family describes the type of bonding: -*ane,* saturated; -*ene,* double bond; -*yne,* triple bond.

alkane
```
      H H
      | |
    H-C-C-H
      | |
      H H
```

alkene
```
      H H
      | |
    H-C=C-H
```

alkyne   H—C≡C—H

10. A "straight-chain" carbon compound does not occur in a straight line because the bond angle between two carbon-to-carbon bonds is 109°. Since the four bonds occur at the vertices of a tetrahedron, there are actually no straight chains.

Page 223 (63M). Investigations
1. Reports should discuss availability of coal and environmental aspects of its production and use.
2. The local gas company can furnish some material. Various environmental publications will have information on shortages of natural gas.
3. Reports will vary depending on types of dyes chosen. Mordants used to "set" various kinds of dyes include: trivalent chromium complexes, metallic hydroxides, tannic acid.
4. Students could compare mileage and use of gasoline with amount of pollutants in air.

Unit Four Changes in Matter

Goal: Students will gain an understanding of how matter changes through solution formation and chemical reactions.

Unit Four, Chapter 1
Solutions

PERFORMANCE OBJECTIVES
Goal: Students will gain an understanding of the main properties of solutions, using the terms solute, solvent, concentration, and saturation.
Objectives: Upon completion of the reading and activities and when asked to diagram, demonstrate, or respond either orally or on a written test, students will:

1:1	P	compare and contrast liquid, gaseous, and solid solutions.
1:2	S/P	conduct an activity to demonstrate the energy change which occurs as a solid dissolves in a liquid.
1:3	S/P	conduct an activity to demonstrate the difference in the rate a large crystal and the rate the same quantity of small crystals will dissolve in a solvent.
1:3	K	list the three factors which affect the solution rate of a solid in a liquid.
1:3	K	list the factors which affect the solution rate of gases in a liquid.
1:4	K	state the general rule concerning organic solvents and inorganic solvents and the materials they dissolve.
1:4	S/P	conduct an activity to demonstrate the solubility of oil in an organic solvent and in an inorganic solvent.
1:5-6	P	compare and contrast the solutions made from polar compounds and nonpolar compounds and explain the reasons for the electrical conductivity of these solutions.
1:7	S/P	conduct an activity to determine the solubility of salt in water.
1:8	S/P	conduct an activity to determine the concentration of a solute in a solvent.
1:9	P	differentiate between saturated, unsaturated, and supersaturated solutions.
1:9	S/P	conduct an activity to demonstrate that crystallization occurs in a supersaturated solution as it cools.
1:10	S/P	conduct an activity to devise a test for water of hydration in crystals.
1:11	K	describe the effect of a solute on a solvent's boiling point and on a solvent's freezing point.
	S/A	When conducting activities and experiments, students will use laboratory materials and equipment in the prescribed manner.

Upon completion of the reading and activities, students will exhibit an interest in science by:

A	reading unassigned literature related to ideas presented in the chapter.
A/S	voluntarily conducting experiments at home to determine the boiling points and freezing points of various solutions.

EQUIPMENT FOR ACTIVITIES
Equipment
   balance
   beakers (125-ml and 250-ml)
   bell wire
   Bunsen burner
   cotton, absorbent
   dropper bottles, 5
   dry cells, 2
   evaporating dish
   filter paper
   flasks (250-ml), 2
   forceps
   funnel
   glass slides
   glass stirring rod
   glass tubing
   graduated cylinder (50-ml)
   litmus paper, red and blue
   medicine droppers
   microlamp with socket
   microscope
   ring stand and ring
   rubber stoppers (to fit flasks)
   rubber tubing, thick-walled
   straw
   thermometer (Celsius)

test tubes
test tube rack
watch glasses
wire gauze

Reagents
alcohol, ethyl
ammonium chloride (solid)
calcium chloride
copper (II) sulfate (crystals)
distilled water
hydrochloric acid
ice cubes
mineral soap
naphtha
potassium sulfate
soap
  bar
  liquid
soda water (cold)
sodium carbonate
sodium chloride (solid)
sodium hydroxide (solid)
sodium nitrate (crystals)
sodium sulfate (crystals)
sodium thiosulfate (crystals)
sugar
vegetable oil
washing soda

Page 227 (3M). Activity

	water	*alcohol*
NaCl	soluble	insoluble
mineral oil	insoluble	insoluble
ethyl alcohol	soluble	soluble
sugar	soluble	soluble

Page 229 (5M). Problems

1. The sample with very small crystals will dissolve first because of the large surface area exposed.
2. In both, chemical bonds are broken and re-formed. Energy is given up or absorbed.

Page 229 (5M). Experiment

This experiment illustrates the energy change which takes place as a solid dissolves in a liquid. Ammonium chloride causes a decrease in temperature; sodium hydroxide causes a great increase in temperature. Be careful because beaker may become hot.

Page 230 (6M). Problem

3. Since the solution becomes hot, the heat released is greater than the heat absorbed.

Page 231 (7M). Activity

Do not agitate. Small crystals should dissolve more quickly. Be sure to check flasks periodically throughout the week.

Page 231 (7M). Text Question

Dividing a cube to calculate the surface to volume ratio.

	Each Edge	Area of face		Number of faces		Number of cubes		Total Surface
First cube	20 cm	400 cm^2	×	6	×	1	=	2400 cm^2
Second cube	10 cm	100 cm^2	×	6	×	8	=	4800 cm^2
Third cube	1 cm	1 cm^2	×	6	×	8000	=	48,000 cm^2

Page 233 (9M). Activity

Oil will not dissolve in water but will in naphtha. When alcohol is added to the water and oil, the oil will not dissolve.

Page 234 (10M). Problem

4. Ionically bonded molecules dissociate in water. The molecules break up into ions each surrounded by water molecules. Molecular (covalently bonded) compounds ionize in water. Ions form but instantaneously react with the water molecules to form hydronium ions.
Dissociation—potassium bromide
Ionization—ammonia

Page 236 (12M). Problem

5. Ions. Sulfuric acid is the electrolyte.

Page 236 (12M). Activity

This is a simple test for electrolytes. Pure water is a poor conductor of electricity. If the wires of the circuit are placed in water, little or no current should flow. The bulb will burn dimly or not at all. By adding an electrolyte (something that will dissociate or ionize in water) to the water, ions will form to carry the current.

NaCl is an electrolyte, alcohol is not. HCl and potassium sulfate are electrolytes, sugar will dissociate somewhat.

To make the bulb burn brighter, increase the concentration of the electrolyte or choose a substance that dissociates more completely.

Page 237 (13M). Problems
6. cold
7. cold

Page 239 (15M). Activity
Any convenient salt such as NaCl, $NaNO_3$, or KNO_3 will be very satisfactory for this activity. To be sure that the volume of solution is as accurate as possible, measure the volume of the solution after it has been filtered. This can be done easily if the filtrate is collected in a graduated cylinder. Table for data:
1. Amount of solution _____ml
2. Mass of solution + dish _____g
3. Mass of dish + salt _____g
4. Mass of water (Step 2 − Step 3) _____g
5. Mass of dish _____g
6. Mass of salt (Step 3 − Step 5) _____g

Calculate the mass of salt dissolved in 20 ml of water:

$$\frac{\text{Mass of salt (Step 6)}}{\text{Volume of water (Step 4)}} = \frac{x}{20 \text{ ml water}}$$

If the water is heated, more salt will dissolve. Repeat the activity with the water at 70°-80° C.

Page 239 (15M). Problems
8. (a) Sodium nitrate is soluble.
   (b) Silver phosphate is not soluble.
   (c) Barium chloride is soluble.
   (d) Ammonium chloride is soluble.
   (e) Aluminum hydroxide is not soluble.
   (f) Magnesium carbonate is not soluble.
9. (a) Na^+, NO_3^-
   (c) Ba^{2+}, Cl^-
   (d) NH_4^+, Cl^-
10. more dilute

Page 240 (16M). Activity
A straw hydrometer will give a relative (and very approximate) value of specific gravity. The specific gravities of the salt solutions will depend upon the concentration of each salt. Add enough salt to make the solution saturated but filter out undissolved crystals. Temperature can have a direct effect on solubility as shown in Figure 1-20. Adding heat may help more solute molecules overcome their mutual attraction and enable them to mix with the solvent.

Page 241 (17M). Activity
Crystallization should occur as soon as the crystal is dropped in. The same experiment could be repeated and a crystal of sodium chloride added to the hypo solution. Because sodium chloride is not the right shape, crystallization would not take place. Sodium chloride is the wrong model for hypo crystallization.

Page 243 (19M). Activity
Copper sulfate crystals lose their water of hydration at 100° C. The crystals will turn into white powder. Some crystals may form from the white powder by absorbing water.

Page 243 (19M). Activity
$Na_2SO_4 \cdot 10\ H_2O$ efflorescent (loses water of hydration at 100° C)
$CaCl_2$ deliquescent
$CuSO_4 \cdot 5\ H_2O$ slowly efflorescent, white when dehydrated
(washing soda) $Na_2CO_3 \cdot 10\ H_2O$ (loses water at MP 32.5-34.5° C) efflorescent at MP 32.5-34.5° C

Page 244 (20M). Activity
The boiling point should be elevated due to presence of salt in the water. Boiling point elevation occurs because the vapor pressure of the solvent is lowered by the solute particles. Fewer overall solvent particles implies fewer escaping as vapor.

Page 244 (21M). Problem
11. No, salt water would boil at higher temperature than fresh water because of the increased concentration of dissolved salts in sea water.

Page 245 (22M). Problems
12. Salt reduces the freezing temperature of water so it will melt the ice if temperatures are not too low.
13. To make the ice melt at a lower temperature.

Pages 246-248 (22M-24M). Study Questions
A. True or False
1. False (To form a solution, a solute must be dissolved by a solvent.) 2. True 3. False (A gaseous solution can be formed by dissolving a gas in another solution.) 4. False (Water is a solvent that will dissolve most inorganic compounds.) 5. True 6. False (Organic solvents usually dissolve organic solutes.) 7. True 8. True 9. False (Crystals which lose their waters of hydration easily are efflorescent.) 10. True

B. Multiple Choice
1. lighter fluid 2. Silver 3. organic 4. ions 5. supersaturated 6. $NaNO_3$ 7. lower 8. naphtha 9. g/ℓ 10. dilute

C. Completion
1. water 2. dissociate 3. sugar 4. polar 5. ionization 6. organic 7. organic 8. electrolyte 9. water 10. lower

D. How and Why
1. Change 50 ml to 0.05 liter.
$$\frac{50 \text{ g}}{1 \text{ liter}} = \frac{x}{0.05 \text{ liter}}$$
$x = 2.5$ g
2. Agitation, pulverization, and heat determine rate of solution.
3. At 20° C, 35 to 40 g dissolve. At 40° C 60 to 65 g dissolve. The solubility at 20° is about half the solubility at 40°.
4. Listed in order of the most soluble to the least soluble: (b) ammonium nitrate, (a) lead chloride, (d) calcium sulfate, (c) silver chloride.
5. If 100 ml of solution contains 50 g, then 60 ml of solution contains 30 g. Pour 60 ml of solution into a 100-ml graduate and fill the graduate with water.
6. The solution contains ions, and it is probably an inorganic solute in water.
7. Change 1 liter to 1000 ml.
$$\frac{50 \text{ g}}{300 \text{ ml}} = \frac{x}{1000 \text{ ml}} \quad x = 167 \text{ g}$$
8. Examples of household substances that dissolve in water: table salt, table sugar, baking soda, boric acid. Substances that dissolve in alcohol: iodine, colognes, perfume.
9. The major difference is the degree of concentration. An unsaturated solution holds less solute than it could at a given temperature; a saturated solution, the exact amount; a supersaturated solution, a greater amount.
10. Using NH_4Cl as an example, when ammonium chloride is dissolved in water, the solvent-solvent bonds of the water and the solute-solute bonds of the ammonuim chloride are broken. The water ions and the ammonuim chloride ions form a solvent-solute bond and energy is released. Refer to Figure 1-6, p. 230 (6M).

Page 248 (24M). Investigations
1. Silica gardens are made of "water glass," sodium silicates dissolved in water. Different colors are added and as crystals grow, a "garden" appears.
2. Fractional crystallization is a method for physically separating compounds. Most substances have a unique solubility in water at a given temperature. For example, at 70° C, potassium bromide is less soluble than potassium nitrate. If the water in a solution containing equal concentrations of these two compounds is evaporated at 70° C, the potassium bromide will crystallize first.
3. A hydrometer is used to find the specific gravity of the water-antifreeze mixture.
4. Sample graph:

5. For variation, some students might try keeping some of the crystallization jars at different temperatures and noting day-to-day progress of each.

Unit Four, Chapter 2
Chemical Reactions

PERFORMANCE OBJECTIVES
Goal: Students will gain an understanding of the conservation of matter and energy and how energy changes accompany chemical reactions.
Objectives: Upon completion of the reading and activities and when asked to diagram, demonstrate, or respond either orally or on a written test, students will:

2:1	S/P	conduct an experiment and an activity to demonstrate that there is no change in mass as a result of a chemical change.
2:2	K	explain the purpose and construction of a chemical equation.
2:2	P	compare and contrast precipitates, reactants, and products.
2:3-6	K	define and give an example of replacement reactions, decomposition reactions, and synthesis reactions.
2:3-6	S	write the equations for a given set of reactions.
2:3	S/P	conduct an activity to demonstrate a double replacement reaction.
2:4	S/P	conduct an activity to demonstrate a single replacement reaction.
2:5	S/P	conduct an activity to illustrate a decomposition reaction.
2:6	S/P	complete and write equations which illustrate a synthesis reaction.
2:7	P	compare and contrast exothermic reactions and endothermic reactions and indicate an example of each.
2:8	K	differentiate between molecular mass and formula mass.
2:9	S	determine the amount of product formed in a chemical reaction when given the amount of reactant(s).
	S/A	When conducting activities and experiments, students will use laboratory materials and equipment in the prescribed manner.

Upon completion of the reading and activities, students will exhibit an interest in science by:

- A reading unassigned literature related to ideas presented in the chapter.
- A/S volunteering to help care for and maintain laboratory materials and equipment.

EQUIPMENT FOR ACTIVITIES
Equipment
balance
beaker (250-ml)
bell wire
D.C. power supply (6-volt) or 4 dry cells
electrolysis apparatus (Hoffman)
filter paper
flasks (250-ml)
funnel
glass tubing
graduated cylinder (50-ml)
medicine dropper
microlamp
rubber stoppers (to fit flask, two-hole)
test tube
test tube (small enough to fit inside flask or use small pill bottle)
thistle tube
watch glass
wood splint

Reagents
barium chloride
calcium carbonate
calcium oxide
copper (II) sulfate (powdered)
copper wire
distilled water
hydrochloric acid (1M)
hydrochloric acid (dilute, 0.3M)
hydrogen peroxide (3%)
lead metal strip
lime water
manganese dioxide (solid)
phenolphthalein
silver nitrate solution
sodium chloride solution
sodium hydroxide (dilute, 0.3M)
sodium hydroxide solution (0.1M)
sodium nitrate solution
sulfuric acid (concentrated)
zinc metal strip

Page 255 (31M). Problem
1. (a) $NaBr(aq) + AgNO_3(aq) \rightarrow AgBr(s) + NaNO_3(aq)$

69T

(b) $Ca(NO_3)_2(aq) + K_2SO_4(aq) \rightarrow$
$CaSO_4(s) + 2\ KNO_3(aq)$
(c) $2\ KCl(aq) + Pb(NO_3)_2(aq) \rightarrow$
$2\ KNO_3(aq) + PbCl_2(s)$
(d) $3\ Ca(OH)_2(aq) + 2\ Fe(NO_3)_3(aq) \rightarrow$
$2\ Fe(OH)_3(s) + 3\ Ca(NO_3)_2(aq)$
(e) $3\ MgSO_4(aq) + 2\ Na_3PO_4(aq) \rightarrow$
$Mg_3(PO_4)_2(s) + 3\ Na_2SO_4(aq)$
(f) hydrogen sulfide plus mercury (II) chloride in water yields 2 hydrogen chloride plus mercury (II) sulfide

Page 255 (31M). Activity
A blue precipitate forms and the solution turns colorless if reaction goes to completion. Adding more sodium hydroxide and removing precipitates drives reaction further to the right.
$CuSO_4(aq) + 2\ NaOH(aq) \rightarrow$
$Cu(OH)_2(s) + Na_2SO_4(aq)$

Page 256 (32M). Activity
$Cu(s) + 2\ AgNO_3(aq) \rightarrow Cu(NO_3)_2(aq) + 2\ Ag(s)$
The silver plates out as a gray material on the wire. The solution turns blue due to the copper compound in solution.

Page 258 (34M). Activity
Copper metal is deposited on zinc strip. Silver metal is deposited on lead.
$CuSO_4(aq) + Zn(s) \rightarrow ZnSO_4(aq) + Cu(s)$
$2\ AgNO_3(aq) + Pb(s) \rightarrow Pb(NO_3)_2(aq) + 2\ Ag(s)$

Page 260 (36M). Activity
$2\ H_2O_2 \rightarrow 2\ H_2O + O_2(g)$
MnO_2 acts as a catalyst to decomposition. A glowing splint bursts into flame in the presence of oxygen.

Pages 260-261 (36M-37M). Problems
2. single replacement, double replacement, decomposition, synthesis
   (a) double replacement, (b) synthesis
3.
   (a) $2\ Mg(s) + O_2(g) \rightarrow 2\ MgO(s)$
   (b) $Fe(s) + Cu(NO_3)_2(aq) \rightarrow$
   $Cu(s) + Fe(NO_3)_2(aq)$
   (c) $2\ H_2O(l) \xrightarrow{elec} 2\ H_2(g) + O_2(g)$
   (d) $2\ Hg_2O(s) \rightarrow 4\ Hg(s) + O_2(g)$
   (e) $AgNO_3(aq) + KI(aq) \rightarrow$
   $AgI(s) + KNO_3$
   (f) $CaI_2(aq) + Cl_2(g) \rightarrow$
   $CaCl_2(aq) + I_2(g)$
4. $S(s) + O_2(g) \rightarrow SO_2(g)$

(a) yes (b) yes (c) solid (d) yields (e) synthesis (f) sulfur dioxide

Page 262 (38M). Activity
Use care in putting thistle tube into the stopper. Lubricate tube before inserting and hold with towel to guard against cuts if breakage occurs.
Flask: $CaCO_3(s) + 2\ HCl \rightarrow$
$CaCl_2(aq) + CO_2(g)$
Beaker: $CO_2(g) + Ca(OH)_2(aq) \rightarrow$
$CaCO_3(s) + H_2O$
Heat is produced (exothermic reaction). Ask students to give equations for reactions taking place. All three types of end reactions (gas, precipitate, and water) are present here.

Page 264 (40M). Problem
5. (a) Na_2SO_4
   Na $2 \times 23 = 46$
   S $1 \times 32 = 32$
   O $4 \times 16 = 64$
   $\overline{\qquad 142}$
   (b) $CaCO_3$
   Ca $1 \times 40 = 40$
   C $1 \times 12 = 12$
   O $3 \times 16 = 48$
   $\overline{\qquad 100}$
   (c) NH_4NO_3
   N $2 \times 14 = 28$
   H $4 \times 1 = 4$
   O $3 \times 16 = 48$
   $\overline{\qquad 80}$
   (d) $CuSO_4$
   Cu $1 \times 64 = 64$
   S $1 \times 32 = 32$
   O $4 \times 16 = 64$
   $\overline{\qquad 160}$
   (e) $AgBr$
   Ag $1 \times 108 = 108$
   Br $1 \times 80 = 80$
   $\overline{\qquad 188}$
   (f) K_3PO_4
   K $3 \times 39 = 117$
   P $1 \times 31 = 31$
   O $4 \times 16 = 64$
   $\overline{\qquad 212}$

Page 265 (41M). Problems
6. $C(s) + O_2(g) \rightarrow CO_2(g)$
   12g $\longrightarrow$ 44g

7. NaOH(aq) + HCl(aq) →
   NaCl(aq) + H₂O(l)
   40g ─────────────→ 18g
8. 2 C(s) + O₂(g) → 2 CO(g)
   32g → 56g (2 × 28)

Pages 266-268 (42M-44M). Study Questions

A. True or False
1. False (Silver chloride is insoluble in water.)
2. True 3. True 4. True 5. True 6. False (An equation may be balanced by changing coefficients.) 7. False (The molecular mass of H_2 is 2.) 8. True 9. True 10. True

B. Multiple Choice
1. exothermic 2. iodine 3. ions 4. remains the same 5. 85 6. 44 7. coefficients 8. exothermic 9. decomposition 10. replacement

C. Completion
1. synthesis 2. mass 3. decomposition 4. 136 5. silver chloride 6. K⁺, NO₃⁻ 7. (double) replacement 8. ionization 9. carbon monoxide (CO) 10. water (H₂O)

D. How and Why
1. $\dfrac{28 \text{ g}}{56 \text{ g}} = \dfrac{x}{88g}$
   $x = \dfrac{(28 \times 88)}{56}$ g
   x = 44g
2. (a) gas—C(s) + O₂(g) → CO₂(g)
   (b) water—NaOH(aq) + HCl(aq) →
       NaCl(aq) + H₂O(l)
   (c) precipitate—
       AgNO₃(aq) + NaCl(aq) →
       NaNO₃(aq) + AgCl(s)
   Answers will vary in all three answers.
3. There are the same number and kinds of atoms on each side of the equation. Therefore, the mass before and after a reaction must be the same.
4. Water plus electricity yields hydrogen plus oxygen
   2 H₂O(l) —elec→ 2 H₂(g) + O₂(g)
5. Endothermic reactions require the constant addition of heat for the reaction to be sustained; exothermic reactions give off heat as they proceed.
6. Changing formulas would indicate a change of reactants or products. Formulas represent the actual elements and/or compounds involved. Only coefficients may be changed to balance an equation.
7. Carbon plus oxygen yields carbon monoxide
   2 C(s) + O₂(g) → 2 CO(g)
8. (a) Na₂S(aq) + 2 AgNO₃(aq) →
       2 NaNO₃(aq) + Ag₂S(s)
   (b) 3 H₂(g) + N₂(g) → 2 NH₃(g)
   (c) 2 KClO₃(s) → 2 KCl(s) + 3 O₂(g)
   (d) 3 CuSO₄(aq) + 2 Al(s) →
       Al₂(SO₄)₃(aq) + 3 Cu(s)
   (e) 2 Na(s) + 2 H₂O(l) →
       2 NaOH(aq) + H₂(g)
9. (a) Na₂CrO₄(aq) + PbCl₂(aq) →
       2 NaCl(aq) + PbCrO₄(s)
   (b) Cl₂(g) + 2 NaBr(aq) →
       2 NaCl(aq) + Br₂(g)
   (c) Mg(ClO₃)₂(s) —Δ→ MgCl₂(s) + 3 O₂(g)
   (d) 2 H₂(g) + O₂(g) → 2 H₂O(l)
   (e) 3 Ca(OH)₂(aq) + 2 FeCl₃(aq) →
       2 Fe(OH)₃(s) + 3 CaCl₂
10. 8.(a) double replacement
    (b) synthesis
    (c) decomposition
    (d) single replacement
    (e) single replacement
   9.(a) double replacement
    (b) single replacement
    (c) decomposition
    (d) synthesis
    (e) double replacement

Page 269 (45M). Investigations
1. (a) Bubbles of gas are given off.
   (b) sodium hydrogen carbonate in water solution plus heat yields carbon dioxide
   (c) 2 NaHCO₃(aq) → Na₂CO₃ + CO₂ + H₂O
   (d) Reaction occurs, heat is given off, a gas escapes.
   (e) Reaction occurs, heat is given off, a gas escapes. Cream of tartar tastes sour.
   (f) Baking powder fizzes in water (gas is given off). Baking powder contains sodium bicarbonate and cream of tartar.
   (g) Biscuits, cakes, some types of breads need baking powder to make them rise.
2. The solvay process is a method of preparing sodium carbonate (washing soda) and sodium bicarbonate (baking soda) from limestone, coal, and salt.

Unit Four, Chapter 3
Acids, Bases, and Salts

PERFORMANCE OBJECTIVES
Goal: Students will gain an understanding of the properties of acids, bases, and salts.
Objectives: Upon completion of the reading and activities and when asked to diagram, demonstrate, or respond either orally or on a written test, students will:

3:1-2	P	compare the properties of acids with the properties of bases and indicate examples of acids and bases.
3:1	S/P	conduct an activity to demonstrate the dehydrating power of concentrated sulfuric acid.
3:1	S/P	conduct an experiment to demonstrate the different activity rates of three different acids when these acids are in contact with mossy zinc.
3:2	S/P	conduct an experiment to demonstrate properties of a base.
3:3	K	describe the purpose of indicators and list examples of indicators used.
3:3	S/P	conduct an activity to demonstrate the use of an indicator in determining which solutions are acids and which solutions are bases.
3:4	P	determine the relationship of hydroxide and hydronium ions with acids and bases.
3:5	S	use universal indicator paper to test the pH of liquids.
3:5	P	compare the pH values of some common acids and bases.
3:6	S/P	conduct an activity to produce a salt as a result of mixing an acid and a base.
3:7	K	define anhydride and list examples of anhydrides.
	S/A	When conducting activities and experiments, students will use laboratory materials and equipment in the prescribed manner.

Upon completion of the reading and activities, students will exhibit an interest in science by:

A	reading unassigned literature related to ideas presented in the chapter.
A/S	volunteering to help prepare materials for use in experiments.
A/S	volunteering to help care for and maintain laboratory materials and equipment.

EQUIPMENT FOR ACTIVITIES
Equipment
 balance
 beaker
 Bunsen burner
 buret
 buret clamp
 drinking straw
 evaporating dish
 graduated cylinder
 labels
 litmus, red and blue
 ring stand
 safety apron
 safety glasses
 test tubes, 6
 test tube rack
 universal indicator paper
 wire gauze

Reagents
 ascorbic acid
 ammonia
 calcium oxide
 fruit juice
 hydrochloric acid, dilute
 indophenol
 lemon juice
 liquid soap
 milk (fresh, sour)
 petroleum jelly
 phenolphthalein
 soda pop
 soda water
 sodium bicarbonate, dilute
 sodium hydroxide, 0.1M
 sulfuric acid, dilute, concentrated
 table sugar
 vinegar
 zinc (mossy)

Page 274 (50M). Problems
1. (a) $Pb(s) + H_2SO_4(aq) \rightarrow PbSO_4(s) + H_2(g)$
 (b) $2\ Al(s) + 6\ HCl(aq) \rightarrow 2\ AlCl_3(aq) + 3\ H_2(g)$

(c) 2 Al(s) + 3 H$_2$SO$_4$(aq) →
Al$_2$(SO$_4$)$_3$(s) + 3 H$_2$(g)
2. HBr, HI, HF

Page 277 (53M). Experiment

The ascorbic acid solution used in this experiment should be a 10% solution. It may be obtained in any drugstore. Dilute further if necessary so that the number of drops of ascorbic acid added to the indophenol can be counted accurately (approximately a 1% solution).

Dilute the common fruit and vegetable juices sufficiently so that 10 to 20 drops of juice added to the indophenol turns it colorless. Dilute all equally so the amounts of vitamin C can be compared with each other.

You may wish to have students add NaHCO$_3$ to the juice samples. (Bicarbonate of soda is often used to preserve the green color of vegetables while cooking.) Note the loss of ascorbic acid. (More juice is needed to bleach the indicator.)

Page 278 (54M). Problems

3. (a) two (b) one (c) three (d) two
4. (a) two (b) one (c) two

Page 281 (57M). Problems

5. hydrochloric acid through acetic acid
6. sodium carbonate through potassium hydroxide
7. stomach contents through milk—acid blood through milk of magnesia—base

Page 283 (59M). Problems

8. (a) 2 KOH(aq) + H$_2$SO$_4$(aq) →
K$_2$SO$_4$(aq) + 2H$_2$O
(b) HBr(aq) + NaOH(aq) →
NaBr(aq) + H$_2$O
(c) Ca(OH)$_2$(s) + 2 HNO$_3$(aq) →
Ca(NO$_3$)$_2$(aq) + 2 H$_2$O
(d) Mg(OH)$_2$(s) + 2 HCl(aq) →
MgCl$_2$(aq) + 2 H$_2$O
(e) Zn(s) + 2 HBr(aq) →
ZnBr$_2$(aq) + H$_2$(g)
9. (a) potassium sulfate
(b) sodium bromide
(c) calcium nitrate
(d) magnesium chloride
(e) zinc bromide
10. Reduces it. H$_3$O$^+$ combines with OH$^-$ to produce water.

Page 284 (60M). Problem

11. (a) basic
(b) acid
(c) acid
(d) basic

Pages 285-287 (61M-63M). Study Questions

A. True or False

1. False (The formula for nitric acid is HNO$_3$.) 2. False (Vinegar contains an acid.) 3. True 4. True 5. False (In a water solution, hydrocholoric acid is more highly ionized than citric acid.) 6. True 7. True 8. True 9. False (A base which has a pH of 8 is a weaker base than a base with a pH of 10. 10. True

B. Multiple Choice

1. sour 2. 2 3. Benzene 4. basic anhydride 5. more than 7 6. magnesium oxide and calcium oxide 7. HCl 8. water 9. more 10. high hydronium

C. Completion

1. Taste 2. a hydronium ion 3. indicators 4. acid 5. hydrogen 6. hydrogen 7. decreases 8. salt 9. increases 10. decreases

D. How and Why

1. neutralization (double replacement)
2. (a) H$_2$SO$_4$ acid   NaOH base
(b) HCl acid   NaOH base
(c) HNO$_3$ acid   NaOH base
3. pH is a measure of the hydronium ion concentration of a solution (negative log of [H$_3$O$^+$]). If a solution has a pH <7 the solution is acid; if the pH = 7, the solution is neutral; if the pH > 7, the solution is basic. The addition of a base increases the pH.
4. by indicators
5. sulfuric acid—fertilizers, dyes, petroleum refining, explosives, electroplating, dehydrating agent

hydrochloric acid—dyes, metal plating, digestive juice, producing other chemicals

nitric acid—fertilizers, explosives, manufacturing plastics
6. When an acid and a base react, the reaction is called neutralization. The replacement reaction forms a salt which is neither

acid nor base and water. Problem 1 is an example, p. 274 (50M).
7. (a), (b) — acid
   (c), (e) — base
   (d), (f) — salt
8. ammonia, lye are used as cleaners
9. Examples are
   (a) $Zn(s) + 2\ HCl(aq) \rightarrow ZnCl_2(aq) + H_2(g)$
   (b) $HCl(aq) + NaOH(aq) \rightarrow NaCl(aq) + H_2O(l)$
   (c) $SO_2(g) + H_2O(l) \rightarrow H_2SO_3(aq)$
   (d) $HCl(aq) + AgNO_3(aq) \rightarrow AgCl(s) + HNO_3(aq)$
10. An acid is a substance which, when placed in water, increases the hydronium ion concentration. A base is a substance that increases the hydroxide ion concentration of a solution. A salt is a substance which is formed in a neutralization reaction. Students could be asked to prepare a chart based on sections 3:1, 3:2, and 3:6.

Page 287 (63M). Investigations
1. Examples are:

Acids	Bases
Aspirin	Window cleaner
Buttermilk	Washing soda
Cream of tartar	Milk of magnesia
Vinegar	Baking soda
Copper cleaner	

2. Results will vary depending on type of detergent.
3. Synthetic fibers hold up in acid since they are "hardened" in acid bath; natural fibers break down. Synthetic fibers react in basic solution.
4. Carbon dioxide in water produces carbonic acid. Oxides of sulfur produce sulfuric acid and other sulfur acids. Oxides of nitrogen form nitric acid and other nitrogen acids. Various chlorine compounds form hydrochloric acid and other chlorine acids.
5. Answers will vary.

Unit Five Heat, Light, and Sound

Goal: Students will gain an understanding of heat as the kinetic energy of molecules, and the wave properties of heat, light, and sound.

Unit Five, Chapter 1
Heat Energy

PERFORMANCE OBJECTIVES
Goal: Students will gain an understanding of kinetic energy and relationships between heat and kinetic energy.
Objectives: Upon completion of the reading and activities and when asked to diagram, demonstrate, or respond either orally or on a written test, students will:

1:1	P	explain the relationship between kinetic energy and potential energy.
1:1	S/P	experiment to demonstrate how heat is produced from kinetic energy in particles of matter.
1:2	S/P	experiment to demonstrate the transfer of heat from a hot body to a cooler body.
1:2	P	compare and contrast conduction, convection, and radiation as methods of heat transfer.
1:2	S/P	experiment to demonstrate the transfer of heat by conduction, convection, and radiation.
1:3	S/P	experiment to determine how much heat is gained by a beaker of water in one minute when heated with a Bunsen burner.
1:3	S/P	conduct an activity to demonstrate how a calorimeter is used to measure heat energy.
1:4	K	define British thermal unit and describe Joule's experiment in which he determined the mechanical equivalent of heat.
1:5	K	define temperature in terms of molecular kinetic energy.
1:6	P	relate the change in phase in a quantity of matter to the amount of heat possessed by that quantity of matter before and after the change of phase.
1:6	S/P	conduct an activity to demonstrate that steam loses heat when it condenses to water.
1:6	P	compare and contrast heat of fusion and heat of vaporization.
	S/A	When conducting activities and experiments, students will use laboratory materials and equipment in the prescribed manner.

Upon completion of the reading and activities, students will exhibit an interest in science by:

A	reading unassigned literature related to ideas presented in the chapter.
A/S	volunteering to design and conduct a demonstration for the class.
A	voluntarily relating ideas presented in the chapter to everyday occurrences and informing class members.

EQUIPMENT FOR ACTIVITIES
aluminum foil
balance
ball, iron with ring
beakers (1 large, 1 small)
bottles, glass pint
Bunsen burner
calorimeter (or materials to make calorimeter—cans, #2½ and #1; electric drill; glass wool; wood to cover large can)
candle
clamp, flask
cork
dowel, 0.5 cm
dye
glass rod
glass tubing
glass wool
graduated cylinder (250-ml)
graph paper
hammer
ice
knitting needle, metal
masking tape
nail
paper cups, 2
paraffin
refrigerator
ring
ring stand and ring
rubber bands
rubber stoppers

ruler
sand
steam boiler
test tube (large Pyrex)
test tube clamp
thermometers, Celsius, 4
vacuum bottle, pint
watch (with second hand)
wood block

Page 291 (3M). Problem
1. (a) falling rock (b) sled going downhill (c) swinging baseball bat (d) car in motion (e) quarterback. Many examples from students.

Page 291 (3M). Activity
Book loses potential energy because it is converted into kinetic energy as the book falls.

Page 292 (4M). Problem
2. (a) mainspring unwinds
   (b) rubber band contracts when released
   (c) opens when released
   (d) moves when air rushes out
   (e) diver jumps off board
   (f) bow string contracts when released

Page 295 (7M). Problems
3. sun, lamp, warm food
4. clouds cut out some radiant heat from sun, turn off lamp or insulate it, cover food or keep in reflective container

Page 296 (8M). Problems
5. metal knitting needle—conductor, glass rod —insulator
6. conductors—metal in pans, water in bath, air in furnace; insulators—air in glass wool, wood, brick
7. reflects incoming heat. See Experiment on p. 294 (6M).

Page 297 (9M). Problems
8. In steam radiator, heat is given off as steam condenses. Heat rises from hot radiator setting up convection currents.
9. An air space is surrounded by insulating materials.
10. Hot air will rise along outside wall. Colder air will sink and travel along floor.

Page 298 (10M). Problem
11. Heat lost to surroundings cannot be calculated so only a well-insulated calorimeter would give an accurate measurement.

Page 299 (11M). Problems
12. 5000 calories heat gained by the water equals heat lost by the metal, excluding heat left in inner chamber.
13. $H = (t_2 - t_1) m$
    $= (100°\text{C} - 25°\text{C}) (500g)$
    $= (75°\text{C}) (500g)$
    $= 37{,}500 \text{ cal}$
14. $H = (t_2 - t_1) m$
    $= (60°\text{C} - 40°\text{C}) (20g)$
    $= (20°\text{C}) (20g)$
    $= 400 \text{ cal}$

Page 300 (12M). Problems
15. Answers will vary.
16. $1 \text{ cal} = 4.4 \times 10^{-3} \text{ BTU}$
    $1 \text{ BTU} = 252 \text{ cal}$

Page 305 (17M). Problems
17. Each gram of ice absorbs 80 calories as it forms.
18. Water as it evaporates from the skin absorbs 540 cal/g.
19. Since steam releases 540 cal/g as it condenses, it would take 54 g of water changing 10°C to produce as much heat.

Pages 307-309 (19M-21M). Study Questions
A. True or False
1. True 2. False (The heat an object contains is measured in calories.) 3. True 4. False (Heat is transferred through water by convection currents.) 5. False (A wound spring is an example of potential energy.) 6. True 7. True 8. True 9. False (Glass is not a good conductor of heat.) 10. True

B. Multiple Choice
1. energy of motion 2. calories 3. average molecular kinetic energy 4. conduction 5. 1 6. 1000 7. calorimeter 8. 1 lb 9. 15,000 10. 40

C. Completion
1. 800 2. lose kinetic energy 3. gain kinetic energy 4. 54,000 calories 5. conduction 6. radiation 7. molecules 8. decreases increases 10. conductors

D. *How and Why*
1. Heat is the total kinetic energy in the molecules of a substance. Temperature is the average kinetic energy, a relative measure of its hotness or coldness
2. kinetic energy—a person walking, an airplane flying, snow falling, a football pass, the wind blowing
   potential energy—water behind a dam, snow on the side of a mountain, a hung-up coat, a person sitting on a chair, an unburnt piece of paper.
3. If you measure the mass of the water in a calorimeter and the change in temperature that occurs, you can calculate the amount of heat in the substance burned.
4. The heat might cause the parts to expand. They then might "freeze" together.
5. The ether absorbs heat as it evaporates. If it drew enough heat from the water, the water would freeze.
6. $H = (t_2 - t_1) m$
   $= (1.5°\ C)\ 1000g$
   $= 1500\ cal$
7. Gain in kinetic energy causes molecules to move apart and the parts to expand.
8.

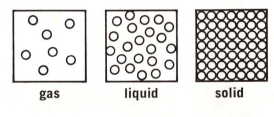

gas   liquid   solid

9. When liquid freon, under pressure, evaporates to a gas, the molecules gain molecular potential energy (heat of fusion), taking on heat from the inside of the refrigerator.
10. Hot air and hot liquid are less dense than cold. As the hot rises, the cold falls setting up a convection current.

Page 309 (21M). Investigations
1. Thermal pollution results when some part of the natural surroundings are abnormally heated. For example, a power plant discharges hot water into a river and the temperature of the river rises. Cooling towers are a partial solution to the problem.

2.

Brass Tube Type Thermostat

3. Building supply stores or hardware stores would have this type of material.

Unit Five, Chapter 2
Heat and Its Uses

PERFORMANCE OBJECTIVES
Goal: Students will gain an understanding of heat energy and its practical applications.
Objectives: Upon completion of the reading and activities and when asked to diagram, demonstrate, or respond either orally or on a written test, students will:

2:1	K	define specific heat.
2:1	S/P	conduct an activity to compare specific heats of some substances.
2:2	K	compare and contrast various types of heating systems.
2:2	S/P	compare an activity to demonstrate the operation of a thermostat containing a bimetallic strip.
2:3	P	state Boyle's law and Charles' law and indicate an example of each.
2:3	S/P	conduct an activity to demonstrate Charles' law.
2:4	P	explain the principles involved in the operation of a refrigeration unit.
2:5	P	explain the relationship between heat energy and mechanical energy.
2:5	K	list various types of engines, describe their operation, and indicate advantages and disadvantages of each.
2:6	P	discuss thermal pollution and suggest possible uses for waste heat.
2:7	K	define cryogenics.
2:7	P	list effects of cryogenic temperatures and suggest practical applications.

S/A When conducting activities and experiments, students will use laboratory materials and equipment in the prescribed manner.

Upon completion of the reading and activities, students will exhibit an interest in science by:
A reading unassigned literature related to ideas presented in the chapter.
A/S requesting permission to conduct further experiments related to ideas presented in the chapter.

EQUIPMENT FOR ACTIVITIES
Equipment
  alcohol
  balloon
  barometers, aneroid
    mercury
  beakers, 2
  bimetallic strip
  broom straw
  Bunsen burner
  dish (for mercury)
  flask (500-ml)
  glass tubing, 80 cm
  graph paper
  hot plate
  metal cans, 2
  metal pieces, 3 (Al, Fe, Cu—all same mass)
  paraffin
  refrigerator
  ring stand and ring
  rubbing alcohol
  rubber band
  ruler
  sand
  tape measure
  test tube clamps, 2
  thermometers, 2
  tongs
  vacuum bottle
Reagents
  alcohol
  dye, dark-colored
  ether
  ice
  water

Page 312 (24M). Problems
1. The specific heat of water is higher than sand, glass, and air.
2. Because it has a high specific heat, it absorbs a relatively large amount of heat per gram.
3. Nearby bodies of water make climate warmer in winter and cooler in summer. The water is warmer than the land in winter and cooler in summer.

Page 317 (29M). Problem
4. Air pressure is greater at sea level and greater under the water's surface. Air pressure is caused by the weight of the atmosphere's mass. The earth at sea level has more atmosphere above it, thus greater force pushing down (weight) than at the top of the mountain. The weight of water above a submerged body makes the force on the body greater than force at the water's surface.

Page 323 (35M). Problem
5. Answers will vary. Some possibilities are more efficient engines for better mileage, catalytic converters and other antismog devices, making engines which run on unleaded gasoline.

Page 327 (39M). Problem
6. good points—provide jobs, new products, improve standard of living; bad points—pollutes, uses raw materials

Page 329 (41M). Problem
7. Cells and tissues are frozen and stored for later study and use. Many surgical procedures are made possible by this practice. Student answers will vary.

Pages 329-331 (41M-43M). Study Questions
A. True or False
1. True 2. False (The specific heat of iron is not greater than that of water.) 3. True 4. False (A hot water heating system is not better than a steam heating system.) 5. False (Cryogenics is the study of very low temperatures.) 6. False (A barometer measures the pressure of a substance.) 7. False (The most common refrigerant in household refrigerators is freon.) 8. False (A rotary engine has no pistons.) 9. False (Absolute zero is $-273°$ on the Celsius scale.) 10. True

B. Multiple Choice
1. insulator 2. currents 3. 500 4. 540 5. thermostat 6. increases 7. $0°K$ 8. cools 9. evaporation 10. under water

C. Completion
1. reaction 2. gases 3. low 4. exhaust 5. less 6. thermal 7. evaporation 8. compressed 9. 0 10. cryogenics

D. How and Why
1. Heated water from industry can be cooled in towers and pools. Excess heat can also be recycled and used in other manufacturing processes.
2. Metal heats faster than water because of lower specific heat. A knife in a heating beaker of water will get hot before the water.
3. Heat in the large bodies of water may prevent late spring frosts that would damage fruit blossoms.
4. A hot water heating system transfers heat by moving hot water from a boiler to radiators inside rooms. A steam system moves steam.
5. Heating and cooling causes the bimetallic strip in the thermostat to bend back and forth. When the temperature becomes too low the strip bends to touch an electrical contact that turns on the heating unit. When the right temperature is reached, the bimetallic strip bends away from the contact and the heater shuts off.
6. The gas laws, Boyle's, Charles', and Gay-Lussac's, relate volume to pressure and temperature.
7. Burning of the gasoline inside the engine's cylinder produces heat which causes gases in the cylinder to expand and exert a force on the pistons. Force makes the pistons move up and down and thereby turn a crankshaft to which they are attached. Motion of the pistons and crankshaft produces power, work ($f \times d$) per unit time.
8. The Wankel, or rotary, engine has a rotor that rotates inside a chamber. A mixture of gasoline and air is sent into the chamber where it is compressed and then ignited by a spark plug. This causes the release of hot gases which exert a force on the rotor, making it rotate in a clockwise direction. The rotor is attached to a crankshaft that turns the wheels of a car.
9. See Section 2:6.
10. Their molecules decrease vibration and take on more orderly arrangements. The resistance to flow of electrical current in metals approaches zero.

Page 331 (43M). Investigations
1. Models are available at hobby shops or department stores. Consider ion, electric, etc.
2. A good geology book would be a reliable source.
3. Some students might be interested in reporting on air conditioning units.
4. A good source would be recent yearbooks for encyclopedias.
5. In certain places, geothermal power has been used for many years.
6. Label rotating blades, stationary blades, and direction of hot gas.

Unit Five, Chapter 3
Waves

PERFORMANCE OBJECTIVES
Goal: Students will gain an understanding of the properties of waves and the electromagnetic spectrum.

Objectives: Upon completion of the reading and activities and when asked to diagram, demonstrate, or respond either orally or on a written test, students will:

3:1	P/S	compare transverse waves with compressional waves and demonstrate the differences.
3:1	K	define wavelength, frequency, and amplitude and indicate their relationships.
3:2	S/P	conduct an activity to determine wave frequency.
3:3	S/P	conduct an activity to determine the length of a sound wave.
3:3	S/P	conduct an activity to demonstrate how beats may be produced by two sounds.
3:4	K	explain the use of a ripple tank in wave studies.
3:5	K	explain the factors determining pitch.
3:5	S/P	conduct an activity to demonstrate that waves can be reflected.
3:6	S/P	conduct an activity to demonstrate that waves can be refracted.
3:7	S/P	conduct an activity to demonstrate the Doppler effect and explain what happens.

3:8 K   define and describe the electro-magnetic spectrum.

S/A When conducting activities, students will use laboratory materials and equipment in the prescribed manner.

Upon completion of the reading and activities, students will exhibit an interest in science by:

A   reading unassigned literature related to ideas presented in the chapter.

A/S volunteering to help maintain and care for laboratory equipment.

A/S volunteering to design and conduct a demonstration for the class.

EQUIPMENT FOR ACTIVITIES
bottle
dowel
dry cell
electric bell
glass plate (to fit in ripple tank)
glass tube, 2.5 × 45 cm
hacksaw blade
medicine dropper
metal washers
overhead projector
pan, flat glass
protractor
rope
rubber bands
ruler
"Slinky" coil spring
test tubes, 6
test tube rack
tubing
  glass
  rubber (heavy wall)
tuning forks, various frequencies attached to resonator boxes
vacuum pump
whistles, 2
wooden block

Page 337 (49M). Problems
1. $\frac{10 \text{ vib}}{30 \text{ sec}} = 0.3$ vib/sec
2. 256 vib/sec

Page 338 (50M). Activity
The loudness decreases since there is less matter (air) inside the jar to transmit the sound waves.

Page 340 (52M). Problem
3. $\lambda = \frac{v}{f}$
   $= \frac{1130 \text{ ft}}{\text{sec}} \mid \frac{\text{sec}}{256 \text{ vib}}$
   $= 4.4$ ft or 1.32 m

Page 341 (53M). Problem
4. $f = \frac{v}{\lambda}$
   $= \frac{335 \text{ m}}{\text{sec}} \mid \frac{1 \text{ m}}{}$
   $= 335$ vib/sec

Page 342 (54M). Problems
5. $f = \frac{v}{\lambda}$
   $= \frac{34{,}000 \text{ cm/sec}}{6 \text{ cm}}$
   $= 5733$ vib/sec
6. $f = \frac{v}{\lambda}$
   $= \frac{344 \text{ m/sec}}{12 \text{ m}}$
   $= 28.7$ vib/sec
7. $f = \frac{v}{\lambda}$
   $v = 344$ m/sec $+ 3$ m/sec for 5° C rise in temperature
   $f = \frac{347 \text{ m/sec}}{12 \text{ m}}$
   $f = 28.9$ vib/sec
8. $v = 344$ m/sec (at 20° C)
   1.61 km $= 5$ sec
   $\frac{5 \text{ sec}}{1.61 \text{ km}} = \frac{10 \text{ sec}}{x}$
   $5x = 16.10$ km
   $x = 3.22$ km
9. by tightening or shortening the string by placing fingers on the frets

Page 345 (57M). Problems
10. Dogs can hear sound frequencies beyond the range of human hearing. The frequency of the whistle exceeds the range of human hearing.
11. The bat emits sounds of very high frequency as it flies. The echoes reflected back to the bat are used to locate surrounding objects and their distances.

12. Sonar sound waves are sent out through the bottom of the ship. By timing the return of the echo, the depth and the location of submerged objects may be determined.

Page 347 (59M). Activity
A simple ripple tank can be made from common materials. A glass baking dish (23 cm × 30 cm × 5 cm) will make a very good container. If desired, a wire screen can be placed on the bottom. Any round stick or dowel rod can be used for the straight wave generator. A medicine dropper can be used for making circular waves. A good light source is an overhead projector. It also allows for projection on a screen. If an overhead projector is unavailable, the dish can be placed on white paper and a flashlight can be used. In all cases, fill the container 1/3 full of water.

Page 350 (62M). Problems
13. The sound waves change speed when they pass from a solid to a gas. This change in speed causes the refraction.
14. The same principle applies as in 13. Any differences in substances through which a wave passes will cause refraction. Refraction always occurs toward the slow side.

Pages 354-356 (66M-68M). Study Questions
A. True or False
1. True 2. True 3. False (When frequency increases, wavelength decreases.) 4. True 5. False (Sound waves cannot travel through a vacuum.) 6. True 7. False (Wave amplitude determines the loudness of a sound wave.) 8. False (Sound waves having a frequency above 20,000 vib/sec are called ultrasonic.) 9. False (Most people can not hear sound with frequencies above 20,000 vib/sec.) 10. False (All visible light waves do not have the same wavelength.)

B. Multiple Choice
1. compressional 2. transverse 3. frequency 4. decreases 5. amplitude 6. cannot be heard by human beings 7. make a vibration in the water 8. remains the same 9. are equal 10. change in velocity

C. Completion
1. position or motion 2. Doppler effect 3. same 4. Cosmic 5. Cosmic 6. glass, air (answers may vary) 7. speed 8. frequency 9. waves 10. same

D. How and Why
1.

2. $\dfrac{15 \text{ waves}}{3 \text{ sec}} = 5$ waves/sec
3. Their speed changes and they are refracted.
4. Transverse wave vibrations are at right angles to the direction the wave is moving. In a compressional wave the vibrations are in the same direction the wave is moving. Transverse wave: light, X rays; compressional wave: sound, wave in a metal spring.
5. It cannot be done. All forms of communication from one point to another require energy waves.
6.

7. The electromagnetic spectrum is a set of invisible, transverse energy waves, ranging from very low frequency to very high frequency. All travel at the speed of light.
8. Infrared waves have a longer wavelength. Ultraviolet waves have a shorter wavelength. They are all forms of radiant energy.
9. Place a vibrator or rippler in the water and slowly move it in the direction of the waves. Then move the rippler away from the waves.
10. $\lambda = \dfrac{v}{f}$
$= \dfrac{3 \times 10^8 \text{ m}}{\text{sec}} \bigg| \dfrac{\text{sec}}{540 \times 10^3 \text{ vib}}$
$= 555$ m, round off to 600

Pages 356-357 (68M-69M). Investigations
1. Relate this to other examples of the Doppler effect. In this case it applies to light waves. This is also another example of spectroscopic observation—similar to but much more refined than flame tests for cation analysis.
2. How does radar relate to echolocation in bats and certain fish?
3. Large lakes often have regular osscillations. Is the motion of waves in them similar to ocean waves?
4. Some new surfing books might provide some answers.
5. Find out how dimensions and the arrangement of a building are important to its acoustic qualities. Can the actual building materials affect its quality?
6. What factors affect the accuracy of these results? How does averaging the results of several trials improve accuracy?

Unit Five, Chapter 4
Optics

PERFORMANCE OBJECTIVES
Goal: Students will gain an understanding of the properties of light and how to use mirrors and lenses to produce images.
Objectives: Upon completion of the reading and activities and when asked to diagram, demonstrate, or respond either orally or on a written test, students will:

4:1	S/P	conduct an activity to demonstrate the characteristics of an image formed by a plane mirror.
4:1-2	P	compare and contrast real images and virtual images and the ways they can be produced.
4:2	S	demonstrate the production of a real image and a virtual image with a concave parabolic mirror.
4:3	S/P	conduct an activity to demonstrate refraction of an object in a clear liquid.
4:4	P	compare convex lenses with concave lenses.
4:4	S	use a convex lens to produce a real image and diagram the paths of the light rays producing the image.
4:5	P	compare the uses of convex and concave lenses in correcting vision problems.
4:6	P	compare and contrast refracting telescopes and reflecting telescopes.
4:7	S	use a prism to separate white light into its component colors.
4:8	P	explain how wavelength and frequency are related to color.
4:9	S	use polaroid filters to demonstrate the polarization property of light.
4:9	S	use a diffraction grating to demonstrate interference of light waves.
4:10	K	describe the photoelectric effect and indicate a device which works on this principle.
	S/A	When conducting activities, students will use laboratory materials and equipment in the prescribed manner.

Upon completion of the reading and activities, students will exhibit an interest in science by:

A	reading unassigned literature related to ideas presented in the chapter.
A/S	requesting permission to conduct further experiments related to ideas presented in the chapter.

EQUIPMENT FOR ACTIVITIES
aluminum foil
candles, 2
cardboard
  piece
  shoe box
coin
concave lens
convex lens
cup
diffraction grating, 3 cm^2
glass, 8 oz tumbler
index card, white
knife
lamp (flashlight)
light meter (or camera with coupled light meter)
meter stick
mirror
  plane
  shaving (magnifying)

paper, white
pencil
polarizing filters, 2
prisms, 2
protractor
ruler
straight pins

Page 359 (71M). Problem
1. Pond, window, car fender, refrigerator, eyeglasses are examples.

Page 364 (76M). Problem
2.

Page 369 (81M). Problems
3. $\dfrac{H_i}{H_o} = \dfrac{D_i}{D_o}$

$\dfrac{10 \text{ cm}}{2 \text{ cm}} = \dfrac{24 \text{ cm}}{D_o}$

$D_o = 48$ cm

4. $\dfrac{H_i}{H_o} = \dfrac{D_i}{D_o}$

$\dfrac{2.5 \text{ cm}}{H_o} = \dfrac{100 \text{ cm}}{10 \text{ cm}}$

$H_o = .25$ cm

Page 370 (82M). Problem
5. increases

Page 372 (84M). Problem
6. real images, otherwise they could not be used to photograph stars

Page 375 (87M). Problems
7. violet
8. red
9. violet
10. red

Page 376 (88M). Problems
11. The color band can be identified by its position in the spectrum.
12. violet

Page 377 (89M). Problem
13. parallel
    perpendicular

Pages 381-383 (93M-95M). Study Questions
A. *True or False*
1. False (A concave lens makes light rays diverge.) 2. True 3. False (The frequency of a light wave determines its color.) 4. False (A parabolic mirror does not always give an enlarged image.) 5. False (The image in a plane mirror is never inverted.) 6. True 7. True 8. True 9. True 10. True

B. *Multiple Choice*
1. real 2. equals 3. reflects 4. both real and virtual 5. it is bent 6. refracted 7. parabolic mirror 8. decreases 9. distance of an image from a convex lens 10. virtual

C. *Completion*
1. reflection 2. refracting 3. parabolic 4. prism 5. violet 6. prism, diffraction 7. spectrum 8. pitch 9. 4×10^{-5} cm to 7×10^{-5} cm 10. polarized

D. *How and Why*
1. Polarizing lenses stop all waves that are not aligned parallel to the axis of the lens. The amount of light traveling through the lens is diminished. If light did not have wave properties, this would not occur.
2. Interference causes reinforcement and cancellation of different wavelengths. At points where a certain wavelength is reinforced a color appears and wavelengths for all other colors are canceled.
3. The photoelectric effect is the release of electrons by some metals when hit by light. Electric eyes and light meters make use of this.
4. A light meter is used to determine the amount of light available for photography or other purposes. Light hitting the meter causes electrons to be released. The number of electrons, and therefore the current, depends upon the amount of light available. The greater the current, the more the arm on the meter moves.
5. Two sides of the tank and the vertical edge between the sides are a prism which can disperse light.
6. Light travels faster in air than in glass. Thus, if light travels from air to glass it should be bent toward the normal. Since the angle with the normal is smaller in (a), (a) is the glass.
7. Sunlight is refracted as it passes from space into the atmosphere. Therefore, the

light from the sun which enters our eyes has been bent from a straight path and the sun appears at a point higher than it really is.
8. Real images can be projected on a screen. Virtual images cannot. A motion picture projector creates a real image; a magnifying glass, a virtual image.

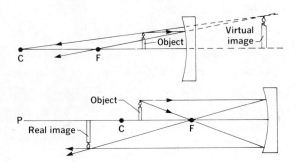

9. An image cannot be seen in a rough surface because the reflected light is scattered rather than reflected in a regular pattern.

10. Farsightedness can be corrected by a convex lens since it causes an image to be formed on rather than in back of the retina when corrected. Nearsightedness is corrected by concave lenses which cause the image to move back to the retina rather than in front of it as when uncorrected.

Page 383 (95M). Investigations
1. Other activities can be devised testing the principles of mirrors and lenses.
2. An alternative to this investigation might be to have students talk with a photographer on the methods used in selecting settings on light meters.

Unit Six   Electrical and Nuclear Energy

Goal: Students will gain an understanding of electrical and nuclear energy as it applies to technological developments.

Unit Six, Chapter 1
Electricity

PERFORMANCE OBJECTIVES
Goal: Students will gain an understanding of the different kinds of electricity and the relationship between electricity and magnetism.
Objectives: Upon completion of the reading and activities and when asked to diagram, demonstrate, or respond either orally or on a written test, students will:

1:1	S	conduct an activity to demonstrate how electrons can be added to or removed from a substance by rubbing two substances together.
1:1	P	compare and contrast positive static electric charges and negative static electric charges.
1:1	P	compare electrons with protons.
1:2	P	contrast electrical conductors and insulators.
1:2	S	use an electroscope to determine when an object is charged positively, negatively, or is neutral.
1:3	S	conduct an activity to demonstrate the charging of a metal rod by induction.
1:2-3	P	compare and contrast the charging of an electroscope by induction and by conduction.
1:4	P	compare and contrast wet cells and dry cells and explain how they can make up a battery.
1:5	K	describe two ways in which electric current can be produced by heat energy.
1:6	S	construct an electromagnet and demonstrate its use.
1:6	S	conduct an activity to demonstrate the presence of a magnetic field around a magnet.
1:6	K	list the properties of a magnet.
1:7	S/P	conduct an activity to produce an electric current through the use of a magnet and a coil of wire.
1:7	P	compare direct current with alternating current.
1:8	K	define ampere, coulomb, volt, ohm, and watt.
1:8	S/P	conduct an activity to demonstrate the relationship among volts, amperes, and ohms in a circuit.
	S/A	When conducting activities, students will use laboratory materials and equipment in the prescribed manner.

Upon completion of the reading and activities, students will exhibit an interest in science by:

A	reading unassigned literature related to ideas presented in the chapter.
A/S	voluntarily constructing a direct current motor and demonstrating its use to the class.
A/S	voluntarily calculating the cost of electricity using the kilowatt hours listed on a monthly electric bill.

EQUIPMENT FOR ACTIVITIES
ammeter
bar magnets, 2
beakers, 2
bottle, glass
comb
copper, strip
   wire
cork
curtain rod (with ball end)
dry cell, 6 volt
   several used
galvanometer
glass rod
graphite
hacksaw
iron filings
metal, foil
   rod
   wire
nail, large
paper, thin
plastic rod
silk, cloth
   thread
sulfuric acid, dilute
variable resistor

wire
wool cloth
zinc strip

Page 390 (6M). Problems
1. In each case, one object either loses electrons or gains electrons resulting in an attraction due to the opposite charges between the two objects.
2. rubbed amber, combing clean hair, electrostatic generator, Leyden jar
3. from the hair

Page 393 (9M). Problems
4. rubber, ceramics, glass
5. Conduction involves direct contact and produces the same charge as the original charged object. Induction does not involve contact and produces a charge opposite to the charge on the original object.
6. With a rubber stopper (or other suitable nonconducting material). Leaves are often enclosed in glass container to prevent discharge to air.

Page 398 (14M). Problem
7. Substances cannot ionize unless in solution and will not effectively carry current.

Page 399 (15M). Additional Information
Thermocouples are used in a kind of thermometer called a *pyrometer*. In a pyrometer, the thermocouple is connected to a circuit containing an electric meter. The meter is scaled in degrees. The greater the current produced by the thermocouple, the higher the temperature indicated on the meter.

Page 404 (20M). Problem
8. Magnetic field induces current in the wire coil. Kinetic energy is changed to electrical energy.

Page 405 (21M). Problem
9. house current

Page 406 (22M). Problems
10. silver and copper
    They have the lowest resistances.
11. too expensive and too soft

Page 407 (23M). Problems
12. $I = \dfrac{V}{R}$
    $I = \dfrac{12 \text{ volts}}{3 \text{ ohms}}$
    $I = 4$ amp
13. $R = \dfrac{V}{I}$
    $R = \dfrac{120 \text{ volts}}{5 \text{ amp}}$
    $R = 24$ ohms

Page 408 (24M). Problems
14. $R = \dfrac{V}{I}$
    $R = \dfrac{6 \text{ volts}}{30 \text{ amp}}$
    $R = 0.2$ ohm
15. 500 W $\times$ 10 hr = 500 W-hr = 5 KWH

Pages 409-411 (25M-27M). Study Questions

A. True or False
1. True 2. True 3. True 4. True 5. True 6. True 7. False (Photoelectric cells convert light energy into electrical energy.) 8. True 9. True 10. False (All ions do not have a net charge of zero.)

B. Multiple Choice
1. a positive charge 2. negatively charged 3. charged 4. conductor 5. insulators 6. repel 7. ammeter 8. magnet and coil 9. decreases 10. Copper

C. Completion
1. loses 2. Like 3. electroscope 4. insulator 5. direct 6. generator 7. induction 8. watts 9. kilowatt-hours 10. high

D. How and Why
1. friction between two bodies
2. kinetic energy
3. A chemical reaction between the chemical solution and metals immersed in the solution releases electrons which form an electric current through an outside circuit.
4. Both are vacuum tubes and both contain a cathode and anode. The heated cathode in the diode releases electrons and these electrons travel to the anode, forming an electric current. The cathode in a photoelectric cell releases electrons when light strikes it and these electrons travel to the anode, forming an electric current.

5. Both the generator and galvanometer contain a wire coil and magnets. The coil of the generator produces an electric current when turned. The coil in a galvanometer rotates when an electric current flows through it.
6. $I = \dfrac{V}{R} = \dfrac{12V}{2 \text{ ohms}} = 6$ amp
7. The Canadian nickel contains nickel metal which is ferromagnetic and attracted to magnets. An American nickel does not contain nickel or any other ferromagnetic metal.
8. Inexpensive. Other examples are ceramic or hard rubber.
9. To discharge clouds to avoid being struck by lightning.
10. Dry cell, wet cell, induction coil and magnet, generator are examples.

Page 411 (27M). Investigations
1. Study the various kinds of electricity generation plants and the environmental effects of each kind.
2. Some students might be interested in finding out about different kinds of motors for various purposes.
3. When working with magnets always be sure to remove your watch. Magnetic fields often affect watch movements.
4. Some bills may indicate "therms" as the unit. In this case try to determine the relationship between therms and KWH and determine cost per therm and cost per KWH. You might ask students why they believe the electric company would use therms.

Unit Six, Chapter 2
Electronics

PERFORMANCE OBJECTIVES
Goal: Students will gain an understanding of the principles involved in electronic devices.
Objectives: Upon completion of the reading and activities and when asked to diagram, demonstrate, or respond either orally or on a written test, students will:

2:1	S/P	conduct an activity to demonstrate a simple series circuit and a simple parallel circuit.
2:2	P	compare the cathode with the anode found in vacuum tubes.
2:2	P	compare a diode vacuum tube with a triode vacuum tube.
2:3	S/P	conduct an activity to demonstrate one way of storing an electric charge.
2:3	P	describe the principle of a capacitor and explain how it is used in a radio circuit.
2:4	K	explain what a rectifier is and what it is used for.
2:5	S/P	conduct an activity with a cathode tube and a magnet to demonstrate the effect of a magnet on a stream of electrons.
2:6	P	compare transistors with vacuum tubes.
2:7	K	define integrated circuit and give one use.
2:8	P	compare and contrast a digital computer and an analog computer.
	S/A	When conducting activities, students will use laboratory materials and equipment in the prescribed manner.

Upon completion of the reading and activities, students will exhibit an interest in science by:

A	reading unassigned literature related to ideas presented in the chapter.
A	voluntarily visiting a computer center and reporting to the class.
A	voluntarily visiting an electric power plant and reporting to the class.

EQUIPMENT FOR ACTIVITIES
aluminum foil
ammeter
bar magnets, varying strength
battery, 6 volt
bell
bell wire
copper wire
Crookes tube (cathode ray tube)
diodes, used
dry cell
electroscope
electrostatic generator
glass plate
jar, glass

magnesium wire
match
microlamps, 3
plastic rod
rubber band
sandpaper
switch
tongs
triode, used
wire loop (connected to nonconducting handle)
wool cloth
zinc strip

Page 413 (29M). Problem
1. battery, coil, switch

Page 415 (31M). Problem
2.

Page 420 (36M). Problem
3. Alternating current would not completely reverse the chemical reaction that produced electrons in the first place.

Page 421 (37M). Problem
4. The electrons rather than returning to original positions are constantly attracted to the positively charged grid thus forcing them to move in one direction in the circuit.

Page 424 (40M). Problem
5. The electromagnet can vary its strength and polarity attracting or repelling electrons at varying degrees and thus cause the beam to change position.

Page 429 (45M). Problem
6. (a) hourglass
   (d) slide rule
   (a) clock
   (d) Geiger counter
   (d) abacus
   (d) fingers
   (d) telephone dial
   (a) hygrometer
   (a) ammeter
   (a) voltmeter
   (a) odometer
   (a) spring scale

Pages 430-432 (46M-48M). Study Questions

A. True or False
1. False (Electrons flow through a circuit from cathode to anode.) 2. False (Like charges repel each other.) 3. True 4. False (The negative plate of a vacuum tube is called the cathode.) 5. True 6. True 7. False (An electron is negatively charged.) 8. False (Electricity is the flow of electrons through a circuit.) 9. True 10. True

B. Multiple Choice
1. filament 2. grid 3. capacitor 4. decreases 5. battery 6. semiconductors 7. less than 8. less than 9. rectifier 10. input

C. Completion
1. charged plates 2. Answers will vary 3. input, storage, arithmetic, output, control 4. program 5. vacuum tube 6. output 7. arithmetic unit 8. Electronics 9. series 10. capacitor

D. How and Why
1. The triode contains a grid which regulates the flow of electrons from filament to plate.
2. One set of plates is positively charged and the other set is negatively charged. The insulator between the plates prevents the electrons from traveling from the negative plate to the positive plate so the electrons are "stored."
3. In both cases the electric current is a flow of ions from cathode to anode.
4. The tungar rectifier changes the alternating current in the filament to direct current in the plate. Positive ions go to the negative filament (cathode). At the same time, electrons stream away from the filament to the positive plate (anode). From here they go into the output circuit. The current produced in the output circuit attached to the plate is direct current. In a direct current, electrons flow in one direction only.
5. The major uses of vacuum tubes are in radio and television equipment, notably transmitters and receivers.
6. Bring a magnet near an operating Crookes tube, or cathode ray tube and the path of the beam will be deflected.

7. Transistors are smaller, cheaper, use less voltage, and do not produce much heat when operating.
8. An analog is something which is similar to something else. The movement of mercury in a thermometer varies directly with changes in temperature. The movement of the needle on a speedometer varies directly with changes in speed (distance/time). Annual rings in a tree trunk equal years of time through which the tree has grown. Thickness of the annual rings represents the amount of rainfall during the tree's growth.
9. The integrated circuit takes up less space than wired circuits. Its reduced circuitry permits its use in small devices.
10. In tuning a radio, the capacitor is adjusted with a knob until the station desired is heard. The tuner (capacitor) changes the AC frequency in the circuit. When the AC frequency equals that of a radio station, that station is heard. If plates of the capacitor are far apart, a low frequency station is heard; if they are close together, a high frequency station is heard.

Page 432 (48M). Investigations
1. Students may wish to find out which tubes do what in a TV set.
2. In particular, they may wish to investigate the use of the cathode ray tube oscilloscope.
3. They may wish to include the use of the various color functions.
4. Students might also investigate the laws governing radio transmitters.
5. Information may be obtained from a telephone company or companies specializing in computers or hand-held calculators.

Unit Six, Chapter 3
Radiation

PERFORMANCE OBJECTIVES
Goal: Students will gain an understanding of radiation and the methods for the detection and measurement of radiation.
Objectives: Upon completion of the reading and activities and when asked to diagram, demonstrate, or respond either orally or on a written test, students will:

3:1	K	describe the characteristics of X rays.
3:1	S/P	conduct an activity to demonstrate the effect of lead shielding on X rays produced by a Crookes tube.
3:2	K	define roentgen.
3:3	P	contrast stable nuclei with unstable nuclei.
3:4	K	list some examples of radioactive isotopes.
3:4	K	list and explain three uses of radioactive isotopes.
3:5	K	describe transmutation.
3:5	P	contrast the differences among alpha, beta, and gamma radiation.
3:6	K	explain the half-life concept as it applies to a radioactive material.
3:7	K	explain the detection of radiation with an electroscope.
3:8	P	compare and describe uses of a cloud chamber and a bubble chamber.
3:9-10	P	compare nuclear emulsions, Geiger counters, and scintillation counters and describe the uses of each.
3:10	S/P	conduct an activity to detect radioactivity with a Geiger counter.
3:10	S/P	conduct an activity to illustrate the relationship between the level of radiation and distance from the radioactive source.
	S/A	When conducting activities, students will use laboratory materials and equipment in the prescribed manner.

Upon completion of the reading and activities, students will exhibit an interest in science by:

A	reading unassigned literature related to ideas presented in the chapter.
A/S	voluntarily constructing and using a cloud chamber to detect background radiation.
A/S	voluntarily constructing and using an electroscope to determine relative radiation levels in the home.

EQUIPMENT FOR ACTIVITIES
aluminum sheet, 2 mm thick
box, square or rectangular
cathode ray tube

corn kernels, 100
electroscope
Geiger counter
meter stick
radiation source
watch

Page 436 (52M). Problem
1. X rays—wavelength 1×10^{-9} to 5×10^{-6} cm. The longest X rays have a wavelength one tenth as long as the wavelength of blue light. Radio waves are 10^6 to 10^{15} times longer than X rays.

Page 443 (59M). Problem
2. $Z = 92$ element—92 protons, 146 neutrons
$Z = 103$ element—103 protons, 154 neutrons
Yes, both are radioactive.

Page 444 (60M). Problems
3. alpha rays—least penetrating power, stopped by paper
beta rays—100 × that of alpha particles, stopped by aluminum 1 cm thick
gamma rays—most penetrating power, stopped by lead or concrete
4. Cosmic rays have shorter wavelengths.

Page 445 (61M). Problems
5. 86 min = 5 grams
2 hr 52 min = 2.5 grams
4 hr 18 min = 1.25 grams
6. Technically forever because a very small fraction would always be left. 99.9% would have decayed after 104 hours.
7. Radon 222—3.82 days
Polonium 214—0.0001 seconds
Uranium 238—4.5 billion years
Uranium 238 is much less radioactive than radon 222. Both are less radioactive than polonium 214.

Page 447 (63M). Problem
8. A charged electroscope loses its charge faster when ionizing radiation is present. The ions formed in the air are attracted to the knob of the electroscope causing the leaves to drop.

Page 449 (65M). Problem
9. The charged particles "expose" grains of silver bromide in the emulsion. In chemical developer, the exposed grains are reduced to silver which appears black. The path of the particles shows up as very short black lines.

Pages 452-454 (68-70M). Study Questions
A. True or False
1. False (A beta particle is actually an electron.) 2. True 3. False (An alpha particle has a positive charge.) 4. True 5. True 6. True 7. False (Radioactivity was discovered by Becquerel.) 8. True 9. False (Uranium 238 is less radioactive than radium 226.) 10. False (The shorter the half-life, the more radioactive the isotope.)

B. Multiple Choice
1. radio waves 2. 3×10^8 m/sec 3. frequency 4. increases 5. Lead 6. roentgen 7. radiation 8. alpha 9. alpha particle 10. flesh

C. Completion
1. negative 2. lost kinetic 3. time, half 4. ionizes 5. supersaturated 6. photographic 7. Geiger counter 8. gamma 9. C 14 10. photon

D. How and Why
1. Inside a vacuum tube a stream of electrons from a cathode are accelerated toward a tungsten anode. When the electrons strike the anode, X rays are emitted.
2. X rays are used to detect the order and spacing of atoms in substances. The X rays are *diffracted* by the atoms in the crystal. Patterns are produced because rows of atoms in a crystal affect X rays. The X rays change direction when they strike an atom. This is similar to the way a diffraction grating affects light.
 Spots form in an X-ray diffraction pattern. This occurs when waves are in phase. The waves are reinforced. Spots do not form where the waves are not in phase. The waves cancel each other or destructive interference occurs. X-ray diffraction patterns help to show the arrangement of atoms in a crystal. See Figure 3-7.
3. X rays and radioactivity ionize the air. Ions (charged particles) are attracted to the electroscope and neutralize the charge on it.
4. Alpha and beta rays are deflected in opposite directions by a magnetic field because

they have opposite charges. The magnetic forces set up by the particles as they move have opposite polarity.

5. A cloud chamber contains a supersaturated vapor in which visible cloud tracks are produced by radioactive particles. A bubble chamber contains a superheated liquid in which a trail of bubbles is produced by radioactive particles passing through it. A nuclear emulsion is a thick layer of gelatin containing silver bromide. It is similar to photographic emulsion. When developed after exposure to radioactivity, a black streak produced in the nuclear emulsion indicates the path of a radioactive particle.

6. The Geiger tube has two electrical connections which are separated from each other by a gas. Radioactivity ionizes particles in the gas, causing a brief current to be carried between the two electrical connections. The current is amplified and detected by a click or a light.

7. Alpha particles are positively charged particles each consisting of a helium nucleus. Speed is between 16,100 and 32,200 km/sec; they are stopped by a thin piece of paper (and are deflected by a magnetic field). Beta particles are electrons (negative charge) which originate from the nucleus. They travel at speeds 100 times that of alpha particles. (They are deflected by a magnetic field.) Gamma rays are waves of radiant energy having wavelength of about 10^{-10} cm. They travel at the speed of light (are not deflected by a magnetic field) and are stopped by several feet of concrete or by several inches of lead.

8. Treatment of cancers, tracers in plants and animals, detection of tumors are examples.

9. Burns, cancer, vomiting, loss of hair, destruction of blood cells, and death are examples.

10. Pass a geiger counter over it. A good guess can be made using the stability criteria on page 442 (58M).

Page 454 (70M). Investigations

1. Reports might contain the different types of radiation used for different diseases. For example, what does cobalt radiation treat?

2. As a class project, a doctor or dentist might be willing to bring in some X-ray photographs and discuss what each tells.

3. Any good encyclopedia or dictionary of famous persons will provide the information needed.

4. Carbon 14 is a beta-emitting isotope. It has a half-life of 5600 years. Carbon 14 decays to form nitrogen 14:

$$^{14}_{6}C \rightarrow {}^{14}_{7}N + {}^{0}_{-1}e$$

one atom of carbon 14 yields one atom of nitrogen 14 plus one beta particle

The amount of undecayed, natural carbon 14 in fossils and archaeological remains is a measure of the age of the material. Carbon-14 dating is so exact that some materials can be dated to within a few decades.

Unit Six, Chapter 4
Nuclear Reactors and Reactions

PERFORMANCE OBJECTIVES

Goal: Students will gain an understanding of the structure of the atomic nucleus, types of nuclear change, and the relationship between nuclear science and technology.

Objectives: Upon completion of the reading and activities and when asked to diagram, demonstrate, or respond either orally or on a written test, students will:

4:1	K	describe the operation of a cyclotron.
4:1	P	explain why all of the particles used as "bullets" in nuclear accelerators possess an electrical charge.
4:1	P	compare the process of accelerating nuclear particles with the principles which cause the armature in an electric motor to turn.
4:2	P	compare and contrast nuclear forces, electrostatic forces, and gravitational forces.
4:3	P	explain nuclear transmutation.
4:4	K	explain the relationship between a nuclear chain reaction and critical mass.
4:4	S	conduct an activity to demonstrate a chain reaction.
4:4	K	indicate what the symbols represent in $E = mc^2$.

4:5	K	list the six main parts of a nuclear reactor and describe the major functions of each part.
4:5	P	explain how energy from nuclear reactor fuel is converted to electrical energy.
4:6	P	compare nuclear fission with nuclear fusion.
4:7	P	explain why scientists are not able to produce a controlled thermonuclear fusion reaction.
4:8	P	list some environmental problems associated with nuclear power plants and indicate some steps taken to alleviate them.
	S/A	When conducting activities, students will use laboratory materials and equipment in the prescribed manner.

Upon completion of the reading and activities, students will exhibit an interest in science by:

- A reading unassigned literature related to ideas presented in the chapter.
- A voluntarily contacting the Energy Research and Development Administration to determine the location of the closest nuclear reactor or particle accelerator, visiting the installation, and reporting observations to the class.
- A/S voluntarily constructing a model of a nuclear reactor or particle accelerator.
- A/S volunteering to collect materials and help set up a demonstration of the rates at which different plants absorb radioactive isotopes.
- A/S volunteering to help care for and maintain laboratory materials and equipment.
- A/S volunteering to help inventory laboratory materials and equipment.

EQUIPMENT FOR ACTIVITIES
board, wooden
mousetraps, several
nails
string

Page 460 (76M). Problem
1. Electrons are not moving, one-dimensional, too large.

Page 462 (78M). Problem
2. $^{4}_{2}He$ The helium nucleus contains two protons and two neutrons for an atomic mass of four a.m.u.'s.

Page 463 (79M). Problems
3. uranium 238, uranium 234, thorium 230, radium 226, radon 222, polonium 218, polonium 214, polonium 210
4. thorium 234, protactinium 234, lead 214, bismuth 214, lead 210, bismuth 210

Page 464 (80M). Problem
5. Atoms different from the reactants are formed as products.

Page 464 (80M). Activity
An illustration of a chain reaction may also be done with matches. Place several matches in clay, ignite one. Discuss the process and relate it to nuclear fission.

Page 470 (86M). Problems
6. Refer to Figure 4-13.
7. This is a safety device used to stop the reaction in an emergency. The control rods absorb the neutrons and completely stop the chain reaction.

Page 473 (89M). Problem
8. Once the techniques for producing the extreme temperatures are perfected, thermonuclear power offers an almost endless supply of energy. The "natural resources" for this process are almost endless. These advantages make thermonuclear power very appealing to all nations.

Page 475 (91M). Problems
9. Nuclear energy is sometimes called "clean energy" since there are no pollutants which are released in the air. This is much unlike that of energy produced from fossil fuels.
10. Answers will vary. Some people object to the building and operation of nuclear power plants because of the cost, danger of radiation accidents, problems with thermal pollution, or danger of waste storage.

11. Answers may vary; Nuclear fusion and gassification of coal may be two such answers.

Pages 476-478 (92M-94M). Study Questions
A. True or False
1. False (A uranium atom has a fewer number of protons than neutrons.) 2. False (Alpha particles are used as atomic "bullets.") 3. False (A proton has the same mass as an electron.) 4. False (The changing of uranium to lead is an example of transmutation.) 5. True 6. True 7. False (The mass of a helium nucleus is less than the total mass of two protons plus two neutrons.) 8. False (Carbon 12 has a stable nucleus.) 9. True 10. True

B. Multiple Choice
1. less than 2. decreases 3. protons 4. lead 5. fuel 6. control rod 7. nuclear fusion 8. unite 9. nuclear forces 10. stable

C. Completion
1. critical mass 2. neutron 3. Turbines 4. transmutation 5. fusion 6. plasma 7. chain reaction 8. moderator 9. lead 10. nuclear particles

D. How and Why
1. A cyclotron is used to accelerate atomic particles to high speeds in mangetic fields. The magnetic field is produced inside the dees of the cyclotron by a large electromagnet. High voltage alternating current produces an electric field along the slit separating the dees. The electric field is constantly reversing from negative to positive many times per second. Protons injected into the center of the dees are forced by the magnetic and electric fields into a circular path, and are accelerated to very high speeds. The particles travel in an ever widening circle, constantly accelerating, until they exit through a window at the edge of the dees.

2. Energy is needed to overcome the nuclear forces which hold the neutrons and protons together.

3. One explanation is that it is analagous to a pile of coal.

4. If the fuel cans absorbed neutrons there would not be sufficient neutrons to maintain the chain reaction.

5. Large amounts of heat are produced in the chain reaction inside a nuclear reactor. If a nuclear fuel had a low melting point, it would melt and the reaction could become uncontrolled.

6. Nuclear reactors produce heat energy. Turbines convert this heat energy into kinetic energy.

7. In nuclear fission, a nucleus is broken apart to form other nuclei. In nuclear fusion, two or more nuclei are fused to become one nucleus. In both cases, the energy comes from the mass that is lost ($E = mc^2$).

8. One experiment for producing a controlled thermonuclear reaction is the heating of hydrogen gas inside a magnetic "bottle." Heavy hydrogen gas is enclosed in a circular aluminum tube and high voltage alternating current is used to heat the gas to a few million degrees for less than a second. Magnetic fields produced by an electromagnet "pinch" the gas and keep it away from the walls of the tube. If a temperature of 100 million degrees can be reached, a thermonuclear reaction will occur inside the tube.

9. Nuclear power plants are "clean" and require little fuel to produce enormous amounts of energy.

10. Nuclear power plants may harm the environment because of radioactive waste, hot water (thermal pollution), and the possibility of escape of radioactivity to the air.

Page 478 (94M). Investigations
1. Find out about "heavy water" and what it is used for.
2. Find out how research in plasma state of matter is related to sustained nuclear fusion reactions.
3. Reports will vary. For example, electronics technician requires two to three years beyond high school for certification.
4. For information look in an encyclopedia or a college physics text. Some students might be interested in reporting on fast-breeder reactors.

6 7 8 9 10 11 12 13 14 15-84 83 82 81 80

FOCUS ON Physical Science

Charles H. Heimler
California State University
Northridge, California

Jack Price
San Diego City Schools
San Diego, California

Charles E. Merrill Publishing Co.
A Bell & Howell Company

Columbus, Ohio
Toronto   London   Sydney

A Merrill Science Program

Focus on Physical Science, Casebound Edition and Modular Editions
Focus on Physical Science, Teacher's Annotated Edition
Focus on Physical Science, Evaluation Program (Spirit Duplicating Masters)
Focus on Physical Science: Activity-Centered Program, Teacher's Guide
Physical Science: A Learning Strategy for the Laboratory
Physical Science: A Learning Strategy for the Laboratory, Teacher's Annotated Edition
Physical Science Skillcards
Focus on Life Science Program
Focus on Earth Science Program

Series Editor: Kenneth E. Rogers
Project Editor: Janet E. Grise
Project Artists: Dennis L. Smith, Larry P. Koons

Cover and Opening Photo Credits and Descriptions

Unit 1 — Interaction of a bicyclist and the simple machinery of a bicycle results in motion. Photo, Gary Walker.

Unit 2 — Mountain scene in British Columbia, Canada illustrates the solid, liquid, and gaseous phases of matter. Photo, William Maddox.

Unit 3 — Diamonds are one form of carbon. This diamond has many facets which reflect and refract light in many directions. Photo, William Maddox.

Unit 4 — Exploding fireworks illustrate one type of chemical reaction. Photo, Edward Young.

Unit 5 — Patterns of rays made by the rising sun filter over the misty land. Photo, Allan Roberts.

Unit 6 — Electricity is produced from nuclear energy at the Point Beach nuclear plant in Two Creeks, Wisconsin. Photo, U. S. Energy Research and Development Administration.

ISBN 0-675-06720-0

Published by
Charles E. Merrill Publishing Co.
A Bell & Howell Company
Columbus, Ohio 43216

Copyright © 1977, 1974, 1969 by BELL & HOWELL
All rights reserved. No part of this book may be reproduced in any form, electronic or mechanical, including photocopy, recording, or any information storage or retrieval system, without permission in writing from the publisher.

Printed in the United States.

Preface

Focus on Physical Science is a practical study of the relationships between matter and energy. Applications of physical laws and chemical processes are current and meaningful. The program develops an awareness of the interdependence of science and technology and of the relationship between process and product of science. Fundamental physical science principles are introduced through student involvement rather than by rote memorization.

This program offers a relevant introduction to the chemical and physical properties of matter, forms of energy, and the laws of motion. Complex ideas are presented simply and then developed logically. Scientific principles are reinforced immediately through activities and experiments in each chapter. Students repeatedly use their experiences in observation, in data gathering, and in studying cause and effect relationships to interpret the physical environment. In emphasizing scientific inquiry, a clear distinction is made between scientific laws and theories. Activities and experiments have been designed to be effective without being overwhelming and time consuming. These activities and experiments make use of inexpensive materials that are readily available.

Focus on Physical Science is divided into six units of three to four chapters each. Each of the twenty-one chapters is divided into sections of related materials. These sections form logical teaching blocks of a convenient length for student assignments. Chapters have been grouped into units which can be studied in a variety of sequences and which can be easily organized into programs to fit any school calendar. For even greater flexibility, the individual units are also available as modules, each with its own table of contents, glossary, and index.

Throughout the program, reading level has been carefully controlled. Photographs, illustrations, charts, graphs, and tables allow students to visualize ideas presented in the text and, therefore, to read with improved understanding. New science words are spelled phonetically when introduced. They are printed in italic or boldface type when they are defined.

Focus pages, *People • Careers • Frontiers,* are newspaperlike pages which feature articles and photographs on current topics. They give additional contemporary emphasis to *Focus on Physical Science*. Some selections illustrate the relevance of physical science to students and describe recent developments. Others point to career opportunities in physical science and related fields through job descriptions or brief biographical sketches.

Questions in the margin help students identify important concepts as they read. Margin questions also may be used to introduce new topics in class discussions and, after a topic has been covered, for review.

Problems interspersed throughout the chapters enable students to immediately apply newly-learned concepts. Problems are also useful for identifying individual difficulties and for ensuring that basic concepts are mastered before more complicated topics are introduced. Mathematics required to do problems is integrated within the text. Thus, students learn basic mathematical skills as they need them to employ physical science concepts. Metric units are emphasized throughout.

Chapter-end features of *Focus on Physical Science* encourage student involvement and increase the flexibility of the program. These features are

- *Main Ideas*—list of important concepts
- *Vocabulary*—list of important science words
- *Study Questions*—questions and additional problem-solving applications of scientific knowledge
- *Investigations*—selected thought-provoking problems and projects
- *Suggested Readings*—literature references to topics discussed.

Focus on Physical Science presents material which is not only necessary for understanding physical science concepts and principles, but also meaningful to the everyday life of the students. Thus, the text involves the student in a relevant, purposeful study of physical science.

During the writing of *Focus on Physical Science,* the authors have had many helpful suggestions from students, teachers, and colleagues. To them, as well as to the editors and reviewers who have contributed to the accuracy and usefulness of the text, the authors offer their thanks and appreciation for the time and effort involved in coordinating the materials within the text.

Contents

1 Measurement and Motion

CHAPTER 1
Physical Science — 2

Chapter 1 discusses the nature of physical science. The interrelationship between science and technology is stressed. Measurements and their applications are emphasized as they relate to science and everyday life.

1:1	Product of Science	3
1:2	Technology	3
1:3	Process of Science	4
1:4	Experiments	7
1:5	Theories and Laws	8
1:6	Physical Science	9
1:7	Measurements	9
1:8	Measuring Length	10
1:9	Measuring Mass and Weight	12
1:10	Measuring Volume	13
1:11	Indirect Measurement	14

CHAPTER 2
Force and Work — 20

Chapter 2 develops the concepts of force, work, and power. Speed, effort force, and distance are discussed as they apply to common examples. Simple and compound machines are presented with an emphasis on how work is made easier with a machine.

2:1	Force	21
2:2	Work	21
2:3	Machines	23
2:4	Mechanical Advantage	24
2:5	Levers	25
2:6	Mechanical Advantage for a Lever	29
2:7	Pulleys	30
2:8	Wheel and Axle	32
2:9	Inclined Plane	33
2:10	Wedge	33
2:11	Screw	34
2:12	Efficiency	35
2:13	Power	38

v

CHAPTER 3
Moving Bodies

3:1	Weight and Mass	46
3:2	Gravity	47
3:3	Speed	50
3:4	Acceleration	51
3:5	Deceleration	54
3:6	Vectors	56
3:7	Velocity	62
		67

Chapter 3 discusses the difference between mass and weight. Speed, velocity, acceleration, and deceleration are some of the major concepts developed. Vectors are introduced and used in readily identifiable examples.

CHAPTER 4
Laws of Motion

4:1	First Law of Motion	72
4:2	Second Law of Motion	73
4:3	Third Law of Motion	75
4:4	Falling Bodies	77
4:5	Relative Motion	80
4:6	Motion in Curves	84
4:7	Momentum	87
		90

Chapter 4 presents Newton's laws of motion and relates them to common examples. Projectile motion and centripetal force are discussed. Additionally, momentum and conservation of momentum are introduced.

2 Properties of Matter

CHAPTER 1
Classification of Matter

1:1	Matter	98
1:2	Elements	99
1:3	Compounds	100
1:4	Mixtures	100
		102

Chapter 1 discusses the classification of matter. Differences between chemical and physical changes are examined. Many activities are performed to observe these changes in matter.

	1:5	Physical Properties	104
	1:6	Chemical Properties	107
	1:7	Physical Change	108
	1:8	Chemical Change	110

CHAPTER 2
Atoms and Compounds — 118

Chapter 2 introduces the atomic theory of matter. Atomic models are presented to show the probable arrangement of nuclear particles. An emphasis is placed on the importance of the electron in chemical bonds.

2:1	Atomic Theory	119
2:2	Subatomic Particles	119
2:3	Atomic Structure	119
2:4	Electron Location	121
2:5	Molecules	123
2:6	Bonding	124
2:7	Valence	126
2:8	Binary Compounds	128
2:9	Polyatomic Ions	130

CHAPTER 3
Solids, Liquids, and Gases — 136

Chapter 3 presents the three major phases of matter: solid, liquid, gas. Solids are subdivided into crystalline solids and amorphous solids. Characteristics of liquids and gases are discussed. Conditions needed for a change in phase are also examined.

3:1	Phases of Matter	137
3:2	Solids	137
3:3	Crystals	137
3:4	Ionic Bonding in Crystals	140
3:5	Covalent Bonding in Crystals	141
3:6	Crystallization	142
3:7	Amorphous Solids	144
3:8	Liquids	146
3:9	Gases	147
3:10	Pascal's Law	149
3:11	Change of Phase	151
3:12	Solid-Gas Change	152
3:13	Liquid-Solid Change	153
3:14	Liquid-Gas Change	155

3 Patterns in Matter

CHAPTER 1
Periodic Table

1:1	Atomic Mass	162
1:2	Mendeleev's Table	163
1:3	Moseley's Table	164
1:4	Isotopes	165
1:5	Average Atomic Mass	168
1:6	Reading the Periodic Table—Columns	169
1:7	Reading the Periodic Table—Rows	170
1:8	Chemical Activity	172
		174

Chapter 1 introduces the periodic table of elements. Practical guidelines are given for identifying properties of each element's atomic structure, and the relative activity of the elements.

CHAPTER 2
Families of Elements

2:1	Halogen Family	180
2:2	Oxygen Family	181
2:3	Nitrogen Family	185
2:4	Alkali Metals	192
2:5	Alkaline Earth Metals	195
2:6	Noble Gases	198
		201

Chapter 2 presents the major families of the periodic table. Emphasis is placed on the similarity of the elements within each family. Many chemical properties are discussed within this context.

CHAPTER 3
Carbon and Its Compounds

3:1	Organic Chemistry	206
3:2	Structural Formulas	207
		208

Chapter 3 introduces organic chemistry. Reasons for the large number of carbon compounds are presented. Saturated and unsaturated hydrocarbons are discussed as they relate to common examples.

3:3	Isomers	210
3:4	Saturated Hydrocarbons	211
3:5	Unsaturated Hydrocarbons	216
3:6	Polymers	217
3:7	Other Organic Compounds	218

4 Changes in Matter

CHAPTER 1
Solutions — 226

Chapter 1 discusses the formation of solutions through chemical processes and physical interaction of solute and solvent. Factors relating to rate of solution are presented. The concepts of solubility, concentration, and saturation are introduced.

1:1	Solutions	227
1:2	Formation of Solutions	229
1:3	Rate of Solution	230
1:4	Solvents	232
1:5	Polar Molecules	233
1:6	Solutions as Conductors	234
1:7	Solubility	237
1:8	Concentration	239
1:9	Saturation	240
1:10	Hydrated Crystals	242
1:11	Properties of Solutions	243

CHAPTER 2
Chemical Reactions

2:1	Conservation of Mass	250
2:2	Chemical Equations	251
2:3	Double Replacement	252
2:4	Single Replacement	253
2:5	Decomposition	256
2:6	Synthesis	258
2:7	Energy and Chemical Change	260
2:8	Molecular Mass and Formula Mass	261
2:9	Mass and Chemical Reactions	263
		264

Chapter 2 presents the principle of conservation of matter and energy. Guidelines for using chemical equations are introduced. Common chemical reactions emphasized are synthesis, decomposition, and replacement. The role of energy in chemical reactions is also a major concept.

CHAPTER 3
Acids, Bases, and Salts

3:1	Acids	270
3:2	Bases	271
3:3	Indicators	275
3:4	Hydrogen and Hydroxide Ions	276
3:5	pH of a Solution	277
3:6	Salts	280
3:7	Anhydrides	281
		283

Chapter 3 discusses acids, bases, and salts. Properties of each are identified and observed in activities. Various indicators for identifying acids and bases are explained and illustrated. Formation of salts through neutralization is presented.

5 Heat, Light, and Sound

CHAPTER 1
Heat Energy

1:1	Kinetic and Potential Energy	290
1:2	Radiation, Conduction, and Convection	291
		293

Chapter 1 discusses kinetic energy and heat as the kinetic energy of molecules. The effect of heat on the properties of matter is emphasized.

x

1:3	Measuring Heat	297
1:4	Joule's Experiment	299
1:5	Molecular Kinetic Energy	300
1:6	Melting and Vaporization	302

Chapter 2 relates heat energy to practical applications. Gas laws are introduced as they apply to common examples. Technological advances in dealing with thermal pollution are stressed. The field of cryogenics is introduced.

CHAPTER 2
Heat and Its Uses 310

2:1	Specific Heat	311
2:2	Heating Systems	312
2:3	Gas Laws	315
2:4	Refrigeration	320
2:5	Heat Engines	321
2:6	Thermal Pollution	325
2:7	Cryogenics	327

Chapter 3 discusses the transfer of energy by waves. Wave properties are introduced as they apply to water, light, and sound.

CHAPTER 3
Waves 332

3:1	Waves	333
3:2	Wave Frequency	336
3:3	Sound Waves	337
3:4	Resonance, Wavelength, and Frequency	339
3:5	Pitch	342
3:6	Volume	344
3:7	Ripple Tank	345
3:8	Reflection	346
3:9	Refraction	348
3:10	Doppler Effect	350
3:11	Electromagnetic Spectrum	352

CHAPTER 4
Optics

4:1	Plane Mirrors	358
4:2	Parabolic Mirrors	359
4:3	Index of Refraction	360
4:4	Lenses	362
4:5	Lenses and Vision	364
4:6	Telescopes	370
4:7	Prisms	371
4:8	Wavelength and Frequency	373
4:9	Polarization and Interference	376
4:10	Photoelectric Effect	376
		379

Chapter 4 describes the properties of light. The use of mirrors and lenses to study light is emphasized. Principles of reflection, refraction, interference, and polarization are emphasized.

Electrical and Nuclear Energy

CHAPTER 1
Electricity

1:1	Electric Charges	386
1:2	Conduction	387
1:3	Electrostatic Induction	390
1:4	Direct Current	392
1:5	Diode and Thermocouple	394
1:6	Magnetism	398
1:7	Alternating Current	400
1:8	Electrical Units	403
		404

Chapter 1 develops the concept of energy as it applies to electricity and its effects. Devices for detecting electrical charges are explained and illustrated. Magnetism is introduced as it relates to electricity. The concepts of alternating current and electrical units are presented.

CHAPTER 2
Electronics

2:1	Circuits	412
2:2	Vacuum Tubes	413
		415

Chapter 2 builds on the study of electricity through a discussion of principles involved in electronic devices. Vacuum tubes, transistors, integrated circuits, and computers are introduced.

xii

2:3	Capacitors		417
2:4	Rectifiers		420
2:5	Cathode-Ray Tube		421
2:6	Transistors		424
2:7	Integrated Circuits		425
2:8	Computers		426

CHAPTER 3
Radiation 434

Chapter 3 discusses radiation, its detection, and measurement. Production of radioactive isotopes, naturally occurring isotopes, and half-life are major concepts.

3:1	X Rays	435
3:2	The Roentgen	439
3:3	Radioactivity	440
3:4	Radioactive Isotopes	442
3:5	Alpha, Beta, and Gamma Rays	444
3:6	Half-Life	444
3:7	Radiation Detection	446
3:8	Cloud Chambers and Bubble Chambers	447
3:9	Nuclear Emulsions	448
3:10	Radiation Counters	449

CHAPTER 4
Nuclear Reactors and Reactions 456

Chapter 4 discusses the relationship between nuclear science and technology. A study is made of the nucleus and three types of nuclear reactions—transmutation, fission, and fusion. The operation of nuclear accelerators and reactors is explained. Environmental factors in the use of nuclear reactors are considered.

4:1	The Cyclotron	457
4:2	Atomic Nucleus	459
4:3	Transmutation	460
4:4	Nuclear Fission	463
4:5	Nuclear Reactors	467
4:6	Nuclear Fusion	470
4:7	Thermonuclear Power	472
4:8	Nuclear Energy and the Environment	473

Appendix A
Metric System 482

Appendix B
Temperature Scales 483

Appendix C
International Atomic Masses 484

Appendix D
Valences 485

Appendix E
The Periodic Table 486

Appendix F
Physical Laws 487

Glossary 490

Index 502

Information provided in these sections is for student use. Explain the function of these sections to the students and encourage them to use these references whenever possible.

Metric units are used internationally in science. It is the major measurement system commonly used by many countries. APPENDIX A is provided for reference. Students should be encouraged to use metric units if they are not already doing so.

APPENDIX B is provided for student use. The Celsius temperature scale is used to familiarize the students with scientific practice. Fahrenheit equivalents are given for those students not already familiar with the Celsius temperature scale.

APPENDIX C is a table of International Atomic Masses. It is presented to enable students to quickly find information regarding all known elements and their atomic masses.

APPENDIX D is a summary of valences of many common atoms and ions. Referral to this appendix will enable students to write and balance simple chemical equations.

APPENDIX E, The Periodic Table, is presented in less detail to provide the information students will be more likely to need once familiar with the detailed table in the text.

APPENDIX F is a list of the major physical laws emphasized throughout the text. It is presented to enable students to quickly refer to the key ideas of each law.

Spend time during the first week of the course explaining the use of the GLOSSARY and PRONUNCIATION KEY. Periodically encourage their use in conjunction with the text and homework assignments. Help students use the GLOSSARY in developing a scientific vocabulary.

Chapter Opening Photo Descriptions and Credits

Unit 1

Chapter 1   Temple of the Inscriptions, Palenque, Mexico   Rich Brommer
Chapter 2   Wheels of steam locomotive   William Maddox
Chapter 3   Lunar Command Module   NASA
Chapter 4   Hang glider   James M. Jackson

Unit 2

Chapter 1   Rusted lock and chain   Paul Poplis/Studio Ten
Chapter 2   Uranium salts   U.S. Energy Research and Development Administration
Chapter 3   Frost on window   Jim Elliot

Unit 3

Chapter 1   Buttons in shells   William Maddox
Chapter 2   Decaying wood in mountain scene   Paul Poplis/Studio Ten
Chapter 3   Candles through a prism   William Maddox

Unit 4

Chapter 1   Taylor River in Colorado   Deborah C. Damian
Chapter 2   Fireplace   Roger K. Burnard
Chapter 3   Salt mine   Morton Salt Company

Unit 5

Chapter 1   Etna volcano in Italy   Photo Researchers, Inc.
Chapter 2   Steel melting in steel mill   U.S. Steel
Chapter 3   Ocean waves breaking at the shore   Craig Kramer
Chapter 4   Reflection of city at night   William Maddox

Unit 6

Chapter 1   Electric power lines at sunset   Rich Brommer
Chapter 2   Light bulb   William Maddox
Chapter 3   Uranium takes its own picture   U.S. Energy Research and Development Administration
Chapter 4   Nuclear reactor   U.S. Energy Research and Development Administration

Unit One

Measurement and Motion

Rich Brommer

1 Physical Science

The nature of physical science is discussed in this chapter. A distinction is made between science and technology. Students will be made aware of the importance of measurements in science and will be given opportunities to become familiar with the methods of science as well as metric, English, and other systems of measurement as they perform a wide variety of experiments.

GOAL: You will gain an understanding of the nature and the methods of science.

For Performance Objectives for each section, see the Teacher's Guide at the front of this book.

Built by the ancient Mayan civilization, the Temple of the Inscriptions still stands near Palenque, Mexico. There are many theories as to why this temple was built. Some scientists believe it was built as a model of the calendar year. Each stone was placed in an exact position. Certainly, careful measurements were made. This early blending of measurement and science led these people to a better understanding of their world. Like the ancient Mayans, people today are still learning about the world through science.

TECHNOLOGY

1:1 Product of Science

Science has two parts—process and product. **The process of science** is the use of scientific methods. It is a special way of exploring our world. The **product of science** is information—the facts discovered and ideas developed by people using the process of science.

The product of science exists in science books, journals, tapes, films, and other records. Information in the science books in your library is part of the product of science.

What is the difference between product and process of science?

Figure 1-1. Alchemists tried to transform lead and other metals into silver and gold. Chemistry, a branch of physical science, developed from this product of science.

1:2 Technology

Technology is based on scientific knowledge.

The application of science for practical benefits is called **technology** (tek NAHL uh jee). Photography and engineering are two examples of technology. The design of a camera begins with knowledge of light and materials. Likewise, the design of a pollution-free engine begins with knowledge of materials, heat, and force. Anti-smog devices, color film, and synthetic fibers are produced through the applied use of science.

Science and technology are interrelated. Scientific knowledge is used to develop new inventions such as the electron microscope or space rockets. In turn, such inventions further scientific discovery. For example, many facts about living cells have been discovered through use of electron microscopes. Rockets make it possible to send scientific instruments into space.

Figure 1-2. Cameras have wide impact in all areas of life, from sports to education to space technology.

Linda Briscoe

Figure 1-3. Modern technology is helping to solve problems of water pollution.

Vincent McGuire

Problems are placed within the chapter to stimulate student involvement with concepts.

PROBLEM

Answers will vary. Examples:

1. Here are four problems of modern technology. Name one way in which science could help solve each problem.
    (a) Heating and cooking with heat from the sun solar cells
    (b) Recycling of wastes chemical precipitation
    (c) Producing fresh water from seawater nuclear reactor
    (d) Finding replacements for fossil fuels seismograph

1:3 Process of Science

Scientists use special methods to develop and test scientific knowledge. These methods include making observations, proposing and testing hypotheses, and stating theories.

seal an object in a box.

Time: 15 minutes.
   ACTIVITY. Your teacher has placed an object in a box and sealed it. Without opening the box, try to find out what is inside. Use your powers of observation. Write down what you know is true about the object in the box. For example, could the object be larger than the box? Is there only one object in the box? From what you know, make a "best guess" about what the object is. This is your hypothesis. Does your "guess" fit all the facts you know about the object?

The interaction of the object and box gives clues. If the object were taped inside the box, it would be a difficult problem indeed.

Observation is basic to the process of science. For example, you look at a thermometer. It reads 25°C. This is an observation. Scientists often use tools to make their observations. Some tools like the

PEOPLE CAREERS FRONTIERS FOCUS ON PHYSICAL SCIENCE

Mobile Lab Run by Students Helps Industries

Pollution control is an important part of many industries. The Illinois Institute of Technology is involved in a large way. The Institute's faculty and graduate students conduct pollution control surveys to help industries determine their problems.

A mobile laboratory is used. It is equipped to analyze industrial problems in air, water, solid waste, and noise. The unit travels to industrial sites to study pollution control systems. From the lab's findings, industries can take steps to correct problems which may exist.

This service has become so popular that many industries are requesting that the surveys be done.

Courtesy of *ChemEcology*, September, 1975.

Students and faculty at IIT are doing their part to help solve pollution problems.

Moving Toward Metric

It has been more than a hundred years since the United States Congress officially approved the metric system. However, the use of the metric system in the U.S. is not widespread as of yet. Many efforts are being made to complete a conversion to the metric system.

A metric board was created by the president. It is the responsibility of this board to coordinate the conversion to metric. The main job of the board is to provide information and make recommendations to the people.

Scientists are already using the metric system as their primary measurement system. They have found that this helps them to communicate with scientists of other nations. Having a common measurement system is much like having a common language.

Schools are doing their part to help with the conversion. Many schools begin teaching the metric system to very young children. Older children are introduced to the units and are offered many opportunities to practice. Pamphlets and other printed material about the metric system go home with the children. Parents are encouraged to read the information and use metric units at home.

Some industries are also changing over to the metric system. Printed labels on food packages often list both English and metric units. Other industries use tools which are designed in metric units.

Figure 1-4. Scientific investigations lead to many practical benefits. One example is the development of special equipment to prepare oranges for the market.

Florida Department of Commerce

How does a conclusion relate to a hypothesis?

Conclusion should support or deny hypothesis.

Figure 1-5. A scientist must observe homing pigeon behavior before a hypothesis can be made.

William T. Keaton, Cornell University, Ithaca, New York

metric ruler, mercury thermometer, and graduated cylinder are simple. Other tools are complex. The microscope, sextant, and telescope are examples of complex tools.

A **hypothesis** (hy PAHTH uh suhs) is a scientific "guess." It is a proposed answer to a question, or a solution to a problem. A scientist can propose a hypothesis based on observations and facts. Then he or she must test the hypothesis. In the previous activity, you could have tested your hypothesis by opening the box and finding out what really was inside. It is not so simple in most scientific investigations. For example, a scientist makes this hypothesis: A homing pigeon uses its ears to find its way to its home loft. To test the hypothesis, the scientist masks the ears of 25 pigeons. He or she releases them at various points far away from their loft. The scientist then waits to see how many pigeons return to the loft.

Scientists explain what is observed. These explanations are called **conclusions**. A **conclusion** is a judgment or decision based on observation. For example, a room thermometer indicates a temperature of 33°C. You may conclude that the room is too warm. You see the sun shining when you wake up in the morning. You might conclude that it is going to be a nice day. In either case, you might be right or wrong. You have made a judgment based on what you observed. In the pigeon experiment, none of the 25 pigeons with masked ears returned to their loft. Thus, the scientist concluded that pigeons use their ears in finding their way home. However, the conclusion need not be correct. Perhaps a storm prevented the flock from returning. Can you think of other possibilities? *Answers will vary.*

1:4 Experiments

In your study of science, you will conduct experiments and other activities. **Experiments** are designed to yield observations under carefully controlled conditions. Keep a record of your work in a notebook. Organize your experimental work as follows:

(1) Problem or purpose. Why is this experiment done? What question do you hope to answer?

(2) Procedure. List the steps in the experiment or activity. What things are you doing?

(3) Observations. What happens? What do you see, hear, or smell? What changes have occurred? How do you know?

(4) Conclusion. Based on your observations, what is your explanation or answer to the question?

In what steps are experiments organized?

U.S. Energy Research and Development Administration

Figure 1-6. Scientists perform many types of experiments. They draw conclusions based on observations.

PROBLEMS

2. Name the problem, procedure, observations, and conclusion for the pigeon experiment.

3. Write down the problem, procedure, observations, and conclusion for the following experiment.

Problem: Does a pigeon use its ears to find its way home?
Procedure: Take pigeons from home, mask ears, let them go.
Observation: No pigeons returned.
Conclusion: Pigeons use ears.

Figure 1-7.

Problem: Does air expand when heated?
Observations: Balloon expands when flask heated; contracts when flask cooled.
Conclusion: Air in balloon expands when flask heated.

Time: 20 minutes.

EXPERIMENT. Carefully insert a glass tube in a one-hole rubber stopper. Attach an uninflated balloon to the glass tube and insert the stopper in a flask. Use a hot plate to heat the flask. What do you observe?

After cooling the flask for a short time, place it in a pan of ice. Explain any change you observe.

Conclusions will vary. Discuss all possibilities.

In the above experiment, could you be sure that only heat is affecting the balloon? Perhaps any balloon joined to a flask will expand. One way to be sure is to use a control. A **control** is a standard for comparison. It is an important feature of many experiments. The control can be part of the procedure. In the heated air experiment, you could assemble two balloons and flasks. You could then treat both exactly the same except that you would heat one and not the other. The unheated balloon would be your control.

PROBLEMS

4. A medical scientist tests a new drug. Two groups of people are selected who have the disease the drug is intended to cure. One group is given the drug. The other is not. What is the control? — group not given drug

5. How would a control improve the pigeon experiment? Describe such a control. Answers will vary. Example: have half of birds with ear masks, half without, test several times from different directions.

1:5 *Theories and Laws*

A scientific **theory** (THEE uh ree) is an explanation based on current observations. For example, there are several theories to explain how birds navigate when they migrate. One theory is that they

How does a scientific law differ from a theory?
Law has stood the test of time.

8 (8M)

Laws of nature merely summarize the effects of certain conditions. Laws do not change; our understanding of them does. Experiments are investigations of the various conditions that produce given results.

MEASUREMENTS

use the earth's magnetic field. Another is that they are guided by the sun. Both theories fit what is known about homing pigeons.

A scientific **law** is a theory that has been upheld for a long period of time. It is supported by a large amount of information. For example, under ordinary conditions, all matter is composed of atoms and molecules. This is a scientific law.

Theories and laws can be changed. They are continually being tested. This is an important part of the process of science. If a new observation shows the theory or law to be incorrect, it is revised or discarded. For example, at one time the following was a law: Matter can neither be created nor destroyed. Then research showed that this was not true. Under certain conditions, matter does change to energy. In outer space, energy changes into matter all the time.

In actual practice, the methods of science are not cut and dried. The work of successful scientists shows that problem solving is not always a step-by-step process. Skill, luck, trial and error, and intelligent guessing all play a part.

U.S. Energy Research and Development Administration

Figure 1-8. Scientific theories and laws lead to new developments. The solar cell, an energy source, is one example.

1:6 Physical Science

Physical science is the study of matter and energy. It has two main branches—chemistry and physics. **Chemistry** is the study of what matter is made of and the changes in matter. It includes such topics as solutions, acids, and bases. **Physics** is the study of how matter and energy are related. It includes such topics as motion, electricity, magnetism, gravity, sound, heat, and light.

What is physical science?

1:7 Measurements

How much material do you need to make a shirt? How much flour, milk, and eggs do you need to make a cake? Without numbers and units, you could not answer these questions. Numbers and units

Asphalt Institute

Figure 1-9. Precise measurements are needed before a road can be constructed.

Figure 1-10. To build a birdhouse, each part must be measured and cut carefully.

are used to express measurements. Measurements are needed for keeping records, solving problems, and doing jobs.

Suppose you wanted to build a birdhouse. First you need a plan. You need materials: wood and nails. You also need tools: hammer, saw, and ruler. You begin by measuring and cutting the birdhouse parts. Then you nail the parts together. If you do not measure correctly, your birdhouse will not be tight and trim. It may not even fit together.

The following scientific questions can only be answered with numbers and units.

(1) How far is the sun from Earth?
(2) How long would it take to go to Jupiter?
(3) How far can you see?
(4) How large is the earth?

You are already familiar with English units of measure. For example, the wheelbase of a car is measured in inches. Cloth is measured in yards. Baking powder can be weighed in ounces or measured in teaspoons. Milk is measured in quarts and gallons.

> Time: 10 minutes.
> ACTIVITY. Obtain a meter stick and yardstick or a metric ruler and English ruler. Compare their lengths and the units into which they are divided. How are they different? How are units on the meter stick similar to units in United States money? *divided into tenths*

Most people in the world do not use English units to express measurements. Over 90 percent of the world's people use another system of units called the **metric system.** Scientists in all countries know and use metric units in their work. This makes it easier for scientists to understand each other's measurements. There is another advantage to the metric system. It is a decimal system just like the United States money system. Metric units are based on 10 and multiples of 10. This makes changing from one unit to another very easy.

Figure 1-11. Some new road signs give distance in both miles and kilometers.

1:8 Measuring Length

The **meter (m)** is the standard unit of length in the metric system. A meter is a little more than 3 in. longer than a yard. One meter is the same length as 39.37 in. (1 m = 39.37 in.).

MEASURING LENGTH (11M)

The meter is divided into 100 units called **centimeters (cm).** Note the prefix *centi-* is similar to cent in the United States coin. There are 100 cents in a dollar. There are 100 centimeters in a meter. One centimeter (1 cm) is 1/100 of a meter.

$$100 \text{ cm} = 1 \text{ m}$$

An even smaller unit is a **millimeter (mm).** The prefix *milli-* means 1/1000 (one thousandth). There are 1000 millimeters in a meter.

$$1000 \text{ mm} = 1 \text{ m}$$

There are 10 millimeters in one centimeter. One millimeter is equal to 1/10 (one tenth) of a centimeter.

$$10 \text{ mm} = 1 \text{ cm}$$

Changing from one unit of length to another is easy. You divide or multiply by 10, 100, or 1000. For example, 945 mm equals 94.5 cm or 0.945 m. You may wish to remind students that division by 10 moves the decimal point one place to the left. Multiplication by 10 moves it one place to the right. Some practice may be useful.

National Bureau of Standards

Figure 1-12. In 1960, the international standard of length was adopted. It is the wavelength of the orange-red light given off by a krypton lamp.

How is a centimeter related to a millimeter and a meter?

Figure 1-13. A meter stick is divided into millimeters and centimeters.

Time: 15 minutes.
  ACTIVITY. *Use a meter stick and a metric ruler to measure the following: (a) length and width of this book in centimeters; (b) length and width of a room in meters, (c) your height in metric units.* Results will vary.

Figure 1-14. Metric units of measurement are used by students in the classroom.

Linda Briscoe   a

F. Bernard Daniel   b

You usually think of distance in miles. For example, it is about 3000 miles from the east coast to the west coast of the United States. In most other countries, however, distance is measured in a metric unit called the **kilometer (km).** The prefix *kilo-* means 1000. So a kilometer is 1000 meters. One mile is the same distance as 1.61 kilometers (1 mile = 1.61 km).

$$1 \text{ km} = 1000 \text{ m}$$

PROBLEM

6. If the speed limit is 55 mi/hr, does a speed of 55 km/hr exceed the limit? Explain.

1:9 Measuring Mass and Weight

Pounds and ounces are English units used to measure weight. **Weight** is a measure of the force or pull of gravity on a body. Your own weight is the force of gravity that pulls you down to Earth. Weight may be measured with a spring scale. The unit of force in the metric system is the **newton (nt)** (Section 2:1).

Mass is the amount of material in a body. Mass does not depend on gravity. The more you weigh, however, the more mass you have. Mass may be measured with a pan balance (Figure 1–16). A body of unknown mass is placed on the left pan of the balance. Metal pieces of known mass are placed on the right pan. When the unknown and known bodies balance, they both have the same mass. The total mass of the pieces on the right pan is the mass of the object on the left pan.

The **gram (g)** is the unit of mass in the metric system. One kilogram is equal to 1000 grams. Remember, the prefix *kilo-* means 1000. A mass of one kilogram weighs about 2.2 pounds.

One page of this book has a mass about 3.25 g. A cubic centimeter of water has a mass of about 1 g.

Figure 1-15. The international standard of mass is a platinum-iridium cylinder. The cylinder has a mass of exactly one kilogram.

National Bureau of Standards

Time: 15 minutes.
ACTIVITY. Obtain a beam balance and measure the mass of five bodies such as a paper clip, pen, notebook, ring, and block of wood. Record your results. How is a beam balance different from a spring scale? When would you use each one? Beam balances measure mass. They are used to compare the masses of small objects. Spring scales measure the force of gravity. Newtons are indicated on the scale itself.

Figure 1-16.

PROBLEMS Answers will vary.

7. What is the total mass in grams for the five objects in the activity above? Change this figure to kilograms.

8. What is your weight in pounds? What is your mass in kilograms?

1:10 Measuring Volume

The **liter** (ℓ) is the unit of volume in the metric system. One liter is equal to about one quart. One liter contains 1000 milliliters (ml). One milliliter is 1/1000 of a liter.

Graduated cylinders are used for measuring volumes of liquid. They are made in many sizes. The level of a liquid in a graduated cylinder shows the volume of the liquid.

A milliliter is about the same volume as one cubic centimeter. One milliliter of water has a mass of about one gram. Therefore, a liter of water is 1000 grams.

What is the main unit of volume in the metric system?

PROBLEM

9. How much water will fill a dish 10 cm × 10 cm × 5 cm? How many grams of water will fill this dish?

volume = 500 cm³
mass = 500 g

Figure 1-17. Each graduated cylinder contains three milliliters of liquid.

FDA Consumer

Figure 1-18. Vincente Hernandez, a chemist, measures the volume of a chemical he is testing.

Figure 1-19.

> Time: 10 minutes.
> ACTIVITY. Obtain three test tubes of different sizes. Fill the smallest test tube with water. Pour the water into an empty graduated cylinder. How much water does the test tube hold? Repeat with the other two test tubes. Results will vary.

1:11 Indirect Measurement

When you measure your height, you are making a direct measurement. You can mark your height on a wall and measure the distance to the floor with a meter stick. Finding your weight is another example of a direct measurement. You step on a scale and read your weight in pounds. However, many measurements are made by indirect methods.

Indirect measurement is a way of measuring something you cannot measure directly. For example, how high is the flagpole at your school? You could directly measure the flagpole with a tape measure. You would need a very long tape measure. How would you get the tape measure to the top of the pole?

You can indirectly measure the height of your school's flagpole by *triangulation* (try an gyuh LAY shuhn). In this method, you measure the distance from the base of the flagpole to a certain point on the ground. Then measure the angle from this point to the top of the flagpole with a sextant. A sextant is an instrument used to measure angles (Figure 1–21).

When is indirect measurement used?

When measurement to be taken is outside range of common measuring device.

Figure 1-20. Why is indirect measurement used to measure this flagpole?

INDIRECT MEASUREMENT

The angle and distance of the flagpole are used to draw a triangle. The flagpole is one of the three sides of the triangle. The diagram is drawn to scale. For example, one centimeter in the diagram might equal one meter on the flagpole. By measuring the length of the flagpole in centimeters on the diagram, you can find the actual height of the flagpole in meters.

group & optional

Time: 45 minutes.

ACTIVITY. Make a simple sextant with a soda straw, protractor, masking tape, string, and metal washer. Tie one end of a 10-cm string to the center of the protractor's straight edge. Tie the other end to the metal washer. Tape the straw lengthwise to the straight edge of the protractor. Objects are sighted by looking through the straw with one eye closed. The string on the curved scale indicates the angle of the object.

Measure the distance from a point on the ground to the base of a flagpole. Then use the sextant to sight the angle of the top of the flagpole from this point. On a sheet of paper, using a scale of 1 cm = 1 m, draw a triangle. First draw a horizontal line to scale, representing the ground. Draw a perpendicular line (90°) to represent the flagpole. Draw a third line at the angle you measured to complete the three sides of the triangle. Measure the perpendicular line to find the flagpole's height. Each centimeter of line equals one meter of pole.

See Teacher's Guide at the front of the book for suggestions.

Students will need help reading the angle.

Figure 1-21.

Students will need help making the diagrams.

MAIN IDEAS

1:1   **1.** Science may be thought of as having two parts—product and process.

1:1, 1:2   **2.** Scientific knowledge is the product of science.

1:2   **3.** Technology is the practical use of scientific knowledge.

1:3   **4.** Hypotheses, theories, and scientific laws are tested by experiments and observations.

1:4   **5.** The process of science includes methods used to solve scientific problems.

1:4   **6.** A control is an important part of most experiments.

For a discussion of the suggested methods of using the materials at the end of the chapter, see the introduction to Teacher's Guide at the front of this book.

1:5   7. An experiment may be recorded in four parts: problem or purpose, procedure, observations, and conclusion.

1:8   8. The meter (m), centimeter (cm), and millimeter (mm) are metric units of length.

1:9   9. The kilogram (kg) and gram (g) are metric units of mass.

1:10 10. The liter (l) and milliliter (ml) are metric units of volume.

VOCABULARY

Write a sentence in which you correctly use each of the following words or terms.

✓chemistry	✓hypothesis	✓observation
conclusion	✓law	physics
✓control	✓liter	scientist
experiment	✓mass	technology
✓gram	✓meter	✓theory

STUDY QUESTIONS

Have students rewrite false statements to make the statements correct.

A. True or False

Determine whether each of the following sentences is true or false. (Do not write in this book.)

T 1. A metric ruler, graduated cylinder, and microscope are tools used in science.

F 2. Product and process of science are both the same. **not**

F 3. A hypothesis is always true. **may be**

T 4. Every experiment has a procedure.

F 5. The control in an experiment is the same as a conclusion. **not**

F 6. A scientific law can never be disproved.

T 7. Metric units have international use in science.

T 8. The metric system of measurement is a decimal system.

F 9. A meter stick and a yardstick both have the same length. **do not**

F 10. The pound is the metric unit of mass. **gram**

Some questions in Parts B and C may have more than one correct answer. Only one answer is required.

B. Multiple Choice

Choose one word or phrase that correctly completes each of the following sentences. (Do not write in this book.)

1. A meter equals *(10, <u>100</u>, 1000, 10,000)* centimeters.
2. The prefix *centi-* means *(10, 100, <u>1/100</u>, 1/1000).*

PHYSICAL SCIENCE   (17M)   17

3. There are *(1, 10, 100, 1000)* millimeters in a centimeter.
4. The prefix *milli-* means *(10, 100, 1000, 1/1000)*.
5. The prefix *kilo-* means *(10, 100, 1000, 1/1000)*.
6. There are *(10, 100, 1000, 10,000)* grams in a kilogram.
7. A kilogram is the mass of about *(1.5, 2, 2.2, 10)* pounds.
8. A milliliter of water has a mass of about *(0.1, 1, 10, 100)* grams.
9. One cubic centimeter equals *(1 ml, 1 ℓ, 1 kg, 1 km)*.
10. There are *(10, 100, 1000)* milliliters in a liter.

C. Completion

Complete each of the following sentences with a word or phrase that will make the sentence correct. (Do not write in this book.)

1. A meter stick is used to measure _____ . length
2. On a scale of 1 mm = 1 m, a centimeter equals _____ meter(s). 10
3. _____ is an example of indirect measurement. Scale drawing
4. The application of science for practical benefits is _____ . technology
5. The metric standard unit of volume is _____ . liter
6. A graduated cylinder contains 15 ml of water. The mass of this water is _____ g. 15
7. A stone is dropped into a graduated cylinder. The volume of water rises from 18 ml to 22 ml. The volume of the stone is _____ ml. 4
8. Metric units are based on ten and units of _____ . 10
9. The volume of a kilogram of feathers is greater than the _____ of a kilogram of lead. volume
10. A _____ is a theory that has been upheld for a long time. law

D. How and Why

1. Name five instruments used to make measurements. What units are used with each instrument?
2. What is physical science?
3. Describe three methods used by scientists.
4. How is science different from technology?
5. What are the advantages of the use of metric units?

Answers to this section are given in the Teacher's Guide at the front of this book.

6. You are riding in an American-made car in a foreign country. A sign you pass shows a maximum speed of 50 km/hr. Your speedometer reads 50 mph. Would you be speeding?
7. Change the following to liters: 250 ml, 1000 ml, 5000 ml.
8. How do you measure mass and volume in a laboratory?
9. How is triangulation used to find height?
10. Change the following to meters: 55 cm, 550 cm, 5500 mm.

Answers to this section are given in the Teacher's Guide at the front of this book.

INVESTIGATIONS

1. Use a 10-ml graduate to measure the volume of a thimble, water glass, teacup, medicine dropper, and soda straw.
2. Use a sextant and triangulation to measure some tall buildings, towers, or other tall structures. Report your results to your class.
3. Write a report on ways a change to the metric system in the U.S. is being made. What other ways do you suggest? Who should be involved?

INTERESTING READING

Baldwin, Gordon C., *Inventors and Inventions of the Ancient World*. New York, Four Winds Press/Scholastic Book Service, 1973.

Bendick, Jeanne, *Measuring*. New York, Franklin Watts, 1971.

Breeden, Richard, *Those Inventive Americans*. Washington, D.C., National Geographic Society, 1971.

Chandler, M. H., *Science and the World Around Us*. Chicago, Rand McNally, 1968.

Gallant, Roy A., *Man the Measurer: Our Units of Measure and How They Grew*. Garden City, N.Y., Doubleday and Co., 1972.

Hayden, Robert C., *Seven Black American Scientists*. Reading, Mass., Addison-Wesley, 1970.

Klein, A. Arthur, *The World of Measurements: Masterpieces, Mysteries, and Muddles of Metrology*. New York, Simon and Schuster, Inc., 1974.

Moore, William, *Metric Is Here!* New York, G. P. Putnam's Sons, 1974.

Moorman, Thomas, *How to Make Your Science Project Scientific*. New York, Atheneum Publishers, 1974.

Pine, Tillie S., and Levine, Joseph, *Measurements and How We Use Them* (The World All Around You Series). New York, McGraw-Hill Book Co., 1974.

Siedel, Frank and James, *Pioneers in Science*. Boston, Houghton Mifflin Company, 1968.

Webster, David, *How to Do a Science Project*. New York, Franklin Watts, Inc., 1974.

Wheels, the drive shaft, and pistons of a large steam locomotive work together to produce motion.

William Maddox

Introduce Chapter 2 by having students describe the characteristics of moving objects. The descriptions should include characteristics such as speed, effort force, and distance. The concepts of force, work, and power are developed in this chapter. The six simple machines are discussed in detail.

2 Force and Work

GOAL: You will gain an understanding of forces, work, simple machines, mechanical advantage, and power.

Machinery is an important part of people's lives. Machines are used in a variety of ways for different purposes. Each machine has a particular use. For example, scissors are used for cutting. Vehicles on wheels are used to move passengers or goods.

The types of machines range from simple to very complex. However, each one has several things in common. These common features are explained by the concepts of force and work.

WORK

2:1 Force

How can you set an object in motion? Kick a can. Throw a ball. Pound a nail into a board. In each case an object is moved. It takes a force to put an object at rest into motion.

A **force** is a push or a pull. For example, a wagon can be pulled or pushed. In either case, a force moves the wagon. When the wagon moves, it is in motion.

Does a force always produce motion? Push down on your desk top as hard as you can or push against the wall in your room. Only an unbalanced force produces motion. Unbalanced means the force you or something exerts must be greater than the force that opposes it. When this happens, motion occurs. **Resistance** (rih ZIS tuhnts) is a force which slows down or prevents motion. *Friction* is an example of resistance.

What is force?

All sports involve forces and motion. Relate these principles to baseball, basketball, football, hockey, and other sports. Have students name the forces they experience in their home or school.

Figure 2-1. When a wagon is pulled or pushed, a force is exerted on the wagon.

Figure 2-2. A force only produces motion when it is greater than the opposing force.

PROBLEMS — Do

1. What force is great enough to move your desk top? *If not fixed in place, a student's arms.*
2. What force moves your body parts? *The forces of muscles on bones.*
3. How could you exert a force to lift yourself? *Sit on chair, place hands on chair, and push down.*

The unit of force in the English system is the pound (lb). Force in pounds can be measured with a spring scale. The metric unit of force is the newton (nt). A *newton* is the unit of force required to accelerate a one kilogram mass at 1 m/sec^2.

Force in pounds can be grasped readily by students because they are familiar with the unit and can measure it with a spring balance. The newton is introduced here to be consistent in the use of metric units. Since the newton is based on acceleration (1 kg at 1 m/sec^2), it is not as easy to understand as metric units for mass, length, and volume.

2:2 Work

A force is needed to do work. Mowing a lawn is work. Washing a car and lifting barbells are other examples of work. In science, work

Figure 2-3. Work is done only when a body is moved. The amount of work done is not affected by the speed with which the body is moved.

What equation is used to calculate work?

A force does not always result in work. Work is done only when the force moves through a distance. If a person holds a 45 nt sack of potatoes he does not do work even though he exerts a force.

Weight of the object can be ignored.

has a precise definition. **Work** is the product of the force applied to an object and the distance the object moves. The object must move; otherwise, no work is done.

To calculate work, use the equation

$$W = F \times D$$

work equals force multiplied by distance

In the English system, the unit of force is the pound (lb). Distance is usually measured in feet (ft). Thus, in the English system, work is expressed in *foot-pounds* (ft-lb). Distance is written before force. In the metric system, the unit of force is the newton (nt) and distance is measured in meters (m). Thus, in the metric system, work is expressed in *newton-meters* (nt-m). Here, force is written before distance.

EXAMPLE 1

How much work is done when a force of 100 lb is used to slide a 600-lb piano 5 ft across a floor?

Solution:
(a) Write the equation: $W = F \times D$
(b) Substitute 100 lb for F, and 5 ft for D:
$W = 100$ lb $\times$ 5 ft
(c) Multiply to find the answer: $W = 500$ ft-lb
(d) Answer: Work $= 500$ ft-lb

EXAMPLE 2

How much work is done when a force of 98 nt is applied in lifting a concrete block 1.5 m?

Solution:
(a) Write the equation: $W = F \times D$
(b) Substitute 98 nt for F, and 1.5 m for D:
$W = 98$ nt $\times$ 1.5 m
(c) Multiply to find the answer: $W = 147$ nt-m
(d) Answer: Work $= 147$ nt-m

MACHINES (23M) 23

PROBLEMS

4. A 15-lb suitcase is lifted 2 ft. How much work is done? 30 ft-lb

5. How much work is done when a force of 3 lb is used to move the suitcase in Problem 4 a distance of 2 ft across the floor? 6 ft-lb

6. Which takes more work, lifting a suitcase 2 ft or sliding it a distance of 2 ft across a smooth floor? Why? See Teacher's Guide.

7. Calculate the amount of work done when a force of 40 nt is used to push a desk 4 m across a room. 160 nt-m

2:3 Machines

Ancient people did most of their work by lifting, pulling, and pushing with their bodies. This took a lot of time and effort. As time passed, people began to find ways to make work easier. For example, large sticks were used to move heavy rocks. Can you think of other examples?

Figure 2-4. Moving a rock is easier when a pole is used as a lever.

A **machine** makes work easier by changing the direction, size, or distance through which a force moves. Therefore, the stick in the example (Figure 2–4) is a machine. In this case, it is a simple machine.

What is a machine?

A machine changes the direction, size, or distance through which a force moves.

Suppose you want to dig a hole to plant a tree. Can you do it using just your fingers? A shovel would make it much easier. A shovel is another example of a simple machine. There are six *simple machines*. They are the lever, pulley, inclined plane, wedge, screw, and wheel and axle.

Name some simple machines.

A *compound machine* is two or more simple machines working together. A sewing machine, gasoline engine, and a washing machine are examples of compound machines. Some can openers, for

Define compound machine.

Figure 2-5. Many of the simple tools used daily are machines.

example, contain inclined planes, a lever, and a wheel and axle. This makes the can opener a compound machine (Figure 2–6).

PROBLEM See Teacher's Guide at the front of the book.

8. How does each of the following machines make work easier?
   (a) bicycle (d) elevator
   (b) oar (e) block and tackle
   (c) sewing machine (f) crowbar

2:4 *Mechanical Advantage*

Have you ever opened a can of paint using a screwdriver to pry off the lid? It was easy. But how hard would it have been if you had only your fingers? You used the screwdriver as a lever and gained a large force to open the can.

Figure 2-6. One type of can opener is a combination of several machines: wheel and axle, wedge, and lever.

LEVERS (25M) 25

The amount by which a machine multiplies the force being applied is called the **mechanical advantage (M.A.).** All machines have a mechanical advantage. It tells us how the machine changes the force it uses. However, the M.A. for a machine is not always greater than one. Sometimes a gain in force is lost to a gain in speed or a change in direction.

There are two types of mechanical advantage. The **ideal mechanical advantage (I.M.A.)** tells us how a machine can ideally change the force. Ideal means neglecting friction. The **actual mechanical advantage (A.M.A.)** tells us how a machine actually changes a force. It includes the effects of friction. In your measurements of mechanical advantage, you will be working with objects in contact with one another. Is it possible to completely eliminate friction in a machine? no

PROBLEM   See Teacher's Guide.

9. Would you measure the A.M.A. or the I.M.A. for a machine with a moving part?

Figure 2-7. Without a lever, a paint can would be very difficult to open.

2:5 Levers

A **lever** is a bar that is free to rotate around a point. It is a simple machine. Some examples of levers are a crowbar, seesaw, shovel, oar, scissors, and bottle opener. Each lever can make work easier. The point where a lever rotates is called the *fulcrum* (FUL kruhm, Figure 2–8). When an effort force is applied to a lever, a resistance can be overcome.

Name four examples of levers.
broom, wheelbarrow, crowbar, tweezers

Linda Briscoe

Figure 2-8. Seesaws are levers. The point at which a seesaw is attached is called the fulcrum.

Figure 2-9. Levers are divided into first, second, and third class levers. These classes are based on the position of the fulcrum, resistance, and effort.

PROBLEM See Teacher's Guide.

10. Three classes of levers are shown in Figure 2–9. How do they differ? Notice the position of the fulcrum for each class of lever.

Figure 2-10.

Time: 25 minutes.

ACTIVITY. (1) Place a book or some heavy object on the edge of a table or desk. Place a ruler under the book with most of the ruler extending beyond the table. Pull up on the end which is not under the book. Notice how easy it is to raise the book. What type of lever have you used? Where is the fulcrum? (2) Now push down on the end of the ruler extending beyond the table. Where is the fulcrum this time? (3) Place the book in the center of the table. Again, put the end of the ruler under the edge of the book. Place one hand on the other end of the ruler. With your other hand, lift up on the center of the ruler. Which type of lever does this represent? Where is the fulcrum? Notice the different forces you had to exert to lift the book. Which type of lever made the task easiest? Hardest?
See Teacher's Guide.

LEVERS

Every lever has two arms. These are called the effort arm and the resistance arm. The **effort arm** is the distance from the fulcrum to the effort force. The **resistance arm** is the distance from the fulcrum to the resistance force.

Every lever also has two moments, effort moment and resistance moment. **Moment** is the force times the length of the lever arm. In the English system, force is measured in pounds and distance in feet. Thus, the English unit for a moment is *pound-foot* (lb-ft). In the metric system, force is measured in newtons and the distance in meters. The metric unit for a moment is *meter-newton* (m-nt). Note that the units for moment (lb-ft and m-nt) are the reverse of those for work. The equation below can be used to calculate the moments of a lever.

$$M = F \times L$$

moment equals force multiplied by lever arm length

Describe the two arms of a lever.

Time: 30 minutes.

ACTIVITY. Obtain a meter stick, 200-g mass, 100-g mass, and a triangular-shaped block of wood, 10 cm long on each side. Use the block as a fulcrum for the meter stick. Set the stick on the block at the 50-cm mark. (1) Place the 200-g mass on one side of the stick. Place the 100-g mass on the opposite side of the fulcrum so the lever is balanced. (2) Move the 200-g mass to another position. How must you move the 100-g mass to balance the stick? (3) After balancing the stick, move the 100-g mass to another position. How must you move the 200-g mass to balance the stick? (4) What is the relationship between the size of the mass and the distance from the fulcrum?

See Teacher's Guide.

Figure 2-11.

Figure 2-12.

Time: 30 minutes.

Do

ACTIVITY. (1) Obtain a yardstick, two equal masses, string, and scissors. Tie a piece of string around the exact center of the yardstick. Then hang the yardstick from a hook or nail on a wall. Or, hang it from an iron stand on a table. Tie string to both masses and hang them on opposite ends of the yardstick. Move the string in the center back and forth until the yardstick is balanced. When the yardstick is balanced, find the distance from the fulcrum to each mass. Record your data in a chart. Was the yardstick with the two equal masses balanced when the string was tied at the center of the stick? *Yes.* If not, explain. (2) Repeat the procedure with two unequal masses. Again, record your results.

When would the moments of a lever be balanced?

The two moments of a balanced lever are equal. Balanced means the lever is not turning. Use the following equation to find the unknown force or lever arm for a balanced lever.

$$F_R \times L_R = F_E \times L_E$$

resistance force × resistance arm length = effort force × effort arm length

EXAMPLE 1

Using a lever, how much force must be applied on a bar to move a rock? Necessary facts are given below.

Given:
Resistance force = 150 lb
Resistance arm = 1 ft
Effort arm = 5 ft

Solution:
$F_R \times L_R = F_E \times L_E$
150 lb × 1 ft = F_E × 5 ft
150 lb-ft = F_E × 5 ft
F_E = 30 lb

Figure 2-13. Levers reduce the amount of force needed to move heavy objects.

Figure 2-14. Mobiles hang correctly only when balanced.

make mobile using fulcrum
IMA
AMA
M = F×L
F_R, L_R, F_E, L_E

EXAMPLE 2

A large metal mobile has a supporting bar 5 ft long. An object is hung 1 ft from the center of the bar. It exerts a force of 10 lb on the bar. A second object is hung so the mobile will balance. How far from the center should the 4-lb object be hung? *Explain*

Given:
Resistance force = 10 lb
Resistance arm = 1 ft
Effort force = 4 lb

Solution:
$F_R \times L_R = F_E \times L_E$
10 lb × 1 ft = 4 lb × L_E
10 lb-ft = 4 lb × L_E
L_E = 2.5 ft

Figure 2-15. A seesaw is a first class lever. The fulcrum is located between the effort and resistance.

PROBLEMS

11. In Figure 2–15, how much force does the girl exert? 300 nt

12. A 100-lb boy sits on a seesaw 3 ft from the fulcrum. Where must a 75-lb boy sit to balance the seesaw? four feet from fulcrum on opposite end

2:6 Mechanical Advantage for a Lever

A lever has a mechanical advantage. To find the I.M.A., measure the length of the effort arm and the length of the resistance arm. Divide the effort arm length by the resistance arm length.

How is I.M.A. for a lever calculated?

$$I.M.A. = \frac{Effort\ Arm}{Resistance\ Arm}$$

EXAMPLE

Find the I.M.A. for a lever with a resistance arm 1 m long. The effort arm is 3 m.

Given:
Effort Arm = 3 m
Resistance Arm = 1 m

Solution:
$$I.M.A. = \frac{Effort\ Arm}{Resistance\ Arm}$$
$$I.M.A. = \frac{3\ m}{1\ m}$$
$$I.M.A. = 3$$

Figure 2-16. Pole vaulters use the pole as a lever to lift their bodies up and over the bar.

Remember, I.M.A. is the ratio of the effort arm length to the resistance arm length. In this case, an effort force applied to the lever is multiplied by 3. The A.M.A. for a lever is less than the I.M.A. What is the explanation for the difference?
A.M.A. takes into account friction which will decrease any advantage.

PROBLEMS

13. What is the I.M.A. for a lever with an effort arm of 5 m and a resistance arm 2 m long? 2.5

14. What is the I.M.A. for a 1-m crowbar when the fulcrum is 0.2 m from the resistance end? 4

Sports Illustrated photo by Neil Leifer © Time, Inc.

Figure 2-17. Pulleys may be either fixed or movable.

How does a pulley make work easier?

By changing the direction or magnitude of the force required to do some work.

Figure 2-18. Heavy objects may be lifted easily with a pulley.
William Maddox

Figure 2-19. To find the ideal mechanical advantage of a movable pulley, count the number of supporting strands.

2:7 Pulleys

A pulley is a simple machine. Study Figure 2–17 and you will see that a **pulley** is really a form of a lever. It is used to move bodies and do work. It can be fixed in one spot or movable.

You can use a pulley to make work easier by changing the direction of a force. For example, you can use a rope around a single fixed pulley to raise some object. You can pull the object up when you are standing on the ground. With a single, fixed pulley the effort force is applied in one direction. The resistance moves in the opposite direction.

Two or more pulleys used together can decrease the force needed to move a body. The I.M.A. of a pulley system equals the number of *supporting strands* (Figure 2–19).

Figure 2-20.

Time: 60 minutes.

ACTIVITY. A pulley may be used to lift objects. (1) Lift a ½-lb weight with a spring scale and observe the reading of the scale. Next, run a piece of string 1 m long through a single movable pulley. Attach each end of the string to a different spring scale as shown in Figure 2–20a. Attach the weight to the pulley. Lift the weight by lifting the spring scales and record the reading on each scale. (2) Arrange pulleys as shown in Figures 2–20b and c. Find the force needed to lift the weight. The force is the reading on the spring scale. How does the number of supporting strings affect the force needed to lift a weight? Predict the force needed to lift the weight in Figure 2–20d.
See Teacher's Guide.

In calculating the I.M.A., the friction and weight of a pulley is not considered. In actual practice, the A.M.A. would be less than the I.M.A. Why?

Note that with an I.M.A. of 2, the effort force moves twice as far as the resistance force. For pulleys with an I.M.A. of 3, the effort force moves 3 ft for each 1 ft the resistance moves.

PROBLEM

15. Give the missing number for each set of pulleys.

Pulleys	Effort Force	Effort Distance	Resistance Force	Resistance Distance	Support Ropes	I.M.A.
Set A	10 lb	2 ft	20 lb	1 ft	2	? 2
Set B	10 lb	3 ft	50 lb	0.6 ft	5	? 5
Set C	5 lb	20 ft	20 lb	5 ft	4	? 4

a
William Maddox

b
William Maddox

Figure 2-21. Wheels are special kinds of levers. The gear, a wheel with teeth, is often used in watches (a). The wheel and axle is commonly used in many forms of transportation (b).

2:8 Wheel and Axle

Bicycles, trains, cars, motorcycles, printing presses, and pulleys run on wheels. Most compound machines have at least one wheel. Often the wheel has teeth cut into it and is called a *gear*.

Observe the wheel and axle in Figure 2–22a. A **wheel and axle** can be considered a variation of a lever. Note that the wheel turns through a larger diameter than the axle. This difference gives a wheel and axle its mechanical advantage.

How is I.M.A. for a wheel and axle calculated?

How can you find the I.M.A. of a wheel and axle? Divide the diameter of the wheel by the diameter of the axle. What is the I.M.A. for a 15.0-cm wheel with a 2.5-cm axle?

$$I.M.A. = \frac{\text{wheel diameter}}{\text{axle diameter}}$$

$$I.M.A. = \frac{15.0 \text{ cm}}{2.5 \text{ cm}}$$

$$I.M.A. = 6$$

Problem See Teacher's Guide.

16. Make a list of machines containing a wheel and axle which you use in everyday life. Which part of the machine is the wheel? Which part is the axle?

a
b

Figure 2-22. Wheels turn through a larger diameter than their axles (a). Many household appliances have wheels which make work easier (b).

WEDGE

2:9 Inclined Plane

A ramp and flight of stairs are both examples of an inclined plane. An **inclined plane** is a slanted surface used to raise objects. A mountain road is an inclined plane. Cars increase their elevations as they go up the road.

Name two examples of an inclined plane.

Less force is needed to lift a body on an inclined plane than when it is on a steep surface. Why? There are two reasons for this. The angle of the moving force is changed. Also, the body is moved through a longer distance than if the body were moved straight up.

Time: 15 minutes.

ACTIVITY. Tie a string to a brick or wooden block. Weigh it with a spring scale. The reading on the spring scale is also the force needed to lift the brick straight up. Set a smooth board against a pile of books to make an inclined plane. Drag the brick up the inclined plane by holding the spring scale attached to the string. Drag the brick at constant speed. Don't jerk it. Read the scale while the brick is moving. The reading on the spring scale gives the force used to pull the brick up the inclined plane. Compare the forces needed to lift and pull the brick. What is the A.M.A. of the inclined plane?
Answers will vary.

Figure 2-23.

The I.M.A. of an inclined plane is its length divided by its height. The longer the inclined plane, the smaller the force needed to move a body on it.

Figure 2-24. Stairways are inclined planes. They make work easier by changing the angle of the force.

PROBLEMS See Teacher's Guide.

17. What are some practical uses of the inclined plane?
18. Explain why a flight of stairs is an inclined plane.

Kathleen Glines

2:10 Wedge

A knife, an axe blade, and a can opener blade are wedges. A **wedge** is one kind of an inclined plane. This simple machine is used for work such as splitting logs. The thin edge of the wedge is placed

Figure 2-25. Some wedges are used to cut and split wood (a). A long, narrow wedge requires a small effort force to overcome a great resistance force (b).

in a crack **in a log and** driven deeper with blows from a mallet. This forces the sides **of the** log farther apart and the log finally splits.

The I.M.A. of a wedge is found by dividing the length of the wedge by its thickness. A long, narrow wedge has a greater I.M.A. than a short, wide wedge. For example, when you sharpen a knife, you make the wedge longer and thinner. This increases the mechanical advantage. This makes it easier to do work. It is easier to cut things with a sharp knife.

PROBLEM

19. List some everyday uses of the wedge. knife, razor blade, hatchet, ice pick, wood planer, chisel

2:11 Screw

Why is a screw an inclined plane?

A **screw** is a modified inclined plane. It is an inclined plane wound around a center to form a cylinder. It is like a spiral staircase where the steps are wound around the center.

Figure 2-26. Screws are modified inclined planes.

Figure 2-27. Jackscrews are used in raising cars, houses, or other heavy objects.

Screws have many uses. They are used to hold furniture together. They are often included in tools where a great amount of force is needed. A vise is one example. Imagine how difficult it would be to saw a large piece of wood without holding it down. A vise will hold the wood securely.

A screw has a large mechanical advantage. A very large resistance can be overcome with a comparatively small force. By twisting a screw into wood or metal, a small effort force is used through a large distance. In contrast, when hammering a nail a large force is used. The large force drives the nail a short distance. Not only does a screw take less force, it holds things more securely. The threads on a screw create friction as the screw is twisted into the object. This friction helps hold the screw in place.

Figure 2-28. You can make a screw by wrapping an inclined plane around a pencil.

2:12 *Efficiency*

Most people think machines do work. However, work must be put into a machine before it can do any work for you. A machine merely converts this work into more useful work by changing force, distance, or direction.

Every machine has a work input and work output. **Work input** is the effort force multiplied by the effort distance. **Work output** is the resistance force multiplied by the resistance distance.

$$W_i = F_e \times D_e$$
work input = effort force × effort distance

$$W_o = F_r \times D_r$$
work output = resistance force × resistance distance

The useful work obtained by a machine is always less than the work put into it. Why? Some of the input work is used to overcome

What is the efficiency of a machine?
ratio of work output to work input

Figure 2-29. Sewing machines have many moving parts. They are operated by electric motors.

friction. The ratio of work output to work input is called the **efficiency** (ih FISH uhn see) of a machine. A scissors, knife, and can opener do work when someone uses them. In each case, an effort must be applied to overcome a resistance. Electric motors and engines are used to operate many machines.

EXAMPLE

A crate is dragged up a ramp 20 m long (Effort distance). One end of the ramp is on the ground. The raised end is 5 m (Resistance distance) above the ground. The crate has a force of 300 nt (Resistance force). The effort force is 100 nt. Find the work input and work output.

Figure 2-30. What is the work input and work output involved in moving the crate?

Given:
Effort force = 100 nt
Effort distance = 20 m
Resistance force = 300 nt
Resistance distance = 5 m

Solution:
$W_i = F_e \times D_e$
$W_i = 100 \text{ nt} \times 20 \text{ m}$
$W_i = 2000 \text{ nt-m}$
$W_o = F_r \times D_r$
$W_o = 300 \text{ nt} \times 5 \text{ m}$
$W_o = 1500 \text{ nt-m}$

Why is work output always less than work input?
Some work must be done to overcome friction.

In the example above, work output is less than work input. For an ideal machine they would be the same. But for real machines, work output always is less than work input. You get less work out of a machine than you put into it.

Efficiency of a machine may be calculated as a percent. Divide the work output by the work input. Then multiply by 100.

$$\% E = \frac{W_o}{W_i} \times 100$$

$$\% \text{ efficiency} = \frac{\text{work output}}{\text{work input}} \times 100$$

EFFICIENCY

The following shows how efficiency is calculated for the inclined plane described above.

EXAMPLE

Given:
Work input = 2000 nt-m
Work output = 1500 nt-m

Solution:
$$\% E = \frac{W_o}{W_i} \times 100$$
$$\% E = \frac{1500 \text{ nt-m}}{2000 \text{ nt-m}} \times 100$$
$$\% E = 75$$

PROBLEMS

20. A loading area is 2 m above the ground. A ramp 6 m long extends from the ground to the edge of the loading area. A box of books with a force of 200 nt is dragged up the ramp. The force necessary to drag this box is 100 nt. Identify the effort distance, effort force, resistance distance, and resistance force. *See Teacher's Guide.*

21. What is the work input and work output for Problem 20? $W_i = 600$ nt-m $W_o = 400$ nt-m

22. Find the efficiency of the inclined plane described in Problem 20. $E = 66.7\%$

How can you increase the efficiency of a machine? One way is to reduce friction. For example, sand the surface of a ramp or wax the hull of a boat. Sanding or waxing smooths a surface and reduces friction. Oil and grease are used in many machines to decrease friction. Ball bearings in bicycle wheels and other machines decrease friction. Thus, efficiency is increased.

How do lubricants and bearings increase efficiency? decrease friction

Figure 2-31. Skiers use wax to make their skiis more efficient on snow (a). Frequent oil changes improve a car engine's efficiency (b).

Craig W. Kramer   *Don Parsisson*

Increasing the efficiency of machines is an important step in conserving natural resources. Many machines are run by electricity or fuels such as gasoline. When efficiency is increased, less fuel or electricity is needed to do a given amount of work. Thus, resources are conserved. For example, steps are being taken to improve the inefficient gasoline engine of today. Also, machines are being designed to last longer. Moving parts are made so there is little friction, thus longer wear of parts.

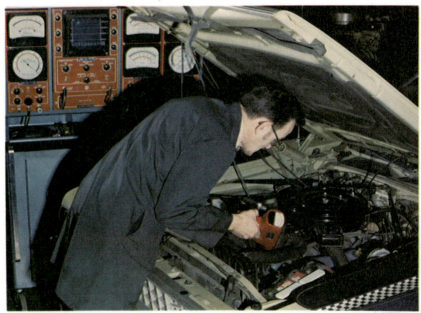

Figure 2-32. Cars need periodic tuning to keep them running efficiently.

Allan Roberts

2:13 Power

Power has a precise meaning in science. **Power** is the amount of work done per unit of time. The more rapidly work is done, the greater is the power. For example, a large engine is more powerful than a small engine. The large engine can do more work in less time. The less time it takes to do work, the more power is used. To find the power for a machine, divide the work done by the time. Use this equation:

What equation is used to calculate power?

$$P = \frac{W}{t}$$

power equals work divided by time

The units for power are ft-lb/sec and nt-m/sec.

POWER

EXAMPLE

A man uses a set of pulleys to lift a 200-lb boat 5 ft in 50 sec. What is the power?

Solution: (a) Write the equation: $P = \dfrac{W}{t}$

(b) Calculate the work done: $W = F \times D$
200 lb × 5 ft = 1000 ft-lb

(c) Substitute 1000 ft-lb for W and 50 sec for t:
$P = \dfrac{1000 \text{ ft-lb}}{50 \text{ sec}}$

(d) Divide to find the answer: $P = 20$ ft-lb/sec

(e) Answer: Power = 20 ft-lb/sec

Horsepower is an English system unit of power. This term was first defined by James Watt, the inventor of the steam engine. Watt determined how much work the average horse could do and compared this with the work done by his steam engine. One **horsepower (hp)** is now defined as exactly 550 ft-lb of work per second. Gasoline engines and other engines are also rated in horsepower.

To calculate horsepower, find the ft-lb of work done per second. Then divide by 550 ft-lb/sec, the work equal to one horsepower.

What is the English system unit of power?

Gary Walker

Figure 2-33. Bicycle speed depends on the horsepower used by the rider. The harder the rider pedals, the faster the bike moves.

40 (40M)   FORCE AND WORK

EXAMPLE

A 150-lb person walks up a flight of stairs 30 ft high in 10 sec. What horsepower is used?

Solution: (a) Calculate the work done: $W = F \times D$
150 lb $\times$ 30 ft = 4500 ft-lb
(b) To find power, divide work by the time:
$$P = \frac{W}{t} = \frac{4500 \text{ ft-lb}}{10 \text{ sec}} = 450 \text{ ft-lb/sec}$$
(c) To find horsepower, divide power by 550 ft-lb/sec:
$$\frac{450 \text{ ft-lb/sec}}{550 \text{ ft-lb/sec}} = 0.82 \text{ hp}$$
(d) Answer: 0.82 hp

PROBLEMS

23. What is the horsepower of an engine which does 2000 ft-lb of work in 4 sec? 0.91 hp

24. A sewing machine operated at full speed does 3000 ft-lb of work in 1 min. What is the horsepower of the sewing machine motor? 0.09 hp

25. A bulldozer pushes 20 tons of soil 100 ft in 2 min. What is the horsepower of the bulldozer? 60.7 hp

Figure 2-34.

Time: 25 minutes.

ACTIVITY. How many horsepower do you use when you go up a flight of stairs? Measure the height of a flight of stairs. Do this by measuring the height of a single step and then multiplying by the total number of steps. Have a classmate clock the time it takes for you to walk and trot up the stairs. Measure and record your weight on a bathroom scale. Power is the rate at which work is done. One horsepower is 550 ft-lb of work per second or 33,000 ft-lb of work per minute (550 ft-lb $\times$ 60 sec = 33,000 ft-lb/min). Calculate the horsepower used when you walk and trot up the stairs.

(a) Calculate work: $W = F \times D$

(b) Calculate power: $P = \dfrac{W}{t}$

(c) Calculate horsepower: $\text{hp} = \dfrac{P}{550 \text{ ft-lb/sec}}$

William Maddox

Figure 2-35. Many washing machines use a ¾-hp motor.

Electric motors and many power tools are rated in horsepower. For example, electric hand drills use a ¼- or ½-hp electric motor. An electric household mixer uses a ¼-hp motor. Name two other home appliances powered by an electric motor.

The watt (w) is the basic unit of power in the metric system. One **watt** is one newton-meter per second $\left(\frac{\text{nt-m}}{\text{sec}}\right)$. This unit was named in honor of James Watt, the inventor of the steam engine. One horsepower is equal to 746 watts.

What is the metric system unit of power?

PROBLEM

26. Use your own experience. You have probably seen each of these machines around your home or school. Rank each machine from the lowest to highest horsepower.
    - (a) eggbeater
    - (b) washing machine
    - (c) compact car
    - (d) minibike
    - (e) jet transport plane
    - (f) train

    lowest (a), (b), (d), (c), (f), (e) highest

MAIN IDEAS

2:1 **1.** Unbalanced forces can produce motion.

2:2 **2.** Work is done when a force is exerted through a distance.

2:3 **3.** Machines help us do work.

2:3 **4.** Machines can change the speed or direction of a force.

2:3 **5.** Machines can decrease the amount of force needed to do work.

2:3 **6.** Most machines may be classified as compound machines. Compound machines are two or more simple machines working together.

42 (42M) FORCE AND WORK

2:4 **7.** The mechanical advantage of a machine is the ratio of the resistance force to the effort force.

2:4 **8.** In figuring I.M.A., friction is not considered.

2:5–2:11 **9.** The six simple machines are the lever, pulley, wheel and axle, inclined plane, wedge, and screw.

2:12 **10.** Work output is always less than work input.

2:12 **11.** Efficiency is work output divided by work input.

2:13 **12.** Power is the rate at which work is done.

2:13 **13.** Power in the English system is measured in horsepower.

2:13 **14.** Power in the metric system is measured in watts.

10-80

VOCABULARY

Write a sentence in which you use correctly each of the following words or terms.

- actual mechanical advantage
- compound machine
- efficiency
- effort arm
- force
- friction
- fulcrum
- horsepower
- ideal mechanical advantage
- mechanical advantage
- moment
- power
- resistance
- simple machine
- watt
- work

STUDY QUESTIONS

Have students rewrite false statements to make the statements correct.

A. True or False

Determine whether each of the following sentences is true or false. (Do not write in this book.)

T **1.** A compound machine is more complex than a simple machine.

F **2.** A pulley is an example of a ~~compound~~ machine. simple

F **3.** The M.A. of a machine is always greater than one. not

T **4.** A force is a push or pull.

F **5.** An eggbeater is an example of a ~~simple~~ machine. compound

F **6.** ~~Pound~~ is the metric unit of force. Newton

F **7.** The efficiency of a machine is calculated by dividing work ~~input~~ by work ~~output~~. output, input

T **8.** There are six simple machines.

F **9.** One horsepower is 550 ft-lb of work per ~~minute~~. second

T **10.** To do work an object must be moved.

FORCE AND WORK   (43M) 43

B. Multiple Choice

Some questions in Parts B and C may have more than one correct answer. Only one answer is required.

Choose one word or phrase that correctly completes each of the following sentences. (Do not write in this book.)

1. Work is done when a body is moved through a distance by a *(force, moment, M.A., fulcrum)*.
2. F × D is the equation used to determine *(power, M.A., work)*.
3. A *(sewing machine, gasoline engine, lever)* is a simple machine.
4. A compound machine has *(one, two, two or more)* simple machines.
5. A single fixed pulley has an I.M.A. of *(1, 2, 3, 4)*.
6. I.M.A. is *(less than, greater than, the same as)* the A.M.A. for a given machine.
7. *(Moment, Resistance, Effort, Fulcrum)* is the point around which a lever rotates.
8. Every lever has at least *(4, 3, 2, 1)* moments.
9. The moments of a balanced lever are *(equal, unequal, less than the M.A.)*.
10. You can measure force with a *(ruler, pulley, spring scale)*.

C. Completion

Complete each of the following sentences with a word or phrase that will make the sentence correct. (Do not write in this book.).

1. A force that slows down or prevents motion is _____. friction
2. The effort arm of a lever is 4 m and the resistance arm is 1 m long. Its I.M.A. is _____. four
3. A block and tackle has four support ropes. The I.M.A. is _____. four
4. A bottle opener is an example of a(n) _____. lever
5. The work _____ of a machine is always less than the work _____. output, input
6. _____ are used to decrease friction. Lubricants
7. Power is the amount of work done per unit of _____. time
8. One horsepower is _____ ft-lb of work/sec. 550
9. A ½-hp motor has more _____ than a ¼-hp motor. power
10. Reducing friction increases the _____ of a machine. efficiency

See Teacher's Guide.

D. How and Why

1. How much work is done when a force of 25 nt is used to slide a 150-nt sofa 10 m across a floor? *250 nt-m*
2. Where is the fulcrum, resistance force, and effort force in (a) the oar of a rowboat, (b) a pair of pliers, (c) a wheelbarrow?
3. Draw a set of pulleys with an I.M.A. of 5. How far will the effort force move if the resistance force moves 1 in.? *5 in.*
4. In what three ways are a lever, wheel and axle, and pulley alike?
5. List six compound machines. Name one simple machine in each.
6. Work input for a block and tackle is 250 nt-m. Work output is 200 nt-m. Find the percent efficiency. *E = 80%*
7. Given: effort arm = 1 ft, resistance arm = 10 ft, resistance force = 50 lb. Find the effort force. Remember that the effort arm × effort force = the resistance arm × resistance force. *F_e = 500 lb*
8. An electric mixer does 24,750 ft-lb of work in 3 minutes. What is the horsepower of the electric mixer? *¼ hp*
9. A 1-hp gasoline engine and a ½-hp motor both do 100 ft-lb work. Which machine can do the work faster? Explain your answer. *1 hp*
10. A pole vaulter weighing 175 lb leaps 16 ft over a bar. How much work is done? *W = 2800 ft-lb*

See Teacher's Guide at the front of the book for answers and suggestions.

INVESTIGATIONS

1. Automobile engines must be "tuned" every so often to maintain their performance. Obtain a book on automobile mechanics and visit a service station to learn how an engine is "tuned."
2. Pulleys may be made from empty thread spools and wire clothes hangers. Cut off the wire of a hanger 20 cm on each side of the hook. Bend the ends and slip them through a spool. Make three spool pulleys in this manner. Using some string, hook two pulleys together to form an I.M.A. of 2. Then hook three pulleys together to form an I.M.A. of 3. Use a spring scale to measure the effort force needed to lift various objects with the pulleys. Record your observations.
3. Obtain advertising material for different kinds of motorcycles, dirt bikes, and minibikes. Make a chart comparing horsepower and gear ratios.

FORCE AND WORK

4. Look up "perpetual motion" in the library and give a report on perpetual motion machines.
5. Make a comparison of fuel economy and horsepower in several types of cars. Explain your findings.

INTERESTING READING

Bulman, A.D., *Models for Experiments in Physics*. New York, Thomas Y. Crowell Co., 1968.

Burlingame, Roger, *Machines That Built America*. New York, New American Library, Inc., 1955.

Gamow, George, *Gravity*. Garden City, N.Y., Doubleday & Company, Inc., 1962.

Munch, Theodore W., *Man the Engineer: Nature's Copycat*. Philadelphia, Westminster Press, 1974.

Urquhart, David I., *The Bicycle and How It Works*. New York, Henry Z. Walck, Inc., 1972.

Zim, Herbert S., and Skelly, James R., *Tractors* (How Things Work Series). New York, William Morrow and Co., Inc., 1974.

Lunar Command Module orbited the moon while the LEM descended to the moon's surface.

NASA

The objectives of this chapter are to discuss the difference between mass and weight and to further develop the concepts of motion including speed, acceleration, and velocity. Vectors are introduced and used in problem solving.

Moving Bodies

GOAL: You will gain an understanding of the differences between weight and mass, speed and velocity, and force and motion.

Hundreds of years of study and research have enabled people to overcome the earth's forces. Launching a rocket was once unthinkable. Yet today, not only are rockets launched, but statellites orbit the earth.

Several engineering, scientific, and mathematical discoveries made trips to the moon possible. Forces exerted by the rocket propelled it into orbit around the earth. Additional forces were needed to overcome the earth's forces to move it into a path around the moon. These achievements are possible only because of an understanding of forces.

WEIGHT AND MASS

3:1 Weight and Mass

All things are attracted to the earth. A skydiver leaping from an airplane falls swiftly toward the ground. Jump up in the air and you come down again. If you accidentally let go of a ball during a game, it falls to the ground. Bodies fall because the earth exerts a force on them. This force is **gravity**. Gravity acts upon all bodies on or near the earth's surface. The force of gravity is measured by **weight**. You can measure weight with a spring scale. Measurements are made using newtons in the metric system. Pounds and ounces are the units for measuring force in the English system.

Figure 3-1. The stretch of the spring inside the scale is proportional to the force which stretches it.

Time: 45 minutes.

ACTIVITY. You can measure the force of gravity with a spring. (1) Cut off the bottom half of a paper cup. With a small piece of string, attach the cup bottom to a spring. Tie the opposite end of the spring to a clamp supported by a ring stand. Bend a paper clip to form a pointer and attach it to the bottom end of the spring. Attach a piece of cardboard in back of the spring with masking tape. Mark a zero on the cardboard opposite the pointer. Now place a metal washer in the paper cup. Mark the new position of the pointer. Add a second washer and mark the new position of the pointer. Repeat this procedure until you have a total of ten washers in the cup. Mark the scale each time. DO NOT OVERLOAD THE SPRING. Why? Remove the washers from the cup. (2) Now weigh separately a marble, thimble, pencil, and pen. Read and record the weight of each in terms of your washer-weight scale. Which weighed the most? Why aren't washers used as standard units of force? They vary in weight.

Figure 3-2.

Mass is different from weight (Section 1:9). **Mass** is the quantity or amount of matter in an object. Examine a book, a pencil, or any solid body near you. Notice that it has a definite mass and occupies space. Gases and liquids also have definite mass and occupy space. Anything that occupies space and has mass is called *matter*. Unlike weight, the mass of a given body remains constant.

How is weight measured?

Figure 3-3.

Time: 45 minutes.

ACTIVITY. Does a body lose mass or weight when submerged in water? (1) Fill a 400-ml beaker half full of water. Place a rubber band around the beaker at the level of the water. Set the beaker on the pan of a balance and balance it. Record the mass. (2) Attach a spring scale to a body (lead sinker) with a string and record the weight. Lower the body into the water until it is submerged. Record the decrease in weight observed on the spring balance. Now move the rubber band to the new level of the water. Remove the body from the water. (3) Add water to raise the water level in the beaker to the rubber band. Record the new reading on the balance (beaker and water). (4) Find the mass of the added water. Subtract the original mass of the beaker and water from the new mass of the beaker and water.

Does the beaker gain mass or weight, or both, when water is added? Why does the body lose weight and not mass when submerged? Compare the change in mass of the beaker plus water with the weight loss of the submerged body. Explain your answer.

The activity illustrates Archimedes' principle. The lead sinker displaces a volume of water equal to its own volume. Weight and mass of the displaced water is less than the weight and mass of the lead. The lead sinker loses weight equal to the weight of the water it displaces due to buoyancy, a force exerted by the water opposite to the force of gravity. When buoyancy is equal to the weight of an object, the object floats.

The beaker gains both mass and weight.

Buoyancy, a force exerted by the water, decreases weight.

The weight loss of the submerged object is equal to the weight of the water added to the beaker. Explanation above.

PROBLEM

1. How does a submarine change its weight when it dives and surfaces? *To submerge, it takes on water to reduce buoyancy. To surface, it forces water out to reduce weight.*

The mass of a body is constant and unchanged regardless of its location. However, the weight of a body can change. Differences in the force of gravity cause differences in weight. For example, on the

How is weight different from mass? Weight is the amount of force of gravity acting on a body and mass is the quantity of matter or "stuff" in the body.

48 (48M)

Figure 3-4. Submarines dive by taking on water to add weight.

moon you would weigh 1/6 of your weight on Earth. Why the difference? Gravity on the moon is only 1/6 as great as gravity on the earth. Yet your mass would be the same on the moon as it is on the earth. Two masses that exactly balance each other on the moon would also balance on Earth.

The earth is not a perfect sphere. If the earth were a perfect sphere, your weight would be the same anywhere on its surface. The earth is slightly flattened at the poles and thicker at the equator. From the North Pole to the equator, the distance from the center of the earth increases by about 20 km. As a body moves away from the center of the earth, gravity decreases. Gravity is less at the equator; weight is less, too. A person who weighs 201 lb at the North Pole would weigh 200 lb at the equator. Weight decreases by about 0.5 percent when a body is moved from the North Pole to the equator.

Figure 3-5. A person can jump higher and much more easily on the moon than on Earth because of the difference in gravity.

a

b

Figure 3-6. A person who weighs 160 lb at the surface of Earth would weigh 40 lb at 12,880 km from the center of Earth and 18 lb at 19,320 km from the center of Earth.

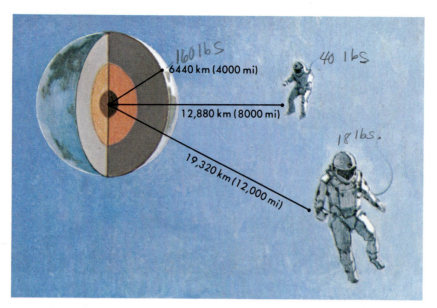

A metric ton is approximately 1.1 English tons.

Remind students that $d^2 = d \times d$. For example, $4^2 = 4 \times 4 = 16$, $8^2 = 8 \times 8 = 64$.

What is Newton's law of gravitation?

Figure 3-7. As a rocket travels farther away from Earth, the gravitational attraction between the rocket and Earth decreases proportionally.

NASA

3:2 Gravity

Most things fall down and not up if you drop them. Gravity pulls bodies to the earth. However, gravity is a property not only of the earth but of all matter. Every body in the universe pulls on every other body. Every body has its own force on other objects. The pull between most objects is too small to be measured except with precise instruments. For example, a five metric ton lead ball attracts a baseball at its surface with a force less than the weight of one mosquito!

Sir Isaac Newton (1642–1727) formulated the law of gravitation during the seventeenth century. A scientific law is an accepted statement based upon a large amount of scientific evidence. However, any scientific law may be disproved by new evidence. Thus, a scientific law is subject to change.

Newton's law of gravitation states that the gravitational attraction (force) between two bodies is proportional to the product of the mass of the bodies divided by the square of the distance between them. In equation form this becomes $F \propto \dfrac{Mm}{d^2}$.

Bodies with a large mass exert a greater gravitational force than bodies with a small mass. For example, the earth exerts a greater force on bodies near its surface than does the moon. This is so because the earth has a greater mass. As the distance between two bodies increases, the attraction between them decreases. For example, as the distance between a rocket and the earth increases, the attraction between them decreases. Double the distance between two bodies and their attraction decreases to ¼ (½²).

SPEED   (51M)   51

PROBLEM

2. Suppose you were 6400 km above the surface of the earth. You would be twice as far from the center of the earth as you are now. The force of gravity on your body would decrease to ¼ (½²). How would this affect your weight? What would you weigh if you were 12,800 km above the earth's surface?

3200 — now
1/9 surface weight   *1/4 surface weight*

Henry Cavendish (1731–1810), an English scientist, accurately measured the gravitational attraction between two bodies. He mounted two small balls on opposite ends of a horizontal rod 2 m long. Then he hung the rod horizontally by a wire (Figure 3–9). Cavendish set rulers at each end of the rod to measure its position. He placed two large masses near the balls at the ends of the rods. The balls were attracted to the large masses. As the small balls moved toward the large masses, the wire twisted. Cavendish measured the change in position of the balls. He used this measurement to calculate the gravitational force between the balls and the large masses.

Figure 3-8. How does distance affect gravitational attraction between two objects?

3:3 Speed

A force can set a body in motion. A body in motion moves a certain distance in a certain unit of time such as a second, a minute, or an hour. **Speed** is defined as the distance a body travels per unit of time. Speed = distance/time.

An automobile speedometer indicates speed in mi/hr or km/hr. Automobiles on a highway may move at a constant speed. Constant speed means that the speed does not vary. For example, a car travels at a constant speed of 50 km/hr. The car travels 50 km in the first

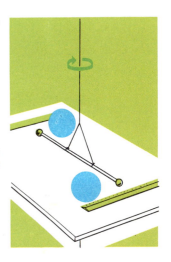

Figure 3-9. Cavendish used his calculations of gravitational force to find the earth's mass.

What is speed?

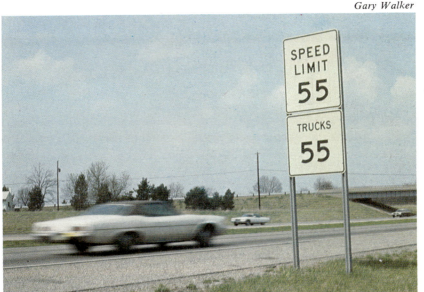

Gary Walker

Figure 3-10. Speed limit signs indicate the speeds at which it is safe to travel.

Figure 3-11. To find the average speed between San Francisco and New York, divide the distance (4800 km) by the total hours of time.

hour and 50 km in the second hour. Thus, it travels a total of 100 km in two hours. When it goes 50 km every hour, it maintains this constant speed.

You can calculate speed, distance, or period of time in motion for a moving body. Use the equation below.

What equation is used to calculate speed?

$$v = \frac{d}{t}$$

speed equals distance divided by time

Have students consult Appendix A. Explain the tables listed and how they may be used as an aid in solving problems.

EXAMPLE 1

What is the speed of a truck which travels 10 km in 10 min at constant speed?

Solution: (a) Write the equation: $v = \dfrac{d}{t}$

(b) Substitute 10 km for d and 10 min for t:
$$v = \frac{10 \text{ km}}{10 \text{ min}}$$

(c) Divide to find the answer: $v = 1$ km/min

EXAMPLE 2

What distance is covered by a police car that travels at a constant speed of 1.5 km/min for 5 min?

Solution: (a) Write the equation: $v = \dfrac{d}{t}$; $d = vt$

(b) Substitute and simplify: $d = \dfrac{1.5 \text{ km}}{\text{min}} \times 5 \text{ min}$

$d = 7.5$ km

SPEED

Problems

3. What is the speed of a bicycle that travels 100 m in 50 sec at constant speed? *2 m/sec*

4. What distance would be covered in 10 min by a train that travels at a constant speed of 500 m in 10 sec? *30,000 m*

5. Which has the greatest constant speed, the bicycle in Problem 3 or the train in Problem 4? *train*

Cars, trucks, trains, and bicycles seldom travel at a constant speed for very long. The speed of a moving body usually increases or decreases as it moves. For this reason, the speed given to a moving body is usually its average speed. To find average speed, use the equation $v \text{ (average)} = \frac{d \text{ (total)}}{t \text{ (total)}}$. Divide the total distance by the total time it takes to travel this distance.

How is average speed different from constant speed?

Average speed is total distance traveled divided by the time required to travel the total distance. Constant speed means that a body moves the same distance in each unit of time.

Problems

6. Compare the motion of the car in Figure 3–12 with that of the car in Figure 3–13. How do they differ? What is the average speed of the car in Figure 3–13? *Car in Figure 3-12 has constant speed. Car in Figure 3-13 has average speed of 24 km/hr.*

Figure 3-12.

Figure 3-13.

Figures 3-12 and 3-13 distinguish between constant speed and motion in which speed changes (accelerated motion).

7. What is the average speed of a commercial jet plane which travels from New York City to Los Angeles (4800 km) in 6 hr? 800 km/hr
8. What is the average speed of an arrow which travels 1000 m in 5 sec? 200 m/sec

Figure 3-14.

Time: 30 minutes.

ACTIVITY. Obtain a board at least 2 m long and 15 cm wide. Place it on a table with one end on a pile of books about 40 cm high. Place a ball or large marble at the high end of the board and gently release it (do not push it). Time its trip down the board with a stopwatch. Mark off and measure in centimeters the distance the marble travels. Find the speed of the ball in cm/sec. Repeat three times and average your answers. Does the marble have a constant speed? Is your answer the speed or average speed of the marble? Explain.
See Teacher's Guide.

Acceleration is produced by a force.

3:4 *Acceleration*

Acceleration (ak sel uh RAY shuhn) is the rate at which speed is changing. Acceleration is caused by a force. For example, the force of a drag racing car's wheels on the road makes the car accelerate. In a rocket, the engine produces the force that accelerates the rocket up and away from the launching pad.

Figure 3-15. Racing cars have high rates of acceleration.

George Silk, Time-Life Picture Agency © Time, Inc.

Union Pacific Railroad

Figure 3-16. Trains accelerate as a result of the force of their wheels on the tracks.

To find acceleration, divide the change in speed by the time taken to change speed. Use the equation

$$a = \frac{v_2 - v_1}{t}$$

acceleration equals the final speed minus the original speed divided by time

What equation is used to calculate acceleration?

A driver increases his speed from 0 km/hr to 150 km/hr in 10 seconds. Acceleration of a drag race car is

$$a = \frac{v_2 - v_1}{t} = \frac{150 \text{ km/hr} - 0 \text{ km/hr}}{10 \text{ sec}} = 15 \text{ km/hr/sec}$$

The acceleration is read as 15 kilometers per hour per second. In each second, the drag racer increases his speed 15 km per hour.

Dragsters accelerate rapidly because the engines have a high horsepower and the rear wheels rotate rapidly.

EXAMPLE

A car starts from a standstill and accelerates to a speed of 50 km/hr in 10 sec. What is its acceleration?

Solution: (a) Write the equation: $a = \dfrac{v_2 - v_1}{t}$

(b) Substitute 50 km/hr for v_2, 0 km/hr for v_1, and 10 sec for t:

$$a = \frac{50 \text{ km/hr} - 0 \text{ km/hr}}{10 \text{ sec}}$$

(c) Subtract and divide to find the answer:
$a = 5$ km/hr/sec

Figure 3-17. Forces and speed provide fun and excitement on amusement park rides. Is the roller coaster <u>accelerating</u> or decelerating?

Most amusement rides provide thrills by rapid accelerations and decelerations which produce forces on the riders.

Kings Island Amusement Park

PROBLEM

9. The speed of a jet plane increases from 450 km/hr to 585 km/hr in 15 sec. Find the acceleration. 9 km/hr/sec

3:5 Deceleration

How does a pilot stop a jet airliner after it lands? Reversing the engines of a jet airplane causes it to slow down. The driver of a car applies the brakes to slow it down. Both the airplane and car are stopped by forces. Decreasing speed is the opposite of increasing speed. The rate at which the speed of an object decreases is called **deceleration** (dee sel uh RAY shuhn). Deceleration means negative acceleration. The greater the force applied, the greater the deceleration. To find deceleration, use the acceleration equation

How is deceleration different from acceleration? Decreasing speed is the opposite of increasing speed (acceleration).

$$a = \frac{v_2 - v_1}{t}$$

EXAMPLE

Application of forces required to decelerate a body results in the generation of heat. A heat shield on a space capsule returning to Earth glows red as it decelerates while falling through the atmosphere. Air exerts the force which decelerates the space capsule.

A car traveling at 30 km/hr is stopped in 3 sec. Find the deceleration.

Solution: (a) Write the equation: $a = \dfrac{v_2 - v_1}{t}$

(b) Substitute 0 km/hr for v_2, 30 km/hr for v_1, and 3 sec for t: $a = \dfrac{0 \text{ km/hr} - 30 \text{ km/hr}}{3 \text{ sec}}$

(c) Subtract and divide to find the answer: (Note: Subtracting 30 from 0 gives -30, a negative answer.)

$$a = \frac{-30 \text{ km/hr}}{3 \text{ sec}} = -10 \text{ km/hr/sec}$$

56 (56M)

DECELERATION

Deceleration is the opposite of acceleration and is in the opposite direction. Acceleration problems have positive (+) answers. Deceleration problems have negative (−) answers. It is standard practice not to write a + sign before a positive number. However, a − sign is always written before a negative number.

You may wish to review negative numbers at this point. A number line is a good tool.

Problems

10. The speed of a jet plane is decreased from 500 km/hr to 400 km/hr in 20 sec. What is the deceleration? *−5 km/hr/sec*

11. A parachute on a drag race car is opened. It slows the speed of the car from 260 km/hr to 130 km/hr in 10 sec. What is the deceleration? *−13 km/hr/sec*

Acceleration and deceleration are opposites. Yet both are produced by forces. Any change in the speed of an object requires the application of a force.

How is a moving body accelerated and decelerated?
application of a force

See Teacher's Guide.

Problems

12. What forces accelerate a passenger car, a drag race car, and a jet plane?

13. What forces decelerate a passenger car, a drag race car, and a jet plane?

A photo essay (pp. 58-61) is included to examine many alternatives in transportation. Forms of land, water, and air transportation are emphasized. Major uses of each particular vehicle are considered. Advantages and

American Airlines

Figure 3-18. Jet airplanes decelerate when the engines are reversed, the flaps are lowered to increase air friction, and when brakes are applied.

disadvantages are also examined. Thought-provoking questions are asked throughout with an emphasis on alternatives with regard to energy conservation.

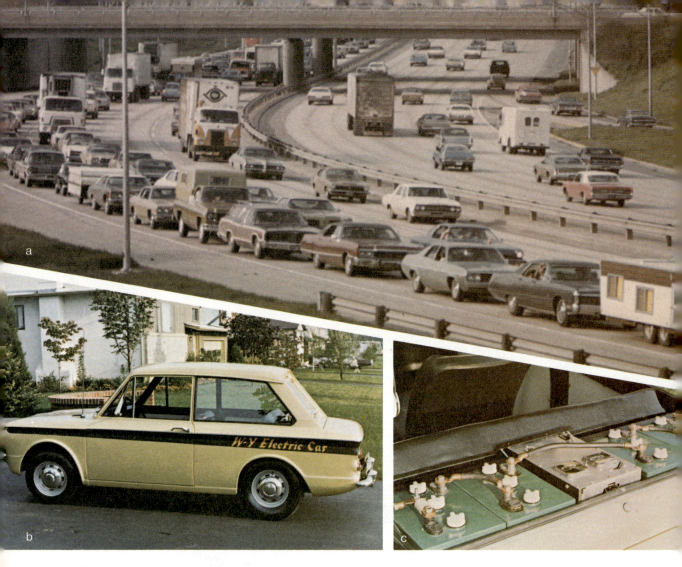

Some Alternatives in Transportation

Transportation takes many forms. Whether or not to use a certain type of transportation depends on many factors. Convenience, comfort, speed, and fuel economy are a few factors which may be considered.

Automobiles

Automobiles are the most popular form of transportation in the United States. In fact, over 107 million automobiles are now registered. Cars outnumber every other type of road vehicle by almost four to one (a). There are many reasons for this popularity. Cars are easy to operate and they come in a variety of sizes and styles. Also, they are very convenient. What are some other reasons for their popularity?

You may wish to expand upon this photo essay and use it as a basis for discussing speed, acceleration, and deceleration.

Experimental Automobiles

New and different types of cars are being developed. Many people want to help conserve gasoline by using different power sources. Others want to have cars which do not pollute the air and are easier to maintain.

An electric car (b) is one type of experimental car. It is designed to run on batteries (c). These batteries can be charged from ordinary house current. Since gasoline is not used, there is no air pollution. Some electric cars reach speeds of 88 km/hr. The cars are easy to maintain and cost very little to run. At this time, they are not widely used. One reason is that they cannot go far before they need recharging.

Mass Transportation

Various types of mass transportation can be found in many cities. Some cities provide a "Park and Ride" service for commuters. People drive their cars only a short distance, park their cars, and ride longer distances on public transportation. This type of transportation is gaining popularity for several reasons. Transporting many people at one time conserves fuel. With fewer cars on the road, there is less air pollution. In some cases, it is less expensive than private transportation.

Buses (d) provide service in many cities, as well as between cities. Bus travel is one form of mass transportation. Subways (e), trains (f), and monorails (g) are other types of mass transit. These systems offer many advantages. They can make many convenient stops. They also can offer a relaxing ride at a fast pace. Are there any other advantages?

Trucks and Trains

Trucks (h) are the most widely used vehicle for transporting goods. Interstate highways and other roads provide convenient routes to and from cities and towns. How many types of trucks are there?

Freight trains (i) are also used for hauling many types of goods. Coal, cars, and refrigerated goods are commonly shipped by rail. Trains are able to haul large amounts of cargo very efficiently when tracks are in good condition. For this reason, many people are encouraging an increase in train service. What changes are needed before more trains can be used?

Airplanes

Airplanes and jets (j) are the fastest way for passengers and goods to travel. Commercial planes can fly to airports in major cities around the world. They offer fast and convenient service. Improvements are continually made to
Other forms of transportation may be considered at this point. Also, an overview of the forms of transportation in your community may offer some interesting insights.

provide even better service. Jets are now being used which fly faster than the speed of sound. These supersonic jets (k) reach destinations in less time than other jets. However, several concerns are being raised. Many people complain about the noise of these jets when they land and take off. Another concern is the amount of fuel used by these jets. Also, some scientists are concerned that these jets may harm the ozone layer. What steps should be taken in these areas?

Ships

Ships and boats are important forms of transportation. Some are used only for pleasure (l). Many are used to carry cargo and passengers on rivers and oceans (m). Others are designed for military use (n). What are some other uses for ships and boats? Are ships being used efficiently? Where can improvements in service be made?

You may wish to expand upon the types of engines and fuels used by the various forms of transportation.

Conclusion

After surveying several types of transportation, many questions can be raised. How important is it for cities to develop mass transit systems? What are some of the ways this can be done? What can the public do to help conserve fuel? How might transportation change in the next twenty years?

Credits: p. 58: a—*U.S. Energy Research and Development Administration,* **p. 58:** b, c—*Electric Vehicle Components Company,* **p. 59:** d—*Cota Transit System,* **p. 59:** e—*Port Authority of New York and New Jersey,* **p. 59:** f—*Canadian National Railways,* **p. 60:** g—*Dick Smith,* **p. 60:** h—*American Trucking Association,* **p. 60:** i—*Paul Poplis/Studio Ten,* **p. 60:** j—*William Maddox,* **p. 61:** k—*British Aircraft Corporation (U.S.A.) Inc.,* **p. 61:** l—*William Maddox,* **p. 61:** m—*Courtesy of Princess Cruises, P & O North America,* **p. 61:** n—*General Dynamics*

3:6 Vectors

When you kick a ball, the ball moves in the direction it is kicked. If two people kick the ball from different directions, how does the ball move? There is a way to explain the effects of forces on bodies. A **vector** (VEK tuhr) is used to represent on paper the amount (magnitude) of a force and its direction of action. The direction the vector points shows the direction the force is applied. The length of the vector shows the amount (magnitude) of force applied. An arrow is used to represent the force vector.

A scale is chosen to represent the quantity. For example, one centimeter (cm) represents one newton (nt) of force (Figure 3–19). Remember that centimeters are metric units of length. Newtons are metric units of force.

The size of the force is converted into the same number of units of length. Using the scale in Figure 3–19, an arrow 5 cm long would equal 25 nt acting in an east direction.

What information is needed to draw a vector? magnitude and direction of force

Figure 3-19. Scales are chosen to show the amount of a force vector.

Problems

14. On graph paper, draw a vector that is 3 cm long. Its direction is north. Use the scale: 1 cm = 5 nt. What is the amount of force of this vector? *If 1 cm = 5 nt, then 3 cm = 15 nt.*

15. On graph paper, draw a vector that is 8 cm long. Its direction is west. Use the scale: 1 cm = 10 nt. What is the amount of force of this vector? *If 1 cm = 10 nt, then 8 cm = 80 nt.*

Two people push a car in the same direction. One person exerts 60 newtons of force and the other person exerts 80 newtons of force. These two forces act as a single force of 140 newtons. The single force which arises from the effects of two or more forces is called the

What method is used to find the resultant of forces acting in the same direction? If forces are in the same direction, simply add them together.

Figure 3-20. Two forces act as a single force of 140 nt on this car.

Figure 3-21. Opposing forces are shown by these vectors.

resultant force. The **resultant** (rih ZUHLT uhnt) is the net effect of several forces. In this case, it is equal to the sum of the individual forces. The resultant is also in the same direction as the two forces acting on the car. In effect, the car is pushed by a force of 140 newtons. Remember, each vector has both magnitude and direction.

In a tug-of-war game, two forces oppose each other. One team pulls in one direction and the other team pulls in the opposite direction. If each team pulls with a different amount of force, what happens? To find the resultant of two opposite forces, find the difference between them. What is the resultant of the forces represented in Figure 3–21? 20 nt

Each team in a tug-of-war pulls with the same amount of force. What do you think happens? When the amount of force exerted by each team is equal, the resultant force is zero. This is called **equilibrium** (ee kwuh LIB ree uhm), the state of balance between equal opposing forces.

Figure 3-22. When opposing forces are in a state of balance, there is equilibrium.

PROBLEM

16. Two teams play tug-of-war. One team pulls with a force of 100 newtons. The other pulls with a force of 75 newtons. Using vectors, find the resultant force. 25 nt in the direction of the first team

You can diagram several forces acting on a single body. The resultant force is found by drawing a force diagram. It is wise to use a ruler and protractor when making vector diagrams. To add force vectors (arrows), place the tail of the second arrow on the head of the first arrow. Then place the tail of the third arrow on the head of the second arrow, and so on. Vectors may be added in any sequence. To find the resultant of these vectors, draw a final arrow from the tail of the first vector to the head of the last vector. This is the resultant vector and **has both** direction and magnitude.

Figure 3-23. Force diagrams are drawn to find resultant forces. A resultant vector is found by placing the tail of each vector against the head of the next vector.

64 (64M)

MOVING BODIES

PROBLEM

Figure 3-24. Defensive driving can help prevent accidents. The resultant force of a chain collision is likely to be great enough to cause harm.

What method is used to find the resultant of several forces acting at angles to each other? Draw a parallelogram using the vector forces as sides. The diagonal is the resultant force.

17. Three cars moving in the same direction collide. The second car hits the rear of the first car with a force of 100 lb. The third car hits the rear of the second car with a force of 50 lb. Find the resultant force on the first car. 150 lb in direction all cars were moving

In a football game, two players may collide. Here two forces may act at an angle to each other. You can find the resultant force in a problem of this kind by drawing a parallelogram. A parallelogram is a four-sided figure with opposite sides parallel.

(1) Represent each force with a force vector. Draw the vectors from the same point to form two sides of a parallelogram. The point represents the place where the two forces act on a body.

(2) Complete the parallelogram. Draw two sides parallel to the vectors that you have drawn to represent the forces.

(3) Draw a diagonal through the point where the forces act. The diagonal is a vector for the resultant force.

(4) Measure the diagonal. Use your scale to convert the measured length to an amount of force.

Figure 3-25. Football players are often tackled by several players coming from different angles.

Courtesy of Ohio State University

PEOPLE CAREERS FRONTIERS FOCUS ON PHYSICAL SCIENCE

Physicists

The work of physicists has resulted in the development of many technical products and improvements in old products. Physicists are concerned with the study of matter and the relationship between matter and energy. This accounts for the wide range of accomplishments within this field. Many of the accomplishments of physicists change the way we live.

Research has led to the development of the transistor and the integrated circuit. These two inventions have made thousands of other things possible. Telephones, computers, calculators, and televisions use the technology of this research.

Most physicists work in the areas of either basic or applied research. There is one main difference between these two areas of physics. Basic research deals with the actual

Many physicists teach basic and advanced principles of physics in colleges and in industries.

principles of physics. Applied research applies the principles of physics.

Some physicists in basic research conduct experiments. Others describe physical concepts in mathematical terms. Many researchers in basic physics combine both aspects by conducting experiments and using mathematical formulas to analyze data.

Applied research physicists use the principles of physics to solve practical problems. New products are often developed by physicists working hand-in-hand with engineers.

The field of physics is very broad. For this reason, many physicists specialize in one area. Some of the main divisions are mechanics (forces and machines), optics (light), and acoustics (sound). Within

each division there may be many subdivision. For instance, one division is called solid-state physics (behavior of materials in the solid state). Ceramics (clay and glass) and crystallography (crystal structure) are two subdivisions within solid-state physics. Although a physicist may have a specialty, his or her work may overlap several different subdivisions.

Dr. Betsy Ancker-Johnson is a physicist working for the U.S. Department of Commerce.

An experimental physicist often builds equipment needed to perform experiments.

Problem

Figure 3-26. To find the resultant force of forces acting at right angles to each other, use the parallelogram method.

18. At an intersection, two cars strike a third car at right angles to each other. One car exerts a force of 300 nt on the third car. The other car exerts a force of 200 nt on the third car. Find the resultant force by the parallelogram method. 360 nt

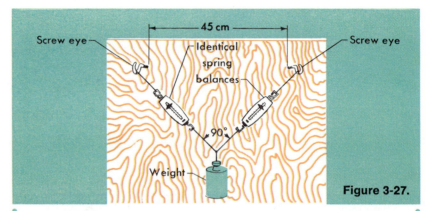

Figure 3-27.

Time: 60 minutes.

DEMONSTRATION. How can spring scales be used to find the components (parts) of a force? (1) Fasten two screw eyes about 45 cm apart near one edge of a piece of plywood 60 cm long and 60 cm wide. Support the board in a vertical position. Hang two identical spring scales, one from each screw eye. Connect the hooks of each spring scale with a string. (2) Read the spring balance scale to find the maximum reading. Obtain a weight that is one half as large as the scale's maximum reading. Attach this weight to the center of the string. The resultant force is straight down from the weight. The reading from each scale shows each component of the resultant force exerted by the weight. (3) Move the weight to different points on the string so that the force components form different angles. Each time record the reading of each scale. (4) Use a ruler and pencil to draw vector diagrams. Show the components and resultants for three different angles between the two force components. How is the size of the forces related to the size of the angle?

Use different weights and repeat steps 3 and 4. What are your conclusions?

The angle between the two strings may be measured with a protractor or drawn on the student's paper by placing the paper behind the strings.

If angle is <120°, each force is <W. If angle = 120°, each force = W. If angle is >120°, each force is >W.

VELOCITY

3:7 Velocity

The speed and direction of an airplane traveling north at 600 km/hr may be shown by a vector. This vector is drawn by using a scale of 100 km/hr = 1 cm. A line, 6 cm long, is drawn pointing to the top of paper (north). The vector which shows both speed and direction is called a velocity vector.

In physical science, speed refers to how fast a body is moving. Velocity (vuh LAHS uht ee) **refers to how fast a body is moving and the direction in which it is moving.**

Problem

19. A motorboat moves south across a river at 20 km/hr. The river current moves at 5 km/hr. Use vectors to find the velocity of the motorboat. Scale: 1 cm = 5 km (See Teacher's Guide.)

Figure 3-28. Vectors can be drawn to show the speed and direction of an airplane. Plotting a course must include an allowance for wind speed and direction.

How can vectors be used to show velocity?

What is the difference between speed and velocity?

Figure 3-29. Sailboat navigation takes wind speed and direction into account.

Allan Roberts

MAIN IDEAS

3:1 1. Weight and mass are different. Weight is the amount of force the earth exerts on a body due to gravity. Mass is the amount of matter in a body.

3:1, 3:2 2. Motion starts and stops through the action of forces.

3:3 **3.** Speed is the distance covered per unit time. Velocity is speed in a given direction.

3:3 **4.** A force must be applied to vary speed or velocity.

3:4, 3:5 **5.** Acceleration and deceleration result from the action of forces.

3:6 **6.** The amount of force may be measured in newtons.

3:6 **7.** A vector represents both magnitude and direction.

3:6 **8.** Force vectors are used to find the resultant of two or more forces acting together.

3:7 **9.** Velocity vectors are used to find the speed and direction of a body in motion.

VOCABULARY

Write a sentence in which you correctly use each of the following words or terms.

acceleration	magnitude	speed
deceleration	mass	vector
equilibrium	resultant	velocity
force	scale	weight
gravity	scientific law	

STUDY QUESTIONS

Have students rewrite false statements to make the statements correct.

A. True or False

Determine whether each of the following sentences is true or false. (Do not write in this book.)

T **1.** It takes a force to produce motion.

T **2.** A body would have the same mass on the moon as it has on Earth.

T **3.** It takes a force to change the velocity of a body.

T **4.** Force may be measured in newtons.

F **5.** Gravity is ~~not~~ a force.

T **6.** Weight is measured in newtons.

T **7.** The resultant is the sum of two or more vectors.

T **8.** The mass of a body may be measured in kilograms.

F **9.** Speed is ~~the same as velocity.~~ not a vector quantity

F **10.** The ~~kilometer~~ is a unit of speed. kilometer/hour

MOVING BODIES (69M) 69

B. Multiple Choice

Some questions in Parts B and C may have more than one correct answer. Only one answer is required.

Choose one word or phrase that correctly completes each of the following sentences. (Do not write in this book.)

1. The *(newton, centimeter, kilogram)* is a unit of force.
2. A car traveling 60 km in 2 hr has an average speed of *(30 km/2 hr, 30 km/hr, 30 km/min, 30 km/sec)*.
3. The formula for speed is $(v = \frac{d}{t}, v = \frac{t}{d}, v = \frac{s}{d})$.
4. When an automobile driver steps on the brake pedal, the automobile *(accelerates, loses velocity, changes direction)*.
5. An example of acceleration is *(15 km/hr, 15 km/min/sec, −15 km/min/sec)*.
6. Velocity may be shown by a *(force, line, vector, unit)*.
7. To find the resultant of two forces acting in the same direction, *(add, multiply, draw a parallelogram)*.
8. To find the resultant of two forces acting at right angles, *(add, multiply, draw a parallelogram)*.
9. Mass is measured in *(meters, kilograms, newtons)*.
10. A mass would weigh more at the *(equator, North Pole, moon)*.

C. Completion

Complete each of the following sentences with a word or phrase that will make the sentence correct. (Do not write in this book.)

1. _____ is a vector quantity. **Velocity**
2. Velocity has both speed and _____. **direction**
3. The resultant of three forces, 30 nt, 50 nt, 100 nt, all acting in the same direction is _____ nt. **180**
4. In the state of equilibrium, the resultant force is _____. **zero**
5. A vector shows both the amount and _____ of a force. **direction**
6. When a drag race car leaves the starting line and increases speed, it is _____. **accelerated**
7. A(n) _____ is the metric unit of force. **newton (nt)**
8. Acceleration is produced by a(n) _____. **force**
9. _____ occurs when the brakes of a bicycle cause it to slow down or stop. **Deceleration**
10. Deceleration is _____ acceleration. **negative**

D. How and Why

1. A car travels 120 km in 2 hr. What is its average speed in km/min? 1 km/min

2. A car going 10 km/hr accelerates to 50 km/hr in 6 sec. Find the average acceleration. 6.7 km/hr/sec

3. A bobsled has an average acceleration of 1 meter per second starting from rest. How fast is it going after 6 sec? 6 m/sec

4. What is the average speed of the bobsled in Question 3? 3 m/sec

5. How much distance is covered in 6 sec by the bobsled in Question 3? 18 m

Figure 3-30.

6. (a) 23 km/hr
   (b) 2 km/hr
   (c) 2 min to 2.7 min
   (d) 0.5 min to 2 min, 2.7 min to 4.2 min, and 4.8 min to 5 min

6. A teenager bicycles as fast as possible from home to a store 1 km away. On the way the rider goes over a hill. Look at Figure 3–30 and find
   (a) the rider's highest velocity
   (b) the rider's lowest velocity
   (c) the time at which the rider is accelerating
   (d) the time at which the rider is decelerating

7. A car traveling at a speed of 30 m/sec is stopped with a deceleration of 6 m/sec. How far does the car go before stopping? 75 m How long does it take to stop the car? 5 sec

See Teacher's Guide for answers to questions 8-10.

8. Why must a pilot include headwinds, tailwinds, and crosswinds when making a flight plan?

9. A sailor attaches a large fan to the stern of a sailboat. The fan is powered with a gasoline engine so that it will blast air against the sail. Will the fan move the boat? Explain your answer.

10. Why can a hammer exert a force many times its own weight?

MOVING BODIES

INVESTIGATIONS

1. Find out how forces can make an airplane accelerate, decelerate, and change direction in flight. Learn the use of ailerons, flaps, and elevators. Using a model airplane, report your findings to the class.

2. Obtain a book on sailboats and learn how wind and water forces can make a sailboat sail against the wind.

3. Find out how the airspeeds of airplanes have changed over the past 50 years. Make a chart with illustrations to show this development.

INTERESTING READING

Bendick, Jeanne, *Motion and Gravity*. New York, Watts, 1972.

Bergmann, Peter G., *Riddle of Gravitation*. New York, Scribner Library, 1968.

Burlingame, Roger, *Machines That Built America*. New York, New American Library, Inc., 1955.

Gamow, George, *Gravity*. Garden City, N.Y., Doubleday & Company, Inc., 1962.

Grey, Jerry, *The Facts of Flight: A Franklin Institute Book*. Philadelphia, Westminster Press, 1973.

Legunn, Joel, *Motion*. Munkato, Minnesota, Creative Education Press, 1971.

See Teacher's Guide at the front of the book for answers and suggestions.

James M. Jackson

The objectives of this chapter are: To discuss Newton's laws, projectile motion, and motion in curves; to discuss the effects of gravity on motion; and to develop an understanding of momentum.

 # Laws of Motion

GOAL: You will gain an understanding of Newton's laws, the effects of gravity on motion, projectile motion, motion in curves, and momentum.

Physical laws are those which explain natural phenomena. These laws have been proven over and over again. Some examples of these laws are the laws of motion. They explain the relationships between forces and objects.

The motion of a hang glider is not haphazard. There is a reason behind each twist or turn and every other action it takes. As the hang glider falls toward the earth, every movement counts. The position of the pilot's body and the way he or she handles the glider is very important. The pilots must recognize the physical laws affecting them and plan their course with these laws in mind.

FIRST LAW OF MOTION

4:1 First Law of Motion

You are riding in an automobile. The driver suddenly applies the brakes. You tend to keep moving. The tendency of a body to keep its present state of motion is called **inertia** (in UHR shuh). Inertia keeps you moving in a straight line, even though the car has stopped. The pull of a seat belt brings you to a halt. If you do not wear a seat belt, you may get hurt. You may continue to move forward and hit the windshield.

What is inertia?

Inertia is the reluctance of a mass to change its state of rest or motion.

Transportation Research Center of Ohio

Figure 4-1. When a car stops rapidly or crashes into another object, inertia throws its passengers forward. When seatbelts are worn, many injuries and deaths are prevented.

Time: 10 minutes.

ACTIVITY. Set a glass tumbler on a desk or table. Lay a card flat on top of the tumbler. Place a coin on the center of the card. Flick the card with your finger so it moves out from under the coin. If you do this fast enough, the coin will fall into the glass when the card flies away.

Figure 4-2.

Time: 10 minutes.

ACTIVITY Tie a light string to a heavy hammer or flatiron. Pull the object slowly up from the floor. Then pull hard on the string while the object is on the floor. Record and explain your observations.

A well known example of inertia is the magician's trick of pulling a tablecloth out from underneath a table set with dishes.

Figure 4-3. Inertia would keep the rider moving over the jump even if a horse refuses.

Give an example of inertia.

Courtesy of Kodansha, Ltd.

Figure 4-4. It takes a force to start motion.

LAWS OF MOTION

Sir Isaac Newton (1642–1727) formed three scientific laws which explain the movement of bodies. **Newton's first law of motion** states:

A body remains at rest unless a force makes it move. A force is required to change the speed or direction of a moving body.

This law means that it takes a force to start and stop motion. It takes a force to change the speed or direction of a body in motion. In other words, bodies have inertia. Bodies at rest tend to remain at rest. Bodies in motion tend to remain in motion. It takes a force to overcome the effects of inertia. A force is required to accelerate a body and a force is required to decelerate it.

EXAMPLE 1

The electric motor in a slot car makes the wheels turn. The force of the wheels against the track makes the car move forward. As the car rounds a curve, the force of the track against the car makes it change direction. When the power is shut off, friction force gives the car a negative acceleration and makes it stop.

EXAMPLE 2

A sailboat floats on a lake with no wind. The sailors have two choices: (1) start to paddle, (2) wait for the wind. A breeze comes up and exerts a force on the sails. The boat moves. To change direction, the skipper moves the rudder right or left. The force of water on the rudder makes the boat turn.

EXAMPLE 3

A girl is standing in a bus. The bus suddenly moves forward and the girl falls backward. Her body tends to remain at rest (motionless) while the bus moves. When the bus stops suddenly, the girl tends to fall forward because of inertia.

PROBLEM See Teacher's Guide.

1. Identify the forces acting in each of the examples above. What effect does each force have on speed and direction of the moving body?

Time: 10 minutes.

ACTIVITY. Stand a nickel or quarter on edge on a 8×12-cm paper. Try to jerk the paper from under the coin without upsetting the coin. What does this illustrate? First law of motion

SECOND LAW OF MOTION (75M) 75

PROBLEMS See Teacher's Guide.

Problems 2-9 should be discussed in class. Ask students to name additional examples which illustrate the principles involved.

2. What forces put the following objects in motion: car, arrow, jet airplane, roller skates?

3. What forces stop or change the motion of the following objects: rocket, submarine, surfboard, car, bowling ball?

4. In which of the cases in Problem 3 is gravity involved? Explain your answer.

5. Why are seat belts used in automobiles and airplanes?

4:2 Second Law of Motion

Hit a ball with a bat and the ball flies away. The ball is accelerated by the bat at the moment the bat strikes the ball. Acceleration of the ball depends on mass and force. The harder you hit the ball, the faster it moves. A ball with small mass travels faster than a ball with large mass when hit with the same force. How far can you hit a baseball? A professional baseball player may hit a homerun ball over 130 m.

Editorial Photocolor Archives, Inc.

Figure 4-5. The greater the force with which the bat strikes the ball, the greater the acceleration of the ball as it moves away from the bat.

Figure 4-6. When hit with the same force, a small ball will go farther than a large ball.

Explain the second law of motion.

Hitting a ball illustrates **Newton's second law of motion:**

Acceleration of a body increases as the amount of force producing the acceleration increases. The larger the mass of the body, the larger the force needed to produce acceleration.

Force equals mass multiplied by acceleration

$$F = m \times a$$

The second law of motion means that the harder you hit a ball, the faster it goes and the farther it travels. If the same force is applied to a ball with a large mass and a ball with a small mass, the smaller ball will go farther. A larger force is needed to send the larger ball the same distance as the small ball.

A ball has a mass of 0.5 kg. It is hit with a force of 50 nt and travels 100 m. If the mass of the ball had been 1 kg, it would have gone half as far or 50 m. If the force had been 100 nt on the first ball, it would have traveled twice as far or 200 m. The larger the force the greater the acceleration, if the mass remains constant. The larger the mass the smaller the acceleration, if the force remains constant.

EXAMPLE 1

The drawn string of a bow is released by an archer. The arrow speeds to the target. The stronger the force of the pull, the faster the arrow hits the target.

EXAMPLE 2

A driver controls the acceleration of his car with the gas pedal, called the accelerator. By feeding more gas into the engine, more force is created. The car speeds up.

EXAMPLE 3

Heavy (more massive) football players often play on the line. They can exert a large force to stop players on the other team. Players with less mass than those on the line often are used as backfield players. They carry the ball and catch passes. Backfield players must be able to accelerate quickly. Less mass makes for faster acceleration since there is less mass to put in motion.

EXAMPLE 4

The fastest drag racers have a small chassis with a large horsepower engine for rapid acceleration.

Figure 4-7. Bees accelerate easily due to their small mass and powerful wings.

Alvin E. Staffan

PROBLEMS

6. Is it easier for a fly or a bee to accelerate when taking off? Explain. The fly. It has less mass.

7. When a sports car and a loaded moving van both are traveling at a speed of 30 km/hr, which vehicle requires more force to stop? Explain. The van. It needs more force since it has more mass for the same amount of deceleration.

8. List three examples of the second law of motion from your everyday life. Student answer.

9. Explain how each example above illustrates the second law of motion. Student answer.

4:3 Third Law of Motion

Imagine that you are ice skating at a rink. Hold on to the railing with both hands and push off. What happens? Turn on the water in a rotary lawn sprinkler and the sprinkler arm turns. Water is forced out of the sprinkler by pressure. The water exerts a back force that

Linda Briscoe

Figure 4-8. In a tug-of-war, the team that exerts greater force is able to move the other team across the line.

Figure 4-9. Water pressure creates the force which turns the sprinkler arm.

What is the difference between action and reaction forces?

makes the sprinkler arm turn. Push down on your desk top as hard as you can. The desk exerts an upward force on your hand at the same time.

When a force (action force) is exerted on an object, the object exerts an equal force (reaction force) in the opposite direction. In the first two examples, you know that there is an equal and opposite force exerted because there is movement. The third example is a little more difficult to understand since motion is not created.

Forces described above are examples of **Newton's third law of motion:**

For every force, there is an equal and opposite force.

The two forces that always act together are called action force and reaction force. Exert an action force on an object and the object exerts a reaction force. The reaction force is equal in amount to the action force and acts in the opposite direction.

Figure 4-10.

Time: 15 minutes.

ACTIVITY. Attach a spring scale to the leg of a desk or table. Connect the scale hook to the hook of a second spring scale. Exert a force on the scale. Keep the force constant and read both scales. Repeat with different amounts of force. What do you observe? The force readings on the two balances are always equal.

PROBLEMS

10. The earth exerts a force on you. What is the reaction force? Your weight, a force, down on the earth.

11. As you stand, you exert a force on the floor. What is the reaction force? Upward force of the floor on your feet.

12. How does the recoil of a cannon illustrate Newton's third law? See Teacher's Guide.

Time: 10 minutes.

ACTIVITY. Obtain a toy balloon and blow it up. Hold the open end of the inflated balloon closed, then release it. Explain why the balloon moves. What causes the action force and the reaction force?

Air pushes against inside of balloon as it escapes. The balloon at the same time pushes against air.

PEOPLE CAREERS FRONTIERS FOCUS ON PHYSICAL SCIENCE

A Fill-up Costs Thirty Cents

Imagine an automobile that uses no gasoline, emits no pollutants, uses no spark plugs, oil, or air filters, and has no muffler or tail pipe. In addition, the car makes almost no sound and is inexpensive to operate.

All of these features can be obtained in the electric car built by Paul Wergin and Dave Yates in Reynoldsburg, Ohio. They rescued a car from a junkyard and converted it to battery power. The engineering backgrounds of both of these men enabled them to solve many of the problems encountered in making this conversion.

It took them about 14 months to change the car from gasoline power to electric power. They worked in their spare time in Mr. Wergin's garage. The total cost of the conversion was about $1400.

The top speed of the car is 88 km/hr and it has a 64 km range. It is powered by eight golf cart batteries which are recharged in 6 hours from any electrical outlet. A "fill-up" of electricity costs only about 30 cents. The car seats four adults comfortably and can be driven as easily as any small car.

Since the electric car is quiet, clean, and inexpensive to operate, Mr. Wergin and Mr. Yates believe that many people are interested in buying them. Some electric cars are being sold at this time. Mr. Wergin and Mr. Yates also believe that more will be sold due to a shortage of petroleum. It is predicted that by 1985, one-half of the cars on the road will be electrically powered. The car built by these two men certainly shows that this is a real possibility.

••••••••••••••

Courtesy of Mr. Paul Wergin.

Driving an electric car is much like driving any other small car.

Paul Wergin checks the wiring in the electric car as Dave Yates looks on.

Figure 4-11.

Time: 15 minutes.

ACTIVITY Take two spring scales. Fasten them together. One person holds one scale while another person pulls on the other scale. Look at the reading on the scales and see who is pulling harder. This shows Newton's third law. Fasten three scales together in a line. Again, one person holds the scale on one end while another person pulls on the scale on the other end. What is the reading on all three scales?
All three scales have the same reading.

PROBLEMS

13. How are action and reaction forces produced as you press a pencil against a paper while writing? *Pencil pushes on paper; paper pushes against pencil.*

14. How would the motions of a toy balloon and rocket engine be different if there were no gravity? How would these motions be different if there were no air resistance? *See Teacher's Guide.*

15. Which law of motion is illustrated by each of the following examples?
    (a) A person jumps to a dock from a boat. The boat moves away from the dock. *Newton's third law.*
    (b) A galloping horse comes to a sudden stop. Its rider is thrown over the head of the horse and lands on the ground. 1st
    (c) A golf ball can be driven 150 m if hit hard enough. 2nd
    (d) A train stops suddenly; the freight in a boxcar falls over. 1st
    (e) A team in a tug-of-war game pulls the other team with all its strength. The team being pulled harder lets go of the rope. The other team falls backward. *Newton's third law.*

(b) *Newton's first law.*
(c) *Newton's second law.*
(d) *Newton's first law.*

Figure 4-12. Parachutes cause a drag force which prevents acceleration. This causes a body to fall at a constant velocity.

Walt Craig

4:4 Falling Bodies

From a tenth-story window, a bowling ball and a golf ball are dropped. Which ball strikes the ground first? — *Neglecting air resistance, the bowling ball and golf ball will strike the ground at the same time.*

Aristotle (AR uh staht uhl, 384–322 B.C.), a Greek philosopher, stated that when two different bodies are dropped from the same height, the heavier body will strike the ground first. Aristotle's hypothesis claimed that a heavier body (large mass) falls faster than a lighter body (small mass). A *hypothesis* (hy PAHTH uh suhs) is a proposed solution or explanation for a problem. We do not know if Aristotle ever performed an experiment to test his hypothesis.

Aristotle's hypothesis was accepted until the time of Galileo (gal uh LEE oh, 1564–1642), an Italian scientist. Galileo believed

Figure 4-13. Divers, regardless of mass, fall at the same rate.

that all bodies, regardless of mass, fall at the same rate. Galileo performed an experiment to test his hypothesis. Galileo timed the motion of a ball rolling down a smooth groove on an inclined board. The movement of a ball down an inclined board is caused by gravity. Speed of the ball can be measured in the same way as a freely falling body. At equal intervals of time, Galileo marked the distance the ball had traveled.

Time: 60 minutes.

ACTIVITY. How does the speed of a body change as it falls? (1) Motion along an inclined plane is a special case of free-fall. Nail two boards, measuring 15 cm wide and 4-m long, together to form a trough. Paste a 5 cm strip of aluminum foil on one side of the trough. Paste 1-cm square pieces of foil along the opposite side as shown in the diagram. The aluminum squares must be 2.5 cm apart. Connect each foil piece to a long wire connected to a dry cell. Connect the dry cell to a bell and then connect the bell to the aluminum strip. "Liquid" or "cold" solder (SAHD uhr) can be used to attach the wire to the foil. (2) Stand the trough up and tilt at a slight angle. Run a metal ball down the trough. If a metronome is available, use it to time the speed of the ball. Set it for 4 beats/sec. Why does the bell ring more often as the ball goes down the ramp? At what point is the ball's speed greatest? The bell rings often farther down the ramp because it accelerates (its velocity increases) as it goes down the ramp. Velocity is greatest at the end of the ramp.

Figure 4-14.

Figure 4-15. The force of gravity causes the metal ball to accelerate as it rolls. How much farther will the ball travel in the next second if it continues down the ramp?

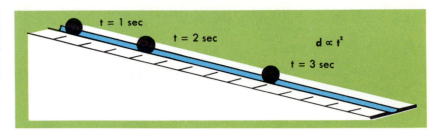

t	t²	d spaces	Final v spaces/sec
1	1	1	2
2	4	4	4
3	9	9	6
4	16	16	8

Galileo's hypothesis was that the distance a ball travels increases with each unit of time. What did he discover in his experiment? The ball moved four times as far the second time interval as it did the first time interval. It moved nine times as far the third time interval. Galileo found that the distance traveled was always proportional to the square of the time elapsed (Figure 4-15). The relationship that Galileo discovered is expressed as

$$d \propto t^2$$

distance object travels varies directly with time

How did Galileo's results compare with yours in the activity above?

Suppose you repeated the above activity with a bowling ball and a golf ball. Would the time intervals differ? No. The distance traveled per second is the same for the bowling ball and the golf ball. Acceleration for both balls is the same.

Yes. Released at the same time both would accelerate at the same rate and have the same velocity because there would be no air resistance.

Define uniform acceleration.

Near the surface of the earth, falling bodies of high density accelerate at a rate of about 9.8 meters/second/second. This means the speed of a falling body increases 9.8 m/sec for each second it falls. If it starts at rest, at the end of one second, it is traveling at 9.8 m/sec. At the end of the next second, its speed is 19.6 m/sec. How fast will it be falling after 3 seconds? Eventually the object will reach a point where it will stop accelerating. This is known as the *terminal velocity*. It is reached when the upward force caused by air resistance is equal to the downward force of gravity. The net force is then zero. The body will keep falling at a constant speed: no acceleration. The value 9.8 m/sec² is usually indicated by *g*. The symbol *g* is the acceleration caused by gravity.

Low density bodies, such as feathers, Ping-Pong balls, and open handkerchiefs, fall more slowly. They encounter more air resistance when they fall. If you measured the fall of feathers, Ping-Pong balls, and handkerchiefs in a vacuum, you would find that they also accelerate at a rate of 9.8 m/sec².

Figure 4-16. Would the illustration be different if the two handkerchiefs were in a vacuum? Why?

To find the velocity of a falling object, use this equation:
$$v = gt$$
velocity = gravitational acceleration (9.8 m/sec²) multiplied by time

Due to air resistance, a parachutist in a free fall may reach a terminal or maximum velocity of about **120 mi/hr** before opening his chute. When the chute is open velocity may be reduced to about **14 mi/hr**.

FALLING BODIES

EXAMPLE

A billiard ball is dropped from the roof of a building. It takes 3 sec to strike the ground. What is the velocity of the billiard ball at the instant it strikes the ground?

Solution: (a) Write the equation: $v = gt$
(b) Substitute 9.8 m/sec² for g and 3 sec for t:
$$v = \frac{9.8 \text{ m}}{\text{sec}^2} \times 3 \text{ sec}$$
(c) Multiply 9.8 m by 3 sec to find v
(d) Answer: $v = 29.4$ m/sec

PROBLEM

16. A rock falls from a cliff and takes 2 sec to reach the ground below. What is the velocity (m/sec) of the rock as it strikes the ground? *19.6 m/sec*

To find the distance that a body travels when it falls from rest, use the equation:
$$d = \tfrac{1}{2} gt^2$$
distance equals ½ (gravitational acceleration × time squared)

No. It would continue to fall back and forth through the tube. When falling toward the center of the earth it would accelerate. After passing the center of the earth it would decelerate until it reached zero velocity at the end of the tube (Earth's surface) and then start falling again back down through the tube.

How can you calculate the velocity of a falling body?

According to legend Galileo (1564-1642) dropped two cannon balls, one ten times heavier than the other, from the leaning tower of Pisa. Both cannon balls were seen to strike the ground simultaneously.

How can you find the distance a body falls from rest during a given time?

Figure 4-17. If a ball were dropped into a tube extending through the center of the earth, would the ball come to rest (a)? Why? When a ball is thrown up into the air, it decelerates due to gravity (b).

Example

A stone falls from the edge of a roof to the ground. If it takes 2 sec for the stone to fall, how high is the building in meters?

Solution: (a) Write the equation: $d = \frac{1}{2} gt^2$
(b) Substitute 9.8 m/sec² for g and 2 sec for t:
$$d = \frac{1}{2} \times \frac{9.8 \text{ m}}{\text{sec}^2} \times (2 \text{ sec})^2$$
(c) Square the 2 sec, multiply by 9.8 m and ½, and divide by sec²
(d) Answer: $d = 19.6$ m

Problems

17. A person drops a rock from the center of a bridge. The rock splashes in the water 3 sec later. How high is the bridge in meters? 44.1 m

18. A ball is thrown straight up into the air. The ball takes 1 sec to fall to the ground from its highest point. How high does the ball go? 4.9 m

4:5 Relative Motion

Suppose you are standing in a moving jet airplane. You jump up two feet off the floor. Will you land in the same spot on the floor when you come down from your jump? Remember, you are moving forward all the time you go up and come down. On a separate sheet of paper, draw the approximate path of your jump.

[You will land in the same spot. You are traveling forward at the same speed as the airplane and you keep moving forward with the airplane while jumping.]

A large stone is dropped from the top of the mast of a moving ship. Does the stone fall to the deck directly below the point from which it was dropped? Or does the stone land in front of or behind the mast? Assume that the mast is perpendicular to the water's surface. Also, remember the ship is moving forward as the stone falls.

Figure 4-18. Both the ship and the stone have the same forward velocity.

RELATIVE MOTION

The falling stone lands on the deck directly below the point from which it was dropped. Before it was released, the stone was moving forward at the same velocity as the moving ship. The stone maintained its forward velocity during its fall. While falling, the stone had two velocities: forward and downward. The forward motion caused it to continue in the same path as the boat during its fall. The stone did not land behind the mast. It fell to a point on the deck directly below the place from which it was dropped.

Time: 15 minutes.

ACTIVITY How does the velocity of a ball change during its flight? (1) Figure 4-19 shows a ball in motion. The ball was thrown into the air at a trajectory (truh JEK tree) or curve of 27°. The time interval between each position of the ball is 1/30 sec. Place a piece of thin centimeter graph paper on top of the drawing. Mark each position of the ball with a dot. (2) Remove the graph paper. Draw straight lines connecting every third position of the ball. The time between three positions of the ball is 0.1 sec, because $3 \times 1/30$ sec = $1/10$ sec = 0.1 sec.

Each straight line (covering three positions of the ball) represents the average velocity during each 0.1 sec of flight. At what point is the velocity greatest? At what point in its flight is the change in velocity greatest? What two forces are acting on the ball?

The path of the ball has two components, horizontal and vertical. To the left of the ruler the components are up and to the right. To the right of the ruler the components are down and to the right. Gravity decelerates the ball as it goes up and accelerates it as it comes down. Velocity is greatest at the beginning of the motion. Change in velocity (deceleration) is greatest in the path to the left of the ruler. Two forces acting on ball: gravity and the throwing force which propelled it forward.

Figure 4-19.

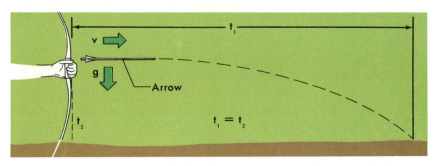

Figure 4-20. Both the released arrow and an arrow dropped from the same height as the bow hit the ground at the same time.

When aiming a bow and arrow at a target, a person should actually aim above the target to compensate for the fall of the arrow.

A bow releases an arrow horizontal to the ground. How long does it take for the arrow to strike the ground? The time depends only on the arrow's downward acceleration caused by gravity. The forward velocity has no effect on the time it takes to fall. Experiments prove this fact. The time it takes for an arrow to strike the ground when it is released from a bow is clocked. Then the time is clocked for an arrow to strike the ground when it is dropped from the bow. The forward velocity has no effect on the downward velocity. The force on the arrow from the bow is horizontal and the force of gravity on the arrow is downward.

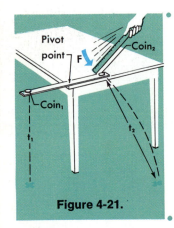

Figure 4-21.

Time: 10 minutes.

ACTIVITY. Nail the center of a 60-cm stick to the corner of an old wooden table. Be certain you have permission to put a nail in the table. The stick should be free to rotate around the nail. Set it so half the stick is over the table and half is over the floor. Place a coin on the end of the stick over the table. Place another coin on the end of the stick over the floor. With a ruler, strike sharply the end of the stick on the table and the coin. Do both coins hit the floor at the same time? How is this activity related to the path of an arrow (Figure 4-20)? The inertia of the coin on the left causes it to fall off the stick when it is struck out from underneath the coin.

What is a parabola?

What is a projectile?

What are the parts of a projectile's motion?

To get a ball over the plate in the strike zone, a pitcher must throw the ball slightly upward rather than horizontally. Instead of traveling a straight path, the ball makes a curved path in its flight from the mound to home plate. This curved path is called a *parabola* (puh RAB uh luh).

Bodies such as stones, balls, or other objects which are thrown or shot are called *projectiles* (pruh JEK tulz). A projectile has two kinds of motion—*horizontal* and *vertical*. The curved line of a parabola shows the result or combination of these two motions. To hit a target, you cannot throw or shoot straight at it. You must

Figure 4-22. Pitchers throw baseballs in a parabola because the ball begins to fall as soon as it is released.

Can a pitcher throw a strike in a straight line? No. The path of a pitched ball is always a parabola because the ball begins falling as soon as it leaves the pitcher's hand. Velocity of a fast ball in the major leagues averages about 100 mi/hr.

Modern highways have curves of large radius. This reduces the amount of centripetal force needed for the car to travel the curve and makes it less likely for the car to go off the outside edge.

allow for the object's downward velocity caused by gravity. The paths of baseballs, footballs, arrows, and all other projectiles are explained by the laws of motion.

4:6 Motion in Curves

What kind of push or pull do you feel in a car when it rounds a sharp curve? Your body may slide sideways. You feel as though you are being pushed outward.

It takes a force to keep a body moving in a curved path. This force is called **centripetal** (sen TRIP uht uhl) **force**. Centripetal force acts toward the center of the curve (Figure 4-24). The centripetal force of the road on a car's tires pushes inward on a car rounding a curve. If the car goes around the curve too fast, inertia may cause it to go off the road. Highways are banked on curves to increase centripetal force. Banked means the outside edge is higher than the inside edge. Banked roads increase highway safety.

Gravity of the sun is the centripetal force which causes planets to travel in orbits around the sun. The earth's gravity is the centripetal force which keeps a satellite in orbit.

Opposite reaction of car to body | Observed motion of body

William Maddox

Figure 4-23. Banked roads help cars go around curves safely.

What forces act on your body as you go around a curve in a car?

Figure 4-24. Inertia causes the passenger to travel in a straight line as the car curves to the left. Centripetal force of the car door is equal and opposite to the **outward force of the girl.**

Figure 4-25.

"Crack the whip" on roller skates or ice skates involves a centripetal force on each skater in the whip. If the end skater is let go when the whip "cracks" inertia causes him to fly off in a straight line.

Time: 5 minutes.

ACTIVITY. Do this activity out-of-doors. Attach a strong string to a ball. Swing the ball in a circle over your head. Do you pull on the string to keep it taut? How does the force on the ball change if you swing it faster or slower? What would happen to the ball if you let go of the string? In which direction would the ball travel?

Centripetal force keeps the ball in the above activity moving in a circle. As Newton's first law predicts, it will fly off in a straight path if you let go of the string.

Time: 30 minutes.

ACTIVITY. Draw a large circle on the floor or pavement with chalk. Place a Ping-Pong ball on the circle. Provide two students with a ruler each. Push the Ping-Pong ball around the circle by using the ends of the rulers. Make a diagram of the circle and ball on a piece of paper. Draw two arrows to show the two directions the ball is pushed to make it go around the circle. Which arrow represents centripetal force on a ball swinging in a circle?

Figure 4-26.

Time: 20 minutes.

ACTIVITY. Centripetal force. (1) Arrange the apparatus shown in Figure 4-26. Hold the tube with one hand and the string with the other. Whirl the stopper over your head. (2) Repeat with 6 washers on the clip, but this time do not hold the string. Whirl the stopper at a rate which keeps the clip in the same position. Have a classmate measure 30 sec with a watch while you count the number of revolutions. Calculate the period of the revolutions. The time divided by the number of revolutions is the period. (3) Repeat the procedure with 3 and 9 washers. Record the periods for 3, 6, and 9 washers.

Draw a graph plotting the periods and the number of washers. How is the period related to the mass of washers on the end of the string? The number of washers on the string is a measure of the centripetal force. How is the centripetal force affected by changes in stopper velocity? The period varies inversely as the mass of the washers. Centripetal force varies directly as the velocity.

Great Adventure Amusement Park a Allan Roberts b

Figure 4-27. Many amusement park rides are exciting because of centrifugal force (a). Blood and other substances can be separated by spinning them in a centrifuge (b).

Centrifugal (sen TRIF ih guhl) **force** refers to the apparent pull away from the center when a body moves in a curve. You have had this experience when rounding a curve on a bicycle or in a car, bus, or train. It provides many of the thrills you get on amusement park rides.

Some automatic washing machines use circular motion. The wet clothes are spun in a circle after washing. Water flies out of the clothes through holes in the tub. The tub pushes the clothes toward the center and keeps them moving in a circle.

A washing machine spinning water out of clothes acts as a centrifuge. A *centrifuge* (SEN truh fyooj) is a machine used to separate substances by spinning them. One kind of centrifuge holds test tubes containing mixtures of liquid and fine solid particles. As the test tubes spin, the solid particles move to the bottom. Centripetal force keeps the liquid and test tube moving in a circle. When whirling a ball around your head on a string, you must pull inward to keep the ball moving. The ball tends to keep moving in a straight line due to inertia. The outward pull you feel on the string is a fictitious or imaginary force sometimes called centrifugal force. Actually, if you were to release the ball, it would travel in a straight line. The inertia of the stone keeps it going in this straight line once the force is not acting on it.

What is the difference between centripetal and centrifugal force?

Centrifugal force is a fictitious or imaginary force used to explain motion along a curve. Centripetal force is a real force which causes bodies to travel in a curved path.

PROBLEMS   See Teacher's Guide.

19. Why might a car slide off an icy road when the car rounds a curve?

20. Hold on to a rubber band tied to a pencil. Whirl the pencil in a circle. Why does the rubber band stretch?

21. How does the banking of a road on a curve affect the centripetal force which acts on a car?

4:7 Momentum

How is momentum related to mass and velocity?

Every body in motion has **momentum** (moh MENT uhm). This is the quantity of motion. The amount of momentum depends on mass and speed. The more mass and speed, the greater the momentum. A baseball has more momentum than a tennis ball when they travel at the same speed. Why? The baseball has more mass. Suppose a truck and a sports car go down a freeway together at 88 km/hr. Which vehicle has more momentum? The truck has more momentum because it has more mass.

Why does a moving truck have more momentum than its driver?

Which has more momentum, a fast-pitched softball or a slow-pitched softball? The fast-pitched softball has more momentum because of its greater speed. An arrow released from a bow has more momentum than a Ping-Pong ball thrown by hand. Very high speed gives the arrow a larger momentum.

The slow pitched ball can be stopped with less force because it has the smaller momentum.

The greater the momentum of a body, the more force it takes to stop it. A body at rest has zero momentum. Doubling the speed of a body doubles its momentum. A 4-ton truck moving 8 km/hr has the same momentum as a 2-ton car moving 16 km/hr. When they are both moving with the same speed, the 4-ton truck has the greater momentum. Why?

A pendulum illustrates the principle of momentum. The larger the mass of the pendulum the greater its momentum.

PROBLEMS

22. Which ball has more momentum at a forward velocity of 5 m/sec, a billiard ball or a tennis ball? Why? *The billiard ball has larger mass.*

23. A golf ball and a tennis ball of the same mass are both traveling at 10 m/sec. Compare the momentum. *The momentums are equal.*

Figure 4-28. Huge waves give a surfer large momentum.

William Huber

Figure 4-29. When two bodies interact, the change in momentum of one body is always equal and opposite to the change in momentum of the other body.

When a rifle is fired, the bullet is pushed out in one direction and the rifle kicks back in the other direction. The momentum of the bullet and rifle are equal and opposite.

If two roller skaters at rest push against each other, they will roll away in opposite directions. The skater with the larger mass will move with less speed than the skater with the smaller mass. However, the momentum for the two skaters will be equal and opposite.

Suppose two moving billiard balls collide. Each billiard ball has momentum before and after the collision, but the total momentum of both balls does not change. The velocities of the balls may change as they hit. If the speed of one increases, the speed of the other must decrease. Momentum is conserved. The total momentum for the

A moving billiard ball which decreases in velocity loses in momentum. A billiard ball which gains velocity also gains momentum.

Collisions between swinging pendulums illustrate conservation of momentum.

Although the pellet has a small mass its high velocity gives it a very large momentum.

The Boeing Company

Figure 4-30. A pea-sized pellet, traveling at a high speed, wrecked these sheets. The pellet punched a neat hole in the first sheet. Metal fragments tore larger holes in the next four sheets.

Explain conservation of momentum.

Momentum may be transferred from one object to another. But total momentum is never increased.

two balls before and after the collision is the same. The total change in momentum as a result of the collision is zero.

Roller skaters and billiard balls are examples of the *law of conservation of momentum*. This principle states that momentum cannot be created nor destroyed. When two bodies interact, one body gains momentum and the other body loses momentum. The total does not change.

MAIN IDEAS

4:1 **1.** Inertia is the tendency of a body at rest to remain at rest. It is also the tendency of a body in motion to remain in motion.

4:1 **2.** It takes a force to start a body moving and a force to stop motion. It also takes a force to *change* the speed or direction of an object.

4:2 **3.** Rate of acceleration and deceleration depends on the amount of force and mass of a body. $F = m \times a$.

4:3 **4.** For every force (action) there is an equal and opposite force (reaction).

4:1, 4:2, 4:3 **5.** Newton's laws explain how forces and motion are related.

4:4 **6.** Bodies near the earth's surface fall at a uniform rate of acceleration, 9.8 m/sec^2.

4:4 **7.** The path of a projectile is curved. The projectile's flight has a horizontal and a vertical motion.

4:5 **8.** Centripetal force acts inward on a body moving in a curve.

4:6 **9.** The apparent outward force on a body moving in a curve is called centrifugal force.

4:6 **10.** Every moving object has momentum which depends on mass and speed. The law of conservation of momentum states that momentum can neither be created nor destroyed.

VOCABULARY

Write a sentence in which you correctly use each of the following words or terms.

acceleration	gravity	parabola
action force	horizontal	projectile
centripetal force	inertia	reaction force
deceleration	momentum	

LAWS OF MOTION   (93M)   93

STUDY QUESTIONS

A. True or False

Determine whether each of the following sentences is true or false. (Do not write in this book.)

Have students rewrite false statements to make the statements correct.

T   **1.** A force is needed to stop a moving body.

T   **2.** Acceleration is always caused by a force.

F   **3.** It takes ~~the same~~ force to accelerate ~~both~~ a golf ball ~~and~~ base- *greater, than a* ball from rest to a speed of 16 m/sec.

T   **4.** Reaction force is equal and opposite to the action force.

F   **5.** ~~Inertia~~ makes a rotary sprinkler spin. *Action-reaction forces*

F   **6.** A hypothesis is always correct. *not*

T   **7.** A falling body accelerates at a rate of 9.8 m/sec^2.

F   **8.** To hit a distant target, a bow is aimed ~~directly at~~ the target. *above*

T   **9.** Centripetal force increases as a merry-go-round increases speed.

T **10.** A baseball gains momentum when hit with a bat.

B. Multiple Choice

Choose one word or phrase that correctly completes each of the following sentences. (Do not write in this book.)

Some questions in Parts B and C may have more than one correct answer. Only one answer is required.

1. Force is measured with a *(scale, meter stick, graduated cylinder)*.

2. It takes *(more, less, the same)* force to accelerate a car as/than it does to keep it at constant velocity.

3. A rocket accelerates because of *(action-reaction, inertia, centripetal)* force.

4. Traveling at 5 km/hr, a *(tennis ball, golf ball, bowling ball)* would have more momentum.

5. The ratio $d \propto t^2$ means that d is *(equal to, greater than, proportional to)* t^2.

6. A hypothesis is a(n) *(fact, law, educated guess)*.

7. When an object falls, its acceleration is *(9.8 m/sec, 9.8 m/sec^2, 32 m/sec)*.

8. A projectile's path is a *(circle, straight line, parabola)*.

9. According to Newton's first law, every object has *(motion, acceleration, inertia)*.

10. The apparent force you feel on many amusement park rides is *(centripetal, centrifugal, action)* force.

C. Completion

Complete each of the following sentences with a word or phrase that will make the sentence correct. (Do not write in this book.)

1. _____ keeps a car moving in a curved path on a highway. *Centripetal force*
2. A(n) _____ is a unit of force. *newton, pound*
3. The attractive force between two bodies is called _____. *gravity*
4. For every action force there is an equal and opposite _____ force. *reaction*
5. A projectile in flight has two motions: horizontal and _____. *vertical*
6. The point in which a falling object stops accelerating is known as _____. *terminal velocity*
7. As a body falls, its downward velocity _____. *increases*
8. As a body falls, its rate of _____ does not change. *acceleration*
9. A body at rest has _____ momentum. *zero*
10. Deceleration is caused by _____. *forces opposing motion*

See Teacher's Guide.

D. How and Why

1. Give examples of inertia. How can inertia cause an accident?
2. Which of Newton's laws of motion applies to each of these cases?
   (a) it takes more push to start a car moving than to keep it rolling *first*
   (b) rocket engine *third*
   (c) drag chute on a racing car *second*
   (d) a classmate dives off a skateboard and each goes in an opposite direction *third*
3. An airplane loses a wheel while in flight. What is the vertical speed of the wheel after it falls for 3 sec? *29.4 m/sec*
4. How can you use a falling stone to judge the height of a bridge?
5. A person throws a ball upward with an initial velocity of 9.8 m/sec. How long does it take for the ball to reach zero velocity? *1 sec*
6. Why is the path of a projectile a parabola?
7. In shooting an arrow, Robin Hood had to aim at a mark above his target. Explain.
8. How is momentum related to the mass and speed of an object? Give examples.
9. How does centripetal force work in a centrifuge?
10. Compare the falling speed of 2 sheets of paper, one crumpled, one not. Is there any difference? Explain.

LAWS OF MOTION

INVESTIGATIONS

See Teacher's Guide at the front of the book for answers and suggestions.

1. Make a model of an airplane. Make a drawing of your model. Label the parts of the airplane that control the speed and direction of the airplane's flight. Explain the forces involved in changing speed and direction.

2. Obtain information on rockets and rocket fuels. Learn how engineers use Newton's laws in designing a rocket and planning a rocket flight to the moon.

3. Head-on crashes are serious problems on many highways. Investigate the use of safety equipment on highways and in cars to reduce the force of these crashes. How do these devices help save lives?

INTERESTING READING

Basford, Leslie, *The Science of Movement: Foundations of Mechanics and Sound*. London, Sampson, Low, Marston & Company, 1966.

Dwiggins, Don, *Robots in the Sky: Explorers of Our Solar System* (Modern Science Series). Chicago, Children's Press, Inc., 1972.

Fermi, Laura, and Bernardini, Gilberto, *Galileo and the Scientific Revolution*. New York, Fawcett World Library, 1965.

Fisher, S. H., *Table Top Science: Physics for Everyone*. Garden City, N.Y., Natural History Press, 1972.

Helman, Hal, *Energy and Inertia*. New York, Lippincott and Co., 1970.

Lewis, Richard S., *The Voyages of Apollo: The Exploration of the Moon*. New York, Quadrangle/The New York Times Co., 1974.

Valens, Evans G., *Motion*. Cleveland, World Publishing Company, 1965.

Unit Two

Properties of Matter

Paul Poplis/Studio Ten

The objectives of this chapter are: to learn some ways in which matter is classified, to study some differences between chemical and physical changes, and to perform some activities to observe chemical and physical changes in matter.

1 Classification of Matter

GOAL: You will gain an understanding of the ways in which matter is classified and the differences between physical and chemical changes.

Scientists study the surrounding world to learn how materials are alike and different. Every material has at least one property that makes it different from any other material. Applying this knowledge leads to improved products. For example, metal is used instead of wood in file cabinets. Why? Glass is used instead of plastic in cookware. Why?

The materials used to make a lock have special properties. What property explains the rust on a lock? Would it have rusted if some other materials were used? These are questions which are answered by studying the properties of matter.

MATTER (3M) 99

1:1 Matter

Matter is anything that has mass and takes up space. Mass is the amount of material a body contains. It can be measured. Can you think of anything that is not matter? Are thoughts and ideas matter? No Is heat matter? Is air matter? Yes
No

> Time: 30 minutes.
>
> ACTIVITY. Obtain a glass milk bottle and a two-hole rubber stopper to fit the neck of the bottle. Insert a funnel into one hole of the stopper. CAUTION: Moisten the stem of the funnel tube with water or mineral oil. Hold it with a rag or towel as you slide it into the stopper. In the same way, insert a 10-cm piece of glass tubing into the other stopper hole. Now fit a 15-cm piece of rubber tubing over the top end of the glass tube. Insert the stopper firmly in the bottle neck. Clamp the rubber tube so no air can escape through it. Pour 10 ml of water into the funnel. What do you observe? Next, unclamp the rubber tube. What happens to the water? Explain what you observe. Some water will run into the bottle as the air compresses. As the tube is unclamped, the water will displace air in the bottle. Since air occupies space, it is matter.

Figure 1-1.

The activity above illustrates that two pieces of matter cannot occupy the same place at the same time. This is a property of matter. When a ship sinks, it displaces enough water to make room for the ship. When a nail is pounded into a board, the nail displaces some of the wood.

Would melting ice in an iced drink make it overflow?

Melting ice in a glassful of liquid does not cause an overflow. Ice displaces about the same volume of water that it will create when melted.

Robert Neulieb

Remind students to weigh all dry materials on a piece of paper. Chemicals and other loose materials should never be weighed directly on a balance.

Figure 1-2. Pan balances are used to measure mass.

Figure 1-3. These early symbols were used by alchemists.

1:2 Elements

Elements 104 and 105 have been produced but they have not been officially named.

Matter is made up of basic substances called elements. An **element** cannot be broken down into simpler substances by ordinary means. Eighty-eight elements have been found naturally on the earth. At least fifteen have been produced in the laboratory. Two common elements in air are oxygen and nitrogen. Carbon, iron, and aluminum are other common elements.

There is a shorthand way to write the names of elements. Circles, dots, and lines were once used as symbols for elements. Today scientists use letters of the alphabet. Table 1–1 gives the names of some of the common elements and the symbols used to represent them.

What other elements can you name?
Many elements could be named; steel is not an element, nor is brass or bronze.

Table 1–1. Some Common Elements

Element	Symbol	Element	Symbol
Aluminum	Al	Mercury	Hg
Carbon	C	Nitrogen	N
Chlorine	Cl	Oxygen	O
Copper	Cu	Silver	Ag
Hydrogen	H	Sodium	Na
Iron	Fe	Sulfur	S
Magnesium	Mg		

PROBLEMS

1. Use Table 1–1 to find the name of each of the following elements: O, C, Mg, Hg, Ag, Na, Cl, Fe.

2. Name the element in Table 1–1 that:
   (a) rusts iron
   (b) is black carbon
   (c) is used in thermometers mercury
   (d) you need to breathe oxygen
   (e) is added to water in swimming pools chlorine

1:3 Compounds

How is a compound different from an element?

Two or more elements can combine chemically to form a **compound.** "Combine chemically" means the elements join together in a way that makes them very difficult to separate.

COMPOUNDS

A compound has an identity all its own. It may be much different from the elements that form it. All samples of a given compound are made of the same elements. For example, sodium chloride (table salt) is a compound. It is always composed of sodium and chlorine. No other elements are included. Carbon dioxide is also a compound. It is always composed of carbon and oxygen.

Elements in a given compound are always combined in the same ratio. The ratio between sodium and chlorine in sodium chloride is always one part sodium to one part chlorine (1:1). The ratio between carbon and oxygen in carbon dioxide is always one part carbon to two parts oxygen (1:2). Water is another example of a compound. Every sample of water contains two parts hydrogen to one part oxygen (2:1).

Formulas are often used to represent compounds. In chemical formulas, symbols show which elements are present. The formula for sodium chloride is NaCl. The formula for carbon dioxide is CO_2. A small number to the right and slightly lower than the symbol is called a subscript. *Subscripts give the ratio in which the elements are combined in the compound.* The subscript 2 in CO_2 means two parts oxygen. Absence of a subscript next to C means one part carbon. A subscript 1 is never used in a chemical formula. The symbol for the element stands for one part. For example, NaCl means a ratio of one part sodium to one part chlorine.

Water has the formula H_2O. The subscript 2 means two parts hydrogen. What does the symbol O mean? *one part oxygen*

HCl (hydrochloric acid)—hydrogen, chlorine; H_2SO_4 (sulfuric acid)—hydrogen, sulfur, oxygen; HNO_3 (nitric acid)—hydrogen, oxygen, nitrogen.

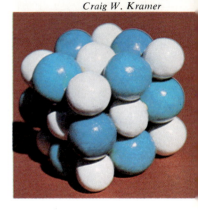

Figure 1-4. Sodium and chlorine always combine in the same ratio (1:1) to form sodium chloride.

What is a subscript?

1. HCl = hydrochloric Acid
2. H_2SO_4 = Sulfuric Acid
3. HNO_3 = Nitric Acid

PROBLEMS

3. NH_3 is the formula for ammonia. What elements does it contain? *nitrogen, hydrogen* What is the ratio between these elements? *1:3*

4. Laughing gas is a compound containing a ratio of two parts nitrogen to one part oxygen. What is its formula? *N_2O*

5. Name the elements in each of the compounds in Table 1-2.

Table 1-2. Some Common Compounds and Their Formulas

Compound		Formula
Cane sugar	carbon, hydrogen, oxygen	$C_{12}H_{22}O_{11}$
Rust	iron, oxygen	Fe_2O_3
Baking soda	sodium, hydrogen, carbon, oxygen	$NaHCO_3$
Hydrogen peroxide	hydrogen, oxygen	H_2O_2

What are some other compounds?

Other compounds include sand (SiO_2), grain (ethyl) alcohol (C_2H_5OH), rubbing (isopropyl) alcohol (C_3H_7OH), and chalk ($CaCO_3$).

William Maddox　　　　*Craig W. Kramer*　　　　*Lorie Hand*

Figure 1-5. Mixtures do not always have the same composition throughout.

1:4 Mixtures

Two or more elements or compounds can be mixed together without combining chemically. Such a combination is called a **mixture**. Each element or compound in a mixture keeps its identity. Mixtures can be separated by physical or mechanical means. For example, a wire screen can be used to separate a mixture of pebbles and sand.

How can mixtures be separated?

A mixture may or may not have the same composition throughout. Air is a mixture of nitrogen, oxygen, and several other gases. However, the composition of air varies from place to place. The exact amounts of nitrogen and oxygen in air can vary. Also, air in a large industrial city may contain smoke and dust particles that would not be found in the air over a mountain lake.

Other examples of mixtures are a cement sidewalk, a glass of iced tea, and a handful of soil. Can you name the parts which make up these mixtures? What other mixtures can you name?

Cement sidewalk: Calcium sulfate ($CaSO_4$), sand (SiO_2), water (H_2O); iced tea: tea, water, ice; soil: sand, clay, rocks, etc.

PROBLEM

6. How could you separate a mixture of iron filings and salt? *use magnet*

Figure 1-6.

Time: 45 minutes.　　　See page 117 (21M).
ACTIVITY. CAUTION: All activities using chemicals should be performed only under the direct supervision of a teacher.

Mix 25 g of sand and 25 g of table salt on a piece of paper. Examine the mixture. How can you separate the two substances? First, add the mixture to 250 ml of hot water. Stir. Pour off the water into a glass funnel fitted with a paper filter. Catch the filtrate in a clean 400-ml beaker. Allow the filtrate to evaporate over a warm hot plate.

Sulfur cannot dissolve in water. How would you separate a mixture of sulfur and sand? *Sulfur and sand can be separated by the use of carbon disulfide (CS_2) or carbon tetrachloride (CCl_4) which dissolve sulfur. Neither experiment should be carried out by the students.*

Time: 20 minutes.

ACTIVITY. CAUTION: Provide adequate ventilation.
Mix 5 g of iodine crystals with 5 g of iron filings in a clean, dry 400-ml beaker. Cover with a large watch glass. Place an ice cube in the watch glass. Heat the beaker with a low flame for a few minutes. What do you observe? Describe another way to separate iodine and iron. Do not allow I_2 vapor to escape into the room. This may be a class demonstration. Purple fumes (I_2 vapor) rise from the mixture and condense in steel gray crystals on the watch glass. I_2-Fe mixture could also be separated by a magnet or by dissolving iodine in alcohol.

Figure 1-7.

Time: 60 minutes.

ACTIVITY. Place 250 ml of a mixture of salt and water in a 400-ml flask. Bend a piece of glass tubing so that one part is 10 cm long and the other part is 30–35 cm long. CAUTION: Insert glass tubing with care. Make sure the ends are rounded and smooth. Moisten the tube with water or mineral oil. Hold it with a rag or towel. Then slide it through the hole in the stopper. Set the stopper tightly in the neck of the flask. Insert the other end of the glass tube into a test tube. Heat the mixture with a Bunsen burner flame and allow it to boil gently for 10 min. CAUTION: Do not let the flask boil dry. How is the water in the test tube different from the water in the flask? The water in the flask is salty; in the test tube, pure.

Use care in inserting tubing. Glass tubing can be bent using a wing tip covered flame, heating thoroughly, and bending quickly against gravity. This is a simple distilling apparatus.

Be sure to emphasize the safety factor of not tasting substances in the laboratory.

To determine how the water is different, have students test (a) the original solution, (b) the distillate, and (c) the solution left in the flask. Each of these three liquids may be carefully evaporated in a watch glass. Salt should appear in (a) the original solution and (c) the flask solution, but not (b) the distillate.

Figure 1-8.

Problem

7. How can the following types of mixtures be separated?
   (a) liquid-liquid mixtures distillation
   (b) solid-liquid mixtures filtration

103   (7M)

Figure 1-9. Each substance has a different density. A material with a low density does not sink as much as one with a high density.

What is density?

1:5 Physical Properties

Suppose you have four test tubes in a rack. Each test tube is filled with a liquid. The liquid in the first test tube is blue. In the second test tube, the liquid has a bad odor. A small steel ball floats on the liquid in the third test tube. When you hold the fourth test tube in your hands, the liquid evaporates rapidly. How can you determine whether any of the liquids is water?

One way to help determine whether a liquid is water is to compare observable features of the liquid with water. Is water normally blue? Does it have a bad odor? Will a steel ball float in it? Does it evaporate rapidly? Such features are called physical properties. A **physical property** depends only upon the substance itself. It may be observed without changing the chemical composition of the substance.

Color, shape, hardness, and density are physical properties. **Density** is the mass of a substance per unit of volume. It may be expressed in grams per cubic centimeter (g/cm^3). For example, water has a density of 1 g/cm^3.

Table 1–3. Densities of Common Substances

Substance	Density (g/cm^3) (at room temperature)
Water	1.0
Sugar	1.6
Table salt	2.2
Aluminum	2.7
Iron	7.9
Copper	8.9
Lead	11.3
Mercury	13.6
Gold	19.3

You have probably heard the old riddle: Which weighs more, a pound of lead or a pound of feathers? Both have the same weight, one pound. However, lead has a greater density. Density is a basic property of a substance. Often a substance can be identified by its density. Steel and polished aluminum may look alike, but they have different densities. You would easily know the difference between a sack of lead and a sack of feathers because of their difference in density. Minerals also have certain densities and are often identified by this property.

Time: 30 minutes.

ACTIVITY. Find the density of a rectangular wooden block. Measure the length, width, and height of the block in centimeters. Calculate the volume of the block by the formula: volume = length × width × height (v = lwh). This gives you the number of cubic centimeters (cm³). Use a balance to find the mass of the block in grams. Calculate the density of the block by the method given below.

Figure 1-10.

To find the density of a substance, you must know its mass and volume. For example, a certain block with a volume of 5 cm³ has a mass of 4 g. Its density is

$$\text{Density} = \frac{\text{mass}}{\text{volume}}$$

$$\text{Density} = \frac{4 \text{ g}}{5 \text{ cm}^3} = 0.8 \text{ g/cm}^3$$

How can you find the density of a stone? It has uneven surfaces so you cannot find its volume by measuring with a ruler. You can find the volume of the stone through an indirect measurement. Tie a string around the stone and lower it into a graduated cylinder containing water (Figure 1–11). Water rises in the graduate as it is displaced by the stone. The amount the water rises is the volume of the stone.

Time: 30 minutes.

ACTIVITY. Find the density of a small stone. First use a balance to find the mass of the stone. Then fill a 25-ml graduate to the 15-ml mark. Tie a string around the stone and lower it into the water until it is completely submerged. Record the increase in water level. This is the volume of the stone. Use the formula to find the density of the stone.

Problems

8. Density determines the use of many materials. Explain how the density of each substance listed affects its uses: aluminum, balsam wood, lead, cast iron, styrofoam. Answers will vary. See Teacher's Guide.

9. Compare the densities of oil and water. See Teacher's Guide.

Figure 1-11.

106 (10M) CLASSIFICATION OF MATTER

Figure 1-12. Pure water boils at 100° Celsius.

What are the boiling and freezing points of water in °C? 100°, 0° respectively

Other physical properties include taste, odor, freezing point, and boiling point. Sometimes odor and taste are also considered to be chemical properties.

The freezing point of a liquid is the temperature at which it changes to a solid. The boiling point is the temperature at which a liquid rapidly changes to a gas. These two temperatures are specific properties of a substance. Unknown liquids are often identified by measuring their freezing and boiling points.

Measurements of freezing point and boiling point as well as other temperatures, are made using the *Celsius* (SEL see uhs) *temperature scale*. Celsius temperature has international use in science and everyday use in many countries. The freezing point of pure water is 0° on the Celsius scale. The boiling point is 100° C. There are 100° (100° − 0°) between the freezing and boiling points on the Celsius scale (Figure 1–12). One Celsius degree is 1/100 of the difference between the freezing and boiling points of water.

Figure 1-13.

This activity will take approximately 45 minutes. If a shorter time is desired, let the ice partially melt before the class period begins.
Freezing should occur in less than 10 minutes.

ACTIVITY. *Freezing point of water*. Fill a 15-ml test tube one-half full of water. Place it in a 500-ml beaker. Fill the beaker with crushed ice. Place a thermometer in the test tube and a thermometer in the ice. Sprinkle 250 g of salt over the ice. Record the temperature of both the water and the salt-ice mixture every minute. Stir the ice gently with a glass stirring rod as it cools the test tube. CAUTION: Do not allow the mercury in a thermometer to fall below the printed scale. Handle thermometers with care!

Graph your data for the changes in temperature in the test tube water and ice-salt mixture. Compare the changes in temperature. Explain any physical changes you observe. Caution students not to drop thermometers. Students should remove the test tube and allow the ice to thaw before removing the thermometer from the test tube.

PROBLEM Answers will vary: color, shape, size, etc.
10. What physical properties could you use to distinguish between the following pairs of materials?
    (a) coal and snow color, melting point, density
    (b) strawberry ice cream and vanilla ice cream color, taste
    (c) soda pop and water density
    (d) lead and aluminum density
    (e) salt and sugar taste
    (f) a baseball and a football shape

Figure 1-14. What physical properties are shown by these balloons?

William Maddox

1:6 *Chemical Properties*

Suppose you have four test tubes. Each contains a liquid. To determine whether any one of the four liquids is water, you can see how each reacts with other substances. Then, compare your observations with the way water reacts. When iron filings are sprinkled into the first test tube, the liquid bubbles and a gas escapes. This gas will burn with a blue flame. When iron filings are sprinkled into the second test tube, another gas is given off. But this time it has an unpleasant odor. What does water do when iron filings are added to it? Try it. Observe any change that takes place. Does either of these two test tubes contain only pure water? Neither is water.

Meanwhile, the liquid in the third test tube has turned black. A small nail in the fourth test tube has taken on a coating of some other metal. Is either of these two liquids pure water? No

You might want to carry out this experiment. In the first test tube use dilute HCl; in the second, concentrated H_2SO_4; $AgNO_3$ solution in the third; $CuSO_4$ in the fourth. The first gas is H_2 and the second is H_2S. Neither test tube contains water. Water does not react with iron filings when they are sprinkled into it. Try it as a control to the first two test tubes. When silver nitrate is exposed to light it turns black (silver is formed). The coating on the nail in the fourth test tube is copper.

Carl England

Figure 1-15. Chemical properties depend upon a substance's reactions with other substances.

108 (12M)   CLASSIFICATION OF MATTER

Name a chemical property of iron.
It rusts (combines with oxygen).

The properties described in these liquids are chemical properties. **Chemical properties** are those that depend upon the material's reaction with other materials. For example, some materials combine with oxygen and burn. Some materials react with other materials to produce gases or metals.

PROBLEMS

11. Name five substances that burn. *Examples: paper, wood, sulfur, manufactured fibers, etc.*

12. Is burning a <u>chemical</u> or physical property? Why? *It depends upon uniting with another substance, usually O_2.*

1:7 Physical Change

When a pane of glass breaks, the size of the glass changes. However, the pieces still contain the same substances in the same ratios as the original pane of glass. When a piece of wood is shaped into a shelf or a chair, it is still wood. Only its size and shape have changed. When an object changes in size, shape, or form, it undergoes a **physical change.** In a physical change, only physical properties are altered.

One of the most common physical changes is a change of phase. Matter may be divided into three states or phases: solid, liquid, and gas. At room temperature and normal atmospheric conditions, all substances have a certain phase. For example, at room temperature and sea level pressure, oxygen is a gas, marble is a solid, and water is a liquid.

What are the three physical phases of water?
ice, liquid water, water vapor

Temperature and pressure can affect the phase of a substance. A substance may change its phase if the temperature or pressure is

Figure 1-16. Physical changes involve changes in size, shape, or form.

Carl England

PEOPLE CAREERS FRONTIERS FOCUS ON PHYSICAL SCIENCE

Industrial Pollutants 'Scrubbed'

Smoke, dust particles, and gases are often given off by smoke stacks of certain industrial furnaces. Many salvage companies produce this type of pollution as a result of melting down scrap metals for recycling. Many of these companies take several precautions to eliminate or reduce pollution.

Many companies have found that dust particles are among the most difficult to remove. For this reason, several efforts were made to find a solution. This resulted in the development of a new method called wet scrubbing. This method removes smoke, dust and gases from the smoke stack.

Gases are first humidified and then passed through the scrubber. The scrubber is a series of trays with holes through which water flows. Water flowing through the trays rapidly cools the hot gases. This rapid cooling releases dust and smoke particles from the gases. Water condenses on the particles making them larger and easier to collect. After this process is completed, the stack only gives off steam and mist. The water used in the process is collected and recycled through the plant.

Courtesy of the Union-Tribune Publishing Co.

An environmental engineer inspects the wet scrubber's operation.

Certification of Appreciation goes to Firestone

An engineer at the plant compares the original waste water (right) with the treated water leaving the pollution control system.

One plant of the Firestone Tire and Rubber Company is located in Louisiana. This plant manufactures many types of rubber. As a result, many different kinds of pollutants are produced by the plant. They are removed from the plant in wastewater. In order to meet federal standards and protect wildlife, Firestone engineers began looking for ways to solve the pollution problem.

The first step was to install underwater screens. These screens were used to collect large pieces of rubber. Chemicals were then added to the water. These chemicals caused small solids to clump together. Using air, these solids were forced to the top of a special chamber and skimmed off. The remaining wastewater was then treated again.

All of these efforts, plus continual checking and sampling, brought the pollutant levels of the water to safe levels. As a result, this plant was given a certificate of appreciation for outstanding work in this field.

Adapted from "Expanded Treatment Cuts Multi-Product Water Pollutants," *ChemEcology,* November, 1975.

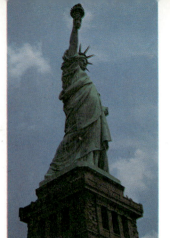

Edward Young

Figure 1-17. Copper undergoes a chemical change when exposed to air.

changed. Water can be changed to ice by lowering the temperature or changed to steam by raising the temperature. Have you ever packed a snowball? The pressure and warmth of your hands caused the snow to melt. The water then refroze to ice when you released the pressure. Because the snow changed only in form, it had undergone a physical change.

1:8 *Chemical Change*

What happens when a piece of wood is burned? Heat, light, and smoke are given off. A small pile of ashes is left. Has the substance been changed? More has occurred than just a change in appearance. The composition of the materials has changed. New substances with different properties appear. When this happens a **chemical change** has occurred. Chemical changes usually involve the release of heat, light, or electricity. A comparison of physical and chemical changes is given in Table 1–4.

How does a chemical change differ from a physical change?

Substances remaining after a chemical change are different from the original substances.

Table 1–4. Physical and Chemical Changes	
Physical Change	**Chemical Change**
Little or no energy lost or gained	Heat, light, or some other form of energy lost or gained
Original substances remain; however, size or form may change	Original substances are changed to other substances
Can be used to separate mixtures	Can be used to decompose or form compounds

Figure 1-18. Chemical changes involve changes in composition.

Diamond International Corp.

Robert Neulieb

Paul Poplis/Studio Ten

CHEMICAL CHANGE

Compounds can be broken down, or decomposed, by chemical change. For example, an electric current can be passed through water. This causes the water to decompose to hydrogen and oxygen. The properties of hydrogen and oxygen are different from the properties of water. Pour a few drops of vinegar on some baking soda. Is this a physical change or a chemical change? Why? *If vinegar (acetic acid, CH_3COOH) is poured on baking soda ($NaHCO_3$) a chemical change takes place. CO_2 is released along with heat.*

Time: 30 minutes.
ACTIVITY. Mix equal parts of powdered sulfur and iron filings on a piece of paper. Wrap a magnet in a plastic bag. Pass it through the mixture several times. What do you observe? How can you separate the two elements without a magnet? CAUTION: Provide adequate ventilation and wear safety glasses. *Dissolve sulfur.*

Mix the sulfur and iron filings again. Fill a Pyrex test tube one-third full of the mixture. Heat with a Bunsen burner until the mixture becomes red hot. Allow the test tube to cool. Wrap it in a towel. Use extreme caution in breaking the glass with a hammer. Pass a magnet over the material left in the test tube. Now can you separate the iron from the sulfur? What change took place? *No, a chemical change has taken place. Iron and sulfur have formed a compound (iron sulfide, FeS).*

Figure 1-19.

Time: 20 minutes.
ACTIVITY. CAUTION: Do this activity under teacher supervision. Wear protective glasses. Always handle acids with care.

Place 3 ml of dilute hydrochloric acid in a test tube. Add a tiny piece of mossy zinc to the acid. Loosely cover the end of the test tube for a few seconds. Then cautiously point the test tube toward a Bunsen burner flame. Did a chemical change take place? *yes* How do you know? *Bubbles of gas appear, test tube warms. Hydrogen gas is produced and burns with a "bark."*

Figure 1-20.

112 (16M)   CLASSIFICATION OF MATTER

PROBLEMS

13. Which of the following is a chemical change?
    (a) piling rocks on top of each other
    (b) burning sulfur
    (c) breaking a window
    (d) baking a cake

14. Which of the following is a physical change?
    (a) opening an envelope
    (b) burning paper
    (c) paneling a room

Figure 1-21.

Direct students to outline their methods of separation and obtain instructor approval before doing this activity.

It might not be necessary to do this activity if previous ones have been done successfully.

Time: 45 minutes.

ACTIVITY. What are some methods of making physical separations? For this activity, you will need the following materials: mixtures of water and sand, sugar and water, salt and sand, salt and iron; test tubes, beakers, funnel, filter paper, magnet, Bunsen burner, ring stand and ring, asbestos pad, watch glass.

How can you separate a mixture of sand and table salt? Would it be possible to pick out all the crystals of salt? [no] Is there some liquid that will dissolve one substance and not the other? Devise a method to separate the salt and sand mixture and the water and sand mixture. Show your teacher the two separated substances from each mixture. [By physical means. water]

How can you separate a mixture of salt and iron filings? Is there something that will dissolve one and not the other? [water] Is there something else that will affect one but not the other? [magnet] Devise a method to separate the mixture of salt and iron filings. Show your teacher the two separated substances.

A sugar solution is a mixture of sugar and water. How can you recover the sugar? [Evaporate the water.] How can you separate the mixture of sand and water? [Evaporate the water or pour it off through a filter.]

PROBLEMS

15. How could you separate the following mixtures?
    (a) sulfur-sand [carbon disulfide]
    (b) iodine-iron filings [heat or magnet]
    (c) salt-iodine [heat or alcohol]
    (d) sand-sugar [water and filter]

16. How could you separate water into hydrogen and oxygen? What kind of change is this? [electrolysis, chemical change]

Time: 30 minutes.

ACTIVITY. Separation of two liquids. For this activity, you will need the following materials: 5% alcohol-water mixture, distilling flask, condenser, rubber tubing, stopper and thermometer, ring stand and ring, asbestos pad, Bunsen burner. CAUTION: Alcohol burns easily. Handle it with care.

Into the distilling flask, pour the alcohol-water mixture. Place the stopper with the thermometer into the neck of the flask and begin heating the flask gently. Record the temperature at which the first drops fall into the beaker. [The first drops should fall in the beaker about 75-80°C.] Continue recording the temperature at one-minute intervals. How will you be able to tell when all the alcohol is gone? [The temperature will rise quickly to 100°C.] Have you separated the two liquids? [Yes.] Where is the water? [In the flask.]

Figure 1-22.

Problems

17. What kind of separation occurred in the above activity? **physical**
18. What is the purpose of the water in the condenser? **Cold water cools the gas to condense it.**

Grumman Allied Industries, Inc.

Figure 1-23. What property of aluminum makes it a suitable material for canoes? **lightweight**

Time: 30 minutes.

ACTIVITY. CAUTION: Use care in handling acid. Pour it under teacher supervision. How can you identify a chemical change?

For this activity, you will need dilute hydrochloric acid, aluminum squares, beakers, watch glasses, ring stand and ring, asbestos pad, and Bunsen burner.

Pour a little of the dilute hydrochloric acid in a watch glass. Evaporate the acid to dryness over a water bath. Describe the result. *Nothing left in the watch glass.*

Observe and record the physical properties of the small square of aluminum. *bright, shiny, metallic, thin sheet*

Place the square of aluminum in a test tube. Add hydrochloric acid slowly. Continue to add acid very slowly until the aluminum has disappeared. Record what you observe. Feel the test tube bottom. *Aluminum dissolves, bubbles of gas formed, test tube becomes warm.*

Pour a little of the liquid from the test tube into a watch glass. Evaporate it to dryness over a water bath. Describe what you observe. *White crystals (AlCl₃) left on watch glass.*

Figure 1-24.

Problems

19. Why do you evaporate the hydrochloric acid in the above activity? *To show that HCl did not leave the crystals.*
20. What chemical changes did you observe in this activity? *Aluminum dissolves in HCl, new compound formed (white crystals), H₂ gas formed, test tube became warm.*
21. What substance is left after you evaporate the test tube solution? *Aluminum chloride (AlCl₃).*

MAIN IDEAS

1:1 **1.** Matter is anything that has mass and takes up space.

1:2 **2.** Elements are basic substances. They cannot be broken down by ordinary means.

1:3 **3.** Two or more elements can combine to form a compound.

1:4 **4.** Mixtures are made of elements or compounds which are not chemically combined.

1:5 **5.** The physical properties of a substance depend only on the substance. Some physical properties are color, melting point, and density.

1:6 **6.** The chemical properties of a substance depend upon its reaction with other substances.

114 (18M)

CLASSIFICATION OF MATTER

1:7 **7.** A physical change does not change the composition of a substance. Only its size, shape, or form changes.

1:8 **8.** A chemical change changes the composition of a substance. New substances with different properties appear.

VOCABULARY

Write a sentence in which you correctly use each of the following words or terms.

1. chemical change
2. chemical formula
3. chemical property
4. compound
5. density
6. element
7. formula
8. gas
9. liquid
10. matter
11. mixture
12. physical change
13. physical property
14. solid
15. subscript

STUDY QUESTIONS

A. True or False

Determine whether each of the following sentences is true or false. (Do not write in this book.)

Have students rewrite false statements to make the statements correct.

T **1.** Water is matter because it has mass and takes up space.

F **2.** Ideas are matter because they have mass. *not, no*

F **3.** Making ice cubes is a ~~chemical~~ change. *physical*

T **4.** Boiling point and freezing point are physical properties of matter.

F **5.** Sodium chloride is ~~an element~~. *a compound*

F **6.** The composition of a mixture ~~never~~ varies.

F **7.** Elements in compounds can be separated by ~~physical~~ means. *chemical*

F **8.** Mixtures can only be separated by ~~chemical~~ means. *physical*

T **9.** Chemical changes produce new substances with new chemical properties.

T **10.** A substance in the solid phase can be changed to the liquid phase.

B. Multiple Choice

Choose one word or phrase that correctly completes each of the following sentences. (Do not write in this book.)

Some questions in Parts B and C may have more than one correct answer. Only one answer is required.

1. Air is a(n) *(element, compound, __mixture__)*.

2. Salt water is a(n) *(__mixture__, compound, element)*.

3. (Breaking, Melting, *Burning*) is an example of a chemical change.
4. (Lemonade, Iced tea, *Water*) is not a mixture.
5. (Density, *Burning*, Color) is not a physical property.
6. Iron usually exists as a (*solid*, liquid, gas).
7. At room temperature, air is usually a (liquid, *gas*, solid).
8. A substance may change its phase if the (size, *temperature*, shape) is changed.
9. (*Rusting*, Freezing point, Boiling point) is a chemical property.
10. Carbon is an example of a(n) (compound, *element*, mixture).

C. Completion

Complete each of the following sentences with a word or phrase that will make the sentence correct. (Do not write in this book.)

mixture 1. Matter which varies in composition is called a(n) _____ .

physical 2. Heating a frying pan is an example of a(n) _____ change.

temperature, pressure 3. Substances can be forced to change their phases through changes in _____ and _____ .

physical 4. Freezing point and boiling point are _____ properties.

chemical 5. Compounds are decomposed by _____ changes.

low 6. Something which evaporates easily usually has a(n) _____ boiling point.

physical 7. Shape is a(n) _____ property.

Density 8. _____ may be measured in grams per cubic centimeter.

chemical 9. Heat and light are often released in a(n) _____ change.

taste 10. The property of _____ should not be tested in a school laboratory.

See Teacher's Guide for 1-6.

D. How and Why

1. What are some chemical and physical properties of water?
2. If a clear liquid turns blue while you are not in the room, has a chemical change taken place? Explain your answer.
3. What properties would help you describe an apple?
4. What kinds of properties are in your answer to Question 3?
5. How could you prove that helium has mass?
6. What are the basic differences between mixtures and compounds?

CLASSIFICATION OF MATTER (21M) 117

7. Name three common mixtures. Name three common compounds. *mixture—lemonade, concrete, soil, air, etc.*
compounds—water, sugar, ammonia, salt
8. What properties would a manufacturer look for in a material suitable for auto seat covers? *strength, resilience, color, wearability*
9. How could you find out if a liquid is pure water or salt water without tasting it? *Evaporate a small amount to determine whether there is a crystalline residue.*
10. How could two liquids be separated using a distilling flask? *See Activity on page 113 (17M).*

INVESTIGATIONS

See Teacher's material at front of book for suggestions.

1. Obtain various samples of wood and/or metal. Devise tests to compare the physical properties of the samples.
2. Obtain information on the use of ethylene glycol and alcohol as an antifreeze. Make graphs showing the amount needed to prevent freezing at different temperatures.
3. Determine the boiling points of vegetable oil and of salt water.
4. Visit a materials testing laboratory. Learn what a Brinell test is. Find out how it is used in the laboratory.

INTERESTING READING

"Fingerprinting Marble." *Science Digest,* LXXII (December, 1972), pp. 30–31.

Jaffe, Bernard, *Chemistry Creates a New World,* New York, Thomas Y. Crowell Company, 1957.

Kelman, Peter, and Stone, A. Harris, *Mendeleyev: Prophet of Chemical Order.* New York, Prentice-Hall, 1969.

Kendall, James, *Great Discoveries by Young Chemists.* New York, Thomas Y. Crowell Company, 1954.

Lapp, Ralph E., *Matter.* Time-Life Books, New York, Time Inc., 1969.

Pringle, Laurence, *Recycling Resources.* New York, Macmillan Publishing Co., Inc., 1974.

Vaczek, Louis, *The Enjoyment of Chemistry.* New York, Viking Press, Inc., 1965.

For page 102 (6M): Observe caution! Make a filter to fit the funnel by folding the filter paper in half and then in quarters. Pull one side out to make the cone. Two substances in a mixture can be separated physically if a solvent for only one can be found. If the substance can then be separated from the solvent by evaporation or some similar means, the substances are separated. In this case salt dissolves in water and passes through the filter. If the filtrate is allowed to evaporate, salt crystals appear.

These three uranium salts have different atomic composition, therefore, different appearances.

U.S. Energy Research and Development Administration

Chapter 2 introduces the atomic theory of matter and discusses the concept of a model to represent an atom which cannot be observed directly. The importance of the electron in chemical bonds, both ionic and covalent, is stressed.

2 Atoms and Compounds

GOAL: You will gain an understanding of the nature of ionic and covalent bonds in terms of the atomic theory and electron structure.

An atom of one element is different from an atom of any other element. This is explained by differences in structure. These differences also explain why atoms combine in certain ways. Compounds resulting from the combination of certain atoms will have certain features.

The three compounds shown in the photograph have something in common. They all contain atoms of uranium. They are all uranium salts. However, there are differences in color. What is the explanation for these color differences?

ATOMIC STRUCTURE (23M) 119

2:1 Atomic Theory

Suppose you could divide an element into two pieces. Then you continued to divide each piece into smaller and smaller pieces. Finally, you would not be able to divide a piece and still have pieces of the same element. The smallest piece of an element which still has the properties of that element is called an **atom.** All elements are composed of atoms.

The idea of atoms has been around since ancient Greek civilization. John Dalton (1766–1844), an English chemist, proposed an atomic theory. Dalton's atomic theory states that all matter is made of small particles called atoms. Dalton also believed that all atoms of the same element were exactly the same. Later experiments have supported some of Dalton's ideas. However, some of his views have been proven incorrect.

What is Dalton's atomic theory?

2:2 Subatomic Particles

Dalton correctly believed that all matter is made of atoms. He wrongly assumed that atoms cannot be divided. Scientists have found more than one hundred smaller, or *subatomic,* particles. Chemists are usually concerned with only three of these particles: electron (ih LEK trahn), proton (PROH tahn), and neutron (NOO trahn).

An **electron** has a negative charge. Its mass is very small. If 1×10^{29} electrons (1 followed by 29 zeros) were put together they would have a total mass of only about one gram. One electron has a radius so small that 25×10^{11} (25 followed by 11 zeros) electrons could fit on a one-centimeter line. There is some disagreement about whether the electron is a wave, a particle, or both. For our purposes, it will be considered a particle.

A **proton** has a mass more than 1800 times larger than an electron. Yet the proton is still very small. More than 6×10^{23} protons (6 followed by 23 zeros) have a mass of only about one gram. The positive charge on a proton is the same size as the negative charge on an electron. A proton has a slightly smaller radius than the electron.

A **neutron** has a slightly larger mass than a proton. As its name suggests, the neutron is neutral. It carries no charge.

What are the three subatomic particles of interest to chemists?

Scientific notation might be a new concept to some students. Explain that it is a method of writing numerals for large or small numbers using exponents, or powers of 10. A numeral is written as a number between 1 and 10 multiplied by a power of 10. Use some examples written out. For example: $2 \times 10^5 = 200{,}000$; $2 \times 10^{-5} = 0.00002$

2:3 Atomic Structure

Scientists often use models to help explain a scientific idea. A model is simply a way of looking at an idea in order to make it more understandable. Many people make model airplanes or ships. Often

Figure 2-1. Models show certain properties of the original objects they represent.

How does the electron cloud model differ from the Bohr model?

Figure 2-2. Electron cloud models show a cloud of rapidly moving electrons (a). An early atomic model showed the electrons embedded in the nucleus (b). A later concept, the Bohr model, was patterned after the solar system (c).

social studies classes will make models of frontier villages or old castles. Architects and engineers make models of homes or bridges they plan to build. In each case new ideas may cause the model to be changed. The model is never exactly the same as what it represents. It may be smaller or larger. Often it is made from different materials. A model shows certain properties of the original as accurately as possible based on known facts and ideas.

One early model of the atom showed electrons lying in a ball of positively-charged material. This model is similar to a snowball with pebbles in it. Later experiments led to the **Bohr model,** named after the Danish scientist Niels Bohr (1885–1962). In this model, an atom is similar to our solar system. The protons and neutrons form a central core or nucleus (NOO klee uhs). The electrons revolve around this nucleus in certain paths called orbits.

Again, more experiments with better equipment have led to a new atomic model, the **electron cloud model.** In this model the nucleus also contains protons and neutrons. The electron moves so fast that it would probably not look like a small particle moving in a path. Rather, it would look like a cloud that is formed by the electron's

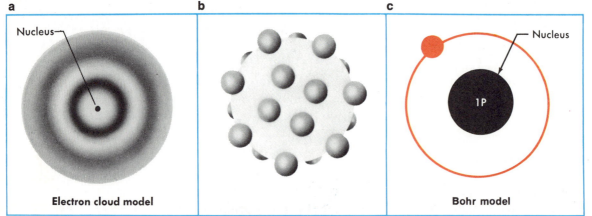

ELECTRON LOCATION

rapid motion. This cloud is something like fan blades at high speed. The whirling blades of the fan look like a cloud, not like single blades moving in a certain path. As electrons move, they appear to form a cloud of negative electricity around the nucleus. The nucleus of an atom is dense, tiny, and positively charged.

Unlike the paths of planets in our solar system, electron paths are constantly changing. For this reason, the electron cloud model is based upon the probable paths of electrons.

All atoms of the same element have the same number of protons. For example, any hydrogen atom has one proton in its nucleus. Any carbon atom has six protons in its nucleus. However, some atoms of an element may have more neutrons than other atoms of the same element. **Atoms of the same element with different numbers of neutrons are called isotopes** (I suh tohps). For example, hydrogen has three isotopes. A hydrogen atom may contain no neutrons. Another hydrogen atom may contain one neutron. Still another may contain two neutrons. The number of protons in the nucleus of an atom determines the element. The number of neutrons determines the isotope of the element. Every element has at least two isotopes.

PROBLEM

1. How does the number of neutrons in an atom affect the mass of an element? *See Teacher's Guide.*

Figure 2-3. Electrons moving around the nucleus may look like fast moving fan blades.

What are isotopes?

Figure 2-4. Deuterium is an isotope of hydrogen which has one neutron and one proton.

Table 2–1. Atomic Particles of Some Elements

Element	Nucleus Proton (+)	Neutron	Electron (−)
Hydrogen (H)	1	0	1
Helium (He)	2	2	2
Lithium (Li)	3	4	3
Beryllium (Be)	4	5	4
Boron (B)	5	6	5
Carbon (C)	6	6	6
Nitrogen (N)	7	7	7
Oxygen (O)	8	8	8
Fluorine (F)	9	10	9
Neon (Ne)	10	10	10

2:4 Electron Location

An atom is electrically neutral because the number of electrons in an atom equals the number of protons. The positive charge of the

Why are atoms neutral?

Figure 2-5. Electrons are found in certain energy levels.

In each shell there are one or more electron paths called orbitals. Each orbital can contain no more than two electrons (one pair of electrons). The orbitals are shaped like dumbbells or concentric spheres.

Why is the number of electrons in the outermost shell important?

protons balances the negative charge of the electrons. For each proton in the nucleus, one electron is in orbit around the nucleus.

Electrons circle the nucleus in certain **energy levels,** or **shells.** Only two electrons can orbit the nucleus in the first shell. The first shell is the energy level closest to the nucleus. The second shell of an atom can hold up to eight electrons. The third shell can hold up to 18 electrons. Higher shells sometimes hold as many as 32 electrons.

Electrons tend to fill the energy levels closest to the nucleus. A magnesium (Mg) atom contains 12 protons, 12 electrons, and 12 neutrons. In the nucleus of the atom are 24 particles—12 protons and 12 neutrons. The 12 electrons are arranged in pairs within the shells. The first shell has one pair of electrons. The second shell has four pairs of electrons. The two remaining electrons of the magnesium atom are in a third shell.

Some atoms have more than three occupied energy levels. Lawrencium (lah REN see uhm) (Lw), an element with 103 electrons, has seven shells containing electrons. Other elements may have electrons in fewer than three shells. Each hydrogen (H) atom contains only one electron. How many occupied shells does hydrogen have?

Electrons in the outer energy level have the most effect on an element's chemical properties. These electrons are most commonly involved in chemical change. They also determine some physical properties. For these reasons, the number of electrons in the outermost shell of an atom is very important.

> Time: 20 minutes.
> ACTIVITY. Draw diagrams showing the Bohr model structure of oxygen, nitrogen, and fluorine. Use the information given in Tables 2–1 and 2–2.

Table 2–2. Electrons in Shells

Shell	Total Electrons Possible	Cumulative Number of Electrons
1	2	2
2	8	10
3	18	28
4	32	60
5	32	92
6	10	102
7	2	104

2:5 Molecules

An atom is the smallest particle of an element. It is the smallest part of an element that can take part in a chemical change.

When atoms combine chemically, they form **molecules.** There can be molecules of elements and of compounds. A molecule of an element always contains two or more atoms of the same kind. A molecule of a compound always contains two or more atoms of different elements. If a molecule is subdivided, it is decomposed into the atoms which make it up. Figure 2–6 shows how atoms may combine to form molecules.

What is the difference between an atom and a molecule?

The atom is the smallest particle that can exist as an element; a molecule is a group of two or more atoms.

Figure 2-6. If each of these molecules were decomposed, atoms of what elements would result?

- -

Time: 25 minutes.
ACTIVITY. Models of molecules may be made with candy gumdrops and toothpicks. Different colored gumdrops represent different kinds of atoms. Obtain some gumdrops and toothpicks and make models of the molecules shown in Figure 2–6. Are your models exactly like real molecules? Explain. *No. The angles are probably incorrect since it is difficult to maintain 109° throughout. Also, the sizes of the atoms are probably proportionally inaccurate.*

Carbon dioxide has the chemical formula CO_2. This formula shows that each molecule of CO_2 contains one carbon atom (C) and two oxygen atoms (O_2). The symbol for an element stands for one atom of the element. A number to the lower right of the symbol is called a subscript. A subscript indicates the number of atoms when the number is more than one.

A chemical formula may also be used to represent two or more atoms of the same element combined chemically. For example, oxygen atoms in air are usually combined in pairs. Thus, the formula for free oxygen is O_2. This represents one molecule of oxygen.

What does S_8 represent?

S_8 means a molecule of sulfur composed of eight sulfur atoms.

Lorie Hand

Figure 2-7. Sodium bicarbonate (NaHCO₃) and ammonia (NH₃) are common compounds used in the home.

Sodium bicarbonate, a household chemical, has the formula NaHCO₃. This formula shows that each molecule of sodium bicarbonate contains one sodium atom (Na), one hydrogen atom (H), one carbon atom (C), and three oxygen atoms (O₃). Aluminum sulfide has the formula Al₂S₃. Each molecule of aluminum sulfide contains two aluminum atoms (Al₂) and three sulfur atoms (S₃).

Problems

2. Assume that each of the following formulas represents one molecule of a substance. What kinds of atoms and how many of each are represented?
   (a) HCl *1 hydrogen, 1 chlorine*   (e) F₂ *2 fluorine*
   (b) Na₂O *2 sodium, 1 oxygen*   (f) Fe₂S₃ *2 iron, 3 sulfur*
   (c) KOH *1 potassium, 1 oxygen, 1 hydrogen* (g) Br₂ *2 bromine*
   (d) H₂SO₄ *2 hydrogen, 1 sulfur, 4 oxygen*   (h) NH₃ *1 nitrogen, 3 hydrogen*

3. Which of the formulas in Problem 2 represent compounds? What do the other formulas represent? *compounds—a, b, c, d, f, h; elements—e, g*

4. How are symbols and subscripts used to write a chemical formula? *Symbols indicate the kind of atoms in a substance; subscripts indicate the ratio of the atoms.*

2:6 Bonding

Elements combine in the simplest possible ratios. For example, two elements, X and Y, might combine as XY, then XY₂, X₂Y, XY₃, and so on. Scientists now believe that most atoms combine in ways that enable them to complete an outer shell. This arrangement appears to be the most stable form of the atom. A compound is formed by the gain, loss, or sharing of electrons.

Complete 8.

Figure 2-8. Sodium and chlorine atoms are neutral. The number of electrons equals the number of protons in each atom.

Sodium atom   Chlorine atom

Figure 2-9. Hydrogen and chlorine share electrons to form a compound by covalent bonding (a). Sodium transfers an electron to chlorine to form a compound by ionic bonding (b).

When two or more atoms form a compound, they become bonded together. For example, a sodium atom has 11 electrons arranged in shells as in Figure 2–8. Since it also has 11 protons, it is electrically neutral. A chlorine atom has 17 electrons arranged as shown in Figure 2–8. It, too, is neutral, since the number of protons in the nucleus is 17. Suppose a sodium atom and a chlorine atom come close together. The electron in the outer shell of the sodium atom may transfer to the outer shell of the chlorine atom. The outer energy level of each atom is now full. The sodium atom loses an electron and becomes positively charged. The chlorine atom gains an electron and becomes negatively charged. The two atoms now have opposite charges. They are attracted to each other and bond together to form a compound. In the new compound, the number of electrons and protons is equal. Thus, the compound is neutral.

When an atom loses or gains an electron, the atom becomes a charged particle called an **ion**. Therefore, the type of bonding in which electrons are transferred is called **ionic** (i AHN ik) **bonding**. The positive sodium ion is shown as Na^+. The negative chloride ion is shown as Cl^-.

In another type of bonding, electrons are shared by atoms in the molecule. This is called **covalent** (koh VAY luhnt) **bonding**. Hydrogen has one electron and one proton. Figure 2–9a shows how chlorine and hydrogen share electrons. Both fill their outer energy levels. Hydrogen now has two electrons in its shell which completes the first energy level. Chlorine now has eight electrons in its third shell. This completes the third energy level.

When compounds are formed, the outer electrons of the atoms are rearranged. This changing of outer electrons results in new properties. Thus, the compound will have different properties than those of the elements that make up the compound.

PROBLEM

5. How are the properties of NaCl different from Na and Cl?

How do sodium and chlorine form an ionic bond?

Why is a compound neutral?

See Teacher's Guide at the front of this book.

2:7 Valence

What is valence?

Valence is the name given to the combining ability of an atom. Valance indicates the number of electrons an atom gains, loses, or shares in forming a compound. Sodium can lose one electron so it has a 1+ valence. Chlorine can gain one electron so it has a 1− valence.

Figure 2-10. Atoms which lose electrons have positive valences. Atoms which gain electrons have negative valences. One lithium atom combines with one fluorine atom because of valence (a). One magnesium atom combines with two chlorine atoms because of valence (b).

The net valence for a compound is zero. Therefore, when sodium (1+) and chlorine (1−) combine, one atom of sodium bonds with one atom of chlorine. Thus, the formula is NaCl.

Hydrogen has a valence of 1+. One atom of hydrogen (1+) bonds with one atom of chlorine (1−) to form HCl. Magnesium has a valence of 2+. One atom of magnesium (2+) combines with two atoms of chlorine since each chlorine atom has a 1− valence. Thus, the formula for the compound is $MgCl_2$.

PROBLEM

6. Hydrogen has a valence of 1+ and oxygen has a valence of 2−. What is the formula for a compound formed by H and O? H_2O

Some elements have more than one valence. For example, carbon has valences of 2+ and 4+. Thus, carbon forms two compounds with oxygen: CO and CO_2. In CO, there is one atom of carbon (2+) and one atom of oxygen (2−). In CO_2, there is one atom of carbon (4+) and two atoms of oxygen. Each oxygen atom in CO_2 has a 2− valence, totaling 4−. Iron can have 2+ or 3+ valences. If more than one valence is possible, the valence intended is written in parentheses after the element's name. For example, iron (II) always has the valence 2+; iron (III) always has the valence 3+. Valences of some common elements are listed in Table 2–3.

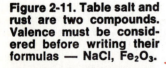

Figure 2-11. Table salt and rust are two compounds. Valence must be considered before writing their formulas — NaCl, Fe_2O_3.

Robert Neulieb

Table 2–3. Valences of Some Common Elements

1+	2+	3+	1−	2−
Silver, Ag^+	Iron (II), Fe^{2+}	Iron (III), Fe^{3+}	Chlorine, Cl^-	Sulfur, S^{2-}
Sodium, Na^+	Calcium, Ca^{2+}	Aluminum, Al^{3+}	Iodine, I^-	Oxygen, O^{2-}
Potassium, K^+	Barium, Ba^{2+}		Bromine, Br^-	
Hydrogen, H^+	Copper (II), Cu^{2+}		Fluorine, F^-	
Lithium, Li^+	Magnesium, Mg^{2+}			
Copper (I), Cu^+				

What elements in the list have two valences?
copper, iron

EXAMPLE

Find the formula for a compound of silver and sulfur.

Solution: Silver has a valence of 1+, and sulfur, in this case, has a valence of 2−. Thus, two atoms of silver are needed to combine with one atom of sulfur. The formula for this compound is written **Ag_2S**. (Note: The symbol of the element with the positive valence is always written first.)

You may wish to teach a simple method for writing formulas.
1. Write each symbol—Al O.
2. Write valence above each symbol—$\overset{+3}{Al}\ \overset{-2}{O}$.
3. Delete + and −, then crisscross valences to make subscripts.
$\overset{+3}{Al_2}\diagdown\overset{-2}{O_3}$
Remind students that a subscript is never written. Absence of a subscript means 1.

PROBLEM

7. Write formulas for the following combinations of elements:
(a) sodium and bromine NaBr
(b) potassium and iodine KI
(c) hydrogen and bromine HBr
(d) hydrogen and sulfur H_2S
(e) magnesium and fluorine MgF_2
(f) calcium and chlorine $CaCl_2$
(g) lithium and sulfur Li_2S
(h) aluminum and chlorine $AlCl_3$
(i) copper (II) and sulfur CuS

Figure 2-12. When copper (II) combines with sulfur, copper (II) sulfide is formed.

Craig W. Kramer

2:8 Binary Compounds

What are binary compounds?

All of the compounds in the preceding problem are binary compounds. **Binary (BY nuh ree) means composed of only two elements.** To name binary compounds, the element with the positive valence is mentioned first. Then the element with the negative valence is given, using the ending -ide. Thus, $MgCl_2$ is magnesium chloride. HCl is hydrogen chloride. $FeCl_2$ is iron (II) chloride, read as "iron two chloride." CuF is copper (I) fluoride, read as "copper one fluoride."

EXAMPLE

What is the name of FeS?

Solution: Iron can have a valence of either $2+$ or $3+$. In most binary compounds, sulfur has a valence of $2-$. Only one atom of iron and one atom of sulfur are indicated in this molecular formula. The valences must be equal and opposite. Thus, the iron is iron (II). The name of the compound is iron (II) sulfide.

PROBLEMS

8. Name each of the following compounds:
   (a) NaCl sodium chloride
   (b) CuBr copper (I) bromide
   (c) BaS barium sulfide
   (d) MgO magnesium oxide
   (e) KI potassium iodide
   (f) $MgBr_2$ magnesium bromide
   (g) CaS calcium sulfide
   (h) CuO copper (II) oxide
   (i) $FeCl_3$ iron (III) chloride
   (j) FeO iron (II) oxide

9. Write formulas for each of the following compounds:
   (a) calcium bromide $CaBr_2$
   (b) potassium oxide K_2O
   (c) aluminum chloride $AlCl_3$
   (d) iron (III) iodide FeI_3
   (e) copper (I) sulfide Cu_2S
   (f) lithium fluoride LiF
   (g) sodium bromide NaBr
   (h) copper (II) chloride $CuCl_2$

FDA Consumer

Figure 2-13. Chemist, Sylvia Gonzalez, uses complex equipment to test for the presence of certain compounds.

PEOPLE CAREERS FRONTIERS
FOCUS ON PHYSICAL SCIENCE

Chemical Engineer

Many industries employ chemical engineers. A chemical engineer is often involved in the development of a new product. He or she applies laboratory discoveries usually made by other people. Many are involved in the overall operation of a laboratory or industrial plant. They make inspections and solve problems as they arise. Equipment is often improved with their help.

A high school diploma with a strong background in science is encouraged for a person desiring to become a chemical engineer. Additional training needed for this career includes a bachelor's degree in chemical engineering.

•••••••••••••

Adapted from *Your Tomorrow — A Guide to Careers in the Chemical Industry*.

Roberta Sahlin is a chemical engineer working in the product development department of her company.

Other Chemistry Careers

There are many career opportunities in chemistry. Most of them require some training after high school. Some require training for one or two years. Others require advanced degrees in college.

Teaching is one type of career in chemistry. Chemistry teachers may be found in high schools, junior colleges, small colleges, and large universities. A strong background in chemistry is needed at all of these levels. Advanced college degrees are needed for those teaching at the college level.

Research is another area in which chemists work. They are employed by industry, governments, hospitals, and other institutions. Their work is varied. Some chemists may develop new materials; others

Research chemists discover or develop new products in chemical industries.

may experiment with existing products. Research chemists usually have several degrees in chemistry. A master's degree and/or a doctorate degree is often desired.

Chemists are needed in many other areas as well. Many companies employ chemists in sales departments. A chemist employed in sales would have to enjoy working with people. A degree in business, as well as a degree in chemistry, is encouraged for such a position.

Chemists with the ability to write well, are often employed by industries and publishers. Chemistry journals, magazines, pamphlets, and books are just a few publications in which a chemist could be involved.

A chemist working for the National Bureau of Standards may check standard chemicals.

2:9 Polyatomic Ions

What is a polyatomic ion?

Not all compounds are binary compounds. Often, compounds contain more than two elements. Two or more elements sometimes combine to form a polyatomic (pahl ee uh TAHM ik) ion. A **polyatomic ion** is a group of atoms which act together as one ion or charged atom. Table 2-4 lists some common polyatomic ions and their valences.

Table 2-4. Some Common Polyatomic Ions and Their Valences

Name	Valence	Representation
Ammonium	1+	NH_4^+
Chlorate	1−	ClO_3^-
Nitrate	1−	NO_3^-
Carbonate	2−	CO_3^{2-}
Sulfate	2−	SO_4^{2-}
Phosphate	3−	PO_4^{3-}

How many oxygen atoms are there in a sulfate ion?
Four oxygen atoms in a sulfate ion.

Compounds which contain polyatomic ions are named in much the same way as binary compounds. The positive part of the compound is given first, followed by the name of the negative polyatomic ion or negative valence ion. For example, the compound formed by sodium and the sulfate ion has the formula Na_2SO_4. It is called sodium sulfate. The compound formed by the ammonium ion and sulfur is $(NH_4)_2S$. Its name is ammonium sulfide. Parentheses and the subscript 2 indicate that two ammonium ions balance the valence of sulfur.

Figure 2-14. Tin oxide (TiO_2) is a binary compound. What makes it different from a polyatomic ion? Two elements form a compound, not ions.

William Maddox

EXAMPLE

What kinds of atoms and how many of each are in one molecule of barium nitrate?

Solution: First a formula for barium (Ba^{2+}) nitrate (NO_3^-) must be found. Based on valences, this formula would be $Ba(NO_3)_2$. One barium atom is in a molecule of this compound. Each nitrate ion has one nitrogen atom and three oxygen atoms. The subscript applies to the whole nitrate ion. Two nitrogen atoms and six oxygen atoms must be in one molecule of barium nitrate.

Figure 2-15. Two ammonium ions combine with one atom of sulfur to form ammonium sulfide.

Problems

10. Write a formula for each of the following compounds:
    (a) sodium nitrate NaNO₃
    (b) silver sulfate Ag₂SO₄
    (c) iron (II) chloride FeCl₂
    (d) potassium phosphate K₃PO₄
    (e) copper (II) iodide CuI₂

11. Name the following compounds: See Teacher's Guide.
    (a) Na₂SO₄
    (b) (NH₄)₃PO₄
    (c) FeO
    (d) AgNO₃
    (e) KBr

12. What kinds of atoms and how many of each are present in the compounds listed in Problems 10 and 11? See Teacher's Guide.

Use extreme care in performing this experiment. Use U.S.P. KClO₃. The test tube may be clamped to a ring stand for the ten minute heating.

Time: 45 minutes.
    DEMONSTRATION.   CAUTION: This experiment is to be done by the teacher wearing eye protection.
    Find the percent of oxygen in potassium chlorate. Find the mass of a clean, dry test tube and add 3 g of powdered potassium chlorate to the tube. Hold the tube with a test tube clamp. Heat the lower end of the test tube with a low Bunsen burner flame for 5 min. Gradually make the flame stronger, until it reaches its hottest point. Heat for 10 min. Allow the test tube to cool. Find its mass again. To find the percent of oxygen compute the mass of oxygen lost. Divide by the original mass of the potassium chlorate. Multiply by 100.
The mass of the oxygen lost equals the mass of the test tube and potassium chlorate minus the mass of the test tube and contents after heating and cooling.

$$\% \text{ O}_2 = \frac{\text{O}_2 \text{ lost}}{\text{KClO}_3 - 3 \text{ g}}$$

Figure 2-16.

Help the students devise a chart for data. A possible chart is given in the Teacher's Guide at the front of this book. Be sure to demonstrate to the students the calculation of finding the percentage of composition. Students will be confused if they do not understand this thoroughly.

MAIN IDEAS

2:1 1. All elements are made of atoms.
2:2 2. Three major subatomic particles are the proton, neutron, and electron.

2:3 3. The present "model" of the atom is a nucleus containing the protons and neutrons. An "electron cloud" surrounds the nucleus.

2:3 4. Isotopes are atoms with the same number of protons but different numbers of neutrons.

2:4 5. Electrons are arranged in shells surrounding the nucleus.

2:5 6. Atoms combine chemically to form molecules.

2:6 7. In ionic bonding, electrons are gained or lost. In covalent bonding, electrons are shared.

2:7 8. The combining ability of an atom or group of atoms is called "valence."

2:8 9. Binary compounds are composed of two elements.

2:9 10. Some compounds contain polyatomic ions. A polyatomic ion is a group of atoms which act together as one ion.

VOCABULARY

Write a sentence in which you correctly use each of the following words or terms.

1. atom
2. atomic shell
3. binary compound
4. covalent bond
5. electron
6. electron cloud
7. ion
8. ionic bond
9. isotope
10. model
11. molecule
12. neutron
13. polyatomic ion
14. proton
15. valence

STUDY QUESTIONS

A. True or False

Determine whether each of the following sentences is true or false. (Do not write in this book.)

T 1. Models are sometimes used to explain theories.

T 2. Molecules are formed when atoms form covalent bonds.

T 3. Electrons have a negative electric charge.

F 4. The mass of an electron is greater than the mass of a proton.

T 5. All atoms of the same element contain the same number of protons.

T 6. Atoms of the same element may contain different numbers of neutrons.

F 7. All atoms of the same element have the same mass.

ATOMS AND COMPOUNDS (37M) 133

T 8. The positive charge of the protons in an atom is equal to the negative charge of the electrons.
F 9. Electrons in the outer shell of an atom have ~~little~~ effect upon its chemical properties. *great*
T 10. The valence of an element tells the number of electrons which may be lost, gained, or shared by its atoms.

B. Multiple Choice

Choose one word or phrase that correctly completes each of the following sentences. (Do not write in this book.)

Some questions in Parts B and C may have more than one correct answer. Only one answer is required.

1. Modern atomic theory is based on the work of *(Galileo, Aristotle, Dalton)*.
2. A(n) *(molecule, atom, proton)* is the smallest particle of a compound.
3. The compound $Mg(NO_3)_2$ contains *(mercury, neon, oxygen)*.
4. A molecule is *(positive, negative, neutral)*.
5. The compound iron (II) sulfide has the formula *(FeS, Fe_2S, FeS_2)*.
6. A polyatomic ion is a group of atoms which act together as *(one ion, two ions, three ions)*.
7. A magnesium atom can form a compound by giving up *(one, two, three)* electrons.
8. A(n) *(neutron, proton, electron)* has a positive charge.
9. The first energy level can contain at most *(2, 6, 8)* electrons.
10. A molecule of $Al_2(SO_4)_3$ contains *(4, 3, 12)* atoms of oxygen.

C. Completion

Complete each of the following sentences with a word or phrase that will make the sentence correct. (Do not write in this book.)

1. Potassium has a valence of _____ . *1+*
2. In forming compounds, potassium _____ electrons. *loses*
3. The formula X_3Y shows that for each atom of Y, there are _____ atoms of X. *three*
4. When electrons are shared by atoms in a molecule, _____ bonding occurs. *covalent*
5. When an atom gains or loses an electron, a(n) _____ is formed. *ion*

isotopes **6.** Elements which have the same number of protons but different numbers of neutrons are called _____ .

two **7.** A binary compound contains atoms of _____ elements.

Ionic **8.** _____ bonding occurs when electrons are transferred.

positively **9.** The electron cloud model of the atom has a(n) _____ charged nucleus in the center.

nucleus **10.** Neutrons and protons are found in the _____ of the atom.

See Teacher's Guide at the front of this book.

D. How and Why

1. How does covalent bonding differ from ionic bonding?
2. Name the compounds represented by the following formulas: (a) NaCl, (b) NH_4NO_3, (c) $Ca_3(PO_4)_2$.
3. Write the formulas for the following compounds: (a) potassium sulfate, (b) sulfur dioxide, (c) mercury (I) sulfide.
4. Draw a diagram to show how magnesium bromide might be formed.
5. What are the differences between a proton, electron, and neutron?
6. What is the location of the electrons in the shells in an oxygen atom?
7. What are the main ideas in Dalton's theory? How have these ideas been modified by later experimentation?
8. An atom of an element has electrons distributed in energy levels in this manner: 2, 8, 2. What would you expect its valence to be? Why? What kind of bonding might it have?
9. What kind of atoms and how many of each are represented by the formula $Mg(NO_2)_2$?
10. How can carbon form the two compounds CO and CO_2?

See Teacher's material at front of book for suggestions.

INVESTIGATIONS

1. Find the chemical formulas for a number of common household compounds.
2. Report on the life of Niels Bohr.
3. Using the Bohr model, draw the electron structure of an atom with nine electrons.

ATOMS AND COMPOUNDS

4. Construct Bohr models of atoms. Use clay or styrofoam balls to represent electrons, protons, and neutrons. Thin copper wire will hold the balls in place.

5. Construct some molecular models. Use styrofoam balls, or gumdrops, and toothpicks.

INTERESTING READING

Adler, Irving, *The Elementary Mathematics of the Atom*. New York, John Day Company, 1965.

Drummond, A. H., Jr., *Molecules in the Service of Man*. Philadelphia, Lippincott, 1972.

Ellis, R. Hobart, Jr., *Knowing the Atomic Nucleus*. New York, Lothrop, Lee and Shepard Co., 1973.

Freeman, Ira M., and Patton, A. Rae, *The Science of Chemistry*. New York, Random House, Inc., 1969.

Grunwald, Ernest, and Johnsen, Russell H., *Atoms, Molecules and Chemical Change*. New York, Prentice-Hall, Inc., 1965.

Hyde, Margaret Oldroyd, *Atoms Today and Tomorrow*. New York, McGraw Hill Book Co., 1970.

Jensen, W. B., "Chemist's Annotated Mother Goose of Modern Bonding Theory." *Chemistry,* XLV (June, 1972), pp. 13–15.

Silverstein, Alvin and Virginia, *Frederick Sanger: The Man Who Mapped Out a Chemical of Life*. New York, John Day Publishing Co., 1969.

Jim Elliott

Solid substances with a regular geometric form are called crystals. Particles in crystals are held together through ionic bonding, covalent bonding, metallic bonding, and other forces. Solids which have no crystalline shape are said to be amorphous. Liquids and gases are substances which flow. By altering conditions, changes of phase can take place for most substances.

3 Solids, Liquids, and Gases

GOAL: You will gain an understanding of the main features of solids, liquids, and gases and the reasons for changes in phase.

The formation of ice crystals is fascinating. Many intricate patterns form when water changes to frost on a window pane. Snowflakes also have many different shapes. Looking at a single snowflake, one can see very delicate features. It has been claimed that no two snowflakes are alike. What causes these differences? Do other types of crystals display similar characteristics? Many questions such as these are answered in the study of matter.

CRYSTALS (41M) 137

3:1 Phases of Matter

Matter, under ordinary conditions, exists in three common phases: solid, liquid, and gas. Each phase of matter has different properties. For example, liquid water is different from solid ice. When a substance changes from one phase to another, there is a change in some of the physical properties of the substance.

3:2 Solids

One phase of matter is the solid. **Solids** have a definite shape and a constant volume. The particles (atoms, ions, or molecules) in solids are held together by strong forces. Ice is a solid. What other solids can you think of? There are two types of solids: crystalline (KRIS tuh lyn) and amorphous (uh MOR fuhs). The type depends on how the particles that make up the solid are arranged.

Figure 3-1. When a candle burns, wax changes from a solid into a liquid.

Describe the solid phase.

3:3 Crystals

A **crystal** is a type of solid which has a regular geometric form. Every crystalline element or compound has a certain geometric shape. Many compounds can be identified by their crystal form.

Do all crystals have the same shape?

Crystals of the same substance have the same shape. However, crystals of each substance have characteristic shapes.

> Time: 10 minutes.
> ACTIVITY. One common crystalline solid is table salt (NaCl). Pour a few crystals of table salt onto a piece of colored paper. Examine the salt with a magnifying glass. Compare the shape of the crystals. Compare the size of the crystals. Draw the shape of a salt crystal. Is each side the same or are some sides different from others? Sides are squares or rectangles.

Charles and Nancy Knight, National Center for Atmospheric Research

Figure 3-2. Snowflakes are crystals. They are always six-sided, but no two are exactly alike.

Figure 3-3.

Figure 3-4. Two kinds of ions make up the sodium chloride crystal (a). A crystal of sodium chloride looks like a cube (b).

a

b

Courtesy of Kodansha, Ltd.

Time: 30 minutes.

ACTIVITY. Obtain some different kinds of crystals from home or the school home economics department. Sugar and Epsom salt are examples. Observe each type of crystal under a magnifying glass. Try to pulverize (crush) several crystals of each type. Prepare a chart showing relative size, shape, strength (easy or hard to pulverize) of each type. Include other properties you observe.

Crystals contain atoms, ions, or molecules. For example, a graphite crystal and a diamond both contain carbon atoms. A sodium chloride crystal contains sodium and chloride ions. Ice contains water molecules. The structure within each crystal has three dimensions. The structure and shape depends on the order, arrangement, and types of particles.

Surfaces of crystals are called **faces**. The faces form definite angles with each other. For example, the faces of a salt crystal are at 90° angles to each other. How many faces does a salt crystal have? A crystal can be split and each piece will have the same number of faces and the same angles. The same basic structure is repeated throughout each piece. In other words, a large crystal of a substance will have the same shape as a small crystal of the same substance.

Time: 40 minutes.

ACTIVITY. Place several Rochelle salt crystals on a glass slide. Observe under a microscope. Make a sketch of their shape. Repeat with alum, nickel sulfate, and sodium nitrate crystals. Compare the crystal shapes. See Teacher's Guide at the front of this book.

If you examine a crystal, you see that some of the faces look alike. For example, a salt crystal looks the same if you turn it 90° left or right or up or down. This property is called **symmetry** (SIM uh tree). Symmetric (suh MEH trik) objects can be divided by a plane, line, or point. Each half will be equal in size, shape, and function (Figure 3–6). Some crystals are symmetric with respect to a plane and some with respect to a point. Some are symmetric with respect to a straight line. This straight line is called an *axis of symmetry*. Figure 3–6 shows some examples of symmetry.

Axes of symmetry are important when considering cleavage of a crystal. **Cleavage** (KLEE vij) is the tendency of a crystal to come apart when hit by a sharp blow. Not all crystals have this property

Figure 3-5. Many crystals have structures which resemble building frameworks (a). The repeating structure of a crystal is similar to a repeating wallpaper pattern (b).

What is symmetry?

Symmetry is similarity of form or arrangement on either side of a dividing line, plane, or point.

Axes, plural of axis.

Name three things that show symmetry.

Answers will vary.

Demonstrate the building of a two-dimensional pattern from a unit cell such as a square. Repeat the square in both the horizontal and the vertical directions. Have the students visualize the repetition of the square in the third dimension. The three-dimensional pattern will be cubic.

Figure 3-6. People and butterflies are symmetric with respect to a plane. Wheels are symmetric with respect to a point.

140 (44M)   SOLIDS, LIQUIDS, AND GASES

Figure 3-7.

to the same degree. Some crystals simply crumble when hit. Others, such as mica, can be pulled apart easily. The areas along which a crystal separates are called *cleavage planes*.

> Time: 20 minutes.
> ACTIVITY. Obtain a piece of mica. Stick a pin into the edge of the crystal. Work the pin back and forth to cleave off a small piece. Observe the mica crystal under a microscope. Draw a diagram of its shape.

3:4 Ionic Bonding in Crystals

For discussion of additional attractive forces in a crystal, see Teacher's Guide, p.49T.

In a crystal composed of ions, the ions are held together by ionic bonding. **Ionic bonding** results from the strong attraction between ions with opposite charges. Ionic bonds hold the crystal together. For example, sodium chloride crystals are made of positively charged sodium ions and negatively charged chloride ions. Each chloride ion is surrounded by six sodium ions. Each sodium ion is surrounded by six chloride ions.

Sodium chloride and other crystalline ionic compounds do not have a molecular arrangement. The formula NaCl gives only the ratio of sodium ions to chloride ions in a crystal. It is not a formula for a molecule.

> Time: 25 minutes.
> ACTIVITY. Obtain six small styrofoam balls, one large styrofoam ball, and some toothpicks. Arrange all seven balls to form the most compact structure possible. Use toothpicks to hold the balls together. The small balls represent sodium ions. The large ball represents a chloride ion. Combine your model with those of several of your classmates. Each pair of sodium ions should be separated by only one chloride ion. What does this larger model represent?

Figure 3-8. Hardness and shape of a crystal are related to how a crystal is bonded.

Ward's Natural Science Establishment, Inc.

Ward's Natural Science Establishment, Inc.

Time: 40 minutes.

DEMONSTRATION. This experiment is to be performed by your teacher only. CAUTION: Do not touch either sodium dichromate or sodium hydroxide. Wear eye and clothing protection.

Mix 60 g of sodium dichromate in 130 ml of hot water in a beaker. Slowly add 7.5 g of lithium carbonate. When the bubbling of carbon dioxide stops, add 8 g of solid sodium hydroxide. Cover and allow to stand. Observe any crystals which form. If crystals do not form in a day, add a few tiny sodium dichromate crystals. The crystals are yellow and hexagonal.

Figure 3-9.

A crystal built up by ions is called an ionic crystal. Ionic bonding produces crystals which are hard and brittle. These crystals have high melting points and they do not conduct electricity. This is because the outer electrons in each ion in the crystal are held tightly. However, a melted crystal or a *melt* can conduct a current. When an ionic crystal melts, its ions are no longer held together. Therefore, the ions are free to move and they may conduct a current.

What are the features of an ionic crystal?

3:5 Covalent Bonding in Crystals

Some crystals are formed by covalent bonding. In **covalent bonding** the electrons are shared and the covalent bonds between the atoms hold the crystal together. The entire crystal becomes one huge molecule. Diamonds are formed by this type of bonding. Each carbon atom in a diamond crystal is bonded covalently to four other carbon atoms. Such a crystal is said to have a *three-dimensional strong bond*.

The properties of diamonds are typical of crystals which are covalently bonded throughout. They are extremely hard, have high

The carbon atoms in the "giant molecule" of diamond are bound together by strong covalent bonds. The molecules of molecular compounds are held to each other by much weaker van der Waals forces. To melt diamonds or other compounds having a covalent lattice crystalline structure, the individual covalent bonds must be broken. This requires energy and such compounds melt at high temperatures.

What are the features of a crystal which is covalently bonded?

Figure 3-10. Three-dimensional strong bonds between carbon and silicon explain the hardness of silicon carbide.

Figure 3-11. Differences in the properties of diamonds (a) and graphite (b) are the result of different crystal structures.

Diamonds and graphite are allotropes because they are different molecular (crystalline) forms of the same element, carbon.

How are carbon atoms bonded in a graphite crystal?

Describe metallic bonding.

Figure 3-12. Silicon carbide is very hard. For this reason, it is often used in the making of grinding wheels.

W. Keith Turpie

melting points, and do not conduct electricity. Some compounds such as silicon carbide (SiC) also crystallize covalently in a three-dimensional strong bond. In these cases the attraction is between molecules.

Graphite crystals in a "lead" pencil contain covalent bonds. Each carbon atom in a graphite crystal is covalently bonded to three others in the same plane. These *two-dimensional strong bonds* are not as strong as three-dimensional strong bonds. This bonding partly accounts for the fact that graphite is not as hard as diamond. The planes in graphite easily slide over each other. This property makes graphite a very good lubricant (LOO brih kuhnt) and a useful writing material. As it moves across paper, a pencil lays down a thin but continuous layer of graphite (Figure 3–11b).

Metals tend to crystallize in simple patterns. Atoms of metals arrange themselves in layers. In **metallic** (muh TAL ik) **bonding, the outer electrons of the atoms move throughout the crystal and are shared equally by all the ions.** The free electrons in a metal help explain some of the properties of metals. Because electrons are free to move throughout the structure, metals conduct electricity. Metals are not brittle because metallic ions in layers can slide over each other and may be shifted without shattering the crystal. Metals may be drawn out to form wire or hammered into thin sheets without breaking.

3:6 *Crystallization*

Crystals are formed in different ways. Snowflake crystals form when water vapor in cold air at high altitude changes to the solid phase. Iodine vapor will form iodine crystals on cool glass. Salt crystals form when the water in salt water is evaporated. Metal crystals form when molten metal is cooled to a solid.

Figure 3-13. Metals are able to be pulled out into wires (a). They are also able to be hammered into thin sheets (b).

Time: 40 minutes.

ACTIVITY. Obtain three evaporating dishes. Add 10 ml of copper sulfate (CuSO$_4$) solution or Epsom salt solution to each dish. Let the first dish stand at room temperature. Heat the second dish in a water bath. Add 2–3 ml of dissolved gelatin to the third dish. Watch the crystals form. Compare the sizes of crystals in each dish. How did each form? *Dissolve one small package of unflavored gelatin in 25 ml of cold water.*

Any soluble salt can be used for the solution.

Name three ways crystals can form.

Crystals can be formed from vapor, hot melts, and solutions.

Time: 30 minutes.

ACTIVITY. Slowly melt some sulfur in a test tube over a Bunsen flame. Describe your observations. How is this process different from dissolving sugar in water? Pour the liquid into a paper cone of filter paper. When a crust forms on the melted sulfur, break it open. Do you observe any crystals? *yes*   *See Teacher's Guide.*

Figure 3-14.

U.S. Geological Survey

Figure 3-15. Lava is liquid rock. When it cools it becomes a solid again.

Figure 3-16.

Time: 35 minutes.

ACTIVITY. Add 130 g of Rochelle salt to 100 ml of water in a beaker. Heat the mixture and stir until all the salt is dissolved. Allow the solution to cool. Add 9 g of Rochelle salt to the mixture. Pour the solution into a small cap-covered jar. Attach a large Rochelle crystal to a thread, suspend it in the solution, and allow the crystal to stand undisturbed for a week. Does the size of the crystal <u>increase</u>, decrease, or remain the same? Does the shape of the crystal change? How?

PROBLEMS See Teacher's Guide at the front of the book.

1. How is melting of a substance different from dissolving?
2. How does the formation of crystals from a melt differ from formation of crystals from a solution?

3:7 Amorphous Solids

Many solids, such as glass, have no regular crystalline shapes. Such solids are **amorphous solids.** Glass has two properties of a solid—definite shape and constant volume. However, it has no regular crystalline structure. Plastics, such as lucite and celluloid, are also amorphous solids.

What happens when glass breaks? Amorphous solids do not have cleavage axes and they have no regular face angles when broken. They chip or leave depressions when broken.

How does glass differ from a crystal?

Glass has no regular pattern, no cleavage axes, no specific face angles, no specific structure.

PROBLEM

3. Why are wax, fat, and plastic classified as amorphous solids?
They have no regular crystalline structure yet they are solids.

a   b

Figure 3-17. Glass can be molded into a variety of shapes and can be used in many ways. Fiberglass campers (a) and glassware (b) are just a few examples.

William Maddox

PEOPLE CAREERS FRONTIERS
FOCUS ON PHYSICAL SCIENCE

Yvonne Brill

Yvonne Brill is a propulsion engineer. She is involved in the analysis and design of spacecraft propulsion systems. She has played a major role in the design of many weather and communication satellites. One project for which she was responsible is the propulsion system design in an atmosphere explorer satellite.

Mrs. Brill prepared for this career in many ways. She obtained both a bachelor of science degree and a master's degree in chemistry. Also, she worked for a variety of companies specializing in the design of rockets and other aircraft. All of these experiences gave Mrs. Brill the background necessary to be a propulsion engineer.

• • • • • • • • • • • • •

Courtesy of Copley News Service.

Yvonne Brill uses a model to point out the features of one of the propulsion systems she has designed.

A. Murty Kanury, Fire Engineer

A. Murty Kanury is interested in a special area of physics—fire engineering. He has devoted many years studying fires, explosions, smoke, and forest fire management.

Mr. Kanury is concerned because there are over three million fires every year in the United States. As a result, tremendous amounts of property are destroyed. Even more important, almost half a million people are injured in fires every year. Of the people injured, over twelve thousand lose their lives.

Not only is Mr. Kanury concerned, but many other people are as well. A commission has been formed to help with fire prevention. This commission, the National Commission on Fire Prevention and Control, has made three major recommendations. (1) It is important for the fire services (fire departments) to be knowledgeable about all types of fires. In this way, fires can be extinguished as quickly as possible. (2) It is recommended that information be gathered for study. This will help prevent fires and control many of the types of fires that occur. (3) Furthermore and very important — the public should be educated in fire prevention.

• • • • • • • • • • • • •

Courtesy of McGraw-Hill Book Company.

Mr. Kanury's work may help firefighters in their efforts to control and prevent fires.

Figure 3-18. Liquids take the shape of their containers.

Why is the water the same level in all the containers shown?
The molecules at the top are all at the same potential energy level. The level of the water is the lowest potential energy level of the system.

3:8 Liquids

Liquids have no definite shape. They take the shape of their container. However, the volume of a liquid remains constant except when the temperature is changed. Molecules of liquid are not tightly bonded. Thus, they are free to move and slide freely over each other. Because liquids have no rigid form, the molecules tend to move toward the area closest to the ground. Thus, in a series of interconnected containers, the liquid will be at the same level in all the containers (Figure 3–19).

Figure 3-19. When two containers are connected, the water levels become equal.

Figure 3-20.

Time: 35 minutes.

ACTIVITY. Stretch a piece of rubber tubing over the mouth of a thistle tube. Attach with a rubber band. Insert the end of the thistle tube into one end of a rubber tube. Connect the other end of the rubber tube to a U-shaped glass tube which is one-third full of water. Hold the thistle tube at various depths in a large, deep container of water. Point the mouth of the thistle tube up, down, and sideways, and observe the movement of water in the U-tube. How is pressure in a liquid affected by depth and direction? The pressure is affected only by depth.

146 (50M)

Time: 20 minutes.

ACTIVITY. (1) Obtain a 25-ml and a 50-ml graduated cylinder. Measure exactly 25 ml of water with the small graduate. Pour this water into the 50-ml graduate. Measure 25 ml more water with the small graduate and pour it into the 50-ml graduate. (2) Repeat the procedure using alcohol instead of water. How much is 25 ml plus 25 ml? (3) Using the small graduate, measure and add exactly 25 ml of water and 25 ml of alcohol to the 50-ml graduate. What is the combined volume of the alcohol and water? Explain what you observe. *The alcohol molecules move into spaces between the water molecules. The mixture of alcohol and water is a liquid-liquid solution since the mixture is uniform throughout.*

Figure 3-21.

In most cases, the particles in a liquid are farther apart than the particles in a crystal of the same substance. Thus, there is more empty space between liquid particles. Other particles can fill these spaces.

Time: 20 minutes.

ACTIVITY. Fill a 250-ml beaker one-half full of marbles. Fill another 250-ml beaker one-half full of BB pellets. Note: Be certain you are accurate in determining the half-way point in each beaker. What is the total volume of the marbles and the BB pellets? Add the BB's to the marbles and mix well. What is the new total volume? Explain the results. *BB's fit between marbles.*

3:9 Gases

Gases have no definite shape and no constant volume. Like liquids, gases take the shape of their containers. The atoms or molecules in gases are separated by large distances. Because gases are mostly empty space, the gas molecules can be forced closer together. Gas molecules are only very weakly attracted to one another. Therefore, they can move farther apart and completely fill containers of various volumes and shapes.

Gas molecules are constantly in rapid random straight line motion. The average gas particle travels at a speed of nearly 400 m per second under standard conditions. However, the molecules collide with (bump into) each other and with the sides of their container. Collisions of gas molecules with the walls of the container create pressure in the **container**. If the collisions are **increased**, the pressure is increased.

What are the main properties of a gas?

Figure 3-22. Balls in a vibrating box collide with the walls and with each other (a). If the volume is decreased, the pressure increases (b). Increasing the number of balls, increases the number of collisions (c).

What causes the pressure on a container filled with a gas?

collision of molecules

PROBLEM

4. What happens to the pressure inside an auto tire as air is released? Pressure is decreased.

As the number of gas molecules in a container increases, the pressure increases (Figure 3–22c). This is due to an increased number of collisions with the container wall. Does the pressure in a car tire increase or decrease as it rolls over hot pavement at high speeds? Why? Heat causes molecules to move more rapidly. When gas molecules are heated, they move faster and hit the walls of the container more often. This causes a flexible container such as a balloon to expand. Closed rigid containers, such as the tank in Figure 3–24 or a tire, register a pressure increase.

Figure 3-23. When gas is released from the container on the right, lower pressure results. Fewer molecules collide with each other.

Figure 3-24. When heat is added to the container on the right, higher pressure results. Heat causes more gas molecules to collide.

PASCAL'S LAW (53M) 149

Suppose one liter of hydrogen and one liter of oxygen are mixed in a one-liter container. Together the gases are compressed into one liter of oxygen-hydrogen mixture. Twice as many molecules now occupy the same volume. The pressure of the mixture is twice the original pressure of the separate gases. Like liquids, the volume of mixed gases may not be the sum of their separate volumes. In this case two liters are mixed to make one liter.

If the volume of a gas is reduced without any change of temperature, the pressure increases.

PROBLEM

5. When you blow up a balloon, how does your breath cause the balloon to expand? Is the pressure inside the balloon increased or decreased? Addition of more and more molecules causes more collisions.

3:10 Pascal's Law

A gallon jug is filled with water and sealed with a cork. Then the cork is hit with a hammer. If the cork is hit hard enough, the bottom of the jug might fall out. The pressure of the hammer on the cork is carried by the water to the bottom of the jug. Here the pressure is on a larger area, making the total force much greater. Thus, the bottom could break off.

A balloon filled with water reacts differently than a balloon filled with air. If both are dropped on the ground, the one filled with water will probably burst. However, the balloon filled with air will bounce. In the water balloon, the force produced when striking the ground

Carl England

Figure 3-25. Pressure applied to a liquid in a container is transmitted to all surfaces.

Pressure is the force per unit area, $P = \frac{F}{A}$. Total force on a surface is the pressure times area, $F = P \times A$.

Figure 3-26. Balloons filled with air bounce. Balloons filled with water break. Why?

SOLIDS, LIQUIDS, AND GASES

breaks the balloon. It is transmitted to all surfaces of the balloon. However, the air balloon bounces because it absorbs the force. The air inside the balloon quickly compresses and then expands again.

Pressure on a gas, such as air, causes the volume of the gas to decrease. This is not so with a liquid. Increased pressure does not compress a liquid any significant amount.

The compressibility of a liquid is so slight that it may be ignored in most scientific and practical considerations.

PROBLEM

6. Why are automobile tires filled with air and not with a liquid?
Air "gives" when hitting bumps, etc. by compressing. A liquid does not.

Blaise Pascal (1623–1662), a French scientist, proposed what is now called **Pascal's law.** If pressure is applied to a liquid in a closed container, the pressure is transmitted unchanged to all surfaces of the container.

State Pascal's law and give two examples of its application.

Figure 3-27.

Time: 30 minutes.

Be careful when performing this activity because the water sprays in all directions. It would be a good idea to do it outside with a hose if possible. The pressure exerted by the water is transmitted equally to all surfaces. Water flows from each hole at the same speed.

DEMONSTRATION. Obtain a hollow rubber ball. Drill or bore ten small holes evenly spaced over the ball. Insert a glass tube into the ball. Connect the tube to a piece of rubber tubing. Connect the rubber tube to a water faucet and place the ball in a sink. Make sure all connections are tight. Gently turn on the water. How does this demonstration illustrate Pascal's law? How does a sprinkler hose illustrate the law?
Pressure is equal in all directions.

A hydraulic (hy **DRAH** lik) lift operates by Pascal's law (Figure 3–28a). A force exerted on a small area causes a pressure in the liquid. This pressure is transmitted equally throughout the liquid. A small force on the small piston produces a large force on the large piston. A force of 1 newton exerted on 1 cm² (small piston) will transfer 100 newtons of force to the piston with an area of 100 cm².

Figure 3-28. Hydraulic lifts are an application of Pascal's law (a). They are used to lift heavy objects (b).

$$P = \frac{f}{a} \quad P = \frac{F}{A}$$
$$\frac{f}{a} = \frac{F}{A}$$
$$\frac{1 \text{ nt}}{1 \text{ cm}^2} = \frac{F}{100 \text{ cm}^2}$$
$$F = \frac{100 \text{ cm}^2 \times 1 \text{ nt}}{1 \text{ cm}^2}$$
$$F = 100 \text{ nt}$$

Will Miles

The same principle applies to hydraulic jacks used to lift heavy objects and to hydraulic brakes found in motor vehicles.

PROBLEM

7. Hydraulic brake lines contain a liquid called brake fluid. Why must brake lines be free of air for the brakes to work properly?
The air will compress and the brake force will not be transmitted to the brake shoes on the wheels.

3:11 *Change of Phase*

Most substances can exist as a solid, liquid, or gas. Solid ice melts to form liquid water when heated. Water in a lake evaporates to form water vapor. Water vapor can condense to liquid water inside a car and fog the car's windows. In each case, there is a change of phase.

A change in the phase of a substance is explained by the kinetic (kuh NET ik) theory. The kinetic theory states that the particles of a substance are in motion. As heat is added, the particles move faster. If heat is removed (cooling) the particles slow down. Heat is the kinetic energy of the moving particles. In a phase change, particles may separate or move closer together. They may become more or less attracted to each other.

What may happen to a substance's particles in a phase change?

Figure 3-29. Ice melting into water is one kind of change of phase.

You may wish to have students record the temperature each minute and then graph the temperature change for each activity. Plot temperature against time.

Figure 3-30.

Time: 25 minutes.

ACTIVITY. Place one ice cube in a glass of water. Place a thermometer in the mixture. Check the temperature every few minutes until the ice cubes are entirely melted. Where did the heat come from that melted the ice? Was there a change in temperature of the solution while the ice was melting? What happened to the heat?
No   melted ice

Time: 35 minutes.

ACTIVITY. Suspend a thermometer in a beaker of boiling water. Record the temperature every few minutes as you gradually increase the heat under the beaker. Continue until the water is nearly gone. Was there a change in temperature? What happened to the added heat? vaporized water

The temperature rises to 100°C. Then the temperature remains constant although more heat is added. The heat is used to vaporize the water.

PROBLEMS

8. A bottle of milk will likely crack if it is frozen solid. Do water molecules move closer together or <u>farther apart</u> when water freezes?

9. A drop of water is placed in a one liter jar. The water evaporates. Do the water molecules move <u>farther apart</u> or closer together?

3:12 Solid-Gas Change — Sublimation

If solid iodine is kept in a closed <u>container, purple iodine vapor can be seen above the crystals. Iodine changes directly from the solid to the gas phase.</u> It does not normally enter the liquid phase.

LIQUID-SOLID CHANGE (57M) 153

The gas particles that escape from the solid crystals are I_2 molecules. **Sublimation** (suhb luh MAY shuhn) is the name given to the direct change from a solid to a gas phase.

Most solids expand when they are heated. Particles in solids vibrate about fixed points. If heat is added to the solid, the rate of the vibrations increases. The particles in the crystal move back and forth and collide with each other with a greater force. Due to the increased force of the collisions, the particles move farther apart. As more heat is added, some of the particles may acquire enough energy to break the bonds that hold them to other particles. In that case, they escape into the air and form a vapor or gas.

To crystallize a substance from the gas form, the gas may be cooled, or exposed to high pressure. Also, the gas may be cooled at the same time it is placed under high pressure. In most cases, the gas becomes a liquid as an intermediate step before it becomes a solid. However, it is possible for a solid to be formed directly from a gas. The CO_2 (carbon dioxide) fire extinguisher is a good example of this phase change. In the fire extinguisher, CO_2 gas is kept under pressure. As the pressure is released, some of the high energy CO_2 molecules escape. This lowers the average kinetic energy of the remaining molecules. Their temperature drops to a point below the freezing temperature of carbon dioxide. These molecules form a solid and fall as "snow."

What is sublimation?

Phosphorus is condensed from a gas to a solid under water.

The solid carbon dioxide has several advantages over water: it does not conduct electricity; it is much colder than water, thus lowering the kindling temperature; it replaces oxygen essential for combustion to continue; it sublimes making cleaning no problem.

3:13 Liquid-Solid Change

A liquid forms a solid when the liquid is cooled to its freezing point. As heat is removed, the liquid particles begin to slow down and move closer together. The particles move into normal solid

Figure 3-31. Carbon dioxide, in the form of dry ice, changes directly from a solid to a vapor (a). Carbon dioxide changes directly from a gas to a solid when released from a fire extinquisher (b).

a

Lorie Hand

b

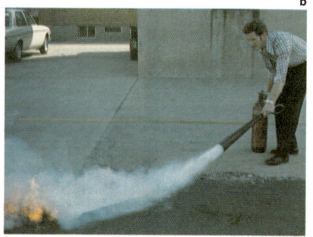

Will Miles

Figure 3-32. Water and ice can both exist at 0°C. Heat is added to change ice to water. Heat is removed to change water to ice.

Lester V. Bergman & Associates, Inc.

What is seeding?

Crystals form around impurities in the substance or around irregularities in the container. Once a small crystal is started, the rest of the substance crystallizes on this base.

phase pattern. In a crystalline solid the change from liquid to solid phase may occur by seeding or chance. *Seeding* means to add a small crystal of the substance to the liquid. An impurity in the substance may also serve as a seed. In the phase change, particles begin to crystallize around the impurity. The liquid remains at the freezing temperature until the entire substance is crystallized.

When a liquid fails to crystallize at its freezing point, it is supercooled. Normally, water freezes at 0°C. Under some conditions, however, water may exist as a supercooled liquid at temperatures below 0°C.

Figure 3-33. Cloth, Rubber band, Thread, Potassium bromate solution, Seed crystal

Time: 45 minutes.

ACTIVITY. Crystals can be grown from a seed crystal. To prepare seed crystals, make a saturated solution of potassium bromate in 100 ml of distilled water. Place 28 ml of this saturated solution in a glass jar. Let it evaporate for a few days until the crystals reach from 3–6 mm in length. Remove the crystals and allow them to dry. CAUTION. Be sure to wash your hands thoroughly before and after handling crystals. This is done to avoid contaminating the crystals and harming your skin.

Obtain a large glass jar. Using a thread longer than the jar, tie it around one seed crystal with a slip knot. Lower the seed crystal into the jar containing the remaining potassium bromate solution. Cover the jar with a clean cloth. Secure the thread and cloth with a rubber band. Allow the solution to evaporate at room temperature. Observe daily.

LIQUID-GAS CHANGE (59M) 155

3:14 Liquid-Gas Change *evaporation*

Liquids can enter the gas phase by evaporation and boiling. At any temperature the surface molecules of a liquid can escape and enter the gas phase. This change from liquid to gas is called **evaporation**.

If you leave water or alcohol in an open container it evaporates away. Why? Molecules of a liquid are held together by attractive forces. Because they are in constant motion, these molecules continually bump into each other. Through their collisions with other molecules, molecules at the liquid's surface are constantly gaining enough energy to escape. The escaping molecules form a vapor.

When heat is added to a liquid, the rate of evaporation increases. Increased evaporation causes the vapor pressure of the liquid to increase. The temperature at which the liquid's vapor pressure equals the atmospheric pressure is the liquid's *boiling point*. For example, at 760 mm of pressure water boils at 100°C. Ethyl alcohol at the same pressure boils at 78.5°C. When a liquid boils there is a rapid change from the liquid to the gas phase.

Craig W. Kramer

Figure 3-34. Gas bubbles form within a liquid when the liquid reaches its boiling point.

What is evaporation?

PROBLEMS

10. Is the boiling point of water at 1000 mm pressure greater or less than 100°C?

11. Why does food cook faster in a pressure cooker? — The pressure cooker increases the boiling point of water and as a result, the temperature inside the cooker is hotter than under normal conditions. Thus, the food cooks faster.

The change from a gas to a liquid is known as **condensation**. Condensation can occur when pressure is applied to a gas or when the gas is cooled. Pressure forces the gas molecules closer together. Reduced temperature causes them to slow down. The two processes

William Maddox

Figure 3-35. Propane gas is liquefied for easier transportation.

Figure 3-36. Chlorine can be liquefied in the laboratory.

cause the molecules to come together. Under the right conditions of pressure and temperature, the gas forms a liquid. Figure 3–36 shows one laboratory method for liquefying chlorine by cooling. What is the pressure on the chlorine gas?

Many gases are liquefied or condensed for easier transportation and use. The fuels propane and butane are two examples of gases which are transported and stored as liquids under pressure. As the pressure is released, the liquid becomes a gas again for use as fuel. For example, propane gas is used in stoves and furnaces after being stored as a liquid.

Heat causes greater pressure on Cl_2 molecules. See Teacher's Guide, p. 51T, for more information on condensation.

MAIN IDEAS

1. Crystals are solid elements or compounds having certain geometric form.
2. Particles in crystals may be bonded together through
   (a) ionic bonding
   (b) covalent bonding
   (c) metallic bonding
3. The type of bonding in a crystal determines many properties of the crystal.
4. In metals, free electrons conduct electricity.
5. Amorphous solids have no regular crystalline shape.
6. Gases and liquids have no fixed shape. They take the shape of their containers.
7. The volume of a gas equals the volume of the container.
8. Pressure applied to a liquid in a closed container is transmitted unchanged to all sides or surfaces of the container (Pascal's law).
9. Changes in phase are caused by changing temperature and/or pressure.

VOCABULARY

Write a sentence in which you correctly use each of the following words or terms.

- amorphous
- cleavage
- cleavage plane
- condensation
- covalent bonding
- crystal
- crystal face
- evaporation
- gas
- ionic bonding
- liquid
- metallic bonding
- pressure
- solid
- sublimation
- symmetry

SOLIDS, LIQUIDS, AND GASES (61M) 157

STUDY QUESTIONS

A. True or False

Have students rewrite false statements to make the statements correct.

Determine whether each of the following sentences is true or false. (Do not write in this book.)

F 1. The molecules of a solid are held together by weak attractive forces. strong ionic, covalent, or metallic bonds

T 2. The surfaces of crystals are called faces.

F 3. All crystals have the same cleavage properties. different

T 4. Ionic crystals have high melting points.

F 5. Crystals can only be formed from a solution.

T 6. Metals are good conductors of electricity because they contain free electrons.

T 7. Glass is a solid that has no definite crystal structure.

F 8. The volume of a liquid can be decreased by increasing the pressure on the liquid in a closed container. gas, gas

F 9. If 10 ml of water is mixed with 10 ml of alcohol the total volume of the mixture will be more than 20 ml. less

T 10. Gas pressure in balloons results from the collision of gas molecules with the inside surface of the balloon.

B. Multiple Choice

Some questions in Parts B and C may have more than one correct answer. Only one answer is required.

Choose one word or phrase that correctly completes each of the following sentences. (Do not write in this book.)

1. Ionic bonding produces crystals which are *(soft, brittle, conductors)*.

2. Metals conduct electricity through their *(central ions, electrons, atoms)*.

3. Metals conduct electricity because *(bonds, electrons, forces)* are free to move throughout.

4. Particles in solids *(always, sometimes, never)* vibrate.

5. An amorphous solid does not have a *(constant volume, definite shape, cleavage axis)*.

6. As the temperature increases, the motion of particles in a liquid *(increases, decreases, remains the same)*.

7. Covalent bonding produces crystals which are *(hard, soft, conductors)*.

8. Gases and liquids *(have constant volume, have definite shape, flow)*.

158 (62M)   SOLIDS, LIQUIDS, AND GASES

Either is correct.   9. Symmetric objects can be divided by a plane or a(n) (*point, face, axis*).

10. (*Iodine*, Table salt, Epsom salt) changes directly from a solid to a gas when heated.

C. Completion

Complete each of the following sentences with a word or phrase that will make the sentence correct. (Do not write in this book.)

? low   1. Covalent crystals have _____ melting points.

Pascal's   2. A hydraulic lift illustrates _____ law.

gases   3. Liquids and _____ take the shape of their containers.

glass, wax   4. One example of an amorphous solid is _____ .

freezing   5. The melting point of a solid is the same as the _____ point of its liquid phase.

temperature, pressure   6. A substance can be liquefied from a gas by _____ and _____ .

vapor   7. Water _____ is a gas.

increases   8. As the temperature of a gas increases, the particle motion _____ .

gas   9. Sublimation is the change in phase from solid to _____ .

0   10. _____ °C is the melting point of ice.

D. How and Why

See Teacher's Guide at the front of this book.

1. How are crystals different from amorphous solids?
2. What kinds of forces exist in crystals?
3. How are crystals formed?
4. Two liters of gas A are added to one liter of gas B in a one-liter container. The temperature remains the same. The combined volume of the two gases is now one liter. Why is the volume of the combined gases less than the sum of their separate volumes? Explain your answer.
5. Why would an air bubble increase in volume as it rises from the bottom of a swimming pool?
6. How do temperature and pressure affect the volume of a gas?
7. How does Pascal's law explain the hydraulic lift?
8. How are liquids and gases similar?

SOLIDS, LIQUIDS, AND GASES (63M) 159

9. Why do diamonds and graphite differ in hardness?
10. How does the kinetic theory explain the phase changes of solids, liquids, and gases.

INVESTIGATIONS

See Teacher's Guide at the front of this book.

1. Obtain a book on refrigeration. Learn how evaporation and condensation are used in mechanical refrigeration. Make a model or diagram to show the major parts of a refrigeration unit.
2. Find out how synthetic diamonds are made. Prepare a report for the class.
3. Make a collection of mineral crystals. Find out what elements are present in each mineral in your collection. Also, find out how the properties of a mineral, such as hardness and density, are related to its composition.
4. Visit a service station. Under the supervision of the station attendant, find out how the hydraulic lift works.

INTERESTING READING

Apfel, R. E., "Tensile Strength of Liquids." *Scientific American,* CCXXVII (December, 1972), pp. 58–62.

Bendick, Jeanne, *Solids, Liquids, and Gases.* New York, Watts, 1974.

Berger, Melvin, *The New Air Book.* New York, Thomas Y. Crowell Co., 1974.

Boys, Charles V., *Soap Bubbles.* New York, Thomas Y. Crowell Co., 1962.

Burke, John G., *Origins of the Science of Crystals.* Berkeley, University of California Press, 1966.

Dwiggins, Don, *Riders of the Winds: The Story of Ballooning.* New York, Hawthorn Books, Inc., 1973.

Griesbach, R. J., "Growing Metallic Crystals." *Chemistry,* XLV (December, 1972), pp. 25–26.

Hyde, Margaret, *Molecules Today and Tomorrow.* New York, McGraw-Hill Book Company, 1966.

Ridpath, Ian, *Man and Materials: Gas.* Reading, Massachusetts, Addison-Wesley, 1975.

Wohlrabe, Raymond A., *Crystals.* Philadelphia, J. B. Lippincott Company, 1962.

Unit Three

Patterns in Matter

Like the elements, these buttons have unique characteristics. Grouping them according to similar characteristics is analogous to how the elements are grouped in the periodic table.

William Maddox

1 Periodic Table

The concept of the combining capacity of elements is studied in greater depth as the student learns about the periodic table of elements. Quantitative aspects are emphasized with the study of atomic mass and atomic number. Students will learn to predict the relative activity of elements by applying the periodic law.

GOAL: You will gain an understanding of the location and use of certain information in the periodic table of the elements.

The concept of classification by similar characteristics is an important one in all branches of science. Emphasize this.

Scientists have found that every element is different. Oxygen is different from lead. Iron is different from sodium. They not only look different, but they are different in the way they react with other elements. These differences are based on differences in their atomic structure.

Although every element has special features, scientists have found similarities among certain elements. A definite pattern was found to exist among certain elements. This discovery resulted in a classification system of the elements.

ATOMIC MASS (3M) 163

1:1 Atomic Mass

An atom is the smallest particle of an element which has the properties of the element. An element is a substance which cannot be broken down into simpler substances. Elements may be classified in groups based on the mass of their atoms. **Atomic mass** is the mass of an atom compared to a standard mass. It is not the actual mass of an atom.

Why is relative atomic mass rather than actual atomic mass used?

Actual atomic mass is too small to be measured accurately in ordinary laboratory conditions.

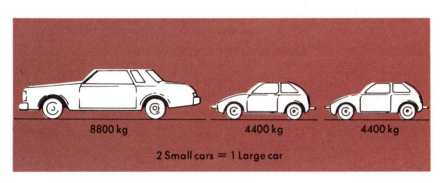

Figure 1-1. One of these small cars has a mass of 4400 kg. The large car has a mass of two small cars. The small car's mass is the standard.

The purpose of this activity is to give insight into determination of relative mass. See Teacher's Guide at the front of this book for a sample data table and answers to questions.

Time: 50 minutes.

ACTIVITY. (1) Find the mass of an empty beaker. Place an equal number of steel ball bearings and glass marbles into the beaker. Find the mass again. Subtract the mass of the empty beaker from the mass of the full beaker. What is the mass of the contents? (2) Take the marbles out of the beaker and find the mass of the beaker and ball bearings. Subtract this mass from the mass of the total contents. What is the mass of the marbles? (3) Subtract the mass of the empty beaker from the mass of the beaker and ball bearings. What is the mass of the ball bearings? (4) Find the simplest ratio of the mass of the marbles to the mass of the ball bearings. Assign the lighter objects a mass of 1. Using this assigned mass, what is the mass of a ball bearing and a marble? Which mass is the standard? See Teacher's Guide.

Figure 1-2.

Carbon 12 is the standard for atomic mass. An **atomic mass unit** is 1/12 the mass of a carbon-12 atom. Atomic mass unit is abbreviated as a.m.u. The masses of all other elements are based on this standard.

An atom of carbon 12 has six protons, six neutrons, and six electrons. The electrons contribute almost no mass. The neutrons and

What is the standard for relative atomic mass?

Figure 1-3. Carbon 12 is the standard for atomic mass.

Table 1–1. **Atomic Mass Units of Some Elements**

Element	Protons	Neutrons	a.m.u.
Carbon (C)	6	6	12
Oxygen (O)	8	8	16
Sodium (Na)	11	11	22
Potassium (K)	19	20	39
Iron (Fe)	26	29	55

protons have nearly the same mass. Each neutron and proton has a mass of 1 a.m.u. If you know the number of protons and neutrons in an atom, you can find its relative mass. For example, a certain atom has 4 protons and 5 neutrons. Its atomic mass, relative to carbon 12, is 9 (4 + 5 = 9).

PROBLEM

1. What is the atomic mass of an atom with 24 protons and 28 neutrons? 52 a.m.u.

1:2 Mendeleev's Table

Scientists believed that there was some order to the elements. Mendeleev (men duh LAY uhf) (1834–1907), a Russian scientist, arranged the known elements into a chart according to their atomic masses. In this order, certain physical and chemical properties of the elements repeated periodically. He called this repetition of properties the *periodic* (pir ee AHD ik) *law*. The chart he drew up became known as the *periodic table*.

Try this before the students do to decide whether you want them to attempt it. Sodium and potassium react violently with water. Lithium could also be used here. Magnesium and calcium will not react with cold water.

What is the basis for Mendeleev's periodic table?

Time: 60 minutes.　　　　　Use caution with this activity.

ACTIVITY. CAUTION: This activity should be done only under direct teacher supervision. Wear eye and clothing protection.

Obtain sodium, potassium, calcium, and magnesium metals. Fill a large beaker or jar three-fourths full of water. Remove the sodium metal from its container with forceps and cut off a piece smaller than a pea. Replace the sodium in its container. Drop the pea-size piece of sodium into the water. Repeat the steps separately with potassium, calcium, and magnesium. Why are sodium and potassium kept in kerosene? Based on your observations, group these four metals into two families. List the observed properties of each family. See Teacher's Guide at the front of this book.

Figure 1-4.

MOSELEY'S TABLE

Elements not yet known could be predicted from Mendeleev's periodic table. There were places in the table where properties seemed to skip an element. These suggested to Mendeleev that some unknown element might belong there. Three elements which Mendeleev suggested—gallium (Ga), scandium (Sc), and germanium (Ge)—were later discovered. All have properties similar to those he predicted.

1:3 Moseley's Table

Errors were found in Mendeleev's table, so attempts were made to improve it. Henry Moseley (1877–1915), a young English scientist, thought that there was a periodic repetition of properties. However, he thought it was due to the number of protons in an atom. He believed that atomic number, rather than atomic mass, was the key factor. This was later found to be true!

Atomic number is the number of protons in the nucleus. Z is the symbol for atomic number. For example:

Hydrogen (H) $Z = 1$ Oxygen (O) $Z = 8$
Nitrogen (N) $Z = 7$ Chlorine (Cl) $Z = 17$

The number of protons equals the number of electrons in an atom. Therefore, the atomic number is also the number of electrons in an atom. No two elements have the same atomic number. Why?

In the modern periodic table (Table 1–2), elements are arranged by atomic number, *not* atomic mass. If elements are arranged in order of increasing atomic number, there is a periodic repetition of properties. This is now called the **periodic law.**

The periodic table shows how elements are classified today. Each box represents one element. The symbol for the element is in the center of the box. The number at the top is the atomic number of the element. The number at the bottom is the average atomic mass of the element. For example, find zinc (Zn). Its atomic number is 30, and its average atomic mass is 65.37. The number(s) at the side of each box show how the atom's electrons are distributed into shells. The number of electrons begins with those in the shell closest to the nucleus.

Figure 1-5. How could these stamps be classified? color, cost

Upon what is the modern periodic table based?

All elements have different numbers of protons. Atoms of the same element have the same number of protons. If two elements had the same number of protons, they would be the same element.

No elements in the table have relative masses which are exactly whole numbers.

Figure 1-6. Each box in the periodic table gives the symbol for the element, its atomic number, its average atomic mass, and the number of electrons in each shell.

Table 1-2.

Noble Gases

					VIIIA
		Nonmetals		Halogens	2 **He** Helium 4.0026

IIIA	IVA	VA	VIA	VIIA	
5 **B** Boron 10.811	6 **C** Carbon 12.01115	7 **N** Nitrogen 14.0067	8 **O** Oxygen 15.9994	9 **F** Fluorine 18.9984	10 **Ne** Neon 20.183
13 **Al** Aluminum 26.9815	14 **Si** Silicon 28.086	15 **P** Phosphorus 30.9738	16 **S** Sulfur 32.064	17 **Cl** Chlorine 35.453	18 **Ar** Argon 39.948

IB	IIB						
28 **Ni** Nickel 58.71	29 **Cu** Copper 63.54	30 **Zn** Zinc 65.37	31 **Ga** Gallium 69.72	32 **Ge** Germanium 72.59	33 **As** Arsenic 74.9216	34 **Se** Selenium 78.96	35 **Br** Bromine 79.909	36 **Kr** Krypton 83.80
46 **Pd** Palladium 106.4	47 **Ag** Silver 107.870	48 **Cd** Cadmium 112.40	49 **In** Indium 114.82	50 **Sn** Tin 118.69	51 **Sb** Antimony 121.75	52 **Te** Tellurium 127.60	53 **I** Iodine 126.9044	54 **Xe** Xenon 131.30
78 **Pt** Platinum 195.09	79 **Au** Gold 196.967	80 **Hg** Mercury 200.59	81 **Tl** Thallium 204.37	82 **Pb** Lead 207.19	83 **Bi** Bismuth 208.980	84 **Po** Polonium [210]*	85 **At** Astatine [210]	86 **Rn** Radon [222]

Rare Earth Elements

63 **Eu** Europium 151.96	64 **Gd** Gadolinium 157.25	65 **Tb** Terbium 158.924	66 **Dy** Dysprosium 162.50	67 **Ho** Holmium 164.930	68 **Er** Erbium 167.26	69 **Tm** Thulium 168.934	70 **Yb** Ytterbium 173.04	71 **Lu** Lutetium 174.97
95 **Am** Americium [243]	96 **Cm** Curium [247]	97 **Bk** Berkelium [247]*	98 **Cf** Californium [251]*	99 **Es** Einsteinium [254]	100 **Fm** Fermium [257]	101 **Md** Mendelevium [258]	102 **No** Nobelium [254]	103 **Lr** Lawrencium [257]

Brackets indicate that the mass number for the isotope of longest known half-life is given. An asterisk indicates that the mass number for the best known isotope is given.

PROBLEMS

2. What is the atomic number of tungsten (W)? 74
3. What element has an atomic number of 6 (Z = 6)? carbon

1:4 Isotopes

Every atom of carbon has six protons. However, some atoms of carbon have six neutrons and some have eight neutrons. Every atom of oxygen has eight protons, but some atoms of oxygen have seven, eight, or nine neutrons. All atoms of an element have the same number of protons. However, they can differ in the number of neutrons. These atoms are called **isotopes** (I suh tohps). Every element has at least two isotopes. Some, like tin, have as many as ten.

Protium (PROHT ee uhm) is the most common isotope of hydrogen. It has an atomic mass of one. It contains one proton in its nucleus (Figure 1–7a). A second isotope of hydrogen is called deuterium (doo TIR ee uhm) or heavy hydrogen. It has an atomic mass of two. Tritium (TRIT ee uhm) is the third isotope of hydrogen. It has an atomic mass of three. This is because it contains two neutrons and one proton in its nucleus (Figure 1–7c). How do you think these isotopes were named? The prefixes *pro-*, *deu-*, and *tri-* mean 1, 2, and 3 respectively.

There are two methods to show the difference between isotopes of an element. One method uses the name of the element followed by the atomic mass. For example, oxygen 16 means the isotope of oxygen which has an atomic mass of 16. Carbon 12 is the isotope of carbon which has an atomic mass of 12. The numeral indicates which isotope is being discussed. Thus, an isotope of hydrogen might be called hydrogen 2, instead of deuterium. What is another name for tritium? hydrogen 3

The second method to show the difference between isotopes uses the isotope's symbol, atomic number, and atomic mass. For example, $^{12}_{6}C$ is the carbon-12 isotope. The 12 is the atomic mass of this isotope. The 6 is the atomic number of the element. $^{23}_{11}Na$ tells the mass (23) and the atomic number (11) of an isotope of sodium.

Figure 1-7. Hydrogen has three isotopes. Protium has one proton, no neutrons (a). Deuterium has one proton and one neutron (b). Tritium has one proton and two neutrons (c).

How many protons are there in $^{25}_{12}Mg$? 12 protons

PROBLEMS

4. How many protons does $^{23}_{11}Na$ contain? 11 protons
5. How many protons and neutrons are in the nucleus of $^{23}_{11}Na$? 11 protons and 12 neutrons
6. How many electrons are in an atom of this isotope? 11 electrons

Figure 1-8. What is the atomic number of each of these atoms? 6, 19, 9

1:5 Average Atomic Mass

Every element with natural isotopes is usually found in nature as a mixture of these isotopes. For example, a sample of chlorine gas is likely to be a mixture of two isotopes. These are chlorine 35 and chlorine 37. The average mass of the atoms in this sample would be greater than 35 but less than 37. Thus, the atomic masses given for elements in the periodic table are **average atomic masses.** They are based upon the atomic masses of the naturally occurring isotopes.

Average atomic mass is found by first separating the isotopes of an element. From this, the amount of each isotope in the mixture is found. An average is then calculated based on these amounts.

What is average atomic mass?

A weighted mass based on the atomic masses of the naturally occuring isotopes. No one isotope will have that mass.

EXAMPLE

Suppose scientists find an element which they call gymnasium. They determine that it has two isotopes: gymnasium 25, which makes up 40% of the sample; and gymnasium 30, which makes up 60% of the sample. What average atomic mass should they assign to gymnasium?

Solution 1: Since gymnasium 25 contributes 40% of the sample, it must contribute 40% of its mass to an average atomic mass. In the same manner, gymnasium 30 must contribute 60% of its mass to an average atomic mass.
Average atomic mass $= (0.40 \times 25) + (0.60 \times 30) = 10 + 18 = 28$ a.m.u.

Solution 2: Consider 100 of the atoms. Since 40 of the atoms of gymnasium have mass 25 and 60 atoms have mass 30, the solution can be found simply by averaging.

$$\text{Average atomic mass} = \frac{(40 \times 25) + (60 \times 30)}{100} =$$

$$\frac{1000 + 1800}{100} = \frac{2800}{100} = 28 \text{ a.m.u.}$$

You may wish to review rounding of numbers. For example, any decimal less than 0.5 is dropped. Any decimal 0.5 or greater raises to the next integer. Examples: 43.48 to 43; 125.089 to 125; 29.52 to 30; 87.503 to 88

Why is atomic mass number used instead of average atomic mass?

Figure 1-9. Members of this family have similar properties. Density, color, and chemical activity are caused by differences in atomic structure.

PROBLEMS

7. Neon exists as two isotopes: 90% is neon 20 and 10% is neon 22. What is the average atomic mass of neon? 20.2 a.m.u.

8. The atomic mass of chlorine on the periodic table is not a whole number. What does this indicate? The element has isotopes.

The atomic mass number is often used instead of the average atomic mass. The **atomic mass number** (A) of an element is its average atomic mass rounded to the nearest whole number. Atomic mass number is sometimes called mass number. For example, the average atomic mass of cobalt (Co) is 58.93. Its mass number is 59 (or $A = 59$). Barium (Ba) has an average atomic mass of 137.34. Its mass number is 137.

	Z	A
Fe	26	56
Ra	88	226
Al	13	27
Au	79	197
Cu	29	64

PROBLEMS

F = 18.9984, Cl = 35.453, Br = 79.909, I = 126.9044

9. What is the atomic mass of F, Cl, Br, I?

10. Find Z and A for lithium (Li), nitrogen (N), and potassium (K).

11. Find Z and A for iron (Fe), radon (Rn), aluminum (Al), gold (Au), and copper (Cu).

	Z	A
Li	3	7
N	7	14
K	19	39

1:6 Reading the Periodic Table—Columns

You can learn much about elements from the periodic table. Each small block within the table contains the symbol, atomic number (Z), and average atomic mass of an element. The symbol represents the name of the element.

In the periodic table, elements are arranged in vertical columns. Each column lists elements with similar properties. For example, fluorine, chlorine, bromine, iodine, and astatine are all in column VIIA. All the elements in a column make up a family. All elements in a family have similar properties.

In column VIIA, the elements have electrons in different shells. However, each element in this column has seven electrons in its outer shell. Therefore, these elements often react in the same way.

All but one of the elements in column VIIIA have eight electrons in their outer shells. Helium has two electrons in its outer shell. Why does helium not have eight electrons in its outer shell? How many electrons do you think an element in column IA has in its outer shell? One electron is in the outer level.   It only has two electrons.

The Roman numerals of the A columns show the number of electrons in the outer shell of each element. Nearly all elements in the B columns have two electrons in their outer shells. Locate the A and B columns in Table 1-2.

PEOPLE CAREERS FRONTIERS FOCUS ON PHYSICAL SCIENCE

Becky Shroeder Makes a Glowing Discovery

Becky Shroeder, age 13, holds a patent for a new device. This invention is a special paper. The paper has a phosphorescent backing which glows in the dark. With the special paper people can see what they write in the dark.

Becky said that the idea for her invention came to her one evening. She was writing something in the car while waiting for her parents. It became dark and she could not see what she was writing.

After working on a solution to her problem, she finally came up with one. It was a special phosphorescent backing sheet. Becky made several attempts before the sheet worked well. She states that this backing sheet will be on the market some day.

....

Courtesy of Associated Press News-features.

Becky Schroeder shows her invention — a special paper which lets people write in the dark.

Gregory Coppa

Gregory Coppa is a chemistry and physical science teacher. His interests in science do not stop when he leaves his classroom. He has many outside interests in science as well. Two major interests include environmental protection and finding new ways of producing energy.

Mr. Coppa has looked into many possible fuel sources. He believes that methane gas is a good power source. He also is interested in methane gas because it can be produced from organic waste. There are many difficulties in disposing of wastes. Therefore, using wastes to produce methane gas could be a solu-

Gregory Coppa

tion to two problems. One problem is producing fuel, the other is getting rid of waste.

Mr. Coppa believes that methane can be produced on a regular basis in methane-production plants. Garbage would have to be separated from glass, metal, paper, and plastic wastes before waste collection. The glass, metal, and paper could be sold to scrap dealers for recycling. This would help pay for the cost of the garbage collection.

Leaves, grass trimmings, and garbage would be trucked to "digesters." Digesters are large airtight containers used to produce methane gas. Sewage systems could even empty into these digesters. In the absence of air, a certain microbe changes carbon dioxide into methane gas. The methane gas produced could be stored for use by local gas companies.

....

Adapted from "Methane: A Neglected Resource," *Chemistry*, December, 1975.

Figure 1-10. Lithium is a metal. It has one electron in its outer shell. *Sodium is a metal; it has one electron in the outer shell and has other physical and chemical properties generally associated with metals such as luster, hardness, etc.*

Elements may be classified as metals or nonmetals. Look at the elements in column VIIIB and column IB. These elements are metals. They have many properties which are alike. Elements in column IA and column IIA are also classified as metals. In general, **metals** have one, two, or three electrons in their outer shells. Elements with more than four electrons in the outer shell are **nonmetals**.

PROBLEMS

12. What change occurs in Z and A as you read down a column? *Z and A increase.*
13. Suppose you are given a periodic table without numbers. How could you determine if one element has more protons than another? *An element would have more protons than any element above it or to the left of it.*

1:7 Reading the Periodic Table—Rows

The periodic table contains horizontal rows. Look at row two. This row lists lithium (Li) through neon (Ne). Each element in the row has different properties. Some of these differences are indicated in the periodic table. What differences are there as you read from left to right (Table 1–3)?

The type of element changes as you read from left to right. Each element is either a metal, metalloid, or nonmetal. Do you know what a metalloid is? A **metalloid** is neither a metal nor a nonmetal. It has properties of both. What is the metalloid in row three? *boron* Other common metalloids are silicon (Si), germanium (Ge), arsenic (As), antimony (Sb), and tellurium (Te).

Each row ends with a gas that contains eight electrons in the outer shell. These gases are very stable. They are called the *noble gases*. Until 1962, it was believed that noble gases did not form

Figure 1-11. Position of an element in the periodic table indicates its properties. The elements become less metallic from left to right across the periodic table.

IA	IIA	IIIA	IVA	VA	VIA	VIIA	VIIIA
Light metals		Metalloid		Nonmetals			Noble gas
3 / 2,1	4 / 2,2	5 / 2,3	6 / 2,4	7 / 2,5	8 / 2,6	9 / 2,7	10 / 2,8
Li	**Be**	**B**	**C**	**N**	**O**	**F**	**Ne**
Lithium 6.939	Beryllium 9.0122	Boron 10.811	Carbon 12.01115	Nitrogen 14.0067	Oxygen 15.9994	Fluorine 18.9984	Neon 20.183

→ Increasing atomic mass →

Table 1-3. Reading the Periodic Table—Left to Right

Properties	Lithium (Li)	Beryllium (Be)	Boron (B)	Carbon (C)	Nitrogen (N)	Oxygen (O)	Fluorine (F)	Neon (Ne)
Atomic number (Z)	3	4	5	6	7	8	9	10
Atomic mass number (A)	7	9	11	12	14	16	19	20
Column	IA	IIA	IIIA	IVA	VA	VIA	VIIA	VIIIA
Number of electrons in outer shell	1	2	3	4	5	6	7	8
How compounds are formed	Gives up electrons	Gives up electrons	Shares electrons	Shares electrons	Shares electrons	Usually shares electrons	Gains an electron	Shares electrons
Type of element	Metal	Metal	Metalloid	Nonmetal solid	Gas	Gas	Gas	Gas

compounds. However, covalent compounds of these elements have now been formed. Neon ($Z = 10$) is the last member of the second row. It is the gas in neon signs.

Row four elements occur in columns which have not appeared in rows one, two, and three. These are the B columns. The metals in the B columns are called *transition metals*. Nearly all of them have two electrons in their outer shell, the fourth energy level.

Name the noble gases.
helium, argon, krypton, xenon, and radon

Problem

14. What change in Z and A occurs from left to right in the periodic table? From left to right, Z and A increase with three exceptions in A.

Texaco, Inc.

Figure 1-12. Boron, a metalloid, is often added to rocket fuel.

1:8 Chemical Activity

The chemical activity of an element can be determined from its position in the periodic table. **Chemical activity** means how easily an element reacts with other elements. For example, oxygen is chemically active. It reacts with most elements to form compounds. The noble gases have low chemical activity; they react with very few elements.

Each metal in column IA has one electron in the outer energy level. However, the outer electron of cesium is much farther from its nucleus than the outer electron of lithium. Cesium has a larger nuclear charge than lithium because it has more protons in the nucleus. It also has more electrons than lithium. In cesium, the electrons between the nucleus and the electron in the outer shell tend to screen the attractive force of the nucleus. Thus, the outer electron is held more loosely in the cesium atom than in the lithium atom. Cesium can lose its electron more easily than lithium can lose its electron. Therefore, cesium is more chemically active than lithium. The same idea holds true for the other metals. Therefore, the most chemically active metals are on the bottom left portion of the chart.

Can you tell the chemical activity of nonmetals by reading the periodic table? Fluorine and iodine combine with other elements. They both attract an electron from another atom. The electrons of the fluorine atom are relatively close to the nucleus. This means the nuclear charge is effective in attracting other electrons. However, the outer energy level of iodine is far away from the nucleus. Its nuclear charge is screened by the electrons. Thus, fluorine has greater attraction for other electrons and is more active than iodine. The most active nonmetals are at the top right of the periodic table.

The column IA metals (alkali metals) easily lose the single outer electron and form extremely stable inert gas configurations. Column IB metals (coinage metals) are noncorrosive and relatively unreactive because loss of the single outer shell electron does not result in the formation of an appreciably more stable ion.

Which is more active, magnesium or barium?

Barium is more active than magnesium. On the periodic table barium is found on the lower left below magnesium.

Name an active nonmetal.
oxygen, sulfur, nitrogen

Figure 1-13. Metal surfaces of buildings often react with elements in the air. These chemical reactions often change the appearance of these surfaces.

Jim Elliott

Time: 60 minutes.   See Teacher's Guide at the front of this book.

DEMONSTRATION. CAUTION: Use care in using carbon tetrachloride. When two or more substances are mixed, a color change may indicate a chemical change. Compare the chemical activity of the column VIIA family. To each of five test tubes, add the materials indicated: (1) Add 5 ml of carbon tetrachloride to 10 ml of potassium iodide solution and shake. Add 5 ml of chlorine water and shake again. (2) Repeat, using bromine water instead of chlorine. (3) Repeat, using potassium bromide solution and chlorine water. (4) Repeat, using potassium bromide solution, iodine solution, and carbon tetrachloride. (5) Repeat, using sodium chloride solution, iodine solution, and carbon tetrachloride. Based on your observations, list chlorine, bromine, and iodine in order of decreasing chemical activity. How are your results related to the position of these elements in the periodic table? Why is fluorine not used in this demonstration? Too reactive.

This activity is to be a teacher demonstration only. Because of the nature of CCl_4, use extreme care throughout. Perform demonstration only under a hood with an operating vent. Be sure to stopper each test tube after adding CCl_4.

Activity series: chlorine, bromine, iodine

Same as the order in the periodic table.

Figure 1-14.

The patterns that have been seen so far are repeated in each row of the periodic table. Moving across the table from left to right, the elements change from metals to nonmetals. Also, bonding changes from ionic to covalent to ionic. In the columns, the most active metals are at the bottom left. The most active nonmetals are at the upper right. Elements in the same column have different size atoms and different chemical activities, but they have similar properties.

Note: Active metals are in the lower left; active nonmetals are in the upper right of the periodic table.

MAIN IDEAS

1:1 **1.** The atomic mass of an element is a relative value with respect to a standard mass.

1:1 **2.** Carbon 12 is the standard for atomic mass. One atomic mass unit (1 a.m.u.) = 1/12 the mass of the carbon-12 atom.

176 (16M)   PERIODIC TABLE

1:2 3. Mendeleev organized the elements according to their atomic masses.
1:2 4. Moseley rearranged the periodic table according to atomic number.
1:2 5. When elements are arranged in order of increasing atomic number, there is a periodic repetition of properties.
1:2 6. The atomic number *(Z)* of an element is the number of protons in the nucleus.
1:4, 1:5 7. Average atomic mass of an element is the average mass of the element's isotopes.
1:5 8. The mass number *(A)* of an element is its average atomic mass rounded to the nearest whole number.
1:6 9. In the periodic table, families of elements occur in columns.
1:7, 1:8 10. The position of an element in the periodic table can indicate its chemical activity.

VOCABULARY

Write a sentence in which you correctly use each of the following words or terms.

all

atomic mass number	chemical activity	metalloid
atomic mass unit	isotope	noble gas
atomic number	mass number	nonmetal
average atomic mass	metal	periodic table

STUDY QUESTIONS

Have students rewrite false statements to make the statements correct.

A. True or False

Determine whether each of the following sentences is true or false. (Do not write in this book.)

T 1. Carbon 12 has a mass of 12 atomic mass units.
T 2. An atomic mass unit (a.m.u.) is equal to 1/12 the mass of a carbon-12 atom.
T 3. An atom with 6 protons, 6 neutrons, and 6 electrons has a mass of 12 a.m.u.
mass F 4. Mendeleev's periodic table was arranged according to increasing atomic ~~number~~.

PERIODIC TABLE (17M) 177

F **5.** Atomic number of an element equals the total number of protons, ~~neutrons, and~~ electrons in an element's atom. *or*

F **6.** The letter ~~Z~~ is used as a symbol for atomic mass. *A*

F **7.** The mass of ~~a proton~~ is so small that it is considered zero. *an electron*

F **8.** Noble gases are chemically ~~active~~. *inactive*

T **9.** Helium is a noble gas.

F **10.** Boron is a ~~nonmetal~~. *metalloid*

B. Multiple Choice

Some questions in Parts B and C may have more than one correct answer. Only one answer is required.

Choose one word or phrase that correctly completes each of the following sentences. (Do not write in this book.)

1. The first member of family VIIIA is (neon, *helium*, argon).
2. Repetition of properties depends on the number of (*protons*, neutrons, shells).
3. (Helium, *Carbon*, Sulfur) has 6 protons in its nucleus.
4. Hydrogen has (2, *3*, 4) natural isotopes.
5. Isotopes differ in the number of (protons, electrons, *neutrons*).
6. Metals are found on the (*left*, center, right) part of the periodic table.
7. Nonmetals are found on the (left, center, *right*) part of the periodic table.
8. Calcium is in the same family as (*magnesium*, potassium, sulfur).
9. Sulfur is a (metal, *nonmetal*, metalloid).
10. Boron has (0, 1, 2, *3*, 4, 5, 6, 7, 8) electrons in the outer shell.

C. Completion

Complete each of the following sentences with a word or phrase that will make the sentence correct. (Do not write in this book.)

1. Like lithium, sodium will form compounds through _____ electrons. *sharing*
2. An example of a compound formed between elements of group IA and group VIA is _____. *Na$_2$O, H$_2$S, etc.*
3. _____ developed a periodic table based on atomic mass. *Mendeleev*
4. Lithium is found in group _____. *IA*
5. Family IIIA elements have _____ electrons in the outer shell. *three*

<small>*cobalt, nickel*</small> **6.** Two members of the transition elements are _____ and _____.

<small>*26, 30*</small> **7.** Iron 56 has 26 protons, _____ electrons, and _____ neutrons.

<small>*protons, electrons*</small> **8.** $Z=9$ tells us that an element has nine _____.

<small>*transition*</small> **9.** Metals in the B columns of the periodic table are called _____ elements.

<small>*greatest*</small> **10.** In metals, chemical activity is _____ when the outer energy level is far away from the nucleus.

<small>*See Teacher's Guide at the front of this book.*</small>

D. How and Why

1. Why is the periodic table of value to scientists?
2. Name five metals and five nonmetals.
3. An element is found 60% as isotope 30 and 40% as isotope 32. What is its average atomic mass?
4. What are some differences between metals and nonmetals?
5. Name five transition elements.

<small>*Included in the Teacher's Guide is a review of the periodic table. The students are asked to fill out, from the information known, a blank periodic table of the thirty known elements found on Mars. The exercise could be used as an open book test to determine how well the students understand the chapter.*</small>

6. An element has $Z=15$ and an atomic mass of 32.7. What can you tell about the element?
7. Using only the periodic table, tell how magnesium differs from chlorine.
8. How are Mendeleev's and Moseley's tables similar? How are they different?
9. How can you tell whether an element is chemically active when reading the periodic table?
10. Why are noble gases not very active chemically? Name two noble gases.

<small>*See Teacher's material at front of book for suggestions.*</small>

INVESTIGATIONS

1. The search for helium is an interesting story. Find out how helium got its name. Why was its discovery so unusual?
2. How did the rare earth elements get their name? Study one of these elements. Determine why it is "rare."
3. John Newlands and Johann Dobereiner made early attempts at classifying the elements. Find out about their work.
4. Write a report comparing the development of the periodic table by Mendeleev and by Moseley.

INTERESTING READING

Asimov, Isaac, *The Search for the Elements.* New York, Fawcett World Library, 1971.

"Evidence for Element 112." *Science News,* XCIX (February 20, 1971), pp. 127–128.

Haines, Gail Kay, *The Elements.* New York, Watts, 1972.

Sanderson, R. T., "How Should Periodic Groups Be Numbered?" *Chemistry,* XLIV (November, 1971), pp. 17–18.

Seaborg, Glenn T., and Valens, Evans G., *Elements of the Universe.* New York, E. P. Dutton & Company, 1958.

Wiegand, C. E., "Exotic Atoms." *Scientific American,* CCXXVII (November, 1972), pp. 102–108.

Wohlrabe, Raymond A., *Metals.* Philadelphia, J. B. Lippincott Company, 1965.

Elements from many of the families can be found either in a free or a combined state in nature. *Paul Poplis/Studio Ten*

Columns of the periodic table are called families. Elements in families exhibit similar properties. The study of families leads to generalizations about chemical

Families of Elements

properties. Among these are diatomic gases, allotropy, photoconductivity, multiple proportions, and spectrum analysis.

GOAL: You will gain an understanding of the properties of chemical families.

Henry Moseley's development of the modern periodic table was a major contribution in chemistry. The organization of the table was based on the number of protons of the elements. This accounted for the periodic repetition of properties.

The table was designed so that each vertical column included elements with some similar properties. Each vertical column on the periodic table represents a family. Each family has features much different from any other family.

HALOGEN FAMILY

2:1 Halogen Family

Table 2–1. The Halogen Family

Element	Z	A	M.P. (°C)	B.P. (°C)	Description
Fluorine (F)	9	19	−223	−187	pale yellow gas
Chlorine (Cl)	17	35	−102	−34.6	greenish-yellow gas
Bromine (Br)	35	80	−7.3	58.8	reddish-brown liquid
Iodine (I)	53	127	114	183	steel-gray crystals
Astatine (At)	85	(210)	—	—	radioactive solid

Chlorine (KLOR een) is added to swimming pool water to kill germs and to laundry water to bleach clothes. As an element, chlorine is a greenish-yellow gas with a sharp odor. Chlorine is a member of the **halogen family,** Column VIIA of the periodic table. In addition to chlorine, the halogen family includes fluorine (FLUR een), bromine (BROH meen), iodine (I uh dyn), and astatine (AS tuh teen). In their uncombined (element) form, all of the halogens are poisonous and burn the skin.

Halogen means "salt-producer." Halogen elements combine with metals to form compounds called *salts*. Sodium chloride (NaCl), or table salt, is the salt with which you are most familiar.

A halogen combines chemically with a metal by ionic bonding. Each halogen has seven electrons in its outer shell. One more electron is needed to complete the outer shell. When a halogen atom combines with a metal, the halogen atom gains that one electron and an ionic bond is formed.

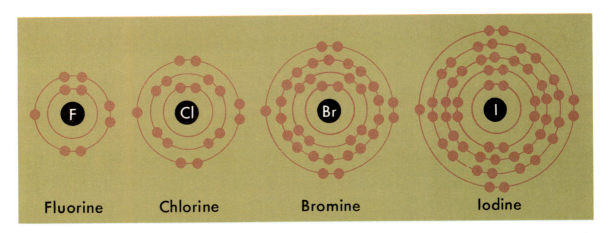

Figure 2-1. Halogens have seven electrons in their outer shells.

Figure 2-2. When potassium and chlorine combine, an ionic bond is formed. Potassium has one more proton than electron and chlorine has one more electron than proton.

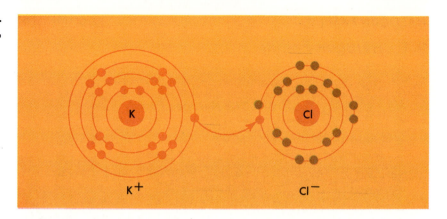

PROBLEM

1. Why do the halogens form ionic bonds when combining with metals? Halogens easily gain electrons.

Halogens can also form covalent bonds. These bonds are found between atoms sharing electrons. Two atoms of a halogen element can share one pair of electrons between them and form a halogen molecule (Figure 2–3). In the gaseous phase, the halogens exist as diatomic molecules. *Diatomic* means that a molecule is composed of two atoms.

Figure 2-3. Two fluorine atoms can share one pair of electrons to form a fluorine molecule.

Two different halogens can also combine covalently to form molecules. One molecule of bromine and chlorine, for example, has the formula BrCl. The outer shell electrons can be shown with an electron dot model, Figure 2–4a. Many other halogen molecules of this type can form.

Figure 2-4. Covalent bonds are formed when two different halogens combine (a). These bonds also form between atoms of a diatomic halogen molecule (b).

In addition to the properties common to this family, each halogen has special properties of its own.

a

b

HALOGEN FAMILY

Fluorine. Fluorine is the most reactive nonmetallic element. It is an extremely corrosive (kuh ROH siv), pale yellow gas. It is never found free in nature. Compounds containing fluorine are called *fluorides*. Free fluorine is obtained by passing an electric current through molten fluorides. The decomposition of a compound into simpler substances by passing an electric current through the compound is called *electrolysis* (ih lek TRAHL uh suhs).

Fluorine reacts explosively with hydrogen to form hydrogen fluoride (HF). In a water solution, hydrogen fluoride can be used to etch glass. Fluorine also combines with oxygen to form many different compounds. The "non-stick" material on cooking utensils is a compound made from fluorine and carbon.

Chlorine. Chlorine is the most abundant halogen. It is twice as plentiful in nature as fluorine and one hundred times more abundant than bromine. Chlorine does not occur free in nature. It is usually found chemically combined with sodium, potassium, magnesium, or calcium. It is usually obtained by the electrolysis of molten sodium chloride or saltwater brine.* It is only slightly less active than fluorine. Unlike fluorine, chlorine can be liquefied easily under pressure.

Chlorine forms compounds with hydrogen and oxygen. Most of these compounds have very practical uses. Many cleaning compounds and bleaches contain chlorine compounds. For example, laundries use a chlorine bleach to whiten clothes. Another type of chlorine product is used to bleach flour and paper. Some chlorine compounds are used to disinfect drinking water.

---

*Brine is a concentrated saltwater or ocean water solution. Chlorides and other compounds such as bromides may also be present in a brine.

Figure 2-5. Fluorides are often used in toothpastes to protect teeth against cavities.

How is fluorine prepared?

Figure 2-6. Teflon® is a compound of fluorine and carbon.

The William C. Pflaum Co.

Name two properties of fluorine and chlorine.
Examples: fluorine—most reactive, never found free in nature; chlorine—most abundant, never found free in nature.

Figure 2-7. Chlorine is often used to disinfect swimming pools.

FAMILIES OF ELEMENTS

Figure 2-8. Iodine is often used to treat minor cuts and scratches.

How is bromine different from chlorine?

Figure 2-9. Iodine is purified through the process of sublimation.

Courtesy of Kodansha Ltd.

Figure 2-10.

Bromine. In nature, bromine is never found as an element. It is always combined as a bromide. Bromides are generally found in seawater and brine wells. Bromine is prepared commercially by treating seawater or brine with chlorine. Chlorine is more reactive than bromine. Thus, chlorine replaces bromine in compounds and free bromine is released. At room temperature, bromine is a dark red liquid with a reddish-brown cloud above it.

Bromine in the form of silver bromide (AgBr) is used to make photographic film. Bromine compounds are added to gasoline to prevent the uneven combustion that causes "knock" in car engines.

Iodine. Iodine, like the other halogens, is found only in the combined state in nature. Like bromine, iodine can be obtained from seawater. Free iodine also results from the burning of certain kinds of seaweed. Impure iodine is often unsuitable for use, so it is purified. Solid iodine can change directly to a vapor without passing through a liquid phase. This is called *sublimation* (suhb luh MAY shuhn). Iodine is purified by first making impure iodine sublime. Then its vapor is crystallized on a cool surface (Figure 2-9).

At room temperature, iodine is a gray, lustrous solid. It has many of the physical properties of a metal. Iodine compounds are essential to the human diet and are also used in medicines. The element iodine is poisonous as are all other halogens. This conforms to the general rule that elements on the right of the periodic table become more metallic near the bottom.

Time: 20 minutes.

ACTIVITY. Obtain a potato, a piece of bread, a banana, a carrot, and some tincture of iodine. Place a small piece of each food in a dish. Put a drop of iodine on each. Record your observations. Iodine is used to test for the presence of starch. Which of these foods contains starch? Try this test on other foods.
CAUTION: Students should not taste any of the foods. Dispose of the tested foods in suitable containers.

CAUTION: Use a well ventilated room for this activity.
Time: 45 minutes. Do not expose students to direct skin contact or allow them to breathe the vapor of iodine.

ACTIVITY. Set up a series of labeled test tubes. Each should contain a single liquid: water, alcohol, and mineral oil. Add a crystal of iodine to each liquid. Mix. Does the iodine dissolve in any of the liquids? Add a drop of liquid starch solution to each and observe any change. Devise an activity to determine whether it is the iodine or the liquid which reacts with starch. You might like to use a control such as distilled water.
You may wish to try other solvents also. Add a drop of liquid starch to each test tube.

OXYGEN FAMILY (25M) 185

Astatine. The last member of the halogen family, astatine, is not found in nature. However, it has been made in the laboratory. It has properties similar to iodine but is a radioactive element. A radioactive element is one in which high energy radiation is released from its nuclei. Most astatine isotopes have short half-lives. This means the nuclei of these atoms break up rapidly to form other elements. Astatine can form compounds with other halogens.

PROBLEMS

2. Write the chemical formula for a molecule of fluorine, of chlorine, of bromine, and of iodine. F_2, Cl_2, Br_2, I_2

3. Draw a diagram of an atom of fluorine and an atom of bromine. How are they alike? See Teacher's Guide for diagram. Each has seven electrons in its outer shell.

4. Give at least one use for each element in the halogen family. See Teacher's Guide.

The name oxygen is derived from the Greek words oxys (sharp) and genes (to form). Lavoisier believed that oxygen was an essential part of every acid. Oxygen is the most abundant element on our Earth and is necessary for the continuous existence of most living things. Twenty-one percent of the atmosphere is oxygen. It accounts for 50% of the weight of rocks and eight-ninths of the weight of water.

2:2 Oxygen Family

Table 2–2. The Oxygen Family

Element	Z	A	M.P. (°C)	B.P. (°C)	Description
Oxygen (O)	8	16	−219	−183	colorless gas
Sulfur (S)	16	32	119	445	yellow solid
Selenium (Se)	34	79	220	685	reddish solid
Tellurium (Te)	52	128	450	1390	gray solid
Polonium (Po)	84	(210)	—	—	radioactive solid

Which member is a gas? oxygen

Column VIA in the periodic table is called the **oxygen** (AHK sih juhn) **family.** Unlike the halogens, the oxygen family members are all found in nature both in the free state and chemically combined. Most members form covalent bonds. Each atom has six electrons in its outer shell. Thus, it must share two electrons with atoms of other elements to form compounds. Sulfur in hydrogen sulfide (H_2S) is an example of an element sharing electrons (Figure 2–11).

The elements of the oxygen family form different molecular types of the same element. These forms are called **allotropes** (AL uh trohps). They result from the formation of molecules with different numbers of the same atoms. Oxygen, for example, exists free as the diatomic molecule, O_2. However, under certain conditions, some

Figure 2-11. In H_2S, sulfur forms a covalent bond with each hydrogen atom.

Electronic structure of H_2S

Figure 2-12. During thunderstorms, some oxygen in the air is changed to ozone.

How is ozone different from O$_2$?
It is a triatomic molecule.

molecules of O$_2$ can be changed into ozone, O$_3$. During thunderstorms, for example, some oxygen in the air is changed to ozone. Both diatomic oxygen molecules and **triatomic** ozone molecules (composed of three atoms of oxygen) are allotropes of oxygen. Oxygen is the only member of the oxygen family which exists as a diatomic gas at room temperature. All other members are solids. Their properties become more metallic as the atomic masses increase.

Oxygen. Oxygen is one of the most reactive nonmetallic elements. Oxygen can be found in chemical combination with nearly every other element. Combined oxygen makes up nearly 50 percent (by mass) of the earth's crust. Approximately 20 percent of the total volume of air is O$_2$.

Figure 2-13.

Time: 30 minutes.
ACTIVITY. Place a piece of steel wool on a cork floating in a pan of water. Cover with an inverted 25-ml graduated cylinder. Allow to stand for one week. Observe the water level and the appearance of the steel wool during this time. Explain your observations.
The water has risen in the cylinder to replace the oxygen which united with the steel wool.

Without free oxygen, most life on Earth could not exist. Compounds of oxygen are also extremely important to people. Water (H$_2$O) is perhaps the most important oxide. Another compound of hydrogen and oxygen is hydrogen peroxide (H$_2$O$_2$). It is used as a disinfectant and as a bleach. Common sand is an oxygen compound called silicon dioxide, or silica (SiO$_2$). Rust is iron oxide (Fe$_2$O$_3$).

Jeff Bates

Figure 2-14. Sand is an oxygen compound called silicon dioxide, or silica. What other oxygen-containing materials are shown? water, air

Time: 90 minutes.

You may wish to use a medicine dropper in place of a dropping funnel.

ACTIVITY. CAUTION: This activity should be done only under the supervision of your teacher.

Arrange the apparatus as shown in Figure 2–15. Slowly drop water from a dropping funnel on 5 g of sodium peroxide. Collect one bottle of oxygen gas by water displacement. Discard the contents of the first bottle since it contains mostly air from the test tube and delivery tube. Collect three more bottles of oxygen. Cover each with a glass plate and stand them upright. Remove the delivery tube from the water. Light a wooden splint and blow it out so it glows red. Thrust the glowing splint into the first bottle of oxygen. What do you observe? Hold a piece of fine steel wool with tongs and heat it until it glows red. Lower it into the second bottle. What do you observe? Use a deflagrating (DEF luh grayt ing) spoon (a special steel spoon for burning substances) to heat a small piece of sulfur until it glows red. Lower it into the third bottle. What do you observe? Name the three oxygen compounds you think are produced.

Figure 2-15.

Splint bursts into flame (O₂ supports combustion). The steel wool glows brightly (rapid oxidation). Sulfur burns with a blue flame. Carbon dioxide, iron (III) oxide, sulfur dioxide are formed.

If reaction is too slow, heat may be added. 30°–40°C is the usual temperature for oxygen generation by this method.

Oxygen is most often prepared commercially by the distillation (dis tuh LAY shuhn) of liquid air. In *distillation*, gases or liquids are separated by making use of differences in their boiling points. Air is a mixture of gases including oxygen and nitrogen. Each gas has a different boiling point. Air is liquefied by pressure and cooling. Then it is allowed to warm. Each gas boils off at a different temperature. Liquid oxygen begins to boil at −183°C. It is drawn off into

What is distillation?

Figure 2-16. Oxygen is given to a patient.

The atoms within the molecules are held together by covalent bonds. The molecules are held together by other attractive forces. Depending on the ability level of your class, you may wish to introduce van der Waals forces.

Figure 2-17. Rhombic sulfur (S_8) is the most common allotrope of sulfur.

another container. Repeating this process produces an almost pure oxygen sample. Also, large amounts of oxygen can be produced by electrolysis of water. Here, an electric current is passed through water. However, this method is expensive on a commercial scale.

Sulfur. Sulfur (SUHL fuhr), like oxygen, is found both free and combined in nature. Sulfur is generally found chemically combined with metals in the form of mineral ores. Most commercial sulfur is obtained from deposits in southern and southwestern United States. Sulfur is mined by the Frasch process (Figure 2–19). This process produces sulfur which is more than 90 percent pure. Like iodine (Section 2:1), sulfur can be purified by sublimation.

Sulfur also exists in several allotropic forms. The most common form is *rhombic* (RAHM bik) sulfur. In this form, eight sulfur atoms are joined in a ring (Figure 2–17). Many other allotropes of sulfur exist as long chains of sulfur atoms.

a

b

Figure 2-18. Sulfur is used in the production of rubber. Raw rubber (a) undergoes many processes before it becomes a finished rubber tire (b).

OXYGEN FAMILY

Sulfur unites with some metals to form compounds called sulfides. It also unites directly with oxygen. Sulfur compounds in the air, such as hydrogen sulfide (H_2S), are responsible for the tarnish on silver. Commercial products which contain sulfur include insecticides, fertilizers, drugs, and rubber.

Table 2–3. Sulfides

Element	Sulfide Compound	Color
Antimony	Sb_2S_3	orange
Arsenic	As_2S_3	yellow
Bismuth	Bi_2S_3	brown
Cadmium	CdS	yellow
Copper	CuS	black
Lead	PbS	black
Silver	Ag_2S	black
Zinc	ZnS	white

This is a method of determining the identity of compounds.

Time: 30 minutes.

ACTIVITY. Place 5 ml of cadmium nitrate, zinc sulfate, antimony chloride, and copper (II) sulfate solutions separately in four test tubes. Label each tube. Cover the label with a blank piece of paper. Have a classmate arrange the test tubes in a rack so you do not know the contents of each. Add a few drops of hydrogen sulfide solution to each. From the color of the solid formed, try to identify the metal. Then check your results against the labels. Table 2–3 lists the colors of various metal sulfides.

Figure 2-19. Water and air are forced down outer and inner pipes. Molten sulfur and water foam are forced up the middle pipe. The sulfur mixture is sprayed into molds where water evaporates and the sulfur remains.

Figure 2-20.

Selenium. Selenium (suh LEE nee uhm) can be found in deposits of free sulfur. It is also an impurity in sulfides and in copper. Most selenium is obtained as a by-product in the electrolysis of copper ore to produce copper.

Selenium is a poison. Plants can absorb selenium from soil and pass it to animals that eat the plant. Insects which feed on plants are often killed in this way. Small amounts of selenium insecticide are put in the soil or sprayed on plant leaves. Selenium then passes through the entire plant without harming it. However, insects eating the plant are poisoned.

190 (30M)　　　　　　　　　　　　　　　FAMILIES OF ELEMENTS

William Maddox

Figure 2-21. Selenium photocells are used in light meters. As the light intensity increases, the current increases, and the arm moves a greater distance.

How does a photocell work?

Rich Brommer

Figure 2-22. Large amounts of selenium are added to the glass used in making red traffic lights.

Polonium was first discovered by the Curie's during the same experiments in which they discovered radium. Formerly it was extracted from pitchblende but now it is synthesized in nuclear reactors. Polonium has a half-life of 138 days which makes it extremely radioactive. After about 138 days a sample of polonium emits only half as many particles per minute as at the start. After 138 more days its activity is again halved and so on.

Selenium has metallic properties such as conducting an electric current. An electric current is a flow of electrons. Metals tend to give up electrons readily (Section 1:6). This property makes metals good conductors because the electrons can move through the metal. Nonmetals tend to hold electrons tightly. Therefore, nonmetals are poor conductors. In the dark, selenium is a poor conductor. However, when exposed to light, selenium gives up electrons and becomes a good conductor. For this reason, selenium is called a *photoconductor*. This means that its ability to pass along electrons is controlled by light.

Photoconductors are used in photographic light meters. One kind of light meter uses a selenium *photocell*. This photocell is made with a small copper plate, a selenium layer, and a gold film that transmits light. Electric wires go to both the copper film and the gold film. Electricity does not flow through the wires until light hits the meter. Then the electrons in the selenium move and an electric current is produced. This causes an arm to move on a dial which indicates the light intensity. As the light intensity increases, the current increases, and the arm moves a greater distance. Selenium photocells are also used in counting people as they enter buildings and for setting off burglar alarms.

Small amounts of selenium are added during the manufacture of glass. Selenium counteracts the green color due to iron impurities in glass. If a great deal of selenium is used, the glass becomes red. This red glass is used in traffic lights.

Tellurium. Tellurium (tuh LUR ee uhm), like selenium, is found in many minerals. It is prepared as a by-product in the refining of ores. It is not a good photoconductor. However, tellurium has some use in the electronics industry. Tellurium is poisonous. It produces a garlic odor on the breath and in the perspiration of people working with it.

Polonium. Polonium (puh LOH nee uhm) is an extremely radioactive metal. As the atoms and molecules undergo changes in the nucleus, high levels of energy are given off. It occurs naturally in pitchblende ore. Marie Curie, a Polish chemist (1867–1934), discovered this element in France in 1898.

PROBLEMS

5. What are some common uses of the elements in the oxygen family?
6. How many electrons are in the outermost shell of each element of the oxygen family?
7. Why is there a similarity in the chemical properties of the elements of the oxygen family?

PEOPLE CAREERS FRONTIERS
FOCUS ON PHYSICAL SCIENCE

Information Chemist

A new and interesting career is that of an information chemist. An information chemist is a specialist who deals with scientific and technical vocabulary. He or she helps other scientists and managers by gathering data.

In order to collect information, an information chemist must be familiar with many sources. Technical records, documents, and patents are just a few sources of information for this type of chemist.

A strong background in grammar and chemistry is needed for this career. A four-year degree in chemistry is also a must.

An information chemist may work in a variety of places. They often work for universities, industries, research centers, or government agencies.

•••••••••••••

Adapted from *Your Tomorrow — A Guide to Careers in the Chemical Industry.*

Manufacturing Chemists Association

Alfreda Sigee chose a career as an information chemist because she likes to locate information for other chemists.

Chemical Technician

A different type of career in chemistry is that of a chemical technician. There is a need for this type of technician in electronics, aerospace, automotive, and chemical industries.

Guild Photographers

This chemical technician works in a research laboratory. He is helping to develop special chemicals used in the manufacture of high quality paper.

FDA Consumer

Many foods are tested to make sure they do not contain harmful chemicals. This technician is preparing green peppers for one type of test. They are being analyzed for the presence of a pesticide.

Chemical technicians perform a variety of tasks. Their responsibilities range from supervising chemistry labs in college to designing equipment. Many are involved in research and analysis of new materials.

To become a chemical technician, many mathematics and science courses should be taken in high school. Many companies hire high school graduates and train them to become technicians. However, most employers encourage applicants to have a two-year degree. This degree is usually called an Associate of Applied Science Degree. It may be obtained at some community colleges or other two-year schools.

Figure 2-23. Nitrogen-fixing bacteria in the roots of certain plants change free nitrogen to nitrate ions. These ions are then absorbed and used by the plants.

2:3 Nitrogen Family

Table 2—4. The Nitrogen Family

Element	Z	A	M.P. (°C)	B.P. (°C)	Description
Nitrogen (N)	7	14	−210	−196	colorless gas
Phosphorus (P)	15	31	44.1	280	white or red solid
Arsenic (As)	33	75	—	—*	gray or yellow solid
Antimony (Sb)	51	122	631	1380	gray solid
Bismuth (Bi)	83	209	271	1500	gray metal

*Gray arsenic sublimes at 450°C.

What are covalent compounds?

Covalent compounds are formed when atoms share electrons.

Figure 2-24. There are five electrons in the outer energy level of each member of the nitrogen family.

Figure 2-25. Two nitrogen atoms each share three electrons. The triple bond of the N_2 molecule makes it extremely stable.

Column VA in the periodic table is called the **nitrogen** (NY truh juhn) **family.** Each member of the nitrogen family has five electrons in its outer shell. Thus, these elements usually form covalent compounds. The family contains a wide range of physical properties. For example, nitrogen is a gas. Both nitrogen and phosphorus (FAHS fuh ruhs) are nonmetals, but bismuth (BIZ muhth) is a metal. Arsenic (AHRS nik) and antimony (ANT uh moh nee) have some properties of both metals and nonmetals. For this reason these two elements are metalloids (Section 1:7).

Elements in the nitrogen family are generally less reactive than elements in the halogen and oxygen families. The five electrons in the outer shell are responsible for this property. It is unlikely that these elements will gain three electrons or lose five electrons. However, they do share electrons with atoms of other elements. In some instances, they share three or even all five electrons.

Nitrogen. Nitrogen is required by every living thing. Air is nearly 79 percent free nitrogen. However, most living things cannot get nitrogen directly from the air. Nitrogen for life comes from compounds found as minerals in the ground, formed during electrical storms, or produced by bacteria.

Like oxygen, nitrogen is usually prepared by the distillation of liquid air. Liquid nitrogen boils at −196°C. Very pure nitrogen can be formed by heating some nitrogen compounds.

Free nitrogen is found as a diatomic molecule. The two nitrogen atoms are held together with a triple covalent bond (Figure 2–25). Two nitrogen atoms each share three electrons. Thus, the nitrogen molecule has little chemical activity. However, the molecule does

NITROGEN FAMILY

Be sure that the students understand the idea of double and triple covalent bonds before proceeding further.

form many compounds which are important to people. One of these compounds is ammonia (NH₃), found in many cleaning compounds. Industry uses nitrogen compounds in making fertilizer and explosives. "Laughing gas," a common anesthetic, is also a nitrogen compound.

Describe a nitrogen molecule.

Figure 2-26.

Time: 45 minutes.

ACTIVITY. A test for the nitrate ion (NO₃⁻). CAUTION: This activity should be done only under the supervision of your teacher.

(1) Add 5 ml of a solution of sodium nitrate or potassium nitrate to a large Pyrex test tube. Add 5 ml of a freshly prepared saturated iron sulfate (FeSO₄) solution. Mix. Then slant the tube. Carefully add 1–2 ml of concentrated sulfuric acid by allowing it to run down the inside of the test tube. Look for a "brown ring" at the line between the acid and mixed solutions.

(2) Repeat using 5 ml of distilled water in place of nitrate solution. Does a brown ring form? Explain.

See Teacher's Guide.

Many different nitrogen-oxygen compounds exist. These compounds illustrate the law of multiple proportions. **The law of multiple proportions** states that the same two (or more) elements may unite to form different compounds. If the mass of one element is held constant, the ratio of the combining masses of the other elements will be in whole numbers. Various nitrogen oxides are shown in Table 2–5. What is the ratio of the masses in each compound?

State the law of multiple proportions.

Table 2–5. Nitrogen Oxides

Formula		Chemical Name	Common Name
N₂O	7:4	nitrogen (I) oxide	nitrous oxide
NO	7:8	nitrogen (II) oxide	nitric oxide
N₂O₃	7:12	nitrogen (III) oxide	dinitrogen trioxide
NO₂	7:16	nitrogen (IV) oxide	nitrogen dioxide
N₂O₅	7:20	nitrogen (V) oxide	dinitrogen pentoxide

The chemical name is generally preferred, but there are many compounds that have long been named by their common names. These more common names are usually retained. Examples are nitrous oxide, nitric oxide.

Phosphorus. Like oxygen and sulfur, phosphorus has allotropes. The two most common are white phosphorus and red phosphorus. White phosphorus is produced from calcium phosphate [Ca₃(PO₄)₂].

Oxides of phosphorus are phosphorus (III) oxide, P₂O₃; phosphorus (IV) oxide, P₂O₄; and phosphorus (V) oxide, P₂O₅.

Figure 2-27. Fertilizers often contain phosphorus compounds.

Name a phosphate found in fertilizer.

DNA is short for deoxyribonucleic acid. Molecules of DNA are long chains interlocked to form a double helix. The molecules are formed by the repetition of a small number of different and comparatively simple chemical compounds.

It is first formed as a gas. Then the gas is condensed under water in the form of P_4 molecules. The water prevents the phosphorus from reacting immediately with the oxygen in air.

Red phosphorus is formed slowly from chains of white phosphorus molecules. Red phosphorus is more stable than white phosphorus. At room temperature, red phosphorus normally has little chemical activity. However, at higher temperatures it forms many compounds.

Like nitrogen, phosphorus forms a number of oxides. Also, phosphates are an important class of phosphorus compounds. For example, calcium phosphate $[Ca_3(PO_4)_2]$ is present in bones. Some phosphates serve as water softeners. Some are used as fertilizers. Ammonium phosphate $[(NH_4)_3PO_4]$ is an important fertilizer. It is used because it contains nitrogen and phosphorus; both are needed for plant growth.

Phosphorus is essential for life. In small amounts, phosphorus provides a means for storing energy in the body. It is found in DNA, a compound in genes. However, in large amounts it harms the human nervous system.

The ease with which phosphorus burns makes it useful in matches. Excessive use of phosphates in detergents may contribute to water pollution. Waste water from the laundry is joined by the runoff from fields fertilized with phosphates and nitrates. These wastes often end up in lakes and rivers. As a result, water plants are fed a diet rich in nutrients. They increase rapidly and use up the supply of oxygen dissolved in the water. Thus, they deprive fish and other aquatic life of oxygen. Many soap industries are reducing the amount of phosphate in detergents. This is an important step in solving this problem.

Figure 2-28. Excess phosphorus in water may cause plant life to multiply until it uses up all the oxygen dissolved in the water.

ALKALI METALS

PROBLEM

8. What can you do to help reduce phosphate pollutants in the environment? See Teacher's Guide.

Arsenic. Arsenic compounds are widespread in nature. The most common consist of arsenic and sulfur. Two allotropic forms of arsenic can be prepared from these compounds. Yellow arsenic, a nonmetal, exists as As_4 molecules. Yellow arsenic will slowly change to gray arsenic, a metal. Perhaps you know that arsenic is a poison. However, it also has uses in medicine. Salvarsan (SAL vuhr san), an arsenic compound, was the forerunner of many of the modern "miracle" drugs.

Antimony and Bismuth. Both antimony and bismuth have metallic properties. Bismuth is a true metal. These two elements have many properties in common with phosphorus and arsenic and form similar compounds. Both antimony and bismuth can be used in alloys with other metals. Bismuth is often included in alloys because it has a low melting point. It is used in automatic sprinkler systems. Heat from a fire melts the bismuth alloy plugs in water pipes. This turns the sprinkler on.

Both antimony and bismuth are used in the plates of storage batteries. Antimony and bismuth also have the unusual property of expanding when they change from the liquid to the solid phase. Thus, when these metals solidify, they expand to fill molds. Most metals would contract away from the walls of molds. The expansion property of antimony and bismuth makes them useful in making plates for printing.

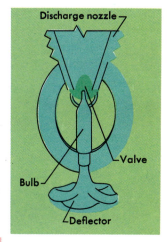

Figure 2-29. Automatic sprinklers have prevented fire damage to many buildings. Bismuth alloys are used in a plug which melts when heated. After the plug melts, water sprays out.

Why are antimony and bismuth useful?

PROBLEMS

9. Give five examples of how the nitrogen family is useful to people. See Teacher's Guide.

10. How many electrons are in the outer shell of each member of the nitrogen family? five

11. What types of bonds are most often formed by members of the nitrogen family? covalent

2:4 Alkali Metals

The **alkali** (AL kuh ly) **metals** are the family of elements in column IA of the periodic table. They have all the features of metals (Section 1:6). They give up their outer shell electrons easily. They usually are shiny and reflect light. They can be pounded into

Table 2-6. The Alkali Metals

Element	Z	A	M.P. (°C)	B.P. (°C)	Description
Lithium (Li)	3	7	186	1336	
Sodium (Na)	11	23	97.5	880	all are silver-
Potassium (K)	19	39	62.3	760	gray metals
Rubidium (Rb)	37	85	38.5	700	
Cesium (Cs)	55	133	28.5	670	
Francium (Fr)	87	(223)	—	—	radioactive solid

sheets and pulled into wires. They are good conductors of electricity and heat. Lithium (LITH ee uhm), sodium (SOHD ee uhm), potassium (puh TAS ee uhm), rubidium (roo BID ee uhm), cesium (SEE zee uhm), and francium (FRAN see uhm) are the most reactive of all the metals. They are never found in the free state in nature. In their element form, the alkali metals are kept under kerosene so they will not react directly with oxygen or water vapor in the air.

All the alkali metals form compounds by ionic bonding because they readily give up their one outer electron to form ions. In fact, cesium gives up its electron when hit with a beam of light. This photoelectric effect is used in a photocell to convert light energy into electrical energy (Section 2:2).

The alkali metals can be identified by *flame tests*. When these elements are heated in a flame some of their electrons gain energy. The electrons lose this energy in the form of light. In the case of potassium, violet light is emitted. Sodium gives a yellow flame and lithium gives a red flame. The names for rubidium and cesium were derived from Latin words describing the color they give off in a flame test. Rubidium gives a red flame and cesium gives a blue flame.

How would sodium and fluorine combine? ionically

The properties of metals are determined by the number of valence electrons available. Column IA metals have only one valence electron per atom and are soft. Column IIA metals have two valence electrons and are harder than Column IA metals. As metallic valence increases, the metals become harder and stronger. Metallic valence refers to the number of free electrons available for metallic bonding.

Dravo Corporation

Figure 2-30. Many metals have properties which make them useful in manufacturing. For example, these newly-formed metal pellets may be easily packaged, moved, then eventually remelted.

Lester V. Bergman & Associates, Inc.

Qualitative analysis is the determination of the elements that are contained in a sample of a substance. The students have already been exposed to one method—the formation of identifiable precipitates. Other methods that they will become acquainted with are electrolysis, titration, flame test, and paper chromatography.

The flame test is an older technique than the other methods and is still extremely important. The flame test method led to the development of the very refined spectrographic techniques that are used in almost every laboratory today. Originally, spectroscopy meant viewing the spectrum produced by a substance, such as that produced when light passes through a prism. It has now come to have a much broader meaning. Spectroscopy now might be interpreted as the broad set of reactions of a substance when it is submitted to a continuous exciting force (heat, in the case of the flame test).

If solutions are relatively pure, some cations can be identified by characteristic flame tests.

Use a length of platinum (or nichrome) wire, clean it and insert it into a solution of the unknown solution. Place the wire in the oxidizing flame of a Bunsen burner. Note the color of the flame. You must be careful that none of the solution falls into the burner, otherwise the succeeding flame tests will be inconclusive.

Copper (emerald green)

Calcium (yellowish-red)

Strontium (scarlet red)

Barium (yellowish-green)

Sodium (yellow)

Potassium (violet)

Rubidium (violet)

Cesium (violet)

Figure 2-31. Flame tests.

Compare with photos on page 197 (37M).

Time: 60 minutes.

ACTIVITY. *Obtain seven test tubes. Label each test tube with one of the following chlorides: lithium, potassium, sodium, barium, calcium, strontium, and copper. Place 5 ml of the corresponding solution in each test tube. Clean a platinum or nichrome wire by dipping it in hydrochloric acid and distilled water in two separate test tubes. Dip the clean wire into one of the sample test tubes. Then hold the wire at the tip of the inner cone of a Bunsen burner flame. Record the color of the flame test for each solution. Clean the wire after each test. When you have become familiar with the colors of flames for each of the samples, ask your teacher for an unknown sample. Identify the metal in the unknown.*

Figure 2-32.

PROBLEMS

12. How many electrons are in the outer shell of an atom of each of the alkali metals? one

13. Why are these elements in the free state stored under kerosene?
They combine explosively with oxygen or water vapor in the air.

2:5 Alkaline Earth Metals

Table 2–7. The Alkaline Earth Metals

Element	Z	A	M.P. (°C)	B.P. (°C)	Description
Beryllium (Be)	4	9	1280±5	2970	very hard silvery metal
Magnesium (Mg)	12	24	651	1107	hard silvery metal
Calcium (Ca)	20	40	842−8	1487	hard silvery metal
Strontium (Sr)	38	88	769	1384	soft silvery metal
Barium (Ba)	56	137	725	1638	soft silvery-white metal
Radium (Ra)	88	(226)	700	1737	radioactive silvery metal

ALKALINE EARTH METALS

The elements in column IIA of the periodic table are called the **alkaline** (AL kuh lyn) **earth metals.** They are also known as the calcium (KAL see uhm) family. This family includes beryllium (buh RIL ee uhm), magnesium (mag NEE zee uhm), calcium, strontium (STRAHNT ee uhm), barium (BAR ee uhm), and radium (RAYD ee uhm).

The alkaline earth metals are very reactive and are not found in the free state in nature. These elements readily give up their two outer electrons and form ions. For this reason, they tend to form compounds by ionic bonding. All of these metals react with water.

Beryllium. Beryllium is found chemically combined in nature in the form of a green mineral. The element itself is usually obtained by the electrolysis of its molten chlorides. Beryllium forms compounds with all of the halogens.

Magnesium. In nature, magnesium is found chemically combined in mineral deposits and in compounds dissolved in seawater. Free magnesium burns with a very bright flame. For this reason it has been used in photographic flashbulbs.

Magnesium is one of the elements found in the green plant pigment, chlorophyll (KLOR uh fil). Some compounds of magnesium are used as medicines. An example is magnesium sulfate which is marketed as Epsom salt.

Calcium. Calcium is one of the most abundant elements in the earth's crust. About three percent of the mass of the earth's crust is calcium compounds. Calcium is never found in the free state in nature. It is usually prepared by the electrolysis of molten calcium chloride.

Calcium compounds are important commercially. Calcium oxide is commonly known as lime. Lime mixed with sand, water, and other additives is used in making mortars and plaster. Lime is also

Describe the alkaline earth metals.

Figure 2-33. The flash seen when a flashbulb goes off is magnesium burning in oxygen.

Caterpiller Tractor Co.

Figure 2-34. Calcium is never found in the free state. Some calcium compounds are obtained by mining.

FAMILIES OF ELEMENTS

Ohio State University Hospital

Figure 2-35. Barium sulfate and X rays are used to detect disorders in the digestive tract.

Figure 2-36. Luminous materials glow in the dark.

William Maddox

used in making glass, dehairing hides, and softening hard water. Calcium sulfate is used in making paints and plasterboard. Calcium compounds are also used in treating soils that are too acid.

Calcium is an important component of bones and teeth. Calcium is essential to the diet of humans and other animals. Milk and other dairy products are excellent sources of calcium.

Strontium. Because strontium is a very reactive metal, it is not found free in nature. It is usually prepared by the electrolysis of molten strontium chloride. Strontium reacts readily with air and water. Therefore, it must be stored under a special liquid in an airtight bottle. The chemical properties of strontium are very similar to those of calcium.

When vaporized in a flame, strontium compounds cause the flame to appear a beautiful shade of red. For this reason, strontium compounds are often used in the manufacture of fireworks.

Barium. Like the other alkaline earth metals, barium is always found in the combined state in nature. Chemically, barium is very similar to calcium and strontium. However, it tends to react more rapidly than calcium and strontium. Barium reacts readily with water, oxygen, and halogens. When vaporized in a flame, barium compounds cause the flame to appear green.

Barium sulfate is used to study the digestive tract. Patients swallow a liquid mixture containing barium sulfate. Because barium sulfate absorbs X rays, a physician can study the digestive tract as the chemical moves through it.

Radium. Radium is even more chemically reactive than barium. It is also radioactive. In nature, it is found in uranium ores such as pitchblende. Usually, it is obtained in the free state by electrolysis of fused radium salts. The metal is silvery white but rapidly turns black when exposed to air.

Radium is used in medicine to treat malignant growths. At one time, it was used to make luminous watch dials. *Luminous* (LOO muh nuhs) means to glow in the dark.

Problems

14. What are some of the common uses for calcium, barium, and strontium? See Teacher's Guide.

15. How many electrons are in the outer shell of each of the alkaline earth metals? two

16. Chlorine combines with all of the alkaline earth metals. Write a chemical formula for the chloride of each of the alkaline earth metals. $BeCl_2$, $MgCl_2$, $CaCl_2$, $SrCl_2$, $BaCl_2$, $RaCl_2$

2:6 Noble Gases

Table 2-8. The Noble Gases

Element	Z	A	M.P. (°C)	B.P. (°C)	Description
Helium (He)	2	4	−272	−269	
Neon (Ne)	10	20	−249	−246	All are
Argon (Ar)	18	40	−189	−189	colorless
Krypton (Kr)	36	84	−157	−153	gases
Xenon (Xe)	54	131	−112	−107	
Radon (Rn)	86	(222)	−71	−61.8	

Florida Department of Commerce

Figure 2-37. Helium filled balloons are lighter than the volume of air they displace.

Column VIIIA of the periodic table includes helium (HEE lee uhm), neon (NEE ahn), argon (AHR gahn), krypton (KRIP tahn), xenon (ZEE nahn), and radon (RAY dahn). These elements are known as the **noble gases.** Until 1962, it was believed that the noble gases would not combine with other elements. However, experiments now show that xenon, for example, can form compounds with fluorine, oxygen, and platinum. Compounds of the noble gases are formed covalently since the outer shell of each noble gas is already complete.

Most of the members of this family were found by chance. For example, helium was found in a study of sunlight before it was discovered on Earth. Argon was found when not all of a sample of a distillation of liquid air could be accounted for. Xenon, neon, and krypton were found by using the techniques that led to the discovery of argon. The last member of the family, radon, is the heaviest gas known. It is the product of the radioactive decay of radium and is itself radioactive.

Why do noble gases form compounds covalently?

Figure 2-38. When electricity is turned on, the neon gas in the tube glows.

Rich Brommer

Some of the compounds of noble gases are: xenon hexafluoroplatinate, $XePtF_6$; xenon difluoride, XeF_2; and xenon trioxide, XeO_3. Some of these compounds are being used experimentally as industrial fluorinating agents.

Problems

17. How many electrons are in the outermost shell of an atom of each of the noble gases? *eight for all but helium*

18. How is helium different from the other noble gases?
Helium has only two electrons. These two electrons fill the first shell. Therefore, helium is stable.

MAIN IDEAS

2:1 **1.** Chemical elements can be grouped in families. Elements in a family all have similar chemical properties.

2:1 **2.** Halogens are the most reactive nonmetals.

202 (42M) FAMILIES OF ELEMENTS

2:2 **3.** The oxygen family elements form allotropes. Allotropes are different molecular forms of the same element.

2:2 **4.** A photoconductor is a substance whose ability to conduct electrons is controlled by light.

2:3 **5.** The nitrogen family elements are less reactive than elements in the halogen or oxygen family.

2:3 **6.** Two or more of the same elements may combine in different ways to form different compounds.

2:4 **7.** Alkali metals are the most reactive metals.

2:4 **8.** The alkali metals can be identified by flame tests.

2:5 **9.** Alkaline earth metals are very reactive and are not found free in nature.

2:2, 2:3, 2:6 **10.** Nitrogen, oxygen, and the noble gases can be produced from the distillation of liquid air.

2:6 **11.** Noble gases are chemically the least active elements.

VOCABULARY

Write a sentence in which you correctly use each of the following words or terms.

allotrope	flame test	photocell
diatomic	law of multiple	sublimation
distillation	proportions	triatomic
electrolysis	metal	

STUDY QUESTIONS

Have students rewrite false statements to make the statements correct.

A. True or False

Determine whether each of the following sentences is true or false. (Do not write in this book.)

T **1.** The elements in the halogen family are all poisonous or harmful in the uncombined state.

diatomic   F **2.** Under normal room temperature and pressure, all of the halogen elements form ~~triatomic~~ molecules.

not   F **3.** Uncombined fluorine is found free in nature.

T **4.** At room temperature and pressure bromine is a red liquid.

gray crystalline solid   F **5.** At room temperature and pressure iodine is a ~~red liquid~~.

T **6.** All elements in the oxygen family have two electrons to share in chemical bonds.

FAMILIES OF ELEMENTS   (43M)   203

T **7.** Arsenic is used in some medicines.

T **8.** Selenium is a good electrical conductor when exposed to light.

T **9.** Heavy growth of water plants in lakes and streams may result from excess phosphate in the water.

F **10.** The ~~high~~ melting point of bismuth makes it suitable for use in automatic sprinkler systems used for fire prevention. low

B. Multiple Choice

Some questions in Parts B and C may have more than one correct answer. Only one answer is required.

Choose one word or phrase that correctly completes each of the following sentences. (Do not write in this book.)

1. (Nitrogen, <u>Sodium</u>, Oxygen) is a solid at room temperature.
2. An element which exhibits photoconductivity is (bismuth, <u>selenium</u>, phosphorus).
3. All members of the halogens have (0, 1, 2, 3, 4, 5, 6, <u>7</u>, 8) electrons in their outer shells.
4. Halogen atoms form compounds with other elements by (covalent, ionic, <u>covalent and ionic</u>) bonding.
5. Phosphorus is not used in the manufacture of (matches, fertilizers, <u>ice cream</u>).
6. Ammonia contains (oxygen, <u>nitrogen</u>, helium).
7. (<u>Bismuth</u>, Sulfur, Antimony) is a true metal.
8. Sulfur is a member of the (halogen, <u>oxygen</u>, alkali metal) family.
9. Phosphorus is a member of the (halogen, oxygen, <u>nitrogen</u>) family.
10. (Nitrogen, Carbon, <u>Helium</u>) is a noble gas.

C. Completion

Complete each of the following sentences with a word or phrase that will make the sentence correct. (Do not write in this book.)

1. Nitrogen is found free as _____ molecules. diatomic
2. The compounds of nitrogen and oxygen illustrate the law of _____. multiple proportions
3. The ability of cesium and selenium to conduct electrons is affected by _____. light
4. Twenty percent of air is _____. oxygen
5. Pure nitrogen is produced by the distillation of _____. air

6. Argon is a by-product of _____ of air. *(distillation)*
7. Each alkali metal has a certain _____ test. *(flame)*
8. The most metallic member of the nitrogen family is _____. *(bismuth)*
9. _____ is the element most like sulfur in physical and chemical properties. *(Selenium)*
10. Calcium is essential to formation of healthy _____ and _____. *(bones, teeth)*

D. How and Why

See Teacher's Guide.

1. What is a family of elements? Give an example.
2. What are the names and formulas of three nitrogen compounds?
3. What kind of bonding is present in compounds containing nitrogen? How does this compare with compounds between the alkali metal and halogen families?
4. How can you distinguish between metallic and nonmetallic members of a family of elements?
5. In what specific ways is sulfur different from oxygen?
6. State the law of multiple proportions. Give two examples of compounds that illustrate this law.
7. How do allotropes differ from isotopes?
8. Why do you think the noble gases were difficult to discover?
9. What is a diatomic gas? Name three and give their formulas.
10. What kind of bonding do you think each of the following compounds would have? Why? (1) boron-nitrogen (2) iron-oxygen (3) magnesium-chlorine (4) sulfur-carbon (5) hydrogen-lithium

INVESTIGATIONS

See Teacher's Guide for suggestions.

1. Visit a nursery or garden shop. (1) From the labels on the pesticides, determine which elements are most used. (2) From the labels on the fertilizers, determine which elements are most often used.
2. Conduct a survey in your local grocery store to determine which detergents are low in phosphates.
3. Visit your local municipal water supply headquarters. Find out how drinking water is purified. List any chemicals added to drinking water in your area.

INTERESTING READING

Asimov, Isaac, *The World of Nitrogen.* New York, Abelard-Schuman, Ltd., 1958.

Flaschen, Steward, *Search and Research: The Story of the Chemical Elements.* Boston, Allyn and Bacon, Inc., 1965.

Freeman, Ira M., and Patton, A. Ral, *The Science of Chemistry.* New York, Random House, 1968.

Froman, Robert, *The Science of Salt.* New York, David McKay Company, Inc., 1967.

"Making Hydrogen a Metal." *Science News,* XCIX (April 3, 1971), p. 231.

Pratt, C. J., "Sulfur." *Scientific American,* CCXXII (May, 1970), pp. 63–72.

Sootin, Harry, *Experiments with Water.* New York, W. W. Norton & Co., 1971.

William Maddox

Taken through a prism, the photograph of one candle represents the element carbon. The wax, wick, and by-products of combustion all contain carbon in some form.

GOAL: You will gain an understanding of the reasons for the large number of carbon compounds.

Carbon forms an exceedingly large number of compounds. A very large percentage of the chemical research in the last few years has involved organic chemistry. In this chapter the students will learn some of the reasons for the large

3 Carbon and Its Compounds

number of carbon compounds—catenation, multiple bonding, and substitution. Saturated and unsaturated hydrocarbons and homologous series are discussed.

What do a diamond and a pencil have in common? Both are forms of the element carbon. Many things contain carbon. Most foods, medicines, fibers, candles, plastics, and detergents contain carbon. Carbon is also found in all living things. Fuels such as gasoline, coal, and natural gas contain carbon.

The abundance of the carbon element has led to a special branch of chemistry. This branch is concerned with the carbon element and all carbon compounds.

ORGANIC CHEMISTRY

3:1 Organic Chemistry

The term "organic" means living. At one time, **organic** (or GAN ik) **chemistry** was the study of materials found in living things. All of these materials contain *carbon*. Later, chemists were able to make some of these carbon materials without using any animal or plant substances. Thus, organic chemistry came to include all carbon compounds.

Carbon is one of the least reactive elements. It combines easily with only a few other elements. Yet, roughly 90 percent of all known compounds contain carbon. More than one million different carbon compounds have been discovered.

One reason for so many carbon compounds is the way carbon atoms bond. Atoms of carbon can join together in long chains or in rings. Other elements may also bond with carbon atoms or with carbon chains or rings. In this way, a great variety of compounds is possible.

In the periodic table, carbon is a member of family IVA. This family also includes silicon (SIL uh kuhn) (Si), germanium (juhr MAY nee uhm) (Ge), tin (Sn), and lead (Pb). Each element in the carbon family has four electrons in its outer shell. Thus, a carbon atom can share electrons with as many as four other atoms.

When a carbon atom shares electrons with four other atoms, the molecule formed has a shape called a *tetrahedron* (teh truh HEE druhn). The angle between each pair of bonds is about 109°. This shape permits each shared pair of electrons to be as far as possible from the other three shared pairs.

What is organic chemistry?
Organic chemistry is the study of carbon compounds.

Carbon forms covalent bonds.

The geometry of carbon compounds is very important.

How does a carbon atom form compounds?
The structure of 1 carbon atom bonded to 4 hydrogen atoms:

$$\begin{array}{c} H \\ | \\ H-C-H \quad 109° \\ | \\ H \end{array}$$

The angle between a double bond and the other single bonds is about 120°.

$$\begin{array}{c} H \quad 120° \quad H \\ \diagdown \quad \diagup \\ C=C \\ \diagup \quad \diagdown \\ H \quad\quad H \end{array}$$

A triple bond forms a linear molecule.

$$H-C\equiv C-H$$

Figure 3-1. Ninety percent of all known compounds contain carbon.

Rich Brommer

Have the students construct the models of molecules illustrated on pages 208 and 209. Styrofoam balls and florists chenille or pipe cleaners are all the materials that you *Ward's Natural Science Establishment* require. Flattening the sides of the styrofoam balls where they

Figure 3-2. When a carbon atom shares electrons with four other atoms, the molecule is in the shape of a tetrahedron.

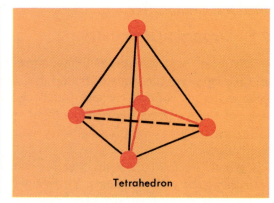
Tetrahedron

Figure 3-3. Carbon atoms can form double covalent bonds and triple covalent bonds.

×C×:C: Double
×C=C: bond

×C×:C• Triple
×C≡C•   bond

A carbon atom can bond with another atom in several different ways by sharing electrons. A single covalent bond is made when one electron pair is shared between atoms. A double covalent bond is formed when two electron pairs are shared. A triple covalent bond is formed when three electron pairs are shared between two atoms.

Bohr model

Electron cloud model

Electron dot model

Structural formula

Figure 3-4. These are four models of the carbon atom.

3:2 Structural Formulas

A *structural formula* is a simple way to show the bonding between atoms. One straight line between symbols represents one covalent bond. Two lines mean a double bond. Three lines mean a triple bond.

Figure 3-5. The following examples are structural formulas and picture models for some carbon compounds containing hydrogen.

You may wish to add additional examples such as C_3H_6 and C_3H_7Cl.

1.

Single carbon to carbon bond; single carbon to hydrogen bond. (C_2H_6 or CH_3CH_3) ethene or ethylene

2. H–C=C–H (with H's above)

Double carbon to carbon bond; single carbon to hydrogen bond. (C_2H_4 or CH_2CH_2) ethane

208 (48M)

are to be joined makes the models more compact. Toothpicks may be used in place of the pipe cleaners if the models are to be glued. Gumdrops may also be used. Each carbon atom has 4 bonds. Each hydrogen atom has 1 bond. Single, double, and triple bonds are indicated by varying degrees of flatness of the joint between two atoms.

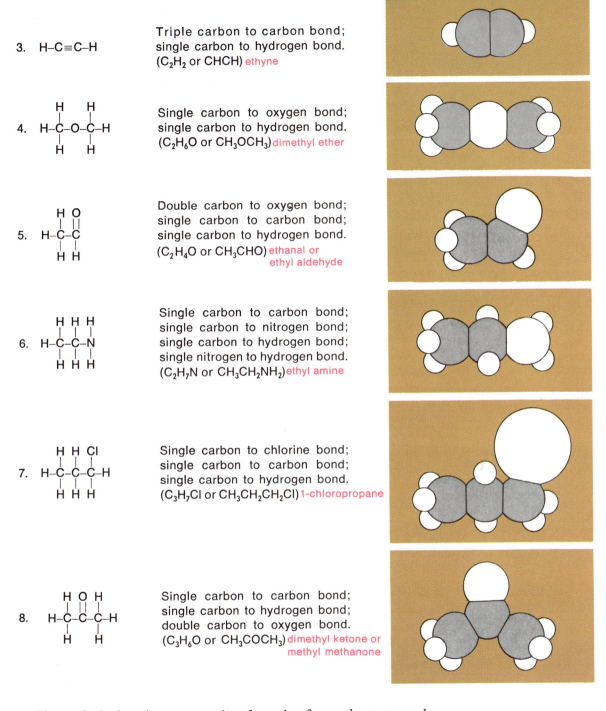

3. H–C≡C–H
Triple carbon to carbon bond; single carbon to hydrogen bond. (C₂H₂ or CHCH) ethyne

4. H–C–O–C–H (with H's on each C)
Single carbon to oxygen bond; single carbon to hydrogen bond. (C₂H₆O or CH₃OCH₃) dimethyl ether

5. H–C–C (with H O double bond on second C, H H on first)
Double carbon to oxygen bond; single carbon to carbon bond; single carbon to hydrogen bond. (C₂H₄O or CH₃CHO) ethanal or ethyl aldehyde

6. H–C–C–N
Single carbon to carbon bond; single carbon to nitrogen bond; single carbon to hydrogen bond; single nitrogen to hydrogen bond. (C₂H₇N or CH₃CH₂NH₂) ethyl amine

7. H–C–C–C–H
Single carbon to chlorine bond; single carbon to carbon bond; single carbon to hydrogen bond. (C₃H₇Cl or CH₃CH₂CH₂Cl) 1-chloropropane

8. H–C–C–C–H
Single carbon to carbon bond; single carbon to hydrogen bond; double carbon to oxygen bond. (C₃H₆O or CH₃COCH₃) dimethyl ketone or methyl methanone

Figure 3–5 also shows two other formulas for each compound. One formula, the *simple molecular formula*, tells the number of atoms of each element in a molecule of the compound. The second formula is the *graphic formula*. It shows number and kinds of atoms

What is the difference between a graphic and a structural formula?

and the structure of the molecule. For example, the simple molecular formula, C_2H_4, shows that one molecule contains two carbon atoms and four hydrogen atoms. The graphic formula, CH_2CH_2, shows the number of hydrogen atoms attached to each carbon atom. Location of atoms in a carbon compound is important. A different location means a different compound with different chemical properties.

3:3 Isomers

Examine the formulas for the compounds in Figure 3–6. Both compounds have the same simple molecular formula. However, each has a different graphic and structural formula. Both molecules have four atoms of carbon and ten atoms of hydrogen. Yet they are completely different compounds. Compounds with equal numbers of the same kind of atoms, but different structures, are called **isomers** (I suh muhrz).

Isomers have different structures due to the way a carbon atom is bonded. Butane is a *straight chain* compound. Here a carbon atom is bonded to no more than two other carbon atoms. Isobutane is a *branched chain* compound. Branched means that some carbon atoms are bonded to three other carbon atoms.

Isomers are compounds which have the same simple molecular formulas but different structural formulas. They might be compared to allotropes.

What are isomers?

Figure 3-6. Butane and isobutane are isomers. They have the same molecular formula but different graphic and structural formulas.

1.
Butane

Single carbon to carbon bond; single carbon to hydrogen bond. (C_4H_{10} or $CH_3CH_2CH_2CH_3$)

Normal butane

2.
Isobutane

Single carbon to carbon bond; single carbon to hydrogen bond. (C_4H_{10} or $CH_3CHCH_3CH_3$)

Isobutane

Often, more than two compounds will have the same simple formula. For example, there are three compounds with the formula C_5H_{12}. See Figure 3–7.

Figure 3-7. These three compounds have the same formula, C₅H₁₂.

normal pentane   isopentane or 2-methylbutane   neopentane or 2,2-dimethylpropane

PROBLEM

1. Do any of the C₅H₁₂ compounds above have branched chains? Explain.

   Yes, two have carbon atoms with more than two other carbon atoms attached.

Time: 35 minutes.

ACTIVITY. Seven isomers have been found for C₅H₁₁Cl. See if you can draw structural formulas for each isomer. Note: The chlorine is always bonded to a carbon atom. Write the graphic formula for each isomer. Obtain styrofoam balls and pipe cleaners. Make a model of at least two of the isomers. See Teacher's Guide at the front of book.

As the number of carbon atoms in a molecule increases, the number of possible isomers also increases. All these isomers may not exist. But the structure of each is possible. Isomers are another reason why there are so many carbon compounds.

Why is there a large number of carbon compounds?

Carbon-to-carbon bonding (catenation); isomeric forms; single, double, and triple bonds

PROBLEMS See Teacher's Guide at the front of this book.

2. Draw the structural formulas for three isomers of C₄H₉Cl. The chlorine is always bonded to a carbon atom.
3. Draw a structural formula for CH₃CH₂CHO.

3:4 Saturated Hydrocarbons

Many of the compounds discussed in the preceding sections contain only carbon and hydrogen. These compounds are called **hydrocarbons** (hy druh KAHR buhnz). Hydrocarbons can be classified into two groups. Those in which all carbon atoms are joined by single bonds are *saturated* (SACH uh rayt uhd) *hydrocarbons*. If, however, two or more carbon atoms are joined by double or triple bonds, the hydrocarbon is *unsaturated*.

Hydrocarbons are classified into series of compounds with similar structure. One group of saturated hydrocarbons is called the *alkanes* (AL kaynz). Since the first member of the alkane series is methane (CH₄), the series is sometimes called the *methane* series. Ethane (C₂H₆), propane (C₃H₈), and butane (C₄H₁₀) are the next three

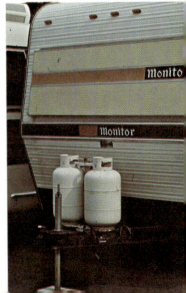

Figure 3-8. Bottled propane gas is often used for heating or cooking.

W. Keith Turpie

members of the series. Methane is found in natural gas. Propane and butane are used as "bottled" gas. Each successive alkane has one more CH_2 group than the alkane before it. How many hydrogen atoms are in one molecule of the alkane containing twenty carbon atoms? *42—two for each carbon atom and two on each end.*

PROBLEM

4. Can you find a general formula for the relationship between the hydrogen and carbon atoms in the alkane series?

Each carbon has two hydrogens except for the two end carbons. Therefore, there will always be twice as many hydrogens as carbons plus two. If the number of carbons is n, then there should be $2n+2$ hydrogens or in general, C_nH_{2n+2}.

Safety precautions: 1. Keep the gas collection bottles away from open flames. 2. Maintain proper ventilation or use the fume hood. 3. Have students wear goggles when they perform this activity.

Have students note the physical properties of the gas.

Methane burns with a blue flame.

Limewater turns milky indicating that CO_2 was a product.

Bromine water remains red in color.

Methane does not change $KMnO_4$ solution.

Time: 2 hours.

ACTIVITY. Crush together 15 g of sodium acetate with 5 g of dry soda lime in a mortar. Fill a test tube one-third full of the mixture. Arrange the apparatus as shown in the diagram. Heat the test tube. Collect the methane in bottles by water displacement. CAUTION: Keep the bottles of gas away from the Bunsen burner flame. Discard the contents of the first bottle of gas. Why? Then collect four bottles.

Place the bottles upside-down on the glass plate when they are filled. Turn upright, removing plate only when adding material.

Insert a burning splint into one bottle. Add 5 ml of limewater and shake. To the second bottle, add 2 ml of bromine water and shake. To the third bottle, add 2 ml of potassium permanganate solution and shake. Note any changes in the three bottles. Record your results. How can you prove that methane in the fourth bottle has a smaller mass than an equal amount of air?

Figure 3-9.

Figure 3-10. Saturated hydrocarbons are single-bonded compounds of hydrogen and carbon.

Table 3–1. Methane Series

Name	Simple Molecular Formula	Graphic Formula	Normal State
Methane	CH_4	CH_4	Gas
Ethane	C_2H_6	CH_3CH_3	Gas
Propane	C_3H_8	$CH_3CH_2CH_3$	Gas
Butane	C_4H_{10}	$CH_3CH_2CH_2CH_3$	Gas
Pentane	C_5H_{12}	$CH_3CH_2CH_2CH_2CH_3$	Liquid
Octane	C_8H_{18}	$CH_3CH_2CH_2CH_2CH_2CH_2CH_2CH_3$	Liquid

Structural formulas of some members of the methane series are given in Figure 3–10. The chains are written as straight lines to make them less confusing. Actually, the carbon chains are not straight. Remember, the angle between each pair of bonds is 109°, not 90°. As a chain grows longer, it is more likely to bend back and forth.

Demonstrate the correct bond angles with ball and stick or styrofoam models.

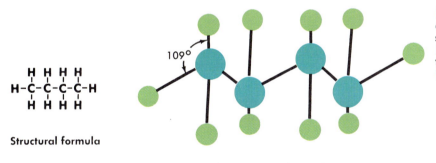

Structural formula

Structural model

Figure 3-11. Hydrocarbon chains are usually represented as straight chains. However, the angle between each pair of bonds is actually 109°.

Time: 25 minutes.

ACTIVITY. Using styrofoam balls and toothpicks, construct a model of the butane molecule. The graphic formula for this molecule is $CH_3CH_2CH_2CH_3$. Remember that angles between pairs of bonds should be about 109°.

As the number of carbon atoms in the methane series increases, the physical phase of the compounds that are formed changes. The first four members of the methane series are gases at room temperature. Starting with five carbon atoms (pentane, C_5H_{12}), a shift from

How does the number of atoms in the methane series relate to physical phase?

Figure 3-12. Fractional distillation is used to refine crude petroleum (a). A fractionating tower (b) separates the various compounds in petroleum.

82

Fractionation separates mixtures of hydrocarbons by piping off compounds as they boil. Boiling points cover quite a range.

Paper chromatography is a useful way of separating chemical compounds for qualitative analysis.

the gas to the liquid phase occurs. Saturated hydrocarbons with more than eighteen carbon atoms ($C_{18}H_{38}$) are waxy solids.

Hydrocarbons with 40 carbon atoms in a chain are known to exist naturally. How many hydrogen atoms would there be in a 40-carbon chain? Can you imagine the possible number of isomers of that compound? To give you an idea of the number, more than 350,000 isomers which have the formula $C_{20}H_{42}$ are possible.

PROBLEM

5. Identify each of these alkanes as either a solid, liquid, or gas.
    (a) C_2H_6 (b) $C_{30}H_{62}$ (c) C_8H_{18} (d) CH_4 (e) $C_{16}H_{34}$
       gas   solid   liquid   gas   liquid

Petroleum is one of the most important sources of saturated hydrocarbons. Most of our petroleum comes from deep underground deposits. Wells are drilled to reach the petroleum. Depending on the location of the well, 60 to 90 percent of the petroleum is composed of saturated hydrocarbons. The various kinds of alkanes are separated by a process called **fractionation** (frak shuh NAY shuhn), a type of distillation. Distillation is a physical separation which depends upon boiling point differences (Figure 3–12).

Figure 3-13.

Time: 30 minutes.

ACTIVITY. Organic compounds can be separated by chromatography (kroh muh TAHG ruh fee). This activity is an example of paper chromatography. Obtain a small glass jar (with lid), white paper towels cut into strips 2 cm wide, and 2 felt-tipped marking pens (different colors and different manufacturers). Fill the jar with 3 ml of water. Cut the strips slightly longer than the jar's height. Draw a thick line with one of the markers across the bottom of the strip 5 cm from the bottom. Attach the strip to the underside of the jar lid with tape. Put the lid on the jar. Observe and describe what happens. Repeat with the second color.

PEOPLE CAREERS FRONTIERS FOCUS ON PHYSICAL SCIENCE

'Fluorine: Sticky Bonds for Safer Drugs'

Medical researchers are designing safer anesthetics and chemicals that show organs in X rays. These new developments result from a characteristic of fluorine. When it bonds to carbon, it won't let go.

Chemists, experimenting with anesthetics containing fluorine, have come to several conclusions. They have found that less is needed to put people to sleep than anesthetics containing chlorine. Also, these chemicals are less active in the body. This means that fewer side effects may result with their use. These fluorine compounds may also be used in another way in the medical field.

New fluoride compounds may replace traditional chemicals used in anesthetics.

Barium- and iodine-containing compounds are generally used for X raying some organ systems. These compounds help show the organs in detail on an X ray.

Some medical researchers believe that fluorine compounds are safer than barium or chlorine compounds. This is because they cannot be broken down. Thus, they pass out of the body within a few hours. On the other hand, barium takes a day or two to pass out of the body.

After thorough testing, these substances may replace some traditional chemicals in the medical field.

• • • • • • • • • • • • •

Adapted from *Science News*, September 6, 1975.

Balloon Investigates Soundness of Ozone Layer

There is much concern that the ozone layer in the upper atmosphere may be destroyed. The ozone layer protects the earth from harmful solar radiation. Scientists have hypothesized that fluorocarbons (floor oh KAHR buhnz) may thin the ozone layer.

Fluorocarbons are released from some aerosol spray cans and from some refrigeration units. The fluorocarbons are broken down into chlorine by ultraviolet radiation. The chlorine is believed to react with ozone.

To study this problem in detail, scientists released a giant balloon. It carried about 450 kilograms of scientific instruments. These instruments measured the amounts and movements of these chemicals. After recording this data, parachutes brought the instruments back to Earth. Scientists are now analyzing the data. This is one of many scientific studies conducted to study the ozone problem.

• • • • • • • • • • • • •

Courtesy of *ChemEcology*, November, 1975.

The crew prepares this helium test-balloon for a touch down.

Figure 3-14. Alkenes have one double bond. Alkynes have one triple bond.

Compare the bonding in the alkenes and alkynes.

| Ethene (C₂H₄) | Propene (C₃H₆) | Ethyne (C₂H₂) | Propyne (C₃H₄) |

Figure 3-15. Propene and the two isomers of butene are in the alkene series. A new way to form isomers is to change the location of the double bond.

Figure 3-16. Some cooking oils and margarines have unsaturated bonds (a). Acetylene, an unsaturated hydrocarbon, is used for welding (b).

3:5 Unsaturated Hydrocarbons

Have the students develop a general formula for the alkenes.

Unsaturated hydrocarbons have double or triple carbon bonds. The term unsaturated is sometimes used to describe cooking oils and vegetable shortenings. Why? *Carbon molecules with double or triple bonds are more easily broken apart, therefore, more digestible.*

Unsaturated hydrocarbons with one double bond are called *alkenes* (AL keenz). Ethylene (ETH uh leen), or ethene ($CH_2=CH_2$), is the smallest possible chain. Other members of the alkene series include propene and the two isomers of butene. Each butene isomer simply has the double bond in a different location.

Another group of unsaturated hydrocarbons is the alkyne (AL kyn) series. *Alkynes* have one triple bond. The simplest and most common triple-bond compound is acetylene (uh SET uhl een), or ethyne (H—C≡C—H). Among others, the alkyne series includes propyne and two isomers of butyne. *Develop a general formula for the alkynes (C_nH_{2n-2}).*

Problem

6. Write structural formulas for the two butyne isomers.

See Teacher's Guide.

As with the alkanes, the alkenes and alkynes with short carbon chains are gases at room temperature. Pentene is a liquid. So is one of the butynes. The larger carbon chains are waxy solids.

a

Rich Brommer

b

W. Keith Turpie

Observe the same safety precautions as in the activity on page 212 (52M).

Time: 90 minutes.

ACTIVITY. CAUTION: *Do* not *perform this activity near an open flame. Wear eye protection.*

Place 2 g of calcium carbide in a flask. Obtain a two-hole rubber stopper to fit the flask. Insert a medicine dropper into one hole of the stopper. Insert a glass delivery tube into the other hole. Fill the medicine dropper with water. Fit the stopper into the flask. Squeeze a few drops of water onto the calcium carbide. Collect three bottles of acetylene gas by water displacement. Discard the first bottle of gas. Keep the next 2 bottles mouth down on glass plates. Turn the second bottle over and add 2 ml of bromine water. Turn the third bottle over and add 2 ml of potassium permanganate solution. Compare your results with the activity on methane, page 212 (52M). Be extremely careful. Acetylene is very flammable. Bromine water bleaches to colorless. KMnO₄ solution is bleached from purple to colorless.

Figure 3-17.

3:6 *Polymers*

The molecules of many compounds can join together to form a very large molecule called a **polymer** (PAHL uh muhr). This process is called *polymerization* (pahl uh muh ruh ZAY shuhn). An example of a polymer is rubber. Synthetic rubber has been made from isoprene and from other unsaturated hydrocarbons. Neoprene rubber, one of the most successful, is made using acetylene. Part of the chain of this rubber has the following structural formula:

What is a polymer?

The formation of Bakelite results from the polymerization of phenol by formaldehyde in the presence of the basic catalyst NaOH.

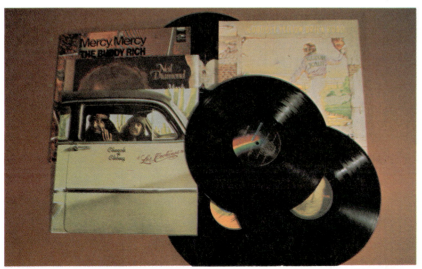

Linda Briscoe

Figure 3-18. Many everyday items are made from polymers.

217 (57M)

Don Parsisson

Columbia Industries, Inc.

Figure 3-19. Polyesters are used to make textiles (a), as well as bowling balls (b).

What are some synthetic fibers?
acrilan, polyester fiber, dacron, kodel, rayon, etc.

Figure 3-20.

What are "ring" compounds?
Carbon compounds like benzene have a ring structure rather than a straight or branched chain. They may be saturated or unsaturated.

218 (58M)   CARBON AND ITS COMPOUNDS

Many plastics are polymers made from alkenes. Plastic bags, refrigerator storage containers, toys, utensil handles, and many other everyday items are made of polyethylene. Polyethylene, as its name implies, is a polymer of ethylene. It is more rigid than the synthetic rubbers. Other compounds based on ethylene are vinyl products. These polymers may include elements other than hydrogen and carbon. Polyvinyl chloride, for example, includes chlorine. Its large molecules may be composed of from 100 to 500 smaller units. Polyvinyl compounds are used in phonograph records, garden hoses, floor tiles, sprinkler tubing, and many other items.

Some polymers do not include hydrogen. Tetrafluoroethylene,

$$\begin{array}{c} F \quad F \\ | \quad | \\ C = C \\ | \quad | \\ F \quad F \end{array}$$, polymerizes and forms the compound used in "nonstick" utensils. This polymer resists heat and chemicals because its fluorine-carbon bond is so strong. It is so tightly bonded that it will not allow anything to "stick" to it. Thus, it can be used as the lining for many kitchen pots and pans. It is also of great use in industry and in the chemistry laboratory for the same reasons.

Many synthetic fibers, such as nylon and orlon, are produced by polymerization. Some are tougher, stronger, and more elastic than many natural fibers. The popular knit clothes are polyester, polymers of organic compounds called esters. They have properties similar to nylon and orlon.

> Time: 50 minutes.
>
> ACTIVITY. Collect small samples of textile materials from home. Wool, cotton, nylon, rayon, orlon, dacron, silk, and linen are good choices. Your teacher may supply some of these. With forceps, hold one sample of each over a flame. Which samples burn? Put a second sample of each in a test tube containing 5 ml of dilute hydrochloric acid. Which samples are affected? Put a third sample of each in a test tube containing 5 ml of sodium hydroxide solution. Which are affected? What does this tell you about the relative properties of the materials? Make a chart to explain your results.

sam- — wool
silk
animal and plant fibers

Textile properties vary because of the differences in chemical composition.

3:7 Other Organic Compounds

Not all hydrocarbons occur as chains; many form *rings*. Both saturated and unsaturated hydrocarbons may form rings. Two compounds which have six carbon atoms in each molecule are cyclo-

OTHER ORGANIC COMPOUNDS (59M) 219

hexane (C_6H_{12}) and benzene (C_6H_6). Are these compounds isomers? The structural formulas for the two compounds are

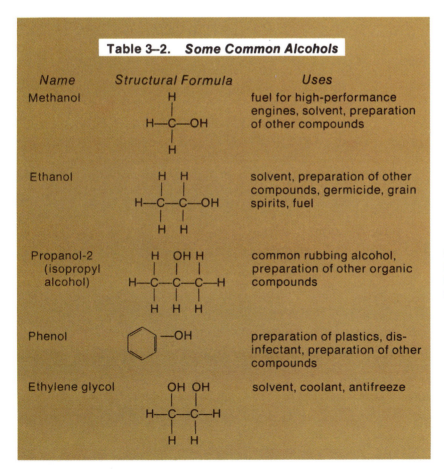

and

Cyclohexane has all single bonds. Benzene has alternating double bonds. To save time and space, cyclohexane is often written as ⬡. Benzene is ⬡. A carbon atom is bonded to one or two hydrogen atoms at each vertex. A vertex is a point where two lines intersect at an angle.

Benzene and cyclohexane are not isomers since they have different simple molecular formulas.

Table 3–2. Some Common Alcohols

Name	Structural Formula	Uses
Methanol	H–C(H)(H)–OH	fuel for high-performance engines, solvent, preparation of other compounds
Ethanol	H–C(H)(H)–C(H)(H)–OH	solvent, preparation of other compounds, germicide, grain spirits, fuel
Propanol-2 (isopropyl alcohol)	H–C(H)(H)–C(H)(OH)–C(H)(H)–H	common rubbing alcohol, preparation of other organic compounds
Phenol	⬡—OH	preparation of plastics, disinfectant, preparation of other compounds
Ethylene glycol	H–C(OH)(H)–C(OH)(H)–H	solvent, coolant, antifreeze

What is a common use for isopropyl alcohol ($CH_3CHOHCH_3$)?
rubbing alcohol

Figure 3-21. Rubbing alcohol is a substituted hydrocarbon.

Among the reasons for the great number of carbon compounds is the existence of substituted hydrocarbons. *Substitution* means that atoms of some other element replace one or more hydrogen atoms in a certain compound.

Carbon tetrachloride (CCl_4) is a substituted hydrocarbon. Each hydrogen atom is replaced by an atom of chlorine. Similar products, such as iodoform (CHI_3) and chloroform ($CHCl_3$), are formed with members of the halogen family.

If a hydrogen atom in a hydrocarbon is replaced by an –OH group, an *alcohol* is formed. You may be familiar with two common alcohols—methyl alcohol (methanol, CH_3OH) and ethyl alcohol (ethanol, CH_3CH_2OH). Table 3–2 lists some of the alcohols with their structural formulas and their uses. Notice that some of the alcohols have more than one –OH substitution.

MAIN IDEAS

3:1   1. Organic chemistry is the study of carbon compounds.

3:1   2. A carbon atom can form four covalent bonds. Carbon combines with other atoms in single, double, or triple covalent bonds.

3:1, 3:3, 3:7   3. There are a great number of carbon compounds because:
    (a) carbon atoms can unite with other carbon atoms to form long chains or rings
    (b) carbon atoms can combine with single, double, or triple bonds
    (c) carbon compounds may have many isomers
    (d) carbon compounds can be formed by substituting hydrogen atoms with other kinds of atoms.

3:3   4. Isomers have the same molecular formulas, but different structural formulas.

3:4   5. Hydrocarbons contain carbon and hydrogen.

3:4   6. In saturated hydrocarbons all carbon atoms are bonded with single covalent bonds.

3:4   7. Alkanes are a group of saturated hydrocarbons.

3:4   8. Petroleum is an important source of unsaturated hydrocarbons.

3:5   9. Hydrocarbons with double or triple carbon bonds are unsaturated.

3:5   10. Alkenes and alkynes are unsaturated hydrocarbons.

3:6   11. Polymers are large molecules formed through the bonding together of smaller molecules.

3:7   12. Ring compounds may be saturated or unsaturated.

CARBON AND ITS COMPOUNDS (61M) 221

VOCABULARY

Write a sentence in which you correctly use each of the following words or terms.

alcohol	hydrocarbon	saturated
alkane	isomer	structural formula
alkene	molecular formula	substitution
alkyne	organic	tetrahedron
graphic formula	polymer	unsaturated

STUDY QUESTIONS

A. True or False

Determine whether each of the following sentences is true or false. (Do not write in this book.)

Have students rewrite false statements to make the statements correct.

F 1. Carbon is in the ~~VA~~ column of the periodic table. IVA
F 2. A carbon atom has ~~six~~ electrons in its outer shell. 4
T 3. Carbon atoms can form double and triple covalent bonds.
F 4. A saturated hydrocarbon has carbon atoms joined by ~~double~~ single bonds.
T 5. The methane series are all hydrocarbons.
T 6. Isomers are compounds which have the same simple formula but different structural formulas.
F 7. Propane, H—C—C—C—H (with H's attached), is a member of the ~~alkene~~ series. alkane
T 8. Petroleum may be separated into gasoline, kerosene, and other fuels and oils.
F 9. Cooking oil is ~~a saturated~~ hydrocarbon. an unsaturated
F 10. A substituted hydrocarbon contains atoms of hydrogen and carbon ~~only~~. and other elements

B. Multiple Choice

Choose one word or phrase that correctly completes each of the following sentences. (Do not write in this book.)

Some questions in Parts B and C may have more than one correct answer. Only one answer is required.

1. All hydrocarbons contain (*carbon*, chlorine, oxygen).
2. The carbon atom has (0, 1, 2, 3, *4*, 5, 6, 7) electrons in its outer shell.
3. Carbon chains are limited to (18, 25, *no known limit of*) carbon atoms.

4. All alcohols have at least one *(NO₃, OH, SO₄)* group.
5. Neoprene rubber is a(n) *(polymer, isomer, allotrope)*.
6. Gasoline is an *(alkane, alkene, alkyne)*.
7. Ethene is a(n) *(saturated, unsaturated)* hydrocarbon.
8. Acetylene is an *(alkane, alkene, alkyne)*.
9. Nylon is a(n) *(isomer, polymer, allotrope)*.
10. CH₃CH₃ is a *(graphic, structural, chain)* formula for ethane.

C. Completion

Complete each of the following sentences with a word or phrase which will make the sentence correct. *(Do not write in this book.)*

structural 1. H—C—C—H (with H's above and below each C) is a(n) _____ formula.

covalent 2. Carbon compounds are formed by _____ bonding.

triple 3. C₂H₂ contains a _____ covalent bond.

substituted 4. Alcohol is a _____ hydrocarbon.

fractionation 5. Gasoline is produced from crude oil by _____ .

polymers 6. Vinyl compounds are examples of _____ .

saturated 7. All carbon atoms are joined by single bonds in a _____ hydrocarbon.

Answers will vary: neoprene, rubber, nylon, vinyl are examples.

8. One example of a polymer is _____ .

methane 9. The first member of the alkane family is _____ .

gases, liquids 10. The methane series members are _____ and _____ at room temperature.

D. How and Why

1. H:C:H (with dots above and below C)

2. Isomers are compounds with the same formula but different structure; isotopes are elements with the same number of protons but different number of neutrons.

1. Draw a diagram of methane (CH₄). Show the outer shell electrons.

2. How do isomers differ from isotopes?

See p.207. 3. What facts account for so many carbon compounds?

See p.219. 4. Benzene and cyclohexane have similarities and differences. What are some of each?

5-9. See Teacher's Guide at the front of this book.

5. Draw the structural formulas for a saturated and an unsaturated hydrocarbon.

6. Write the formula for methane, ethane, butane, and acetylene.

7. Draw a structural formula for each of the following compounds: C₂H₅OH, C₂H₃OH, and C₅H₁₀.

CARBON AND ITS COMPOUNDS (63M) 223

8. What are polymers? List three organic compounds that form polymers.
9. Give a structural formula for one compound in each of these families: alkane, alkene, alkyne. How can you tell which compound is in which family?
10. Why are "straight" carbon chains crooked? C—C bonds are 109°.

INVESTIGATIONS

See Teacher's material at front of book for suggestions.

1. Prepare a report about research on the conversion of coal to fuel gas. Explain how this research can help solve America's energy problems.
2. Prepare a report on natural gas. Include the history of its use, sources of the gas, uses of the gas, and any current information about shortages of natural gas.
3. Organic compounds are used for textile dyes. Prepare a report on the history and uses of dyes.
4. Many automobiles get lower mileage from engines with pollution control equipment. Should pollution control equipment be added to a car if it reduces gas mileage? Why?

INTERESTING READING

Asimov, Isaac, "Is Silicon-Life Possible?" *Science Digest,* LXXII (July, 1972), pp. 56–57.

Chase, Sara H., *First Book of Diamonds.* New York, Franklin Watts, Inc., 1971.

Hahn, Lynn and James, *Plastics.* New York, Franklin Watts, Inc., 1974.

Kaufman, Morris, *Giant Molecules: The Technology of Plastics, Fibers, and Rubber.* Garden City, N.Y., Doubleday & Company, Inc., 1968.

Klein, S. A., "Methane Gas: An Overlooked Energy Source." *Organic Gardening and Farming,* XIX (June, 1972), pp. 98–101

Lambert, Joseph B., "The Shapes of Organic Molecules." *Scientific American,* CCXXII (January, 1970), pp. 58–70.

Ridpath, Ian, *Man and Materials: Coal.* Reading, Massachusetts, Addison-Wesley, 1975.

Squires, Arthur M., "Clean Power from Dirty Fuels." *Scientific American,* CCXXVII (October, 1972), pp. 26–35.

Wohlrabe, Raymond A., *Exploring Giant Molecules.* New York, World Publishing Co., 1969.

Unit Four

The clear water of Taylor River in Colorado emphasizes the importance of water in forming solutions.

Deborah C. Damian

Solutions are formed through chemical processes and physical interaction of solute and solvent. Rate of solution can be increased through heating, stirring, and pulverizing. Generally solvents interact with similar types of solvents (organic or inorganic). This chapter introduces the idea that not all substances are soluble to the same extent. Students will learn that not all solutions have the same concentration. Degree of saturation is one method of describing concentration.

1 Solutions

GOAL: You will gain an understanding of the main properties of solutions and the terms solute, solvent, concentration, and saturation.

When two elements combine to form a compound, a chemical change takes place. A chemical change involves the formation of a new substance and an energy change. For example, when magnesium burns, chemical energy changes into heat and light.

Water is known as the "universal solvent." This means that many things dissolve in it to form solutions. When water and another substance form a solution, is energy released? Does a chemical change take place?

SOLUTIONS (3M) 227

1:1 Solutions

What is a solution (suh LOO shuhn)? A **solution*** is a mixture in which a substance is dissolved in another substance. The **solute** (SAHL yoot) is the substance being dissolved. The **solvent** (SAHL vuhnt) is the substance in which a solute is dissolved. In a solution, two or more substances are completely mixed. The new material formed is exactly the same throughout. When sugar is dissolved in water, sugar is the solute and water is the solvent. Molecules of sugar are distributed uniformly throughout the molecules of water.

What is a solute and a solvent?

Time: 40 minutes.

ACTIVITY. (1) To each of four 15-ml test tubes add 5 ml of water. In the first test tube place a small amount of table salt. To the second add 4 drops of mineral oil. To the third add 4 drops of ethyl alcohol. To the fourth add a small amount of sugar. Place stoppers in each test tube and shake. Record what you observe. Empty and rinse your test tubes with distilled water. (2) Repeat Part 1 using 5 ml of alcohol in each test tube. Add water to the third test tube instead of alcohol. Compare the results of Parts 1 and 2. *See Teacher's Guide at the front of this book.*

Figure 1-1.

The most common solutions are liquid solutions. **Liquid solutions** are those in which solids, liquids, or gases are dissolved in liquids. Water is probably the most common solvent. Unless some other solvent is specified, we assume the solvent is water. For example, a sugar solution is a solution of sugar and water.

What are the three kinds of solutions?

Solutions can also be formed by dissolving solids, liquids, or gases in gases. In this case, a **gaseous solution** is formed. Air is a gaseous solution.

Figure 1-2. Alloys are solutions of at least two metals. Brass is a solution of copper and zinc.

A third type of solution is a **solid solution.** Solid solutions are formed by dissolving solids, liquids, or gases in solids. Carbon steel is a solid solution of carbon in iron. Bronze is a solution of copper and tin. Such solid solutions of metals are called *alloys* (AL oyz).

By mixing certain metals together in the right proportions, an alloy with properties to suit a special purpose can be made. For example, chromium can be alloyed with steel. The chromium-iron-manganese alloy is called stainless steel. It does not rust as does normal steel. Brass is an alloy of copper and zinc. It is stronger and

Jim Elliott

---

*The term "solution" is also used to describe the process of dissolving or going into solution.

Table 1–1. Some Alloys and Their Uses

Alloy	Metals	Typical Uses
Wood's metal	Bi, Pb, Sn, Cd	automatic sprinklers
Commercial bronze	Cu, Sn	jewelry, screens, nuts, and bolts
German silver	Cu, Zn, Ni	silver platings, jewelry
Gold, 14 carat	Au, Cu, Ag	jewelry
Solder	Sn, Pb	electrical wire soldering
Dentist's amalgam	Hg, Ag	tooth fillings
Nichrome	Ni, Cr	electrical heating elements
Monel metal	Ni, Cu, Fe	household appliances
Dow metal	Mg, Al, Mn	aircraft parts

What is an alloy?
Solid solution of two or more metals.

more resistant to corrosion than either copper or zinc alone. Table 1–1 shows common alloys and their uses.

Alloying metals produces changes in density, strength, hardness, and melting point. Alloying may also produce changes in the conductivity of heat and electricity.

Solution takes place as the solvent molecules separate.

Before boiling—acid.

After boiling—neutral. CO_2 more soluble in cold liquid.

ACTIVITY. Half fill a small beaker with cold soda water (carbonated water). (1) Stir the liquid. Explain what you observe. (2) Test the liquid with litmus paper. Explain what you observe. (3) Heat the liquid until boiling. Allow it to cool and test again with litmus paper. Explain. What is the solute in this solution? What is the solvent? water CO_2

Figure 1-3.

FORMATION OF SOLUTIONS (5M) 229

1:2 Formation of Solutions

When sugar is added to water it dissolves to form a solution. First, molecules of sugar on the surfaces of the sugar crystals mix with water. As the outer layers of sugar molecules leave the crystals, more surface is exposed to the water. The dissolving continues through layer after layer of sugar molecules. Eventually, all the sugar molecules are separated and mixed with water.

PROBLEM

1. You are given two 1-g samples of copper (II) sulfate crystals. One sample contains very small crystals. The other contains large crystals. Which crystals will dissolve faster? Explain.
   Small crystals have larger total surface area.

Figure 1-4. Copper sulfate dissolved in water forms copper sulfate solution.

Time: 30 minutes.

EXPERIMENT. CAUTION: This experiment should be done only under the direct supervision of the teacher.
(1) Place a thermometer in a 250-ml beaker one-half full of water at room temperature. Record the temperature. Add 25 g of ammonium chloride (NH_4Cl). Stir to dissolve the solid. Does the temperature <u>increase</u>, decrease, or remain the same? (2) Repeat Part 1 with 10 g of solid sodium hydroxide (NaOH). Compare the results from Parts 1 and 2. *The temperature increases greatly in Part 2; decreases in Part 1.*

Figure 1-5.

Energy changes occur when a solution is formed. Energy is needed to break the chemical bonds that hold the solvent particles together (solvent-solvent bond). Energy is needed to break the chemical bonds that hold the particles of solute together (solute-solute bond). Energy is released when the solvent and solute particles unite (solute-solvent bond).

PROBLEM

2. How is the formation of a solution similar to a chemical change? *Energy change occurs.*

Ammonium chloride dissolves in water. Heat energy first breaks the solute-solute bonds between the ammonium and chloride ions. Then new solute-solvent bonds form and energy is released. The

How is heat used in the solution process?

Figure 1-6. When ammonium chloride is dissolved in water, the solvent-solvent bonds of the water and the solute-solute bonds of the ammonium chloride are broken. The water ions and the ammonium chloride ions form a solute-solvent bond and energy is released.

Figure 1-7. Stirring helps a solute dissolve faster because it exposes molecules more quickly to the solvent.

J. R. Schnelzer

overall effect of dissolving NH_4Cl in water is a decrease in the temperature of the solution. Why? The heat absorbed in breaking the NH_4Cl bonds is greater than the heat released in forming solute-solvent bonds.

PROBLEM

3. As sodium hydroxide is dissolved in water, the temperature of the solution rises. The water becomes hot. Heat is absorbed in breaking the solute-solute bonds. Heat is released in the formation of solute-solvent bonds. Which is greater, heat absorbed or <u>heat released</u>?

1:3 Rate of Solution

Make sure the students understand that the sugar has not changed to a liquid (melted). The sugar is still in its solid phase but the molecules are evenly distributed throughout the solvent. The melting of sugar is a completely different process.

Suppose you stir some coffee or tea after adding sugar to it. Does the stirring help the sugar dissolve? Will sugar dissolve faster in iced tea or in hot tea? Will granulated sugar dissolve faster than sugar cubes? The answers to these questions are based upon factors that affect the rate at which a solute dissolves.

When a solution is stirred, surface molecules of the solute are pulled away faster. Other surface molecules are exposed more quickly to the action of the solvent. Does stirring cause a solution to form faster?

Energy is needed to break the solute-solute bonds and the solvent-solvent bonds. The addition of energy in the form of heat should

RATE OF SOLUTION (7M) 231

cause the bonds to break and speed the dissolving process. Heat causes molecules to move faster. Dissolving solute particles then move away from the surface faster, exposing other particles.

Time: 25 minutes.

ACTIVITY. Find the mass of a large crystal of copper (II) sulfate on a balance. Measure an equal mass of small copper (II) sulfate crystals. Put the large crystal in a 250-ml flask full of water. Seal with a stopper. Put the small crystals in a second 250-ml flask full of water. Seal this flask with a stopper. Allow the flasks to stand for one week. Check the flasks several times during the week. Compare the results.

The small crystals, though they have the same mass, have more surface area and will dissolve faster. Periodic checks should be made throughout the week.

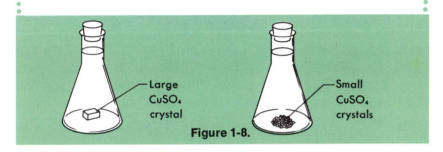

Figure 1-8.

A crushed crystal has more surface area than the original crystal. Consider a cube 20 cm on a side. The area of each face of the cube is 400 cm² (20 cm × 20 cm = 400 cm²). Since a cube has six faces, the total area of the cube is 2400 cm² (400 cm² × 6 = 2400 cm²). If the cube is cut so that it forms eight equal cubes, each 10 cm on a side, the total area will be 4800 cm². Suppose the original cube is cut so that it forms 8000 cubes, each one centimeter on a side. Then the total area will be 48,000 cm² (Figure 1–9). As the cubes are made smaller, more and more area is exposed. If a cube of granulated sugar is crushed and put into water, the area exposed to the solvent

For calculations, see the Teacher's Guide at the front of this book.

Figure 1-9. As a cube is divided into smaller pieces, its total surface area increases.

232 (8M) SOLUTIONS

Figure 1-10. After shaking a warm bottle of pop, gas and liquid rush out of the bottle.

What are three ways to speed solution of a solid?

How can gases be made to dissolve?

If a glass of cold water stands at room temperature, air which was in solution forms bubbles as it comes out of solution. is tremendous. As a result, more particles will be dissolved in a shorter period of time than with a large cube.

To summarize, three ways to increase the rate at which a solute dissolves are (1) heat the solution, (2) stir or shake the solution, and (3) crush the solute.

How does heat affect the solution of a gas in a liquid? Heat increases the amount of solid that can dissolve in a liquid. Just the opposite holds true for gases. Gas molecules are normally farther apart than molecules in a solid. Cooling a gas causes its volume to decrease. The molecules slow down and pull closer together. More molecules are packed into a given space. This greater number of gas molecules can form more bonds with a liquid solvent. Therefore, cooling a liquid allows more gas to dissolve in the liquid.

Do you think that stirring would speed or slow solution of a gas in a liquid? Carbon dioxide gas (CO_2) is dissolved in many kinds of beverages. Have you ever stirred a glass of ginger ale or some other carbonated drink? Does the gas stay in solution? no Before the bottle of soda pop is opened, the gas is under pressure. What happens when the cap is removed from a warm bottle of soda pop which has been shaken? Gas rushes out of the bottle and takes some of the liquid along with it. Gases dissolve better in liquids if the solution is cooled and if pressure is increased. Demonstrate this with a cold bottle of carbonated beverage.

1:4 Solvents

Early chemists searched to find a "universal solvent." But no known solvent will dissolve everything. Water is probably closest to being a universal solvent. It can dissolve many gases, liquids, and solids. However, water will not readily dissolve a number of substances. Grease and carbon tetrachloride (CCl_4) are two materials that do not dissolve in water.

Figure 1-11. Water (inorganic) and oil (organic) cannot mix (a). Dry cleaning fluid removes most soil on clothing because both the fluid and soil are organic (b).

a

Carl England

b

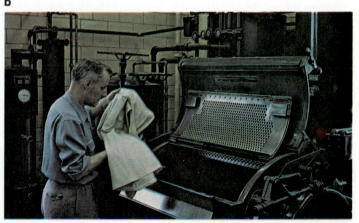

American Institute of Drycleaning

POLAR MOLECULES Point out this rule. Remember (9M) 233
organic compounds contain carbon.

Generally, a solvent will dissolve a solute which is chemically like the solvent. Usually, organic solvents will dissolve organic solutes. Inorganic solvents will dissolve inorganic solutes. Remember, organic compounds contain carbon. Both grease and CCl_4 are organic substances. Carbon tetrachloride, a liquid organic solvent, readily dissolves grease. Benzene, another liquid organic solvent, dissolves grease and CCl_4. Water, however, is inorganic. Water dissolves many inorganic substances, such as table salt.

General rules for solution are not always followed. For example, ethyl alcohol is an organic compound. However, water and alcohol can mix. Water also dissolves some organic substances, such as sugar.

What kind of solutes do organic solvents usually dissolve?

Figure 1-12.

- -
Time: 20 minutes.
ACTIVITY. Place 10 ml of water in one test tube and 10 ml of naphtha (lighter fluid) in another test tube. Add 5 drops of vegetable oil to each and shake. Add 0.5 ml of isopropyl alcohol to the water and shake again. Note the solubility of oil in water, naphtha, and alcohol.
See Teacher's Guide.
- -

Organic solvents are usually used as "dry cleaning" agents because most soil on clothing is organic soil. Before you try to remove some foreign matter from your clothing with a solvent, consider what it is that you are trying to remove. A solvent that will remove chewing gum may also dissolve nylon. Care should be exercised in using any solvent.

1:5 Polar Molecules

What do salt, soap, hydrogen chloride, and sugar have in common? Each is soluble in water. Water dissolves many substances because water molecules are polar. **Polar** means the molecules have a positive charge on one end and a negative charge on the other end.

Most inorganic substances are composed of polar molecules or charged particles. Sodium chloride, for example, is an ionic compound. It is formed through ionic bonding of sodium ions (Na^+) and chloride ions (Cl^-). When sodium chloride is placed in water, the attractive force between the ions in the crystals is lessened. Water molecules surround the ions (Figure 1–14), and the ions are distributed rapidly throughout the solution. When an ionic compound dissolves in water and forms ions, the process is called **dissociation** (dis oh see AY shuhn).

What is a polar molecule?

Figure 1-13. Water is a polar molecule. The hydrogen end is positive and the oxygen end is negative.

Figure 1-14. Dissociation takes place as particles of sodium chloride dissolve in water.

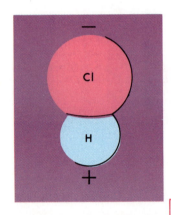

Figure 1-15. Hydrogen chloride is a polar molecule. It is now assumed that H⁺ ions (free protons) are nearly impossible to find in any solution. Free protons would combine instantaneously with a water molecule.

Hydrogen chloride (HCl) is a molecular compound. It is formed through covalent bonding between hydrogen and chlorine. This molecule is bonded by the sharing of an electron pair. The charge of chlorine is large compared to that of hydrogen. Therefore, chlorine controls the electrons most of the time. Thus, the electrons are more likely to be at the chlorine end of the molecule, causing that end to be a negative end. The hydrogen end is positive. Thus, hydrogen chloride is a polar molecule (Figure 1–15).

When hydrogen chloride is placed in water, it forms ions. Both the chloride ion (Cl⁻) and the hydrogen ion (H⁺) form in the water solution. The hydrogen ion (H⁺) combines with a molecule of water (H_2O) to produce an ion called the *hydronium* (hy DROH nee uhm) *ion* (H_3O^+) ($H^+ + H_2O \longrightarrow H_3O^+$). When a molecular compound dissolves in water to form ions, the process is called **ionization** (i uh nuh ZAY shuhn).

PROBLEM

4. What is the difference between ionization and dissociation? Give an example of each. See Teacher's Guide at the front of this book.

Some compounds do not ionize or dissociate when placed in water. For example, sugar is such a compound. The atoms in its molecules are held together by covalent bonds. Sugar is nonpolar. Its electric charges are shared equally throughout the molecule. Neither end is charged, so it is nonpolar. In water, it dissolves but remains as molecules. It does not break up into ions.

1:6 Solutions as Conductors

Handling electrical appliances with wet hands can be dangerous. A person may **receive** a severe shock or **possibly** be electrocuted.

PEOPLE CAREERS FRONTIERS
FOCUS ON PHYSICAL SCIENCE

Modern Alchemist Turns Sludge into Zinc Worth Millions

John Cosgrove, an environmental engineer for FMC Corporation, has developed a way to recover zinc from industrial waste. The zinc is in the compound zinc hydroxide. The zinc hydroxide and waste are in the form of sludge.

Zinc is removed by first heating the sludge until the zinc hydroxide changes from a gel into crystals. Water leaves the mixture as it is filtered. This filtering is much like the action of a drip coffee maker. After a few more processes, a zinc solution is ready to be recycled into the plant.

This process has saved the company millions of dollars.

• • • • • • • • • • • • •

Courtesy of *ChemEcology*, September, 1975.

John Cosgrove, an environmental engineer, has perfected a way to recover zinc from industrial waste.

Mrs. Gwendolyn Veal Albert Environmental Engineer

Mrs. Gwendolyn V. Albert is an environmental engineer. She works for the United States Army Corps of Engineers. She works in the Water Supply Studies Branch in Dallas, Texas. Her job is to find out about present and future water supply needs for areas in southwestern United States.

Mrs. Albert prepared for her job in many ways. She studied chemistry in college and obtained a bachelor's degree. She also completed a master's degree in civil engineering with a concentration in environmental engineering.

Mrs. Albert says that she likes her work because it helps people. Her work is important because the results of her studies will affect the development of communities.

How does Mrs. Albert conduct a study of the water supply in a certain area? First of all, she determines the number of people and industries located in the area. Also, she determines how much water is available. Using mathematical procedures, Mrs. Albert determines if the current water supply is adequate for future needs. If it is not, she predicts what the water needs will be.

A review is made of her study. Her recommendations often result in action. For example, a community may not be expanded if there is an inadequate water supply.

• • • • • • • • • • • • •

Courtesy of the American Association of Physics Teachers.

Gwendolyn Albert discusses a proposed reservoir system.

Impure water can be a good conductor of electricity. A **conductor** is a substance through which electricity can flow readily.

Water conducts an electric current when it contains ions. In general, inorganic compounds which dissolve in water will release ions into solution. The apparatus in Figure 1–16 is used to determine whether a substance releases ions when it dissolves in water. Organic compounds, with a few exceptions, will not produce ions and will not conduct electricity.

Potassium bromide (KBr) is an inorganic compound. It dissociates in water. The ions present (K^+ and Br^-) make the solution a conductor. Substances which can conduct electric currents when in a water solution are called **electrolytes** (ih LEK truh lyts). Potassium bromide is one example.

Electric current in a wire is a flow of electrons. In a solution, an electric current is a flow of ions. Both electrons and ions are charged particles. For an electric current to pass through a solution, ions must be present in the solution.

What is an electrolyte?

PROBLEM

5. Electrical current travels through the storage battery in a car's electrical system. Is the current inside the battery a movement of electrons or ions?

Figure 1-16.

Time: 50 minutes.

ACTIVITY. Prepare a test device for electrolytes similar to that in Figure 1–16. Connect two dry cells to an electric socket containing a 3-V flashlight bulb. Cut one wire in the circuit and bare the wires for about an inch. Obtain five small beakers (125 ml) and pour 50 ml of distilled water in each. Put the two bare wires into the water in one beaker. Be sure that the wires do not touch each other. What change occurs? Sprinkle a few grams of sodium chloride into the water. What happens? Is sodium chloride an electrolyte? Yes

Discuss the reason for using distilled water in this activity.

Clean the wires by rinsing in distilled water. Then place them in the second beaker. What is your observation? Pour 5 ml of alcohol in the water. Is alcohol an electrolyte? No

Clean the wires and repeat with hydrochloric acid, sugar, and potassium sulfate in the other three beakers. Which are electrolytes? What "carries" the current through the solution? How could you make the bulb burn brighter? Devise an activity to test your hypothesis. See Teacher's Guide at the front of this book.

Figure 1-17. It takes hundreds of years for a cave to form. Water carrying dissolved calcium carbonate (from rocks) drips from the ceiling. As the water evaporates, calcite is deposited to form stalactites (top) and stalagmites (bottom).

Sugar in solution does not ionize. A sugar solution contains nonpolar sugar molecules. Because the solution cannot conduct electric currents, it is called a nonelectrolyte. A **nonelectrolyte** is a substance which does not conduct an electric current when dissolved in water. An alcohol-water solution cannot conduct a current because alcohol is an organic compound that does not ionize. Alcohol is a nonelectrolyte.

Name a nonelectrolyte.

1:7 *Solubility*

Table salt is very soluble in water and iodine is very soluble in ethyl alcohol. **Solubility** is the amount of solute that can be dissolved in a specific amount of solvent. When table salt is added to water, the salt dissolves readily to form a saltwater solution. However, only a very tiny amount of table salt dissolves in ethyl alcohol. In contrast, iodine crystals do not dissolve readily in water. When iodine crystals are added to ethyl alcohol, the iodine dissolves readily, coloring the liquid brown.

Raising the temperature increases the solubility of solids in liquids. For example, table salt is more soluble in hot water than in cold water. Just the reverse is true for gases. The solubility of a gas decreases as the temperature is raised.

PROBLEMS

6. Does soda pop hold more carbon dioxide when it is warm or cold?

7. Which can hold more dissolved oxygen, warm or cold lake water?

> Time: 15 minutes.
> ACTIVITY. Place three test tubes in a beaker or test tube rack. Add 10 ml of water to each test tube. Add a small piece of soap to one test tube. Add 0.5 ml of liquid detergent to another test tube. Add 5 drops of vegetable oil to each test tube and shake to mix the contents. Compare the solubility of oil in water, soapy water, and water containing detergent. Oil will not dissolve in water. It dissolves better in water with detergent.

It is often difficult to determine whether a compound will dissolve. It also may be impractical to try to find out. Chemists have determined a few solubility rules which can be used to predict whether an inorganic compound will dissolve (Table 1–2). These rules are based upon observations that have been made during laboratory experiments.

Point out the usefulness of this table.

Table 1–2. Solubility of Common Compounds in Water

Common compounds which contain the following ions are *soluble:*
(a) sodium (Na^+), potassium (K^+), ammonium (NH_4^+).
(b) nitrates (NO_3^-).
(c) acetates ($C_2H_3O_2^-$), except silver acetate, which is only moderately soluble.
(d) chlorides (Cl^-), except silver, mercury (I), and lead chlorides. $PbCl_2$ is soluble in hot water.
(e) sulfates (SO_4^{2-}), except barium and lead sulfates. Calcium, mercury (I), and silver sulfates are slightly soluble.

Common compounds which contain the following ions are *insoluble:*
(a) silver (Ag^+), except silver nitrate and silver perchlorate.
(b) sulfides (S^{2-}), except those of sodium, potassium, ammonium, magnesium, barium, and calcium.
(c) carbonates (CO_3^{2-}), except those of sodium, potassium, and ammonium.
(d) phosphates (PO_4^{3-}), except those of sodium, potassium, and ammonium.
(e) hydroxides (OH^-), except those of sodium, potassium, ammonium, and barium.

EXAMPLE

Will mercury (II) sulfide dissolve in water?

Solution: Check Table 1–2. All sulfides are insoluble, except those listed. Mercury (II) sulfide is not listed. It will not dissolve in water.

Figure 1-18.

Time: 60 minutes. Any salt such as NaCl, NaNO₃, or KNO₃ will work.

ACTIVITY. Find the solubility of table salt in water. Place 20 ml of water in a beaker. Slowly dissolve the salt, with constant stirring, until a small amount of salt lies on the bottom of the beaker and does not dissolve. Filter the solution through a piece of filter paper in a funnel. Find the mass of an evaporating dish. Place the filtrate in an evaporating dish. Find the mass of the dish and contents. Heat with a Bunsen burner flame until all the liquid is evaporated. Allow to cool and find the mass of the dish again. From your measurements, compute the mass of salt dissolved in 20 ml of solution.

See Teacher's Guide at the front of this book for sample data.

Problems

8. Which of the following compounds are soluble in water?
   - (a) sodium nitrate *yes*
   - (b) silver phosphate *no*
   - (c) barium chloride *yes*
   - (d) ammonium chloride *yes*
   - (e) aluminum hydroxide *no*
   - (f) magnesium carbonate *no*

9. If any of the compounds in Problem 8 are soluble in water, what ions, if any, will be found in solution? *(a) Na^+, NO_3^- (c) Ba^{2+}, Cl^- (d) NH_4^+, Cl^-*

1:8 Concentration

A dilute solution has less solute per given volume than a concentrated solution. They are relative terms.

To some people, a glass of lemonade may be too sour. To others, the same lemonade may not be sour enough. To describe a solution such as lemonade, people often use the terms "dilute" or "concentrated." These terms are sometimes misleading. It is often difficult to determine what is concentrated and what is dilute unless measurements are made. **Concentration** is the amount of solute per unit volume of solvent. A solution is generally described giving its concentration as a ratio of so many grams of solute in each liter of solution (g/ℓ).

Figure 1-19. Orange juice is more concentrated than orange drink.

Carl England

Problem

10. A can of frozen lemonade is opened and mixed with water. Does the lemonade become <u>more dilute</u> or concentrated?

Figure 1-20.

Suppose a solution contains 50 g of sugar per liter of water solution. The sugar is distributed uniformly throughout the solution. There are 25 g of sugar in 500 ml and 5 g in 100 ml. If you needed 5 g of sugar, you would simply pour out 100 ml, 1/10 of a liter, and evaporate the water.

- -

Time: 60 minutes.
ACTIVITY. (1) Place 35 ml of water in a beaker. Slowly add table salt with constant stirring until no more will dissolve. A small amount of salt will remain on the bottom of the beaker undissolved. Pour the solution into a 50-ml graduated cylinder. Take a specific gravity reading with a straw hydrometer (Figure 1–20). (2) Repeat Part 1 using three different concentrations of table salt in water. Make a table to compare the specific gravities of the solutions. How might a difference in temperature affect your results? Temperature determines amount of solute to go into solution.

Use a few pellets of lead shot. Measure the density of the distilled water and mark the place on the straw. (This density is the accepted standard with a value of one. Since other specific gravities will be multiples of this, you might want to mark its density as 1 on the straw.)

1:9 Saturation

Not all compounds dissolve at the same rate. For example, at 60°C approximately 110 g of potassium nitrate (KNO_3) dissolves in 100 ml of water. Less than 40 g of sodium chloride dissolves in the same amount of water at the same temperature.

At room temperature, 20°C, 100 ml of water will hold about 40 g of potassium nitrate (KNO_3). If any more KNO_3 is added to the

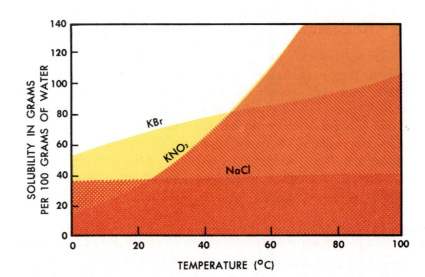

Figure 1-21. Differences in solubility of these salts can be shown with curves on a graph.

SATURATION

solution, it falls to the bottom undissolved. The solution is said to be **saturated** (SACH uh rayt uhd) when it will hold no more solute. However, if the solution is heated to 60°C, the same amount of water can hold nearly three times as much KNO_3. At 60°C, the solution is **unsaturated.** It does not hold all the solute that it can hold at that temperature.

Suppose the same solution is slowly cooled to 10°C so that no crystals form. At 10°C, 100 ml of H_2O is expected to contain only 25 g of KNO_3. However, this solution contains 40 g of KNO_3. The solution is said to be **supersaturated.** It contains more solute than is expected at that temperature. Thus, the same solution could be saturated, unsaturated, or supersaturated depending on the temperature of the solution.

Figure 1-22. Sweetened ice tea is saturated when it will hold no more sugar.

Time: 45 minutes.

ACTIVITY. Dissolve 100 g of "hypo" (sodium thiosulfate) in 100 ml of water in a 250-ml flask. Heat until all the solid dissolves. Remove the flask from the flame. Stopper the flask with a wad of cotton. Allow it to cool. Then remove the cotton and drop a crystal of "hypo" into the liquid. Crystallization should occur. Design an experiment to prove that crystallization would not occur if a crystal of sodium chloride were added to a supersaturated sodium thiosulfate solution.

—Care must be taken not to agitate the flask.

Crystallization should occur as soon as the crystal is dropped in. The same activity could be repeated and a crystal of sodium chloride added to the hypo solution. Because sodium chloride is not the right shape, crystallization would not take place. Sodium chloride is the wrong model for hypo crystallization.

Figure 1-23.

One way to determine whether or not a solution is saturated is to put more solute into the solution. A saturated solution contains all the solute it is expected to contain at that temperature. Additional solute put into a saturated solution will not dissolve. At least, it appears not to dissolve. What actually happens is that some of it does dissolve, but some of it crystallizes out at the same time. The amount of solute in the saturated solution remains the same.

How can you determine whether a solution is saturated or not?

This is an example of dynamic equilibrium.

A solution is a mixture rather than a compound. It does not have a definite composition by weight. The solute can be recovered by physical means. The process of solution may be chemical but the material formed is a mixture.

If a solution is unsaturated, additional solute will dissolve. However, if the solution is supersaturated, the excess solute in solution will crystallize immediately. Why is a solution a mixture and not a compound?

Figure 1-24.

Time: 35 minutes.

ACTIVITY. Prepare saturated solutions of various salts in small dropper bottles. Place one drop of a salt solution on a slide and gently heat over a burner or on the edge of a hot plate. Place the slide under the low power lens of the microscope and watch for crystals to form as the liquid cools. If no crystallization occurs, reheat and observe again. If crystallization is too rapid, add water with the end of a toothpick and repeat.

1:10 *Hydrated Crystals*

Many substances which ionize or dissociate in water solution produce ions that are strongly attached to water molecules. Therefore, when the substances crystallize from solution, water molecules form a part of their crystalline structure. For example, when copper (II) sulfate ($CuSO_4$) crystallizes out of solution, four water molecules are attached to each Cu^{2+} ion and one water molecule is attached to each SO_4^{2-} ion. Thus the ions are said to be **hydrated.** The crystal formed is called a *hydrate.* Many ionic substances form hydrated crystals. The water they contain is called **water of hydration** (hy DRAY shuhn).

Figure 1-25. Deliquescent materials attract and hold water. They are used when a dry environment is desired.

Time: 30 minutes.

ACTIVITY. Place a few crystals of CuSO₄ in the bottom of a Pyrex test tube. Hold the test tube at a 45° angle and heat the bottom strongly. What happens to the crystals? What happens at the mouth of the test tube? What do you suppose causes the color of the CuSO₄ crystals? Place some of the powder remaining in the test tube on a slide. Put a few drops of water on the powder. What happens? Warm the slide gently over the burner. Does a crystal form? What is it? Devise an experiment which uses CuSO₄ to test for water.
See Teacher's Guide at the front of this book.

Figure 1-26.

Some substances give up their waters of hydration much easier than others. In fact, some release them quickly into the air. These compounds are said to be *efflorescent* (ef luh RES uhnt).

On the other hand, some crystals hold their water of hydration so strongly that water from the air is attracted to the crystal. These substances may even gather enough water to form a solution. Compounds which do this are said to be *deliquescent* (del ih KWES uhnt).

What is a deliquescent compound?

Time: 75 minutes.

ACTIVITY. Find the mass of four small beakers, watch glasses, or petri dishes. Place approximately 10 g of sodium sulfate crystals (Na₂SO₄ · 10 H₂O) in the first dish. In the second dish place 10 g of CaCl₂; in the third, 10 g of CuSO₄ · 5 H₂O; and in the fourth, 10 g of Na₂CO₃ · 10 H₂O. Record the mass of each dish every 15 min for an hour or wait until the following day. Has anything appeared to happen? What change occurs in the mass of each container and its contents? Which crystals, if any, are deliquescent? Which, if any, are efflorescent? Which show no signs of change?   CaCl₂
Na₂CO₃•10 H₂O
Na₂SO₄•10 H₂O
CuSO₄•5 H₂O

Figure 1-27.

1:11 Properties of Solutions

Why do some motorists put ethylene glycol (antifreeze) in the radiator of their cars? How does this substance prevent the water in the cooling system from freezing? You may know someone who adds salt to water "to make it hotter" when heated to boiling. Does the addition of salt make water boil at a higher temperature?

Cold weather may cause the radiator to freeze and crack.

The addition of salt raises the B.P. of water.

Figure 1-28. Because ethylene glycol has a high boiling point and can be mixed with water, it is used as a permanent antifreeze for automobile cooling systems.

William Maddox

Time: 30 minutes.

ACTIVITY. Bring water in a beaker to a boil. Record the temperature. Stop heating the beaker. Allow the water to cool slightly. Add 10 g of salt (NaCl) to the water and stir. Heat the water until it boils. Record the temperature again. Was there any change in boiling temperatures? What caused the change? *Adding salt raised boiling point.*

Figure 1-29.

10 g NaCl in water

You may wish to explain boiling point further.

Dissolving a solute in a liquid raises the liquid's boiling point. The kind of solute particles in the solution is unimportant. However, the amount of solute particles in the solution is important. As more solute is added, the boiling point is raised. A smaller proportion of the particles in the solution are solvent particles. More of the solution consists of dissolved particles. Thus, more heat is needed to cause the solvent to evaporate.

How does a dissolved substance affect the boiling point of a liquid?

PROBLEM

11. Would salt water from the ocean have the same boiling point as fresh water from the Great Lakes? *Salt water has higher boiling point.*

SOLUTIONS

Addition of a solute to a liquid lowers the liquid's freezing point. When a liquid freezes, it changes from liquid to solid phase. As it freezes, the liquid forms solid crystals. If a substance is dissolved in the liquid, the particles of solute interfere with crystal formation. More heat must be removed to produce the normal crystal pattern. Thus, the freezing point is lowered as more solute is dissolved in the solvent.

In general, the addition of a solute to a pure liquid causes an increase in the boiling point of the liquid. Addition of a solute causes a decrease in the freezing point.

Figure 1-30. Both freezing and boiling points change when a solute is added to a liquid.

Problems

12. Why is salt spread on ice-covered sidewalks? *The solution has lower freezing point, ice melts*
13. Why is salt mixed with the ice used in making homemade ice cream? *To make the ice melt at a lower temperature.*

Time: 20 minutes.

ACTIVITY. Partially fill a glass with ice and add a small amount of water. Place a thermometer in the glass, stir, and record the temperature. Add a large amount of salt to the ice and water and record the temperature. What changes do you observe? *The solution has a lower F.P.*

Figure 1-31.

MAIN IDEAS

1. Solutions are mixtures of matter which are the same throughout.
2. A solute dissolves in a solvent to form a solution.
3. Solution of a solid in a liquid may be aided by heating the solution, crushing the solute, or stirring.
4. Solution of a gas in a liquid may be aided by cooling the solution or by increasing the pressure.
5. Organic solvents usually will dissolve organic solutes. Inorganic solvents usually will dissolve inorganic solutes.
6. When an ionic compound dissolves in water, it dissociates to form ions.
7. When a polar molecular compound dissolves in water, it releases polar molecules into solution.
8. Substances that form ions in solution and conduct electric current are called electrolytes.

1:8 **9.** The concentration of a solution may be described as the number of grams of solute per liter of solution.

1:9 **10.** Solutions may be saturated, unsaturated, or supersaturated.

1:11 **11.** The boiling point of a solution is generally higher than that of the pure solvent.

1:11 **12.** The freezing point of a solution is lower than that of the pure solvent.

VOCABULARY

Write a sentence in which you correctly use each of the following words or terms.

alloy	hydrated crystal	solute
concentration	ionization	solution
deliquescent	nonelectrolyte	solvent
dissociation	polar	supersaturated
efflorescent	saturated	unsaturated
electrolyte	solubility	water of hydration

STUDY QUESTIONS

Have students rewrite false statements to make the statements correct.

A. True or False

Determine whether each of the following sentences is true or false. (Do not write in this book.)

solute, solvent F **1.** To form a solution, a ~~solvent~~ must be dissolved by a ~~solute~~.

T **2.** Oil will not mix in water.

gaseous F **3.** A ~~solid~~ solution can be formed by dissolving a gas in another gas.

most inorganic compounds F **4.** Water is a solvent that will dissolve ~~everything~~.

T **5.** Ethyl alcohol and water can form a mixture.

F **6.** Organic solvents usually dissolve ~~inorganic~~ solutes.

T **7.** Stirring increases the rate of solution.

T **8.** Ions conduct electricity in a liquid.

efflorescent F **9.** Crystals which lose their waters of hydration easily are ~~deliquescent~~.

T **10.** The addition of solute usually raises the boiling point of a pure liquid.

SOLUTIONS   (23M)   247

B. Multiple Choice

Some questions in Parts B and C may have more than one correct answer. Only one answer is required.

Choose one word or phrase that correctly completes each of the following sentences. (Do not write in this book.)

1. Water will not dissolve *(copper sulfate, lighter fluid, alcohol)*.
2. *(Nitrate, Silver, Sulfate)* compounds are all insoluble in water.
3. Dry cleaning solvents are usually *(inorganic, organic)*.
4. A solution conducts electricity through its *(electrons, ions, polar molecules, atoms)*.
5. If you could dissolve 5 kg of salt in a liter of water, the solution would probably be *(saturated, unsaturated, supersaturated)*.
6. *(Ag_2S, Sugar, $NaNO_3$)* would produce the most ions when added to water.
7. Adding solute to a solution causes the freezing point to *(lower, remain the same, raise)*.
8. Organic solids will generally dissolve in *(water, ammonia, naphtha)*.
9. Concentration of solution is usually expressed as *(g/ℓ, lb/ℓ, oz/ml)*.
10. One gram of salt in ten liters of water would make a *(dilute, concentrated, supersaturated)* solution.

C. Completion

Complete each of the following sentences with a word or phrase that will make the sentence correct. (Do not write in this book.)

1. _____ is the most common solvent. Water
2. When ionic compounds dissolve in water, they _____. dissociate
3. _____ does not ionize when it dissolves. Sugar
4. Water is a good solvent for inorganic compounds because it has _____ molecules. polar
5. _____ is the process in which molecular compounds form ions in solution. Ionization
6. Organic solvents generally dissolve _____ solutes. organic
7. Carbon tetrachloride is a liquid _____ solvent. organic
8. A(n) _____ is a substance which can conduct an electric current when in a water solution. electrolyte
9. Adding _____ to orange juice makes the solution more dilute. water
10. Adding alcohol to water causes the freezing point to _____. lower

D. How and Why

1. If a solution of NaCl contains 50 g in 1ℓ, how much salt would 50 ml contain? *(2.5 g)*

2. List three factors that contribute to rapid solution of a solid solute. *(agitation, pulverization, heat)*

3. From the graph in Figure 1–21, estimate how many grams of KNO_3 will dissolve in 100 ml of water at 20°C. How does this compare with the amount that will dissolve at 40°C? *(35-40 g at 20°C; 60-65 g at 40°C; about half)*

4. List the following in order of solubility in water, using Table 1–2: (a) lead chloride, (b) ammonium nitrate, (c) silver chloride, (d) calcium sulfate. *(b a d c)*

5. A 100-ml solution contains 50 g of solute. How could you make 100 ml of solution of the same material which contained only 30 g of the solute? *(100 ml contains 50 g, 60 ml contains 30 g, Add 40 ml water to 60 ml solution)*

6. A solution conducts electricity. What do you know about the solution? *(It contains ions, probably inorganic.)*

7. A solution contains 50 g of solute in 300 ml of solution. What is the concentration in grams per liter? *(167 g/ℓ)*

8. What are some household substances that will dissolve in water? In alcohol? *(salt, sugar)*

9. What is the major difference between saturated, unsaturated, and supersaturated solutions of the same solute? *(See Teacher's Guide.)*

10. Describe how a crystal dissolves in water. Illustrate with a drawing. *(See Teacher's Guide.)*

(See Teacher's Guide at the front of this book.)

INVESTIGATIONS

1. Find out how to make a "silica garden."

2. Prepare a report on the purification of chemicals by crystallization.

3. Visit a service station to determine how the device for testing antifreeze works. You may find it very close to something you may have already made.

4. Using table salt (NaCl), 100 ml of water, and a thermometer, determine the solubility of NaCl in water at various temperatures. NOTE: Form a saturated solution at room temperature first. Record the mass of salt used—or the volume of the salt if a balance is not available. Make a graph of your results.

5. Grow a large crystal of copper (II) sulfate or alum from a saturated solution.

SOLUTIONS

INTERESTING READING

Asimov, Isaac, "Are Oceans Getting Too Salty?" *Science Digest,* LXXII (April, 1972), pp. 73–74.

Coulson, E. H., Trinder, A. E. J., and Kleith, Aaron E., *Test Tubes and Beakers: Chemistry for Young Experimenters.* Garden City, Doubleday & Company, Inc., 1971.

Holden, Alan, and Singer, Phyllis, *Crystals and Crystal Growing.* Garden City, Doubleday & Company, Inc., 1960.

One of the most basic concepts of all science is the principle of conservation of matter and energy. *Roger K. Burnard*
Chemical equations are used by the chemist to describe chemical change and to demonstrate the law of conservation of mass. Common types of reactions are synthesis, decomposition, single replacement, and double replacement. One of the important ideas in this chapter is that energy changes accompany

2 Chemical Reactions

chemical reaction. Energy is released in an exothermic reaction and absorbed in an endothermic reaction.

GOAL: You will gain an understanding of the conservation of matter and energy and how energy changes accompany chemical reactions.

Burning and rusting are two common chemical reactions. In chemical reactions, new and different substances are formed. What new substances are formed when logs burn or iron rusts? How are these new substances different from the original substances?

Other changes may occur in chemical reactions. Heat or light may be given off. The changes which occur in chemical reactions can be shown by writing chemical equations.

CONSERVATION OF MASS

2:1 Conservation of Mass

When iron rusts, the iron reacts with oxygen to form red iron oxide. The mass of the oxide is equal to the combined mass of the iron and oxygen. No mass is lost or gained in the reaction. Similarly, when hydrogen and oxygen react to form water, the mass of the water is equal to the total mass of hydrogen and oxygen.

Time: 30 minutes.

EXPERIMENT. Place two wooden matches in a flask and seal with a rubber stopper. Place the sealed flask on a balance and record its mass. CAUTION: Stand away from flask as burner is ignited. Ignite the matches by heating the flask with a Bunsen burner. Allow the flask to cool and then find its mass again. Has the mass changed? Explain your observation. *A chemical change does not change the mass that is present.* *no*

Figure 2-1.

In ordinary chemical changes, no matter is lost. The mass of all the substances before a reaction equals the mass of all the substances after the reaction. This statement is called the **law of conservation of mass.** It is a basic principle in the study of chemical reactions.

What is the law of conservation of mass?

Time: 40 minutes.

ACTIVITY. CAUTION: This activity should be done only under the direct supervision of the teacher. Do not get silver nitrate on your hands or clothing as it will leave stains.

Dissolve 5 g of silver nitrate in 150 ml of water in a 250-ml flask. Add 5 ml of sodium chloride solution to a small test tube. Place the test tube inside the flask. Seal with a stopper. Find the mass of the flask and its contents. Tip the flask over so the contents of the test tube mix with the liquid in the flask. Determine the total mass of the flask, test tube, and contents. Explain your results. *The mass remains the same. No mass is gained or lost in a chemical change.*

Caution students to wear clothing protection when handling silver nitrate. Stains may be removed by applying a sodium thiosulfate (Hypo) solution.

Figure 2-2.

Figure 2-3. Industrial precipitators remove waste gas pollutants from the atmosphere.

What do (aq), (l), and (g) indicate in a chemical equation? aqueous, liquid, gas

Figure 2-4. Silver nitrate and sodium chloride solutions react to produce a precipitate, silver chloride.

CHEMICAL REACTIONS

2:2 Chemical Equations

How does one chemist tell another chemist about a chemical change that has been observed? To describe chemical reactions, scientists use chemical equations. A **chemical equation** is a shorthand description made up of symbols and formulas. For example, the chemical equation for a reaction between carbon and oxygen is

$$C + O_2 \longrightarrow CO_2.$$

How do you describe the reaction between solutions of silver nitrate ($AgNO_3$) and sodium chloride (NaCl)? Chemical reactions can be described by using two types of chemical equations: the word equation and the formula equation. Using a *word equation* you can say that silver nitrate reacts with sodium chloride to produce silver chloride and sodium nitrate:

silver nitrate plus sodium chloride yields

silver chloride plus sodium nitrate

A simpler way to explain the reaction is to write a *formula equation:*
Point out the symbol (s).

$$AgNO_3(aq) + NaCl(aq) \longrightarrow AgCl(s) + NaNO_3(aq)$$

Symbols in a formula equation describe how atoms are rearranged in a chemical reaction. The letter (s) means "solid." It shows that a precipitate (prih SIP uh tayt) forms. A **precipitate** is a substance which is separated from a solution by a chemical or physical change. A precipitate is usually a solid which does not dissolve in the solvent. Silver chloride is a precipitate. The symbol (aq) means the compound is dissolved in water; (aq) stand for aqueous. The symbol (l), when used, means the substance is in the liquid phase. The arrow which points to the right ($\longrightarrow$) means "yields" or "produces." Substances to the left of $\longrightarrow$ are called **reactants.** Substances to the right of $\longrightarrow$ are called **products.**

Some reactants will not take part in a chemical reaction unless they are in water solution. In these cases, chemical change takes place through the action of ions. The reaction between silver nitrate and sodium chloride is such a reaction. Both silver nitrate and sodium chloride are ionic compounds. Their ions are held tightly to each other in their crystalline forms. In order for the compounds to react, these ionic bonds must be broken. One way to break these bonds is to dissolve the compounds in water.

When silver nitrate and sodium chloride are dissolved in water, the water molecules separate the ions. The ions are distributed throughout the solution. Silver, sodium, chloride, and nitrate ions are in the solution. When silver ions and chloride ions collide, they bond to form silver chloride. The water molecules are not able to break this bond. Thus silver chloride, because it is not soluble in water, settles out of solution (precipitates). Free sodium ions and

DOUBLE REPLACEMENT

free nitrate ions remain in solution. The precipitate AgCl may be filtered out. Then, when the water is evaporated, sodium nitrate will remain. Since the water molecules no longer hold the ions apart, the compound $NaNO_3$ forms.

Sometimes a gas is formed in solution as a result of a chemical reaction. In this case, the gas bubbles out of solution, leaving the other ions behind. For example, if zinc is added to a water solution of hydrogen chloride, hydrogen gas is formed. Zinc ions and chloride ions are left in solution. The equation

$$2\ HCl(aq) + Zn(s) \longrightarrow ZnCl_2(aq) + H_2(g)$$

shows this. The (g) after H_2 means that hydrogen gas is formed.

There are many different types of chemical reactions. Four main kinds are double replacement, single replacement, decomposition, and synthesis.

2:3 Double Replacement

The reaction between silver nitrate and sodium chloride is called a **double replacement reaction.** In this type of reaction, the reactants switch ions. A precipitate, gas, or water solution is also formed.

A general form of double replacement reaction is shown below. Letters are used to represent the compounds.

General equation for a double replacement reaction
  Word equation:
    AB plus CD yields AD and CB
  Formula equation:
    $AB + CD \longrightarrow AD + CB$

Actual double replacement reaction
  Word equation:
barium chloride (solution) plus sodium sulfate (solution) yields barium sulfate (solid) plus sodium chloride (solution)
  Formula equation:
    $BaCl_2(aq) + Na_2SO_4(aq) \longrightarrow BaSO_4(s) + NaCl(aq)$

In the above reaction, the barium ion (Ba^{2+}) combines with the sulfate ion (SO_4^{2-}) replacing the sodium. The sodium ion (Na^+) combines with the chloride ion (Cl^-) replacing the barium. The newly formed barium sulfate ($BaSO_4$) is a precipitate. The sodium chloride (NaCl) is soluble. Thus, sodium (Na^+) and chloride (Cl^-) ions remain dissolved. NaCl is in solution as $Na+$ and $Cl-$ ions.

Count the number of sodium atoms on the left and on the right sides of the equation. Does the number of sodium atoms on the left

Figure 2-5. Double replacement reactions result in the formation of a precipitate, a gas, or water.

Figure 2-6. Many chemical reactions take place when metal is refined.

How do you know when an equation is balanced?

NaCl is in solution as Na⁺ and Cl⁻ ions.

What is the difference between a coefficient and a subscript?

Coefficients are numerals used to balance an equation. Subscripts give the ratio in which the elements are combined in the compound.

Make sure that the students understand the example before you proceed.

side equal the number of sodium atoms on the right side? Now count the chlorine atoms. Is the number the same on both sides? According to the law of conservation of mass, the number of atoms of an element should be the same on both sides of an equation. By writing the numeral 2 in front of NaCl, the equation can be balanced. An equation is *balanced* when the number and kind of atoms to the left of ⟶ equal the number and kind of atoms to the right of ⟶. The equation is now balanced:

$$BaCl_2(aq) + Na_2SO_4(aq) \longrightarrow BaSO_4 + 2\,NaCl(aq)$$

Numerals used to balance a chemical equation are called *coefficients* (koh uh FISH uhntz). Subscript numbers in a formula should not be added or changed to balance an equation. Changing a subscript changes the formula into a formula for a different compound.

Equations represent chemical changes or reactions. To write a correct equation:

(1) Write a word equation for the reaction.
(2) Write proper formulas for all reactants and products.
(3) See if the equation is balanced. Place coefficients in front of the formulas if needed to balance the equation. *Do not change subscripts to balance equations.*

Example

Sodium hydroxide (NaOH) and iron (III) chloride (FeCl₃) react to form sodium chloride (NaCl) and iron (III) hydroxide [Fe(OH)₃]. NaOH, FeCl₃, and NaCl are in solution. Fe(OH)₃ is a precipitate. You can write an equation for this reaction. This is a double replacement reaction. Iron (III) means that each iron atom has lost three electrons to chloride ions.

DOUBLE REPLACEMENT (31M) 255

Solution: When the iron ions (Fe^{3+}) unite with the hydroxide ions (OH^-), a precipitate forms.

(a) Write the formulas:

$$NaOH(aq) + FeCl_3(aq) \longrightarrow NaCl(aq) + Fe(OH)_3(s)$$

(b) Check the balance:
Hydroxide ions and chloride ions do not balance.

(c) Balance:
Three chlorine atoms are on the left. To have three chlorine atoms on the right, place the numeral 3 in front of NaCl:

$$NaOH(aq) + FeCl_3(aq) \longrightarrow 3\,NaCl(aq) + Fe(OH)_3(s)$$

Now three sodium atoms are on the right. To have three sodium atoms on the left, place the numeral 3 in front of NaOH:

$$3\,NaOH(aq) + FeCl_3(aq) \longrightarrow 3\,NaCl(aq) + Fe(OH)_3(s)$$

Three hydroxide ions are needed on the right. The formula already has three. The iron atoms are equal. The equation is balanced.

Problem

1. Complete and balance the following equations:
   (a) $NaBr(aq) + AgNO_3(aq) \longrightarrow$ __Ag__ $Br(s) +$ __Na__ $NO_3(aq)$
   (b) $Ca(NO_3)_2(aq) + K_2SO_4(aq) \longrightarrow Ca$ __SO_4__ $(s) +$ __2K__ __NO_3__ (aq)
   (c) __2__ $KCl(aq) + Pb(NO_3)_2(aq) \longrightarrow$ __2__ K __NO_3__ $(aq) + Pb$ __Cl_2__ (s)
   (d) __3__ $Ca(OH)_2(aq) +$ __2__ $Fe(NO_3)_3(aq) \longrightarrow$ __2__ Fe __$(OH)_3$__ $(s) +$ __3__ Ca __$(NO_3)_2$__ (aq)
   (e) __3__ $MgSO_4(aq) +$ __2__ $Na_3PO_4(aq) \longrightarrow$ __$Mg_3(PO_4)_2$__ $(s) +$ __3 Na_2SO_4__ (aq)
   (f) Hydrogen sulfide plus mercury (II) chloride in water yields _____ + _____ . 2 hydrogen chloride plus mercury (II) sulfide

---

Figure 2-7.

Time: 25 minutes.

Blue precipitate forms. Copper compounds are generally blue.

ACTIVITY. Place 5 ml of <u>copper (II) sulfate solution</u> in a <u>test tube</u> and add three <s>drops</s> of sodium hydroxide solution. What do you observe? What compound is formed? What color is characteristic of most copper compounds? What other substance must have been formed? Write an equation for the reaction that you think took place. $CuSO_4 + 2\,NaOH \longrightarrow Cu(OH)_2 + Na_2SO_4$

Filter the solution. Can you tell if all of the copper (II) sulfate in the solution has reacted? How? Add an additional drop of sodium hydroxide solution. What change occurs? What does this prove about the first addition of sodium hydroxide? If more precipitate forms, all copper sulfate did not react initially.

What does "go to completion" mean?

All reactions in which a gas, a precipitate, or water is formed are said to "go to completion." This means that all of the reacting substances undergo chemical change and none are left. The reactants are changed totally into the products of the reaction.

2:4 Single Replacement

In a **single replacement reaction,** a free element replaces an element which is combined in a compound. The element being replaced must be similar to the element replacing it. Metals replace metals. Many metals will also replace hydrogen. Nonmetals replace nonmetals.

Can zinc replace copper? yes

AgNO₃ dissolved in distilled water
Figure 2-8.

Time: 35 minutes.

ACTIVITY. Dissolve 2 g of silver nitrate (AgNO₃) in 100 ml of distilled water. Place this solution in a 150-ml beaker. Wind a clean bare copper wire around a pencil to form a coil. Remove the pencil. Leave enough wire to form a hook so that the wire can be hooked over the lip of the beaker. Place the coil in the beaker. Explain what you observe. Allow the reaction to continue overnight. What happens to the copper wire? Why does the liquid turn blue? Silver crystals grow on copper wire. Copper ions in solution give blue color.

Figure 2-9. Jet engines produce heat from single replacement reactions. In these reactions, fuel and oxygen combine to form carbon dioxide and water.

U.S. Air Force Photo

PEOPLE CAREERS FRONTIERS
FOCUS ON PHYSICAL SCIENCE

Metal Recycling: Junk Cars

The Bureau of Mines is concerned with the refining of metals. However, attention is being focused on recovering metals from waste. A lot of metal can be obtained from this source. The recycling of junk autos can provide a large percentage of metal.

About nine million cars, trucks, and buses are junked every year in the United States. Eight million of these are scrapped to recover iron and steel. Half are scrapped by shredding, the other half by taking them apart by hand.

Magnets are used to separate shredded materials. Iron and steel are picked up by giant magnets. Other separation methods are used to recover nonmagnetic metals. Many of the recovered metals are then melted and recycled.

Many of the metal products used today may have been used before. This is one method of conserving natural resources.

* * *

Adapted from the *Phoenix Quarterly*, Fall, 1975.

Two cars are in position for burning in a smokeless junk car incinerator. After the cars are burned, valuable materials are reclaimed and recycled.

Recycling Trash

Many valuable materials are thrown away. Every day people throw away aluminum and steel cans, bottles, jars, paper, and metal foil. These items usually end up in dumps, sanitary landfills, or incinerators.

Concerned citizens are beginning to take measures to prevent the waste from "going to waste." Many of these materials can be recycled and used in a variety of products.

Waste treatment plants are being developed to separate the different types of trash. Paper, metal, and glass are the materials most often recycled. Some plants have conveyer belts which dump refuse into a large tub of water. Rotating blades in the tub move the trash around. Large and heavy pieces sink to the bottom of the tub and are removed. Iron materials are picked out with large magnets. The water and remaining solids from the tub are passed through a series of screens and centrifuges. This process recovers the paper fibers. These fibers are collected and returned to paper manufacturers.

Recycling centers make throw-aways useful again.

General equation for single replacement reaction
　Word equation:
　　A plus BC yields AC plus B
　Formula equation:
　　A + BC ⟶ AC + B

Actual single replacement reaction
　Word equation:
copper (solid) plus silver nitrate (solution) yields
　　　　　　copper (II) nitrate (solution) plus silver (solid)
　Formula equation:
　　$Cu(s) + 2\ AgNO_3(aq) \longrightarrow Cu(NO_3)_2(aq) + 2\ Ag(s)$

In the activity, a deposit of silver forms on the coil and the solution turns blue. This indicates that a copper (II) nitrate solution has formed. Notice that the equation is balanced in the same manner as the equation for a double replacement reaction. Remember, (s) represents "solid."

Figure 2-10.

Time: 30 minutes.
ACTIVITY. Dissolve 10 g of powdered copper (II) sulfate in 100 ml of water. Place a strip of zinc (Zn) metal in the water. What substance forms on the zinc? Write an equation for the reaction. Repeat the procedure using silver nitrate and a strip of lead.

copper metal
Silver is deposited

$CuSO_4 + Zn(s) \longrightarrow ZnSO_4 + Cu(s)$　　$2\ AgNO_3 + Pb(s) \longrightarrow Pb(NO_3)_2 + 2\ Ag(s)$

Sometimes it is difficult to determine whether one substance can replace another. An element can usually replace any element of the same kind below it or to the right of it in the periodic table. For example, iron will replace copper, and chlorine will replace bromine. However, this rule does not always hold true. Lead, for example, will replace silver. Fortunately, experiments can show which substances will replace each other.

2:5 Decomposition

Sometimes a compound breaks down, or decomposes, into other compounds and/or elements. This is called a **decomposition** (dee kahm puh ZISH uhn) **reaction.**

General equation for decomposition reaction
　Word equation:
　　AB yields A plus B
　Formula equation:
　　AB ⟶ A + B

Figure 2-11. Silver plate is made by coating base metals with silver through electrolysis.

Actual decomposition reaction

Word equation:

potassium chlorate (solid) yields
potassium chloride (solid) plus oxygen (gas)

Formula equation:
$$2\ KClO_3(s) \longrightarrow 2\ KCl(s) + 3\ O_2(g)$$

In the above reaction, potassium chlorate is heated. The heat energy causes the potassium chlorate molecules to break apart (decompose) into oxygen gas and solid potassium chloride. When oxygen is free, it exists as a diatomic molecule. Diatomic means that each molecule is composed of two atoms. Bubbles that cause cakes and bread to "rise" are caused by carbon dioxide (CO_2) gas produced by decomposition reactions.

Pennington Bread Company, Washington Court House, Ohio

Figure 2-12. Bubbles of CO_2 in a decomposition reaction cause bread to "rise."

Figure 2-13.

You may wish to discuss the concept of catalysts at this time.
Time: 15 minutes.

ACTIVITY. Place 5 ml of hydrogen peroxide (H_2O_2) in a test tube. Drop a pinch of manganese dioxide (MnO_2) into the liquid. Insert a glowing wooden splint into the mouth of the test tube. What gas is released by the decomposition of the hydrogen peroxide? oxygen Write an equation for the reaction. NOTE: The MnO_2 only serves to start the reaction. It is not chemically changed so it should not be considered part of the reaction.

$2 H_2O_2 \longrightarrow 2 H_2O + O_2(g)$

The MnO_2 serves as a catalyst to the H_2O_2 decomposition. The wooden splint bursts into flame, signifying the presence of oxygen gas.

Some compounds decompose when they are exposed to a form of energy, generally heat, light, or electrical energy. Usually, the form of energy is indicated above the arrow in the equation as $\xrightarrow{\Delta}$ (heat), $\xrightarrow{lt}$ (light), or $\xrightarrow{elec}$ (electrical). When a compound is decomposed by electrical energy, the reaction is called **electrolysis** (ih lek TRAHL uh suhs).

2:6 Synthesis

Synthesis is a process by which something is put together. A **synthesis reaction** occurs when two or more elements or compounds unite to form one compound.

General equation for synthesis reaction
    Word equation: A plus B yields AB
    Formula equation: $A + B \longrightarrow AB$

Actual synthesis reaction
    Word equation:
    sodium (solid) plus chlorine (gas) yields sodium chloride (solid)
    Formula equation:
$$2 Na(s) + Cl_2(g) \longrightarrow 2 NaCl(s)$$

In the above reaction, sodium and chlorine combine directly to form sodium chloride. Notice the symbols (s) and (g) indicate the phase of the substances.

Iron rusting is a synthesis reaction. Iron (Fe) combines with oxygen (O_2) in the air and produces iron (III) oxide (Fe_2O_3):
$$4 Fe(s) + 3 O_2(g) \longrightarrow 2 Fe_2O_3(s)$$

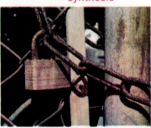

Figure 2-14. When iron rusts, what type of reaction is taking place? synthesis

Ria C. Parody

PROBLEMS
single replacement, double replacement, synthesis, decomposition
2. Name the four types of reactions. Which type of reaction is represented by each equation?
    (a) $3 KOH (aq) + AlCl_3 (aq) \longrightarrow Al(OH)_3 (s) + 3 KCl (aq)$ double replacement
    (b) $C (s) + O_2 (g) \longrightarrow CO_2 (g)$ synthesis

ENERGY AND CHEMICAL CHANGE (37M) 261

3. Complete and balance each of the following equations. In Parts (c) and (f), what type of reaction is taking place?
   (a) Synthesis: 2Mg(s) + O$_2$(g) → 2MgO(s)
   (b) Single replacement: Fe(s) + Cu(NO$_3$)$_2$(aq) → __Cu__ (s) + __Fe__ (NO$_3$)$_2$(aq)
   (c) 2H$_2$O(l) → __2 H$_2$__ (g) + O$_2$(g) decomposition
   (d) Decomposition: 2Hg$_2$O(s) $\xrightarrow{\Delta}$ __4 Hg__ (s) + O$_2$(g)
   (e) Double replacement: AgNO$_3$(aq) + KI(aq) → __Ag__ I(s) + __K__ NO$_3$(aq)
   (f) CaI$_2$(aq) + Cl$_2$(g) → __CaCl$_2$__ (aq) + I$_2$(g) single replacement

4. When sulfur is burned, a very disagreeable substance is produced:
$$S(s) + O_2(g) \longrightarrow SO_2(g)$$
   (a) Is this equation balanced? Yes
   (b) Does this reaction go to completion? Yes
   (c) What does the → mean? Yields
   (d) What kind of chemical reaction does this represent? Synthesis reaction
   (e) What is the name of the gas, SO$_2$(g)? Sulfur dioxide

2:7 Energy and Chemical Change

Energy is either gained or lost during a chemical change. In some reactions, energy is given up as the reactants regroup themselves into new compounds. In other reactions, energy must be continually added to the reactants for a chemical change to occur. If energy is given up, the reaction is called **exothermic** (ek soh THUHR mik). This means that heat is given off during the reaction. If heat or some other form of energy is taken on during the reaction, the reaction is **endothermic** (en duh THUHR mik).

Alternating current would change the polarity of the electrodes 60 times a second. The ions would not collect at either electrode.

Figure 2-15.

You may wish to conduct this activity as a demonstration.
Time: 50 minutes.
  ACTIVITY. CAUTION: When mixing water and acid, always add the acid to the water. Wear eye and clothing protection.
  Add 5 ml of concentrated H$_2$SO$_4$ to 145 ml of water. Add the solution to a Hoffman electrolysis apparatus (Figure 2–15). Connect the terminals to four dry cells connected in series, to a lead storage battery, or to a 6-V D.C. power supply. Collect the gases produced. Test each gas by holding a glowing splint above the stopcock and opening the stopcock. What reaction has occurred? Is the reaction exothermic or <u>endothermic</u>? Write an equation to show the reaction. 2 H$_2$O(l) $\xrightarrow{\text{elec}}$ 2 H$_2$(g) + O$_2$(g)

There will be twice as much H$_2$ as O$_2$ produced. H$_2$ will burn with a blue flame. O$_2$ will cause a glowing splint to burst into flame.

Figure 2-16. Fireworks are exothermic reactions.

William Maddox

What kind of a reaction is the burning of magnesium?

The burning of magnesium is an exothermic reaction. Little heat is needed to start the reaction. After the reaction starts, the heat given off by the union of magnesium atoms and oxygen atoms is more than enough to keep the reaction going.

Electrolysis of water is an endothermic reaction. Water is a stable compound; it does not decompose readily. However, by passing an electric current through water, it can be forced to decompose into hydrogen gas and oxygen gas. The reaction stops as soon as the electric current is stopped. Atoms of hydrogen and oxygen are produced. These atoms give up little energy as they combine to form H_2 and O_2, the normal diatomic forms of the gases. A great deal of energy is added to keep the reaction going. Little energy is given up as the products form. Thus, this reaction is endothermic.

What occurs in an endothermic reaction?

Use care in putting the thistle tube into the stopper. Lubricate with water or glycerin. Hold both parts in several layers of cloth to avoid getting glass into hands if breakage should occur.

Time: 40 minutes.

ACTIVITY. Place 25 g of limestone and 50 ml of water in a flask. Insert a thistle tube and a glass delivery tube into a two-hole rubber stopper. Seal the flask with the stopper. Place the tip of the glass delivery tube in a solution of limewater (calcium hydroxide). Add 25 ml of dilute hydrochloric acid through the thistle tube. Be certain the bottom of the thistle tube is below the surface of the liquid. Note the change in the flask and the limewater. Does an <u>exothermic</u> or an endothermic reaction occur in the flask? How do you know?

Flask: $CaCO_3(s) + 2\ HCl \longrightarrow CaCl_2(aq) + CO_2(g)$

In the flask, chips begin to disappear as they react. Heat is produced (exothermic reaction). Bubbles of CO_2 gas move through the delivery tube to the limewater. $CaCO_3$ disappears in the flask forming CO_2 which reacts with $Ca(OH)_2$ in the beaker to form $CaCO_3$ again. Ask students to give equations for reactions taking place. All three types of end reactions (gas, precipitate, water) are present here.

Figure 2-17.

Beaker: $CO_2(g) + Ca(OH)_2(aq) \longrightarrow CaCO_3(s) + H_2O$

2:8 Molecular Mass and Formula Mass

Molecular mass is the sum of the atomic mass numbers for the atoms in a molecule. Mass numbers may be obtained from a periodic table or a list of mass numbers (Table 2–1).

Table 2–1. Mass Numbers of Some Common Elements

Element	Symbol	Mass Number	Element	Symbol	Mass Number
Aluminum	Al	27	Lead	Pb	207
Barium	Ba	137	Lithium	Li	7
Bromine	Br	80	Magnesium	Mg	24
Calcium	Ca	40	Mercury	Hg	201
Carbon	C	12	Nitrogen	N	14
Chlorine	Cl	35	Oxygen	O	16
Chromium	Cr	52	Phosphorus	P	31
Copper	Cu	64	Potassium	K	39
Fluorine	F	19	Silver	Ag	108
Hydrogen	H	1	Sodium	Na	23
Iodine	I	127	Sulfur	S	32
Iron	Fe	56	Zinc	Zn	65

Carbon dioxide contains one atom of carbon and two atoms of oxygen. Carbon has a mass of 12 and oxygen has a mass of 16. Thus, the molecular mass of CO_2 is $12 + (2 \times 16) = 44$.

What is the molecular mass of oxygen? **32**

Carbon monoxide contains one atom of carbon and one atom of oxygen. The molecular mass of CO is $12 + 16 = 28$.

Ionic compounds do not exist as molecules. The mass of the smallest possible unit of an ionic compound is called the **formula mass.** It is the sum of the mass numbers of the atoms present in a

What is formula mass?

Figure 2-18. CO_2 has a molecular mass of 44.

Figure 2-19. NaCl has a formula mass of 58.

formula of an ionic compound. Molecular mass and formula mass can be calculated in the same way. Sodium chloride is an ionic compound with the formula NaCl. According to the periodic table and Table 2–1, sodium has a mass of 23 and chlorine has a mass of 35. Therefore, NaCl has a formula mass of 58 (23 + 35 = 58).

What is the formula mass of KBr? 119

Molecular mass should be used only for molecular compounds. Formula mass may be used for all compounds. Formula mass is a more general term than molecular mass.

Figure 2-20. This pipe is being cleaned and coated. The coating prevents the iron in the pipe from coming into contact with air and rusting.

EXAMPLE

Find the formula mass of calcium phosphate.

Solution: (a) Write the correct formula: $Ca_3(PO_4)_2$
(b) Analyze the compound:

Number of Atoms	Mass Number	Formula Mass
3 calcium	40	$3 \times 40 = 120$
2 phosphorus	31	$2 \times 31 = 62$
8 oxygen	16	$8 \times 16 = \underline{128}$
		310

(c) Answer: Formula mass = 310

PROBLEM

5. Using Table 2–1, find the formula mass for each of the following compounds:
   (a) Na_2SO_4 142
   (b) $CaCO_3$ 100
   (c) NH_4NO_3 80
   (d) copper (II) sulfate 160
   (e) silver bromide 188
   (f) potassium phosphate 212

2:9 Mass and Chemical Reactions

Carbon burns in air to form carbon dioxide. The equation for the reaction is $C(s) + O_2(g) \longrightarrow CO_2(g)$. Suppose 12 g of carbon combines with oxygen. How much carbon dioxide is formed? You

Marathon Oil Company

MASS AND CHEMICAL REACTIONS (41M) 265

can predict the amount of carbon dioxide formed from its molecular mass.

> The equation shows that one atom of C combines with one molecule of O_2 to yield one molecule of CO_2. Carbon has an atomic mass of 12. Carbon dioxide has a molecular mass of 44. The ratio between the atomic mass of C and the molecular mass of CO_2 is 12 : 44. The ratio of 12 : 44 indicates the number of grams of reactants and products. Thus, 12 g of carbon reacts with oxygen to yield 44 g of carbon dioxide.

How can molecular mass be used to determine the amount of products in a chemical reaction?
Molecular mass is the sum of the masses of the atoms of a molecule.

Figure 2-21. Mass is conserved in a chemical reaction.

Hydrogen gas burns in oxygen to form water. The equation for the reaction is $2\,H_2(g) + O_2(g) \longrightarrow 2\,H_2O(l)$. How much water is formed when 32 g of oxygen reacts with hydrogen? The molecular mass of H_2O can be used to predict the answer.

The equation shows that two molecules of H_2 combine with one molecule of O_2 to yield two molecules of H_2O. A diatomic molecule of oxygen combines with hydrogen. Therefore, the molecular mass of O_2 is 32 (2 × 16). The molecular mass of H_2O is 18. However, the coefficient 2 indicates that two molecules of H_2O are formed. This means that the molecular mass of water (18) is multiplied by 2 (2 × 18 = 36). The ratio between the mass of O_2 and the mass of H_2O is 32 : 36. This indicates the number of grams of reactants and products. Thus, 36 g of water are formed from 32 g of oxygen. How many grams of hydrogen react with 32 g of oxygen?

PROBLEMS

6. How many grams of oxygen combine with 12 g of carbon when CO_2 is formed? $C(s) + O_2 \longrightarrow CO_2(g)$
   12g   44g
7. Forty grams of sodium hydroxide reacts with hydrochloric acid (NaOH + HCl $\longrightarrow$ NaCl + H_2O). How many grams of water are formed? NaOH(aq) + HCl(aq) $\longrightarrow$ NaCl(aq) + H_2O(l)
   40 g   18 g
8. Thirty-two grams of oxygen combine with carbon to form carbon monoxide gas (2 C + O_2 $\longrightarrow$ 2 CO). How many grams of carbon monoxide are formed? 2 C(s) + O_2(g) $\longrightarrow$ 2 CO(g)
   32 g   2(28) = 56 g

You may wish to use a different amount of reactant and set up a proportion to determine the amount of product. For example, you might use
6. 24 g C to yield 88 g CO_2
7. 10 g NaOH to yield 4.5 g H_2O
8. 8 g C to yield 18.7 g (56/3) CO

MAIN IDEAS

2:1   **1.** The law of conservation of mass states that in an ordinary chemical reaction no matter is lost.

2:2   **2.** Chemical equations are used to describe chemical changes.

2:2   **3.** Water, gas, or a precipitate may be formed in a chemical change.

       4. Reactions that can be represented by chemical equations include:

2:3   (a) double replacement reactions

2:4   (b) single replacement reactions

2:5   (c) decomposition reactions

2:6   (d) synthesis reactions

2:7   **5.** Energy is either gained or lost in a chemical change.

2:8   **6.** The grams of a substance involved in a chemical reaction can be found by using molecular mass or formula mass.

VOCABULARY

Write a sentence in which you correctly use each of the following words or terms.

1. coefficients	equation	product
2. conservation of mass	exothermic	reactant
3. decomposition	formula mass	replacement reaction
4. electrolysis	molecular mass	subscript
5. endothermic	precipitate	synthesis

STUDY QUESTIONS

A. True or False

Determine whether each of the following sentences is true or false. (Do not write in this book.)

in   F   **1.** Silver chloride is soluble in water.

      T   **2.** In ordinary chemical reactions no mass is lost.

      T   **3.** A gas can be formed in a chemical reaction.

      T   **4.** A precipitate is an insoluble solid that forms during a chemical reaction.

      T   **5.** Electrolysis is decomposition of a compound by electricity.

coefficients   F   **6.** An equation may be balanced by changing ~~subscripts~~.

2   F   **7.** The molecular mass of H_2 is ~~1~~.

CHEMICAL REACTIONS (43M) 267

T 8. The molecular mass of O₂ is 32.
T 9. A + BC ⟶ AC + B represents a single replacement reaction.
T 10. The formula mass of potassium bromide (KBr) is 119.

B. Multiple Choice

Choose one word or phrase that correctly completes each of the following sentences. (Do not write in this book.)

> Some questions in Parts B and C may have more than one correct answer. Only one answer is required.

1. A reaction that gives off heat is *(exothermic, endothermic, stable)*.
2. Bromine can replace *(fluorine, iodine, iron)* in a chemical reaction.
3. When hydrogen chloride dissolves in water, *(ions, molecules, atoms)* are formed.
4. In a chemical change, the total mass *(increases, decreases, remains the same)*.
5. The formula mass of NaNO₃ is *(85, 85 g, 170, 170 g)*.
6. The molecular mass of CO₂ is *(20, 30, 44)*.
7. To balance equations, *(coefficients, subscripts, formulas)* should be changed.
8. Burning of magnesium is an *(endothermic, exothermic)* reaction.
9. 2 KClO₃(s) ⟶ 2 KCl(s) + 3 O₂(g) is a *(replacement, decomposition, synthesis)* reaction.
10. AB + CD ⟶ AD + CB is a *(replacement, decomposition, synthesis)* reaction.

C. Completion

Complete each of the following sentences with a word or phrase that will make the sentence correct. (Do not write in this book.)

1. C(s) + O₂(g) ⟶ CO₂(g) is an equation which represents a(n) _____ reaction. synthesis
2. A chemical change involves no change in _____ . mass
3. Electrolysis of water is an example of a(n) _____ reaction. decomposition
4. Calcium sulfate has a formula mass of _____ . 136
5. If silver nitrate solution reacts with potassium chloride solution, _____ is the precipitate that forms. silver chloride

268 (44M) CHEMICAL REACTIONS

K⁺, NO₃⁻ **6.** In the reaction in Question 5, _____ and _____ are the ions left in solution.

(double) replacement **7.** The reaction in Question 5 is a _____ reaction.

8. When molecular compounds dissolve to form ions, the process is called _____ .

ionization

Carbon monoxide (CO) **9.** _____ is the compound of carbon and oxygen with a molecular mass of 28.

H₂O **10.** The compound of hydrogen and oxygen with a molecular mass of 18 is _____ .

D. How and Why

44 g **1.** In the reaction represented by Fe(s) + S(s) ⟶ FeS(s), how many grams of iron (II) sulfide will be produced from 28 g of iron?

See Teacher's Guide. **2.** Name a reaction in which each of the following is produced: (a) gas, (b) water, (c) precipitate.

See Teacher's Guide. **3.** Why does a balanced equation agree with the law of conservation of mass?

water yields hydrogen plus oxygen
elec
2 H₂O(l) ⟶ 2 H₂(g) + O₂(g)
4. Write the word equation and chemical equation for electrolysis of water. Balance the equation.

5. How do endothermic reactions differ from exothermic reactions? Endothermic reactions absorb heat as they proceed; exothermic reactions give off heat as they proceed.

See Teacher's Guide. **6.** Why are formulas not changed when balancing equations?

carbon plus oxygen yields carbon monoxide
2 C + O₂ ⟶ 2 CO
7. Write the word equation and chemical equation for the formation of carbon monoxide from carbon. Balance the equation.

8. Balance the following equations:

double replacement (a) Na₂S(aq) + 2AgNO₃(aq) ⟶ 2NaNO₃(aq) + Ag₂S(s)
synthesis (b) 3 H₂(g) + N₂(g) ⟶ 2NH₃(g)
decomposition (c) 2KClO₃(s) ⟶ 2KCl(s) + 3O₂(g)
single replacement (d) 3 CuSO₄(aq) + 2Al(s) ⟶ Al₂(SO₄)₃(aq) + 3Cu(s)
single replacement (e) 2Na(s) + 2H₂O(l) ⟶ 2NaOH(aq) + H₂(g)

9. Complete and balance the following equations:

double replacement (a) Na₂CrO₄(aq) + PbCl₂(aq) ⟶ 2 NaCl(aq) + PbCrO₄(s)
single replacement (b) Cl₂(g) + 2NaBr(aq) ⟶ 2 NaCl(aq) + Br₂(l)
decomposition (c) Mg(ClO₃)₂(s) ⟶ MgCl₂(s) + 3 O₂(g)
synthesis (d) 2 H₂(g) + O₂(g) ⟶ 2 H₂O(l)
double replacement (e) 3 Ca(OH)₂(aq) + 2FeCl₃(aq) ⟶ 2 Fe(OH)₃(s) + 3 CaCl₂(aq)

10. What type of reaction is represented by each equation in Questions 8 and 9?

CHEMICAL REACTIONS

INVESTIGATIONS

1. Sodium bicarbonate is the chemical name for baking soda. In baking, carbon dioxide gas is produced as baking soda is heated. (Baking soda is also called bicarbonate of soda.)
   (a) Place a teaspoon of baking soda in a beaker. Add water. Heat your mixture. What happens?
   (b) Write a word equation for the decomposition of $NaHCO_3$ (baking soda) to carbon dioxide (CO_2) when it is heated.
   (c) Write a chemical equation for the decomposition in (b).
   (d) Place a teaspoon of baking soda in water. Add a drop of vinegar. What happens?
   (e) Place a teaspoon of baking soda in water. Add cream of tartar. What happens?
   (f) Place a teaspoon of baking powder in water. How does it react? How does baking powder differ from baking soda? Read the ingredients on the label of the baking powder can.
   (g) What types of baked goods require baking soda or baking powder?

2. Through library research obtain information about the Solvay process. Prepare a report showing the steps in the process and its commercial importance.

INTERESTING READINGS

Grosswirth, Marvin, "The Wonders of $NaHCO_3$ (baking soda)." *Science Digest,* (March, 1976), pp. 70–75.

Kuslan, Louis, and Stone, A. Harris, *Liebig, The Master Chemist.* New York, Prentice-Hall, 1969.

Marcus, Rebecca B., *Antoine Lavoisier and the Revolution in Chemistry.* New York, Franklin Watts, Inc., 1965.

Courtesy of Morton Salt Company, Division of Morton-Norwich Products, Inc.

The type of mining commonly employed in salt mines is known as the room and pillar method. Salt is removed in a checkerboard pattern, leaving permanent pillars of salt standing for roof support.

3 Acids, Bases, and Salts

Some of the most important compounds in chemistry are the acids, bases, and salts. This chapter will introduce the student to some properties of these substances. The students will become acquainted with various indicators used to identify acids and bases.

GOAL: You will gain an understanding of the properties of acids, bases, and salts.

Salts are very important chemicals. A salt can be produced in the laboratory by combining an acid and a base.

Some salts occur naturally. Sodium chloride or common table salt, is found in natural underground deposits and in seawater. Removing salt from these sources requires special processes and equipment. Once the salt is removed and processed, it is ready for use. In what ways may salt be used?

3:1 Acids

Acids are chemical compounds which have common characteristics such as a sour taste and the ability to corrode metals. In addition, every acid contains hydrogen. Only nonmetals form acids. Many acids are poisonous and corrosive to the skin. For this reason, extreme care should be used when handling acids in the laboratory.

Common acids play an important part in daily life. The label on a bottle of vinegar lists one of its components as acetic (uh SEET ik) acid. Buttermilk contains lactic (LAK tik) acid. We eat citric (SIH trik) acid in lemons, oranges, and grapefruits. Hydrochloric (hy druh KLOR ik) acid in the stomach aids digestion. Some household bleaches are weak solutions of hypochlorous (hy puh KLOR uhs) acid. Automobile batteries contain a sulfuric (suhl FYUR ik) acid solution. There are three major commercial acids. They are sulfuric acid, nitric (NY trik) acid, and hydrochloric acid.

Sulfuric acid (H_2SO_4) is an oily, thick liquid. It is used in the manufacture of paints, plastics, and fertilizers. The solution within a car's storage battery contains sulfuric acid. It is also used to prepare other acids and to act as a dehydrating agent. Dehydrate means to take water away. A wooden stick placed in sulfuric acid becomes charred as the acid removes water from it. Because it is a dehydrating agent, sulfuric acid can burn skin and seriously damage fibers. Always handle it with care.

Sulfuric acid can be produced in the laboratory. Sulfur dioxide can be produced by burning sulfur and collecting the gas. It is then dissolved in water and the solution is treated with hydrogen peroxide (H_2O_2).

Name some common acids.
Some common acids: sulfuric acid, acetic acid, citric acid, hydrochloric acid, tannic acid, boric acid, acetylsalicylic acid (aspirin).

What are the main properties of sulfuric acid?
Sulfuric acid is used as an oxidizing agent and as a dehydrating agent.

Figure 3-1. Each of these materials is acidic or becomes acidic when mixed with water (a). Sulfuric acid forms when sulfur dioxide in smog combines with water (b).

a

Jim Elliot

b

Ohio EPA

Figure 3-2. When an acid reacts with a metal, corrosion often takes place.

Robert Neulieb

Reaction depends on the number of electrons transferred as sulfur changes oxidation states.

$$4\ Zn\ (s) + H_2SO_4\ (conc.) \longrightarrow 4\ ZnO\ (s) + H_2S\ (g)$$

H₂S is very poisonous.

$$Zn\ (s) + H_2SO_4(dil.) \longrightarrow ZnSO_4\ (s) + H_2\ (g)$$

Figure 3-3. Dilute H₂SO₄ and concentrated H₂SO₄ react differently.

Review the distinction between dilute and concentrated. Explain how sulfuric acid may be diluted by adding the acid to water. Stress the safety factor here. Add acid to water; never add water to acid.

Dilute and concentrated sulfuric acid react differently. Dilute sulfuric acid will react with zinc or iron to produce hydrogen. However, when concentrated sulfuric acid reacts with zinc or iron, sulfur dioxide (SO_2) and hydrogen sulfide (H_2S) may be produced instead. Various other sulfides are also formed in the reaction.

Time: 20 minutes.

ACTIVITY. CAUTION: Conduct this activity only under the direct supervision of your teacher. Wear eye and clothing protection.
(1) Place 25 g of table sugar in a beaker. Add 10 ml of concentrated sulfuric acid. (2) Repeat Part 1 with dilute sulfuric acid. Compare your results.

$$C_{12}H_{22}O_{11} \xrightarrow{H_2SO_4} 12\ C + 11\ H_2O$$

Figure 3-4.

This activity demonstrates the dehydrating power of concentrated H₂SO₄. The concentrated acid removes hydrogen and oxygen from the sugar. The dilute acid does not remove water from sugar since the acid is already in water solution.

Nitric acid (HNO_3) is oily but not as thick as sulfuric acid. Nitric acid should be handled with care. If it touches skin, it combines chemically with the protein. A yellow stain results which will gradually wear away.

Nitric acid can be produced in the laboratory. This is done by heating sodium nitrate with concentrated sulfuric acid. Nitric acid does not normally produce hydrogen when it reacts with metals. This is the difference between it and most dilute acids. Some products of nitric acid-metal reactions are nitrogen oxides and various nitrates. Nitrates are important commercially. They are used in making fertilizers and explosives.

Hydrochloric acid (HCl) is produced by dissolving hydrogen chloride gas in water. The hydrogen chloride gas can be produced by heating sodium chloride with concentrated sulfuric acid. The resulting gas is collected in distilled water where it forms hydrochloric acid.

Figure 3-5. Nitrates are used in making fertilizers (a). Nitric acid can be easily produced in the laboratory (b).

What are the main uses for nitric acid?

Figure 3-6. Hydrochloric acid can be produced in the laboratory (a). It can be used to clean metals before they are plated (b).

Engelhard Industries

273 (49M)

Wear safety goggles, safety gloves, and apron and use an exhaust fan.

ACIDS, BASES, AND SALTS

Hydrochloric acid will produce hydrogen when it reacts with metals such as zinc and iron. This acid is not as destructive as sulfuric acid or nitric acid. However, care should be taken when using HCl. HCl fumes can harm the lungs and will react on skin. Hydrochloric acid has many uses. One of these is to clean metals. It is also present in the human stomach in a very dilute form that aids digestion.

Figure 3-7. Hydrochloric acid is sometimes sold under the name "muriatic acid." Muriatic acid is used to remove some types of stains from brick and cement surfaces.

PROBLEM

1. Write balanced equations for the following reactions:
   (a) sulfuric acid (dilute) with lead $Pb\ (s) + H_2SO_4\ (aq) \longrightarrow PbSO_4\ (s) + H_2\ (g)$
   (b) hydrochloric acid with zinc $Zn\ (s) + 2\ HCl\ (aq) \longrightarrow ZnCl_2(aq) + H_2(g)$
   (c) sulfuric acid (dilute) with aluminum
   $2\ Al\ (s) + 3\ H_2SO_4(aq) \longrightarrow Al_2(SO_4)_3\ (aq) + 3\ H_2(g)$

Many other acids are also important. Organic acids contain hydrogen, carbon, and oxygen. Formic acid [methanoic acid] was first found in ant bites and was isolated by distilling ants. Acetic acid [ethanic acid] is a fermentation product and a part of vinegar. A third organic acid, propanoic (proh puh NOH ik) acid is used to retard spoilage in such foods as bread.

What is the main difference between organic and inorganic acids?
Organic acids contain hydrogen, carbon, and oxygen. Inorganic acids do not contain carbon.

Figure 3-8.

Time: 30 minutes.

> **EXPERIMENT.** Add 5 ml of each of the following liquids to separate test tubes: water, dilute hydrochloric acid, vinegar, and lemon juice. Add a small piece of mossy zinc to each liquid. Compare and explain the activity of the acids. What control is used in this experiment? *water*

Have the students devise a means of determining the activity quantitatively. For example, they can count the number of bubbles of gas in x seconds. Dilute HCl is most reactive; lemon juice will probably produce no reaction.

PROBLEM

2. In addition to hydrochloric acid (HCl), other acids are formed from the other elements in the halogen family (Column VIIA of the periodic table). What would you expect the formulas to be for hydrobromic acid, hydriodic acid, and hydrofluoric acid? *HBr, HI, HF*

a

b

Figure 3-9. Glass can be etched by hydrofluoric acid. A design is cut into a wax coating on a glass plate (a). The acid etches the uncoated parts of the plate (b).

Courtesy of Kodansha, Ltd.

Table 3–1. Common Acids

Acetic acid	CH₃COOH	Lactic acid	C₃H₆O₃
Ascorbic acid	C₆H₈O₇	Nitric acid	HNO₃
Carbonic acid	H₂CO₃	Sulfuric acid	H₂SO₄
Hydrochloric acid	HCl		

Some inorganic acids contain both oxygen and hydrogen (oxy-acids). Phosphoric acid (H_3PO_4) and chloric acid ($HClO_3$) are two examples. See Table 3–1 for some acids and their formulas.

3:2 Bases

All **bases** have common characteristics. They generally taste bitter and feel slippery. However, taste and touch are not safe and accurate methods to identify a base. Bases also dissolve fats and oils. All bases contain hydrogen, oxygen, and at least one metal.

A base is also known as an alkali or antacid. Lye, ammonia, and milk of magnesia are common household bases. The most common base is sodium hydroxide. It is a part of lye and is used in making soap. Lye is also used to unclog sink drains since it dissolves oil and grease readily. Ammonia is used in cleaning compounds, such as window cleaners. Milk of magnesia is most commonly used as a laxative.

Figure 3-10. Each of these materials is basic or becomes basic when mixed with water.

> Time: 15 minutes. Observe next day.
> EXPERIMENT. Fill two plastic pans one-half full of water. Add 15 ml of ammonia to one pan. Put a small lump of petroleum jelly in each pan. Let the water stand for several hours. Observe and explain any changes that occur. Point out the control in this activity.

Table 3–2. Common Bases

Name	Formula	Common Uses
Ammonium hydroxide	NH₄OH	household cleaner
Calcium hydroxide	Ca(OH)₂	dehairing hides, manufacture of mortar and plaster
Aluminum hydroxide	Al(OH)₃	deodorants
Sodium hydroxide	NaOH	drain cleaner, soap
Magnesium hydroxide	Mg(OH)₂	laxative, antacid

Name some common bases.

ammonia, lye, baking soda, washing soda, milk of magnesia

Suggestion: Ask students to write an equation for the production of the metal hydroxide formed when calcium reacts with water.

$Ca(s) + 2 H_2O(l) \longrightarrow Ca(OH)_2(aq) + H_2(g)$

3:3 Indicators

Taste is a dangerous way to determine whether something is an acid or a base. Chemicals can harm the tongue, as well as other parts of your body. The use of an **indicator** is a more exact test for an acid or base. Indicators are substances which can turn different colors in solutions. Their colors depend upon whether the solution is an acid or base. *Litmus paper* is one indicator you can use to test for an acid or base. Blue litmus paper will turn red in an acid solution. Red litmus paper will turn blue in a base solution. If neither color of paper changes color, the solution is *neutral*. This means it is neither an acid nor a base.

How do indicators work?

These indicators are organic dyes.

Indicators are only approximate for judging acidity and basicity because of the limitations of the human eye to perceive color change.

William Maddox

Figure 3-11. Red litmus paper turns blue in a base solution. Blue litmus paper turns red in an acid solution (a). This indicator paper is used to test the urine of diabetics (b).

Make sure students add the solid calcium oxide to the water, not the reverse. Reminder: have students wear safety goggles during all activities.

sodium bicarbonate, base; breath + water, acid; calcium oxide, base; milk (fresh), neutral; milk (sour), acid; soda pop, acid; vinegar, acid

Time: 40 minutes.

ACTIVITY. Set six test tubes in a test tube rack. Label each appropriately. Dissolve 1 g of sodium bicarbonate in 10 ml of water in a test tube. Use a straw to bubble your breath through 10 ml of water in another test tube. Dissolve 1 g of calcium oxide in 10 ml of water in a third test tube. Place 5 ml each of milk, soda pop, and vinegar in separate test tubes. Add a piece of red and blue litmus to each of the six test tubes. Determine which are acids and which are bases.

Figure 3-12.

HYDROGEN AND HYDROXIDE IONS (53M) 277

Other common indicators are methyl orange, methyl red, bromthymol blue, and *phenolphthalein* (feen uhl THAYL een). Each has a characteristic color change for acids and bases. For example, phenolphthalein indicator is colorless in an acid solution and pink in a basic solution. Litmus paper and phenolphthalein are the most common indicators used in the laboratory.

Figure 3-13. Phenolphthalein will turn pink in a basic solution.

> Time: 30 minutes.
> EXPERIMENT. Test for ascorbic acid (Vitamin C). Add 10 ml of the indicator, indophenol (0.1 percent solution), to a test tube. Add diluted ascorbic acid to the test tube one drop at a time. Count the number of drops needed to change the blue color to colorless. Repeat this activity using common fruit and vegetable juices which have been diluted. Compare the results of your testing. See Teacher's Guide for additional information in the preparation of this experiment.

3:4 *Hydrogen and Hydroxide Ions*

Pure water contains both water molecules and ions. About one in every 500 million water molecules ionizes. A water molecule ionizes to form a hydrogen (H^+) ion and **hydroxide (OH^-) ion.** The equation for the change is:

$$H_2O(l) \longrightarrow \underset{\text{hydrogen ion}}{H^+(g)} + \underset{\text{hydroxide ion}}{OH^-(aq)}$$

The hydrogen ion produced forms a bond with a water molecule. This particle is called a **hydronium ion.** Its formula is H_3O^+. The equation for the change is

$$H^+(g) + H_2O(l) \longrightarrow H_3O^+(aq)$$

Figure 3-14. If two water molecules collide, they may form a hydronium ion (H_3O^+) and a hydroxide ion (OH^-).

How do acids and bases affect the ion concentration of water?

Acids increase the hydronium ion concentration. Bases increase the hydroxide concentration of water.

In pure water there is an equal number of hydronium and hydroxide ions. However, this ratio changes if an acid or base is added to the water. An acid increases the hydronium ion concentration of water. For example, when hydrochloric acid is added to water, hydronium ions are formed.

$$HCl(g) + H_2O(l) \longrightarrow H_3O^+(aq) + Cl^-(aq)$$

PROBLEM

3. The following acids ionize in water to produce hydronium ions. How many hydronium ions could be produced by one molecule of each of the following acids?
   (a) H_2SO_4 two
   (b) HBr one
   (c) phosphoric three
   (d) carbonic two

Bases increase the hydroxide ion concentration of water. For example, when sodium hydroxide is dissolved in water, hydroxide ions (OH^-) are added. The ionization of sodium hydroxide is shown in this equation:

$$NaOH(aq) \longrightarrow Na^+(aq) + OH^-(aq)$$

However, not all compounds which contain an OH group are bases. Some organic compounds known as alcohols contain an OH group. However, they do not ionize in water to form hydroxide ions (OH^-). Therefore, they are not classified as bases. Although most hydroxides of metals are bases, a few, such as zinc hydroxide and aluminum hydroxide, can act as acids or bases. Reaction conditions determine how each of these compounds will act.

PROBLEM

4. The following bases provide hydroxide ions (OH^-) in water solution. How many hydroxide ions are represented by each of the following formulas?
   (a) $Ca(OH)_2$ two
   (b) NH_4OH one
   (c) $Mg(OH)_2$ two

Figure 3-15. Strength of acids and bases can be determined by how well they conduct an electric current. The stronger the acid or base, the brighter the light.

PEOPLE CAREERS FRONTIERS FOCUS ON PHYSICAL SCIENCE

Industrial Hygienist

There is a growing demand for industrial hygienists. Industrial hygienists are responsible for industrial safety. Checking for any dangerous conditions and finding solutions to problems are two things an industrial hygienist might do.

Companies which make or use chemicals need their help. Many safety measures need to be taken by these companies. For example, some chemicals in spray, aerosol, or vapor forms are harmful if not carefully controlled. If in the air in unsafe amounts, these chemicals may cause skin and/or lung disorders. Therefore, an industrial hygienist's work may include checking the safety levels of these chemicals. This involves taking air samples and testing them. If the levels are unsafe, the hygienist would find methods to control the problems.

The work of an industrial hygienist is not just limited to an industrial plant. Some work in laboratories, while others work in offices. Many industrial hygienists work with engineers, chemists, and medical staff as consultants.

To become an industrial hygienist, it is recommended that chemistry and biology courses be taken in high school. A bachelor's degree in chemistry, chemical engineering, or another science is the next step. After graduation from college, many companies provide a year of on-the-job training. After gaining this experience, a certificate is needed. To receive a certificate, two tests must be passed. One test is taken after one year of on-the-job training. The second test is taken four years later.

• • • • • • • • • • • • •

American Chemical Society *Student Affiliate*, Vol. 7, No. 3, Spring, 1975.

Dale Shapiro, an industrial hygienist, is responsible for making sure the employees at his plant are not overexposed to chemicals.

Food Scientists

It has been estimated that the average family of four eats over 227 kg of food a year. Most of our foods are processed by industries. Many people work in the area of food processing. A very important person in this industry is the food scientist.

Food scientists investigate the chemical, physical, and biological nature of food. They apply this knowledge to the processing and preserving of foods. Their work often includes the area of packaging, distributing, and storage of foods.

Many of these scientists work in research and development. Some work in laboratories or production and processing areas of food plants. Others teach or do basic research in colleges and universities.

Many new protein sources have been developed by food scientists. New foods and processing methods have been developed by others. The flavor, color, texture, and nutrition of many foods have been improved through their work.

A bachelor's degree with a major in food science, chemistry, or biology is required for a job in food science. An advanced degree is needed for many research, teaching, and management jobs.

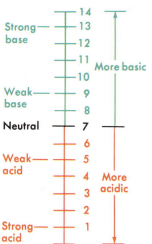

Figure 3-16. pH scales range from 0 to 14.

Acids and bases are classified as strong or weak. The dividing line between strong and weak is not distinct. In general, strong acids and bases ionize readily to form a large number of ions. Weak acids and bases do not ionize readily.

Table 3–3. Strength of Acids and Bases

	Strong	Weak
ACIDS	nitric acid	oxalic acid
	hydrochloric acid	citric acid
	sulfuric acid	acetic acid
	hydrobromic acid	carbonic acid
BASES	sodium hydroxide	ammonium hydroxide
	calcium hydroxide	iron (III) hydroxide
	potassium hydroxide	aluminum hydroxide

3:5 pH of a Solution

pH is defined as the negative log of the hydrogen ion concentration in moles per liter.

The acidity of a solution is expressed in terms of its hydronium ion (H_3O^+) concentration. The symbol for hydronium ion concentration is **pH**.

A pH scale is used to express the acidity of a water solution (Figure 3–16). The pH scale ranges from 0 to 14. Above 7 is basic. Below 7 is acid. Neutral (neither acid nor basic) is 7 on the pH scale.

Pure water has a pH of 7. Strong acids have a pH range of 1 to 2. Weak acids have a pH range from 3 to 5. A strong base may have a pH of 13. Weaker bases may have a pH of 11.

Explain how the concentrations of hydronium and hydroxide ions vary inversely.

The concentration of hydronium and hydroxide ions in a solution varies inversely. This means that as one increases the other decreases. A low pH value indicates a high hydronium concentration. A high pH value indicates a high hydroxide ion concentration.

Figure 3-17. pH meters can be used to determine the acidity of a solution.

Craig W. Kramer

Time: 20 minutes.
ACTIVITY. Test a variety of household liquids with Universal Indicator Paper. Classify each as acid or base. Make a chart indicating the pH of each liquid. Indicate the relative strength of the acids and bases.
Any number of liquids could be used. Try any of those in Tables 3-4 and 3-5.

Table 3–4 lists some common acids and bases and the pH of their solutions of equal concentrations. Table 3–5 lists some common substances and their pH values.

Poisoning in young children often occurs from drinking or eating harmful household substances. Sometimes the substances are strong acids (muriatic) or bases (lye). Have students identify those substances that should be kept out of the reach of young children.

Deborah C. Damian

Table 3–4. pH Values of Solutions of Some Common Acids and Bases

Hydrochloric acid	1.1	Sodium bicarbonate	8.4
Sulfuric acid	1.2	Calcium carbonate	9.4
Citric acid	2.2	Iron (II) hydroxide	9.5
Acetic acid	2.9	Ammonium hydroxide	11.1
Carbonic acid	3.8	Sodium carbonate	11.6
Hydrogen sulfide	4.1	Sodium hydroxide	13.0
Boric acid	5.2	Potassium hydroxide	14.0

Figure 3-18. Which food has the highest pH? Which has the lowest pH?

milk

citrus fruits, apples

Table 3–5. Approximate pH Values of Some Common Substances

Stomach contents	1.6	Milk	6.5
Vinegar	2.8	Pure water	7.0
Apples	3.0	Shrimp	7.0
Orange juice	3.5	Blood	7.35
Carrots	5.0	Sea water	8.4
Urine	6.0	Milk of magnesia	10.5

What is the pH of pure water? pH = 7 (neutral)

Problems

5. Which acids in Table 3–4 have a high hydronium ion concentration? hydrochloric acid through acetic acid

6. Which bases in Table 3–4 have a high hydroxide ion concentration? sodium carbonate through potassium hydroxide

7. Classify each substance in Table 3–5 as an acid or a base. "stomach contents" through "milk" are acids; "blood" through "milk of magnesia" are bases

3:6 Salts

Acids and bases react with each other in a chemical reaction called neutralization (noo truh luh ZAY shuhn). In **neutralization,** the properties of both the acid and the base are destroyed. Neutral indicates that a substance is neither an acid nor a base. This explains why weak bases are used to counteract acids that are spilled on the skin or clothing. Baking soda is a common base used to neutralize acids. Antacids, containing bicarbonate of soda, are used to reduce indigestion resulting from excess stomach acid.

In neutralization, hydronium ions (H_3O^+) of the acid unite with the hydroxide ions (OH^-) of the base to form water (H_2O). This can be written as:

$$\text{hydronium ion} + \text{hydroxide ion} \rightarrow \text{water}$$
$$H_3O^+ + OH^- \rightarrow 2\,H_2O$$

Figure 3-19. In the United States, over 30 percent of the salt comes from underground salt mines.

Courtesy of Morton Salt Company, Division of Morton-Norwich Products, Inc.

What is a salt?
Salts are also produced through direct combination, such as,
2 Na + Cl$_2$ ⟶ 2 NaCl.

If the acid and base are chemically equivalent (both about 0.1 M) only NaCl should remain. Do not taste, however, since some NaOH may still be present. Litmus and/or phenolphthalein could be used to determine neutrality before evaporation.

If the water is evaporated after a neutralization reaction, a solid substance remains. This substance is called a **salt**. It is formed from the positive ion of the base and the negative ion from the acid. For example, when NaOH is neutralized by HCl, NaCl salt is formed.

Time: 35 minutes.

ACTIVITY. Place 10 ml of dilute sodium hydroxide in an evaporating dish. Add 2 drops of phenolphthalein as an indicator. What do you observe? Stir this solution carefully while slowly adding dilute HCl. Add HCl until the solution just becomes colorless. Evaporate slowly over a low Bunsen burner flame. Name the residue which remains. HCl + NaOH ⟶ NaCl + H$_2$O(l)
H$_3$O$^+$ + OH$^-$ ⟶ H$_2$O + H$_2$O

Figure 3-20.

When sulfuric acid reacts with sodium hydroxide, the salt sodium sulfate is formed:

$$H_2SO_4(aq) + 2\ NaOH(aq) \longrightarrow Na_2SO_4(aq) + 2\ H_2O$$

Salts also are formed when an active metal reacts with an acid. A single replacement reaction produces the salt (Section 2:4). For

ANHYDRIDES

example, iron filings in hydrochloric acid will produce hydrogen gas. Iron (II) chloride crystals remain upon evaporation of the water:

$$Fe(s) + 2\ HCl(aq) \longrightarrow FeCl_2(aq) + H_2(g)$$

PROBLEMS See Teacher's Guide at the front of this book.

8. Write balanced equations for each of the following reactions:
   (a) potassium hydroxide + sulfuric acid
   (b) hydrobromic acid + sodium hydroxide
   (c) calcium hydroxide + nitric acid
   (d) magnesium hydroxide + hydrochloric acid
   (e) zinc + hydrobromic acid

9. Name the salt produced in each of the preceding reactions.

10. How does the addition of a base to an acid affect the hydronium ion concentration? Why?

3:7 Anhydrides

When magnesium is burned, white magnesium oxide (MgO) is formed. The oxide dissolved in water produces a colorless solution. If a drop of colorless phenolphthalein is added to the magnesium oxide solution, the solution will turn pink. This color change indicates a base. Sulfur combines with oxygen when it burns forming sulfur dioxide (SO_2) (Figure 3–21). Sulfur dioxide is a gas which is very soluble in water. When dissolved in water, the sulfur dioxide solution is colorless. If a piece of blue litmus paper is added to the sulfur dioxide solution, the paper will turn red. What does this color change indicate? acid present in solution

Similar reactions occur if calcium oxide and carbon dioxide are dissolved in water and tested with indicators. The results show that the calcium oxide solution is a base and the carbon dioxide solution is an acid.

These oxides are called anhydrides. **Anhydride** (an HY dryd) means "without water." Most metallic oxides are bases "without water," or *basic anhydrides*. Most nonmetallic oxides are acids "without water," or *acid anhydrides*.

When water is added to magnesium oxide, the following changes occur:

$$MgO(s) + H_2O(l) \longrightarrow Mg(OH)_2(aq)$$
$$Mg(OH)_2(aq) \longrightarrow Mg^{2+}(aq) + 2\ OH^-(aq)$$

Since the hydroxide ion concentration of the solution is increased, MgO is a basic anhydride.

Ask students why this occurs. Sulfur burned in oxygen produces SO_2. When dissolved in water, it produces sulfurous acid, H_2SO_3. This gives the acid reaction to litmus.

What is an anhydride? Acid or base in which the water has been removed.

Figure 3-21. When sulfur is burned in oxygen, a gas is produced. When the gas is dissolved in water, blue litmus placed in the solution will turn red.

$$S(s) + O_2(g) \longrightarrow SO_2(g)$$
$$H_2O(l) + SO_2(g) \longrightarrow H_2SO_3(aq)$$

When sulfur dioxide is dissolved in water, the following reactions occur:

$$SO_2(g) + H_2O(l) \longrightarrow H_2SO_3(aq)$$
$$H_2SO_3(aq) + 2\ H_2O(l) \longrightarrow 2\ H_3O^+(aq) + SO_3^{2-}(aq)$$

Since the hydronium ion concentration is increased, SO_2 is an acid anhydride.

Like acids, acid anhydrides will react with bases to form salts. Like bases, basic anhydrides will react with acids to produce salts. The following reactions illustrate neutralization of anhydrides:

$$CaO(s) + H_2SO_4(aq) \longrightarrow CaSO_4(s) + H_2O(l)$$
$$CO_2(g) + Ba(OH)_2(aq) \longrightarrow BaCO_3(s) + H_2O(l)$$

Many bases and acids form anhydrides when heated. This occurs when water is driven off:

Base: $\ Ba(OH)_2(s) \longrightarrow BaO(s) + H_2O(g)$
Acid: $\ H_2CO_3(aq) \longrightarrow CO_2(g) + H_2O(g)$

PROBLEM

11. Identify the following oxides as basic or acid anhydrides.

   (a) MgO   basic
   (b) SO_2 acidic
   (c) CO_2 acidic
   (d) CaO   basic

MAIN IDEAS

3:3 **1.** Indicators turn different colors in solutions depending upon the acidity of the solution.

3:4 **2.** Water ionizes slightly to form hydronium ions (H_3O^+) and hydroxide ions (OH^-).

3:4 **3.** Acids increase hydronium ion concentration of a solution; bases increase hydroxide ion concentration of a solution.

3:4 **4.** Strong acids and bases provide large numbers of ions in solution.

3:5 **5.** The pH values of acid solutions range from 0 to 7.

3:5 **6.** The pH values of basic solutions range from 7 to 14.

3:6 **7.** A salt and water are the products of a neutralization reaction.

3:7 **8.** An anhydride is a substance "without water."

3:7 **9.** Oxides of most metals are basic anhydrides.

3:7 **10.** Oxides of most nonmetals are acid anhydrides.

ACIDS, BASES, AND SALTS (61M) 285

VOCABULARY

Write a sentence in which you correctly use each of the following words or terms.

1. acid
2. anhydride
3. base
4. hydronium ion
1. hydroxide ion
2. indicator
3. litmus paper
4. neutralization
1. pH
2. phenolphthalein
3. salt

STUDY QUESTIONS

A. True or False

Determine whether each of the following sentences is true or false. (Do not write in this book.)

Have students rewrite false statements to make the statements correct.

F 1. The formula for nitric acid is NH₃. HNO₃

F 2. Vinegar contains a base. an acid

T 3. The strength of an acid can be determined by electrical conductivity.

T 4. The strength of an acid is measured on a pH scale.

F 5. In a water solution, citric acid is more highly ionized than hydrochloric acid. hydrochloric, citric

T 6. A neutralization reaction is a reaction between an acid and a base.

T 7. OH⁻ is the formula for a hydroxide ion.

T 8. An indicator may be used to determine whether a solution is an acid or a base.

F 9. A base which has a pH of 8 is a stronger base than a base with a pH of 10. weaker

T 10. An acid anhydride will react with a base in the same way that an acid will.

B. Multiple Choice

Choose one word or phrase that correctly completes each of the following sentences. (Do not write in this book.)

Some questions in Parts B and C may have more than one correct answer. Only one answer is required.

1. Acids in food taste (*sour*, sweet, bitter, salty).

2. A strong acid will usually have a pH of (*2*, 5, 7, 8, 11).

3. (Phenolphthalein, Methyl orange, *Benzene*, Litmus) is not an indicator.

4. An oxide of a metal usually is a(n) (acid anhydride, *basic anhydride*).

5. The pH of a dilute NaOH solution is (*more than 7*, 7, less than 7).
6. Examples of a basic anhydride are (*magnesium oxide*, carbon dioxide, sulfur dioxide, *calcium oxide*).
7. Which of the following is an acid: (H₂O, MgO, *HCl*)?
8. Neutralization reactions produce a salt and (a gas, light, *water*).
9. As the amount of HCl in water increases the solution becomes (*more*, less) acidic.
10. A low pH value indicates a (low hydronium, *high hydronium*) concentration.

C. Completion

Complete each of the following sentences with a word or phrase that will make the sentence correct. (Do not write in this book.)

Taste 1. _____ should never be a test for an acid or base in a laboratory.

a hydronium ion 2. A hydrogen ion combines with a water molecule to form _____ .

indicators 3. Bases can be tested safely by using _____ .

acid 4. CO₂ is an example of a(n) _____ anhydride.

hydrogen 5. When an active metal reacts with dilute H₂SO₄, _____ gas is formed.

hydrogen 6. When an extremely active metal reacts with water, _____ gas is formed.

decreases 7. As the acidity of a solution rises, its pH value _____ .

salt 8. When an active metal and an acid react, a(n) _____ is formed.

increases 9. When sodium hydroxide is added to water the pH _____ .

decreases 10. When carbon dioxide is added to water the pH _____ .

See Teacher's Guide at the front of the book.

D. How and Why

1. What kind of reaction is shown by the following equation?
   HCl(aq) + NaOH(aq) ⟶ NaCl(aq) + H₂O(l)
2. What are the "parent" acids and bases for these salts?
   (a) Na₂SO₄   (b) NaCl   (c) NaNO₃
3. What is pH?
4. How are acids and bases detected?
5. List three important industrial acids. What are the primary uses of each?

ACIDS, BASES, AND SALTS

6. Explain how salts are formed through neutralization. Give one example.
7. Classify each substance as an acid, a base, or a salt:
   (a) HNO_2 acid
   (b) $HCOOH$ acid
   (c) KOH base
   (d) CaI_2 salt
   (e) $Ca(OH)_2$ base
   (f) $Fe(NO_3)_3$ salt
8. Name two common household bases. Give their uses.
9. Write an equation which could represent involvement of acids or bases in each of the following: (a) single replacement reaction, (b) neutralization, (c) formation of acid from acid anhydride, (d) double replacement reaction.
10. Compare the properties of acids, bases, and salts.

9. Examples of reactions that could be used:
(a) $Zn(s) + 2\ HCl \longrightarrow ZnCl_2 + H_2(g)$
(b) $HCl + NaOH \longrightarrow NaCl + H_2O$
(c) $SO_2(g) + H_2O \longrightarrow H_2SO_3$
(d) $HCl + AgNO_3 \longrightarrow AgCl(s) + HNO_3$

See Teacher's Guide at the front of the book for answers and suggestions.

INVESTIGATIONS

1. Check the labels on many household products such as patent medicines, kitchen aids, and foods. See how many involve acids or bases.
2. Prepare solutions from liquid synthetic detergents of different brands. Use the same number of drops of each detergent in the same volumes of water. Use a universal indicator to determine the pH of each.
3. Boil some natural and synthetic fibers for about 5 minutes in a weak solution of sodium hydroxide. Test the same type of fibers in dilute sulfuric acid. What do you conclude?
4. Certain gases in the air form acids when dissolved in water. What gases are they? Where do they come from? How do the acids they form affect the environment?
5. Using information from garden books, farm publications, your local garden store, or florists make a list of plants that require acid soil and those that require basic soil. If available, give pH requirements. Find out what methods can be used to make soil basic or acidic.

INTERESTING READING

Beeler, Nelson F., *Experiments in Chemistry*. New York, Thomas Y. Crowell Company, 1952.

Hyde, Margaret, O., *For Pollution Fighters Only*. New York, McGraw Hill Book Co., 1971.

Unit Five

Heat, Light, and Sound

Mt. Etna is an active volcano in Italy. A volcano is a graphic illustration that there is heat in the interior of Earth. Also, it shows that heat is periodically released from the interior.

Photo Researchers, Inc.

1 Heat Energy

Chapter 1 discusses kinetic energy and develops an understanding of heat as the kinetic energy of molecules. Properties of matter affected by gain or loss of heat are discussed. The relationship between work (f × d) and heat is studied in a discussion of Joule's experiment on the mechanical equivalent of heat.

GOAL: You will gain an understanding of kinetic energy and the relationships between heat and kinetic energy.

Heat is obtained from a variety of sources. It is produced from chemical changes such as burning and reactions between certain elements. Nuclear reactions produce large amounts of heat. Heat is even produced by the random motion of particles in all matter.

The sun's radiant energy provides heat to warm the earth. Heat also comes from the earth. How do we know this? What natural occurrences support this evidence?

KINETIC AND POTENTIAL ENERGY   (3M)   291

1:1 Kinetic and Potential Energy

All moving bodies have kinetic (kuh NET ik) energy. A swinging pendulum, a soaring rocket, your beating heart, running water, and moving air are examples of bodies with kinetic energy. **Kinetic energy** is energy of motion. Mechanical energy is another name for kinetic energy.

Define kinetic energy.

PROBLEM

1. Make a list of bodies that have kinetic energy. *Answers will vary, motion must be involved.*

Potential (puh TEN chuhl) **energy** is the energy of position. Potential energy is sometimes called stored energy. This means that the energy is inactive at the moment but has the potential for doing work. For example, water at the top of a dam has potential energy. As the water falls over the dam, its potential energy becomes kinetic energy. Falling water has kinetic energy.

Define potential energy.

Time: 5 minutes.
ACTIVITY. Place a book on a desk top. Raise the book about 20 cm into the air. By raising the book you increase its potential energy. Let the book drop. Does the book gain or lose potential energy? Why? *Potential energy changed to kinetic energy.*

Figure 1-1.

Figure 1-2. Water at the top of these falls has potential energy. Falling water has kinetic energy.

Allan Roberts

Figure 1-3. Heat energy from this fireplace provides warmth.

Gene Rogers

Potential energy can be changed to kinetic energy. Kinetic energy can be changed to potential energy. Under ordinary conditions, energy is never created nor destroyed. What becomes of a falling book's kinetic energy? Some of it becomes the sound you hear when it strikes the desk. The rest is changed to heat energy.

To raise a hammer to a height of 5 m, work must be done to overcome the force of gravity. The hammer gains potential energy, or energy of position. As the hammer is moved upward, its potential energy increases. The higher it is raised, the greater its potential energy. A hammer has more potential energy at 10 m height than at 5 m. If the hammer is dropped, it falls swiftly to the ground. Its potential energy decreases. As the hammer is raised, work is done. It is stored as potential energy. When the hammer is dropped, this energy is released in the form of kinetic energy.

You may wish to discuss potential energy with regard to frame of reference. For example, a hammer lying on the ground does not have potential energy with respect to the ground.

Give an example of potential energy and kinetic energy.

PROBLEM

2. Here are examples of potential energy. Explain how each changes to kinetic energy.

   (a) wound watch — *Flexed steel spring unwinds.*
   (b) stretched rubber band — *Energy used to stretch rubber band is released.*
   (c) camera shutter — *energy stored in spring, released*
   (d) inflated balloon — *Muscles force air into balloon.*
   (e) swimmer on a diving board — *Swimmer jumps into air, gaining height.*
   (f) a stretched archer's bow — *Energy used to stretch bow is released.*

Figure 1-4.

Time: 20 minutes.

EXPERIMENT. Is heat produced from kinetic energy? Obtain two paper drinking cups. Fill one cup one-third full of dry sand at room temperature. Place the end of a thermometer in the sand and record the temperature. Now invert the second cup over the first cup. Seal with a piece of tape. Shake the sand back and forth inside the cups for 10 min. Punch a hole in the top of the cup. Insert the thermometer. Record the temperature again. Is there a change in temperature? Why?
Kinetic energy of the shaking sand is changed to heat energy.

Figure 1-5.

Time: 20 minutes.

ACTIVITY. Hold a small round stick between your hands. Rotate the stick rapidly by moving your hands. Does the temperature of the stick change? Hammer a nail into a block of wood a short distance. With the claw of the hammer, bend the nail back and forth a few times. Now carefully touch the nail with your finger. Is the nail cooler or warmer than before? Take a rubber band and stretch it back and forth rapidly for one minute. Does the band feel warmer or cooler than before you stretched it? Rubber becomes warmer as it is stretched repeatedly.

1:2 Radiation, Conduction, and Convection

Energy can be changed from one form to another. All forms of energy can be changed to heat energy. **Heat** is the internal kinetic and potential energy which flows from one substance to another.

Why is heat a form of kinetic energy? Heat is the kinetic energy of molecules.

All molecules do not vibrate at the same rate.

Figure 1-6.

Time: 15 minutes.

EXPERIMENT. Place some hot water in a large beaker and some cold water in a small beaker. Place a thermometer in each beaker. Record the two temperatures. Then set the small beaker inside the large beaker. Check both water temperatures after 10 min. What is the final temperature in each beaker? Which way does the heat travel? Heat travels from the hot to the cold water.

Suppose you take cold lemonade from a refrigerator and want to keep it cold. If you leave the lemonade on a table, it will warm up. You can put a cold drink in a vacuum bottle and keep it cold for several hours. A vacuum bottle can also be used to keep things hot. For example, hot chocolate or soup stays hot in a vacuum bottle for several hours.

How does a vacuum bottle keep things hot or cold? It prevents heat from easily moving into and/or out of the bottle.

Figure 1-7. Heat exchange between the inside and the outside of a vacuum bottle is prevented by the vacuum (a). Vacuum bottles can keep things hot or cold (b).

Linda Briscoe

Time: 35 minutes.

EXPERIMENT. Obtain a pint-size vacuum bottle and three pint-size clear glass bottles. Cover one bottle with aluminum foil, shiny side in. Cover the second bottle with aluminum foil, shiny side out. Leave the third bottle uncovered. Heat 3 pints of water to boiling. Carefully fill the vacuum bottle and each glass bottle two-thirds full with hot water. Then put a thermometer in each bottle and record the temperatures. Allow each to stand for 30 min. Observe the temperature of the water in the four containers every 5 min. Record your data in a chart or graph. Which water cools fastest? *Uncovered jar cools fastest, jar with foil inward cools slowest.*

Figure 1-8.

How does a vacuum bottle work?

Water cools in all bottles in the experiment above. As it cools, the water loses heat. Heat is lost fastest in the clear bottle. There is little change of temperature in the vacuum bottle. The aluminum foil around the glass bottle prevents heat loss. So does the metal coating of the vacuum bottle. The vacuum between the two walls of a vacuum bottle also reduces heat loss.

Heat travels by radiation (RAYD ee ay shuhn), conduction (kuhn DUHK shuhn), and convection (kuhn VEK shuhn). In **radiation**, heat travels in the form of special energy waves. Heat can travel

Describe radiation.

Craig W. Kramer

Figure 1-9. Electric lamps give off radiant energy in the form of light and heat (a). When hot water or steam passes through the coils in a radiator, heat is given off (b).

through a vacuum by radiation only. Radiated heat energy is reflected by smooth surfaces such as aluminum foil and other shiny metals. The silver coating on a vacuum bottle reflects heat radiation back into the bottle. It also reflects heat rays that strike the bottle from the outside. Reflection by the metal coating reduces the movement of heat into and out of the vacuum bottle.

PROBLEMS

3. Name three things that give off heat by radiation. *Answers will vary.*

4. In each example for Problem 3, tell how the radiation could be reduced or stopped. *Answers will vary.*

Conduction occurs when heat travels through a substance. In a vacuum, no matter is present. There is no conduction through a vacuum. Conduction can occur only through a substance—liquid, gas, or solid. The vacuum in a vacuum bottle is a partial vacuum. Partial vacuum means that most but not all of the air is removed. The partial vacuum in a vacuum bottle cuts down on heat loss by conduction. Some heat may still enter or leave the vacuum bottle. It is conducted through the remaining air. But the heat conduction is small.

When does conduction occur?

Time: 20 minutes.
ACTIVITY. Push one end of a metal knitting needle into a cork. Use the cork as a handle. Place tiny pieces of wax 2 cm apart on the needle. Light a candle and hold the free end of the needle in the flame. Continue heating only the end of the needle until all wax pieces drop off. How long did it take for all the wax to melt? Repeat this activity using a glass rod instead of a metal knitting needle. Compare the conduction in the metal needle with that in the glass rod. *Metal conducts heat faster.*

Figure 1-10.

296 (8M)   HEAT ENERGY

A material through which heat passes easily is called a **conductor**. Heat travels more slowly through insulators. **Insulators** are materials used to reduce heat transfer.

PROBLEMS

5. What is the conductor and insulator in the preceding activity?
6. List 3 heat conductors and 3 heat insulators used in homes. Answers will vary.
7. Why is aluminum foil used as an insulator in many buildings?
It prevents radiation of heat.

Figure 1-11.

•••
Time: 20 minutes.
ACTIVITY. Fill a beaker about two-thirds full of water. Place it on a ring stand. Add a drop of food coloring to the water. Do not stir. Be very careful not to disturb the water in the beaker. Gently heat the beaker and water. Record what you observe. Color moves by convection currents throughout water.
•••

Convection is heat transfer in liquids and gases. In general, when liquids and gases are heated, the molecules move farther apart. In this way, the density of liquids and gases usually decreases as the substances are heated. The less dense part rises in the fluid causing currents that carry heat through the material. For example, the heat from a flame can warm the bottom of a pot of water. Water at the bottom of the pot becomes hot and decreases in density. This lighter water floats upward through the water above and carries heat with it. Winds in the atmosphere and currents in the oceans are caused by convection.

What is convection?

Figure 1-12. Hot water rises because it is less dense than cold or warm water. Differences in density cause convection currents (a). Radiators heat rooms by producing convection currents (b). For maximum efficiency, radiators are installed against outer walls.

a

b

MEASURING HEAT (9M) 297

PROBLEMS

8. Some rooms are heated by radiators. In what ways is heat transferred in warming the room? conduction, convection, radiation
9. Why is little heat lost by convection in a vacuum bottle? Silver walls reflect radiation, vacuum prevents conduction, convection.
10. Which way will convection currents flow from a wall radiator? up and out

1:3 Measuring Heat

The amount of heat energy in a body depends on both the temperature and the mass of the body. A swimming pool full of water has heat energy. So does a dishpan full of water. At the same temperature, the pool has more heat than the dishpan. This is because the water in the pool has a greater mass than the water in the dishpan. Which would lose the most heat if cooled from 30°C to 0°C? The pool would lose the most heat.

Heat is measured in calories. One **calorie** (KAL uh ree) is the amount of heat needed to raise the temperature of one gram of water one Celsius degree. One ml of water has a mass of 1 g.

To raise the temperature of 10 g of water 1 C°, you must add 10 calories of heat to the water. To find the number of calories, multiply the change in temperature by the mass in grams. Use this equation: How are calories calculated?

$$H = (t_2 - t_1) m$$

heat equals the final temperature minus the beginning temperature times mass

Suppose the temperature of 4 grams of water is raised from 20°C to 25°C. The heat added is 20 calories.

$$H = (t_2 - t_1) m$$
$$H = (25° - 20°) \times 4 \text{ g}$$
$$H = 20 \text{ calories}$$

Figure 1-13.

Time: 25 minutes.

EXPERIMENT. Weigh 100 g of water (room temperature) in a 250-ml beaker. Measure and record the temperature. Heat the water with a Bunsen flame for 1 min. Remove the flame and measure the water temperature again. Calculate the calories of heat [$H = (t_2 - t_1) m$] gained by the water. Would the calories of heat be different if there were 200 g of water in the beaker? no How is the size of the Bunsen burner flame related to the calories of heat produced? The larger the flame, the more calories of heat produced.

Figure 1-14. Calorimeters are used to measure the heat value of foods and fuels.

Water is used to measure heat because it is inexpensive, abundant, a good heat absorber, and its mass is easily determined. Heat = mass × temperature change.

calories = g × C°

Strictly speaking, in order for the units to be correct, the right hand side of the equation should be multiplied by the specific heat in cal/g-C°. However, since the specific heat of water is 1 cal/g-C°, this will be omitted to simplify calculations.

Specific heat is the amount of heat lost or gained by a unit mass of substance for each degree change in temperature.

Substance	Specific Heat (cal/g-C°)
water	1
aluminum	0.225
copper	0.0939
iron	0.11

Heat energy is measured with an instrument called a **calorimeter** (kal uh RIM uht uhr) (Figure 1-14). For example, the heat value for a food may be found by burning it in the inner chamber of a calorimeter. Heat produced in the inner chamber is transferred to the water in the outer chamber. This heat gain causes an increase in water temperature. The amount of temperature increase is read on the thermometer. Heat gained by the water is equal to the change in temperature multiplied by the water's mass. The amount of heat gained by the water is the amount of heat produced from the food.

PROBLEM

11. Why must a calorimeter be insulated? *so that all heat is accounted for and does not escape*

Time: 90 minutes.

ACTIVITY. Make a simple calorimeter. Use two clean cans (size number 2½ and number 1). Cover the small can with rock wool or glass wool. Fit it into the large can. Make a cover for the can out of a piece of wood. Drill two holes in the center of the cover. One hole is for a piece of 0.5 cm dowel to be used as a stirrer. The other hole is for a thermometer. Heat 100 g of water to 50° C. Place the water in the inner can and cover. Insert the stirrer and thermometer. Wait 10 min then record the water temperature. Add two ice cubes to the inner can. Cover and stir until the ice cubes are melted. Record the temperature of the water again. From the weight of the water and change in water temperature, estimate the heat it took to melt the ice.

H = 100g × temperature change

JOULE'S EXPERIMENT

EXAMPLE

A student places a piece of hot steel in the inner chamber of a calorimeter. The temperature of 1 kg of water in the calorimeter changes from 25°C to 30°C. Note: 1 kg = 1000 g. How many calories of heat were gained by the water?

Solution: (a) Write the equation: $H = (t_2 - t_1)\, m$
(b) Substitute 30°C for t_2, 25°C for t_1 and 1000 g for m:
$H = (30°C - 25°C)\, 1000\text{ g}$
(c) Subtract and then multiply to find the answer: $H = 5\text{ C}° \times 1000\text{ g}$
(d) Answer: 5000 calories

PROBLEMS

12. How much heat was lost by the metal in the preceding example? *5000 calories*
13. A kettle containing 500 g of water is heated from 25°C to 100°C. How much heat is added to the water? *37,500 calories*
14. A baby bottle containing 20 g of water at 60°C is cooled to 40°C. How much heat is lost by the water? *400 calories*

1:4 Joule's Experiment

James Joule (JOOL, 1818–1889), an English scientist, showed that work can produce heat. Joule measured heat in British thermal units. One **British thermal unit (BTU)** is the amount of heat required to raise the temperature of one pound of water one Fahrenheit degree. If Joule made his observations today, he would use the calorie as a unit of heat.

What is a BTU?

Joule wound a rope on a pulley and attached the pulley to the paddles of a churn filled with water. Then he hung a weight on the rope and let the weight fall from the top of a cliff. As the weight fell,

Figure 1-15. By measuring the temperature before and after the experiment, Joule proved that work produces heat.

the paddles rotated rapidly and stirred the water in the churn. The kinetic energy of the moving paddles heated the water. Joule measured the temperature of the water before and after the weight fell. Knowing the mass of the water, Joule calculated the BTU's of heat gained by the water.

Joule also measured the distance the weight fell. Multiplying weight in pounds by distance in feet, he calculated the work done by the falling weight. This was the same as the work done by the paddles. Work is force exerted through a distance.

What did Joule find out about heat?
A certain amount of work always produces a certain amount of heat.

The work required to produce 1 BTU of heat is called the *mechanical equivalent of heat*. Joule figured the mechanical equivalent of heat to be 778 ft-lb of work. That is, 778 ft-lb produces 1 BTU. BTU is the heat unit used in engineering. It is the unit used in measuring heat loss or gain for air conditioners and heating systems.

PROBLEMS

15. Find the BTU rating of your school furnace and home furnace. Compare the figures. *Answers will vary.*

16. Which is larger, a BTU or a calorie?

Explain the molecular kinetic theory.

Figure 1-16. Water can exist in the gaseous phase. The clouds and steam from the geyser are two examples of vapor.
William Maddox

1:5 *Molecular Kinetic Energy*

All matter is composed of tiny particles called molecules. A *molecule* (MAHL ih kyool) is the smallest particle of an element or a compound which can still be identified as that element or compound. Molecules are in constant motion. This is true even for solids. In solids and liquids, molecules vibrate back and forth. In gases, they fly about in random motion. Since the molecules are in motion, they have kinetic energy called **molecular** (muh LEK yuh luhr) **kinetic energy.** Heat is the molecular kinetic energy within a substance.

This idea of molecules in motion is known as the *molecular kinetic theory*. One test of a theory is how well it agrees with known facts. The molecular kinetic theory may be tested by how well it explains some properties of matter.

Matter can exist in three phases: solid, liquid, or gas. According to the molecular kinetic theory, the molecules in a solid are packed close together. This gives a **solid** a definite size and a definite shape. The molecules in a liquid are farther apart than in a solid. Molecules in a liquid flow over, under, and around each other. Thus, a **liquid** has a definite volume but no definite shape. A liquid takes the shape of its container. The molecules in a gas are farther apart than in a

MOLECULAR KINETIC ENERGY (13M) 301

solid or liquid. They have a rapid, random motion. **A gas** has no definite volume or shape. A gas takes the size and shape of its container. It can expand or be compressed.

When heat is added to a body, its temperature goes up. The heat energy becomes molecular kinetic energy within the body. As a body gains heat, its molecules vibrate faster and faster. As a body loses heat, its molecules vibrate more slowly.

For example, when a balloon is heated it expands. Why? The air molecules gain kinetic energy and move faster striking the sides of the balloon harder, making it expand. You may have opened a glass jar with a tight metal lid by placing the lid under hot water. The metal lid gains molecular kinetic energy and expands more than the glass. Expansion causes the lid to loosen.

In general, substances contract when they cool because their molecules vibrate more slowly and move closer together. Substances expand when heated. Their molecules move farther apart.

How does the molecular kinetic theory explain phases of matter?

You may wish to point out at this time that water expands as it approaches its freezing point.

How does the molecular kinetic theory explain temperature and expansion?

Time: 15 minutes.
ACTIVITY. Take a ring which just fits your finger. Place it in the refrigerator for a few hours. Then try it on. tight Warm the ring in your hand for a few minutes. How does the ring fit your finger now? Why? expansion
loose

Time: 30 minutes.
ACTIVITY. An iron ball and ring like those in Figure 1–17 can show how solids expand. Pass the ball through the ring. Heat the ball over a flame for 10 min. Try to pass the heated ball through the ring. What do you observe? How did heating affect the ball? Allow the ball to cool completely. Again try to pass the ball through the ring. Explain what you observe.
Heat causes expansion and ball will not fit.

Figure 1–17.

Temperature tells how hot or cold something is compared to other things around it. Your body is warm, about 38.1°C, compared to room temperature. Snow is cold, 0°C or less. According to molecular kinetic theory, temperature is the average kinetic energy of molecules in a body or substance. Each molecule has kinetic energy. But the speed of the molecules differs. Some vibrate faster than others. Therefore, the kinetic energy for each molecule in a body is not the same. Average molecular kinetic energy is the total energy

Temperature refers to the average kinetic energy of molecules in a substance. Heat is kinetic energy of molecules. Temperature indicates the direction in which heat travels.

How is temperature different from heat?

Figure 1-18. Ice melts when heat is added.

for all molecules divided by the number of molecules. If heat is added to a body, the temperature increases. Average molecular kinetic energy increases. What happens to temperature when average kinetic energy per molecule decreases?

1:6 Melting and Vaporization

Ice cubes melt if you leave them at room temperature. When a piece of chocolate candy is left in the sun too long, it melts. Heat energy causes substances to melt.

Melting is a change from solid to liquid. How is melting explained by the molecular kinetic theory? When a solid melts, no change in temperature occurs. Its molecules do not gain kinetic energy. Then why is heat needed? It takes energy to change the phase of a substance. When a substance is changed from a solid to liquid phase, energy is absorbed. The heat added to the substance when it melts becomes molecular potential energy.

Molecular potential energy is energy of position. When a solid melts, its molecules move farther apart. They overcome to some extent the forces that hold them together. Molecules have more potential energy when they are farther apart than when they are close together.

Heat is necessary for an object to melt. **Heat of fusion** (FYOO zhuhn) is the amount of heat required to melt one gram of a solid. For example, the heat of fusion for ice is 80 cal/g. When one gram of ice melts, the ice gains 80 calories. Yet there is no increase in temperature. When one gram of water freezes, the water loses 80 calo-

What happens to molecules in melting and evaporation?
Molecules move farther apart.

Figure 1-19. Steel is reheated to temperatures of about 204° C to reduce brittleness.

U.S. Steel Corporation

Figure 1-20. Water at 0° C has 80 cal/g more heat than ice at 0° C (a). Which has the larger volume, the ice cube or the water (b)?

ries. Yet there is no decrease in temperature. In melting and freezing, there is a gain or loss of potential energy. There is no gain or loss of kinetic energy.

Time: 40 minutes.

EXPERIMENT. Fill a large test tube one-third full of water and attach a rubber stopper containing a 45-cm delivery tube. CAUTION: Follow your teacher's directions for inserting the tube into the rubber stopper. Support the test tube in a slanted position with a ring stand and test tube clamp. Set the end of the delivery tube in a small beaker full of water. Put a thermometer in the beaker and record the temperature.

Heat the water in the test tube to boiling. Keep it boiling slowly until you get steam coming through the delivery tube for several minutes. Note any change in temperature of the water in the beaker. Remove the delivery tube from the beaker. Stop heating the test tube. Record the temperature of the water in the beaker. Explain your observations. What effect is there on the amount of heat in the beaker water? — lowers What change in procedure would be needed if you wanted to measure the heat gained by the water? — need to find mass of water

Caution students to be careful of escaping steam. Ask them why steam causes more severe burns than water at 100°C (the 540 cal/g heat of vaporization).

Figure 1-21.

Figure 1-22. Steam at 100° C has 540 cal/g more heat than water at 100° C (a). Water vapor is invisible. Steam, which consists of condensing water vapor, is visible (b).

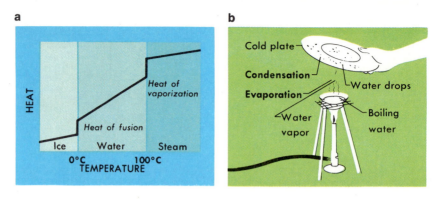

Vaporization (vay puh ruh ZAY shuhn) is a change from a liquid to a gas. After reaching its boiling point, a liquid gains more heat as it vaporizes. For example, water gains 540 cal/g when it boils off in the form of steam. A liquid's temperature does not increase when it changes to a gas. Its molecules do not gain kinetic energy. They gain potential energy. The molecules in a gas are farther apart than the molecules in a liquid. Heat added to the liquid becomes molecular potential energy of the gas molecules.

Condensation (kahn duhn SAY shuhn) is a change from a gas to a liquid. When a gas condenses to form a liquid, it loses heat. But it does not decrease in temperature. The lost heat results from a decrease in the molecular potential energy of the gas as it becomes a liquid.

What happens to molecules in freezing and condensation?
Molecules move closer together.

The amount of heat required to change one gram of liquid to a gas is called **heat of vaporization.** Calculations show that the heat of vaporization for water is 540 calories per gram. Heat of vaporization may be measured by passing steam through water in a calorimeter. Heat lost by the condensing steam may be measured by the increase in temperature of the water. For every gram of steam that condenses to liquid water, the steam loses 540 calories.

Figure 1-23. Condensation often occurs on window panes.

Jim Elliott

Figure 1-24.

Time: 45 minutes.

ACTIVITY. Steam loses heat when it condenses to water. (1) Place 100 g of water (room temperature) in the inner container of a calorimeter. Weigh and record the total weight of the calorimeter. Measure and record the water temperature. (2) Add steam from a steam boiler until the water in the calorimeter becomes hot. Stop the steam and record the water temperature. (3) Weigh the calorimeter again. How many grams of steam were added? (4) Calculate the calories of heat in the room-temperature water: cal = m × t. Calculate the calories of heat in the heated water, using the same equation. The difference in calories is the amount of heat added by the steam.

How many calories were gained from each gram of steam? Your answer is an experimental value for the heat of vaporization of water. Why might this value differ from the true heat of vaporization for water, 540 cal/g?

Experimental error. Some heat is lost from the calorimeter; room may change temperature; condensed water may be carried into the calorimeter from the tube.

PROBLEMS

17. How does the heat of fusion of ice explain its use as a refrigerant? *uses heat as it melts*

18. How does the heat of vaporization of water explain why you feel cooler after a swim? *takes body heat as it evaporates*

19. Why can a steam heating system deliver more heat per hour to a room than a hot water system? *releases heat of vaporization as it condenses*

305 (17M)

Figure 1-25. How does heating the air in a hot air balloon cause the balloon to rise?

What changes occur when there is a gain or loss of potential energy and kinetic energy?

There are two kinds of heat energy in a body: molecular kinetic energy and molecular potential energy. Changes in temperature occur when molecules lose or gain kinetic energy. Changes in phase occur when molecules lose or gain potential energy. Changes in molecular potential energy occur during boiling, melting, freezing, vaporization, and condensation.

MAIN IDEAS

1:1 1. Potential energy is energy of position. Kinetic energy is energy of motion.

1:1 2. Energy can be changed from one form to another.

1:1 3. All forms of energy can be changed to heat.

1:2 4. Heat travels by radiation, conduction, and convection.

1:3 5. Temperature is measured in degrees. Heat is measured in calories.

1:3 6. Heat is the energy of molecules: molecular kinetic energy and molecular potential energy. Temperature is average molecular kinetic energy.

1:5 7. Molecular kinetic energy is the energy of molecules in motion.

1:5 8. The molecular kinetic theory explains some physical properties of solids, liquids, and gases.

1:6 9. Temperature is not changed by melting, boiling, or other changes in physical phase.

1:6 10. Heat is gained or lost during a change of physical phase.

HEAT ENERGY (19M) 307

VOCABULARY

Write a sentence in which you correctly use each of the following words or terms.

BTU	convection	kinetic energy
calorie	energy	melting
calorimeter	heat	potential energy
change of phase	heat of fusion	radiation
condensation	heat of vaporization	temperature
conduction	insulator	vaporization
conductor		

STUDY QUESTIONS

A. True or False

Have students rewrite false statements to make the statements correct.

Determine whether each of the following sentences is true or false. (Do not write in this book.)

- T 1. Heat is a form of energy.
- F 2. The heat an object contains is measured in ~~degrees~~. *calories*
- T 3. Freezing water is an example of a change in physical phase.
- F 4. Heat is transferred through water by ~~conduction~~ currents. *convection*
- F 5. A wound spring is an example of ~~kinetic~~ energy. *potential*
- T 6. A calorimeter measures calories.
- T 7. Heat travels from the sun to Earth by radiation.
- T 8. When the temperature of a gas increases, its molecules vibrate faster.
- F 9. Glass is a good conductor of heat. *not*
- T 10. Temperature is a measure of the degree of hotness or coldness.

B. Multiple Choice

Some questions in Parts B and C may have more than one correct answer. Only one answer is required.

Choose one word or phrase that correctly completes each of the following sentences. (Do not write in this book.)

1. Kinetic energy is (*potential energy, energy of position, energy of motion*).
2. Heat is measured in (°C, °F, *calories*).
3. Temperature is (*total kinetic energy, average molecular kinetic energy, heat energy*).
4. When heat travels through a substance (*convection, conduction, radiation*) occurs.

5. One milliliter of water has a mass of *(1, 10, 100)* gram(s).
6. One liter equals *(100, 1000, 10,000)* grams of water.
7. Heat is measured with a *(thermometer, calorimeter, mercury column)*.
8. One BTU is the amount of heat required to raise the temperature of *(10 ml, 12 oz, 1 lb)* of water 1°F.
9. If 1 kg of water is heated from 30°C to 45°C, the heat added is *(15, 150, 1500, 15,000)* calories.
10. Two grams of water are cooled from 80°C to 60°C. The water loses *(20, 22, 40)* calories.

C. Completion

Complete each of the following sentences with a word or phrase that will make the sentence correct. (Do not write in this book.)

Answer		
800	1.	When 10 g of ice melts, it gains _____ calories.
lose kinetic energy	2.	When substances are cooled, their molecules _____ .
gain kinetic energy	3.	When a solid is heated, its molecules _____ .
54,000	4.	When 100 g of water boils, it gains _____ calories.
Conduction	5.	_____ is the movement of heat through a substance, from molecule to molecule.
Radiation	6.	_____ is a more rapid means of heat transfer than convection and conduction.
molecules	7.	Molecular kinetic energy is the energy of moving _____ .
decreases	8.	When food is placed in a refrigerator, the molecular kinetic energy of the food _____ .
increases	9.	When water is heated, its molecular kinetic energy _____ .
conductors	10.	Heat passes easily through materials called _____ .

D. How and Why

See Teacher's Guide at the front of this book.

1. How is heat different from temperature?
2. List five examples of kinetic energy and five examples of potential energy.
3. How is a calorimeter used to measure heat?
4. Why might the parts of an engine "freeze" if the engine overheats?
5. How is it possible for water at 0°C to melt ice at 0°C with no change in temperature?

HEAT ENERGY

6. A student burned some matches in a calorimeter. The temperature of 1 kg of water increased from 25°C to 26.5°C. How much heat did the matches give off?

7. A drawbridge always has a space between its moving parts. How is this fact related to the molecular kinetic theory?

8. Draw a diagram to show the difference in molecular structure of a solid, liquid, and gas. Draw three boxes 3 cm square. Use small circles for molecules inside the boxes.

9. The freon gas used to cool a refrigerator evaporates and condenses as it passes through coiled pipes. Explain the cooling action of the refrigerant using the molecular kinetic theory.

10. How is density involved in the process of convection? Give an example.

INVESTIGATIONS

See Teacher's Guide at the front of this book.

1. Write a report on how industries are reducing the threat of thermal pollution.

2. Obtain an old thermostat such as those used on gas hot water heaters. Take it apart and learn how it works.

3. Make a collection of insulation materials such as aluminum foil, cork, and glass wool. Obtain information on the insulating properties of each material. Find out the savings in fuel costs that result from proper insulation of a home.

INTERESTING READING

Adler, Irving, *Hot and Cold*. New York, John Day Company, 1959.

Balestrino, Philip, *Hot as an Ice Cube*. New York, Thomas Y. Crowell Company, 1972.

Cobb, Vicki, *Heat*. New York, Franklin Watts, Inc., 1973.

Halacy, D. S., Jr., *The Energy Trap*. New York, Four Winds Press/Scholastic Book Service, 1974.

Keller, A. G., *Theatre of Machines*. New York, Macmillan Company, 1965.

Thompson, Paul D., *Gases and Plasmas*. Philadelphia, J. B. Lippincott Company, 1966.

Wilson, Charles Morrow, *Diesel: His Engine Changed the World*. Princeton, N.J., Van Nostrand Company, Inc., 1966.

Heat is used to melt steel. The steel is then poured into molds and permitted to cool. U.S. Steel Corporation

2 Heat and Its Uses

This chapter further develops the concepts of heat introduced in Chapter 1 and the gas laws are developed. This information is applied to problems of refrigeration, heating systems for buildings, and heat engines. Thermal pollution and possible solutions to this problem are considered. Cryogenics and its applications are also presented.

GOAL: You will gain an understanding of heat and its practical uses.

Heat energy is used in many ways. Heat is needed for our comfort and well-being in cold weather. Office buildings, homes, and schools are heated so that normal activities go on regardless of the weather.

Heat is also used in industry. For example, it is needed to melt steel before molding it into desired shapes and sizes. What are some other uses of heat in industry?

2:1 Specific Heat

Heat a pot of water on a stove for a few minutes and the pot becomes too hot to touch. Yet the water may only be lukewarm. Metals and water do not increase in temperature at the same rate. Metal heats up faster than water.

Figure 2-1.

Time: 30 minutes.
ACTIVITY. Obtain a piece of three different metals. Aluminum, iron, and copper are good choices. All pieces should have the same mass. Place the metal pieces in boiling water for 5 min. With metal tongs, remove each piece from the water and set it on a block of paraffin. Allow the pieces of metal to stand until they are cool. Which metal melts the most paraffin? Which metal has the most heat? Explain any differences. The metal with the highest specific heat will melt the most paraffin. Aluminum should melt about twice as much paraffin as iron or copper. Water with the same mass and temperature would melt over four times more than aluminum. See Table 2–1 for specific heat values.

Specific heat is the amount of heat needed to change the temperature of one gram of a substance one Celsius degree. Specific heat is measured in calories. The **calorie** (KAL uh ree) is a unit of heat (Section 1:3). The specific heat of water is 1 cal/g-C°. One calorie will raise the temperature of one gram of water one Celsius degree.

What is specific heat and how is it measured?

The specific heat of iron is 0.11. This means that it takes 0.11 calories of heat to increase the temperature of one gram of iron one Celsius degree. The higher the specific heat of a given material, the more heat energy needed to increase its temperature. Table 2–1 lists specific heats for several substances. Which of the metals in the above activity has the highest specific heat? Al Which metal has the lowest specific heat? Cu

Table 2–1. Specific Heats of Some Common Substances	
Substance	Specific Heat (cal/g-C°)
Aluminum	0.21
Copper	0.09
Iron	0.11
Water	1.00

EXAMPLE 1

How much heat will increase the temperature of 10 g of water by 15 C°? Multiply the mass by change in temperature. Then multiply by the specific heat.

temperature change times mass times specific heat = calories
15 C° × 10 g × 1 cal/g-C° = 150 cal

Example 2

How much heat is needed to increase the temperature of 10 g of iron 15 C°? Again, multiply mass by degrees change in temperature. Then multiply by the specific heat.

$$15 \text{ C°} \times 10 \text{ g} \times 0.11 \text{ cal/g-C°} = 16.5 \text{ cal}$$

Figure 2-2.

Time: 2½ hours.

EXPERIMENT. Obtain two similar cans and two thermometers. Fill one can with sand. Fill the other with water. Put a thermometer in each can to the same depth and the same distance from the walls of each container. Record the temperature. Allow the cans to stand in the sun for one hour. Record each temperature again. Which can has the higher temperature? Allow the cans to stand in a refrigerator for one hour. Record each temperature again. Which has the higher specific heat, sand or water?

Problems

1. Compare the specific heat of water with that of sand, glass, and air.
2. Why is water used to remove heat from a car engine?
3. How do large bodies of water affect the climate of nearby land areas during winter and summer? Why?

2:2 Heating Systems

Hot water systems are used to heat some homes and other buildings. These systems include a furnace, boiler, and radiators. Radiators in rooms are connected by pipes to a boiler which is heated by a furnace. Usually the furnace and boiler are in a basement. The furnace heats the water in the boiler to about 82°C.

Convection carries the hot water up through pipes to the room radiators. Heat is released into the room from a radiator as the hot water cools. Cooler water in the radiator sinks back down again to the boiler and is replaced by rising hot water. The circulation of water from boiler to radiator is repeated over and over. In some systems, a pump forces the water through the pipes and radiators. In effect, a hot water heating system transfers heat from a furnace to air inside a room.

Figure 2-3. Furnace burners heat water in hot water systems and heat air in forced air furnaces.

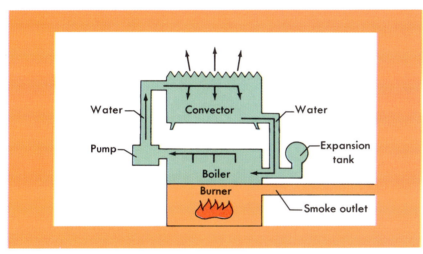

Figure 2-4. In a hot water heating system, heat is released as hot water cools.

A steam heating system is an improvement on a hot water system. In a steam heating system, water is heated under pressure to boiling. Hot steam rather than water is circulated from the boiler to the radiators. Inside a steam radiator, steam condenses to water which runs back down to the boiler.

When steam condenses to water it gives up 540 cal/g without a change in temperature. This figure is known as the **heat of condensation** of water (Section 1:6). If 10 g of steam condenses, 5400 cal of heat are released. Here you see why steam radiators get hotter than hot water radiators. It takes about 50 times as much hot water to give the same heat as condensing steam.

Some heating systems use radiant heat. Radiant heat is carried into a room through radiation. In one kind of radiant heating, electric wires are heated by an electric current. Behind the wires is a shiny metal reflector which reflects heat into the room.

Why is steam heat an improvement over hot water heat?

A substance must absorb as much heat (without a change in temperature) when it becomes a gas as it gives up when it becomes a liquid. As steam condenses it gives off as much heat as it absorbed on vaporizing.

Define heat of condensation.

the amount of heat that a gas gives up (without a change in temperature) as it condenses

Figure 2-5. In a forced air heating system, rooms are heated as warm air circulates.

Some types of furnaces heat air in the furnace with a burner (Figure 2–5). The heated air is transferred to other parts of the building by convection. Frequently a fan is attached to the furnace to help circulate the warm air. This increases the efficiency of the furnace and lowers costs.

New advances have been made in recent years to make use of the sun's energy. Solar heating systems are being tested and used successfully. These systems are found in many homes, offices, and school buildings throughout the world.

Solar heat may be collected by using black metal plates. The plates are black since black absorbs sunlight well. The plates are covered by plastic or glass. This covering reduces the heat loss in the system. Tubes in back of the plates circulate water which collects the heat. The water carries the heat away from the plates and through the system.

Figure 2-6. Solar heating uses heat energy from the sun.

Roger K. Burnard

GAS LAWS

Most heating and cooling systems are regulated by a **thermostat** (THUHR muh stat). A thermostat contains a thin strip that changes shape as it is warmed or cooled. This strip is *bimetallic* (by muh TAL ik) meaning that it has two different metal ribbons joined together. For example, a bimetallic strip may have a layer of brass and a layer of iron.

Metals expand when heated, but different metals expand at different rates. As a bimetallic strip is warmed, one metal expands faster than the other. This unequal expansion causes the strip to bend. When the strip cools, the metals contract and the strip straightens out.

Time: 20 minutes.
ACTIVITY. Obtain a bimetallic strip attached to a wooden handle. Heat the free end of the strip with a Bunsen flame. What change occurs? *The strip bends.* Allow the strip to cool. Then invert the strip and heat again. Does the strip always bend in the same direction? *It always bends toward the iron when heated.* Brass expands faster than iron when heated. Thus, a bimetallic strip bends toward the iron. Which way does a bimetallic strip bend when it is cooled? *Upon cooling the strip straightens out.*

Figure 2-7.

A bimetallic strip in a furnace thermostat acts as a switch to start and stop the system. When cool, the strip touches a contact point. This completes an electric circuit and starts the system. An electric motor pumps fuel to the furnace or an electric fan blows hot air into the area to be heated. As the thermostat warms, the bimetallic strip bends away from the contact point. The circuit is broken open and the motor stops. In effect, the bimetallic strip acts as a switch which turns the heating system on and off.

Describe how a thermostat works.

Figure 2-8. Thermostats regulate most furnaces and air conditioners.

2:3 Gas Laws

Cars and bicycles move on tires inflated with air. When air is pumped into a tire, the air is compressed. It is forced into a smaller space than it occupied outside the tire. The pressure of air inside a bicycle tire may be four times that of the air pressure outside. Suppose someone rides the bicycle many miles on a hot day. An increase in tire temperature may cause the pressure to increase.

Pressure is defined as force per unit area. Air pressure is the push of air on a surface. Pressure can be expressed in both English and metric units. In English units, pressure is stated in pounds per square

William Maddox

Figure 2-9. Mercury barometers (a) and aneroid barometers (b) measure air pressure.

Allan Roberts — *William Maddox*

Torricelli first measured atmospheric pressure in 1643 using a mercury barometer. To this day pressure is measured in millimeters of mercury.

inch or square foot of surface. The average air pressure at sea level is 14.7 lb/in². This value is called one atmosphere of pressure. Two atmospheres of pressure would be 29.4 lb/in². Tire pressure gauges are used to measure the difference between tire pressure and atmospheric pressure. Some automobile tires have a pressure of about 30 lb/in² above atmospheric pressure.

How does a barometer measure air pressure?

A **barometer** (buh RAHM uht uhr) is an instrument used to measure air pressure. In a mercury barometer (Figure 2–9a), a column of mercury is supported by air pressure. The mercury column rises and falls as the air pressure rises and falls. Air pressure may be recorded in millimeters or centimeters of mercury. Air pressure of one atmosphere equals 76 cm or 760 mm of mercury.

Figure 2-10. Scuba divers ascend slowly because of differences in pressure.

Joey Jacques

GAS LAWS (29M) 317

Problem

4. Does your body experience more pressure at <u>sea level</u> or at the top of a mountain? Do you experience more pressure when you swim on the surface of water or <u>under the surface</u>? Why? *Pressure increases as more and more air (or water) exerts force on body.*

Time: 5 minutes daily for at least 5 days.

ACTIVITY. Read a mercury or aneroid (AN uh royd) barometer each day at the same time. Record the air pressure in centimeters of mercury. Why is the air pressure not exactly 76 cm? Do changes occur in the barometer readings? How is air pressure related to weather? *atmospheric pressure changes with weather conditions*

Time: 70 minutes.

EXPERIMENT. Inflate a round rubber balloon. Measure its circumference with a tape measure and determine its volume. Warm the balloon over a heated radiator or let it sit in the sun for 30 min. Calculate the volume now. Put the balloon in a refrigerator and find its volume again when it is cold. How does the volume of the balloon change with change in temperature? Explain your observations. *volume decreases in cold; volume increases with heat*

Figure 2-11.

Gases have three main properties. These are **volume, pressure,** and **temperature.** These properties affect each other. Principles, called the gas laws, help explain these properties and relationships.

Boyle's law states that the volume of a gas decreases as its pressure increases, if the temperature does not change. Molecules of the gas are pushed closer together when the pressure is increased. Thus, the volume decreases.

The reverse occurs when the pressure decreases. The volume of a gas increases. Remove the cap from a bottle of soda pop. Carbon dioxide gas rushes out because it expands with reduced pressure. Because of the spaces between molecules of a gas, a gas can be easily compressed and expanded.

Suppose a closed cylinder contains oxygen gas. A pressure gauge attached to the cylinder reads 70 cm of mercury. What causes this pressure? The gas molecules inside the cylinder contain kinetic energy and are in constant motion. As the molecules move about, they strike each other and the walls of the container. The force of

State Boyle's law.
$P \propto V$ or $P_1 V_1 = P_2 V_2$

Figure 2-12. Carbon dioxide in soda pop expands when the bottle is opened and pressure is reduced.

The Seven-Up Company

Figure 2-13. When the volume of a gas decreases, what happens to the pressure? *increases*

the molecules striking the walls of the container produces the pressure. If more oxygen is pumped into the tank, the pressure increases. An increase in the number of molecules striking the walls of the tank causes an increase in pressure.

State Charles' law.
$V \propto \frac{1}{T}$ $\frac{V_1}{T_1} = \frac{V_2}{T_2}$

Charles' law states that the volume of a gas increases as its temperature increases, if the pressure is not changed. Heating a gas causes it to expand (Figure 2–14). Gas molecules gain kinetic energy when they are heated. They move faster, travel farther, and strike the walls of the container more often. If the walls of the container are flexible, the gas pushes it out. There is an increase in volume.

Figure 2-14. Balloons expand in hot water. Gas molecules gain kinetic energy and are forced farther away from each other.

Figure 2-15.

Time: 35 minutes.

ACTIVITY. Obtain a 500-ml flask and a one-hole rubber stopper to fit it. Moisten a glass tube. Carefully work the tube through the hole in the stopper. Insert the stopper into the flask. Invert the flask. Clamp the flask to a ring stand as shown in Figure 2–15. Place the end of the tube in a large beaker of water. Add some ink to the water. Place both hands tightly against the flask. Hold them there and watch the level of water in the tube. Record what you observe. Explain. *rises*

318 (30M)

PEOPLE CAREERS FRONTIERS FOCUS ON PHYSICAL SCIENCE

Shallow Solar Ponds for Energy Tested

Two model "shallow solar ponds" are being tested near Grants, New Mexico. These ponds were built by a University of California laboratory. The main purpose of these ponds is to provide low-cost, solar-heated water to a uranium processing plant.

Each pond is approximately 60 meters long and 3.6 meters wide. Water is pumped into the ponds each morning. All morning and part of the afternoon, the sun heats the water. By mid-afternoon, the water is at its highest temperature. The use of a six-acre shallow pond system could provide almost half of the energy needed by the plant.

Oil has been traditionally used as the energy source. It is believed that using solar-heated water will save oil. One estimate was that 10,000 barrels a year could be saved.

Researchers also believe that the cost of heating the water by the sun would be cheaper than by other methods.

Courtesy of the *U.C. Clip Sheet*, October 11, 1975.

Lawrence Livermore Laboratory

These "shallow solar ponds" are being tested near Grants, New Mexico.

Solid Wastes: Diamonds in the Rough?

Over 44 kilograms of solid waste is produced everyday for each person in the United States. This includes by-products from agriculture, mining, and industry. Over 2.4 kilograms per person per day is collected by cities and towns. It is nearly impossible to dispose of these solid wastes. They are often dumped into landfills, lakes, and rivers.

Scientists are looking into the possibility of recovering the atoms and molecules from waste. After recovering them, they could be changed into new and useful things.

The most popular method for disposing of city waste is the sanitary landfill. However, there are few places where landfills can be located. For this reason, incineration (burning) is favored. Also, more than three-fourths of city waste is combustible. After burning, the mass and volume of waste materials is decreased about 75 percent. When burned under controlled conditions, glass, metal, and ash residue can be separated from the waste. Many of these materials can then be recycled.

Some incinerators are designed to produce steam. This steam drives turbines which produce electricity. It is estimated that ten to fifteen percent of electric power needed by the United States could come from this source. Solid city waste may prove to be an excellent energy source.

Adapted from "Solid Wastes: Diamonds in the Rough," *The Science Teacher*, February, 1976.

W. Keith Turpie

Many items such as glass, metal, and paper can be used over again.

Figure 2-16. Autoclaves, similar to pressure cookers, are used to sterilize equipment.

320 (32M) $P \propto \frac{1}{T}$ $\frac{P_1}{T_1} = \frac{P_2}{T_2}$ HEAT AND ITS USES

Gay-Lussac's (gay luh SAKS) **law** states that the pressure of a gas increases as the temperature increases, if the volume is not changed. A kitchen pressure cooker can build up pressure to two or three atmospheres. Heating increases the pressure of water vapor inside the cooker. Increases in pressure due to high temperatures have caused accidental explosions of steam boilers. Why do tire blowouts occur most often on hot days at high speeds? Heat increases air pressure inside the tire. General Gas Law combines all three:

$$\frac{P_1 V_1}{T_1} = \frac{P_2 V_2}{T_2}$$

2:4 Refrigeration

Ice is used in cold drinks and picnic coolers. Ice is also used to keep food cold in some storage plants. Ice cools things because it takes on heat from its surroundings. When ice melts, each gram of ice can absorb 80 calories of heat without a change in temperature. This figure is called the **heat of fusion** for ice.

Figure 2-17.

Time: 25 minutes.

ACTIVITY. CAUTION: This activity should be done under the direct supervision of your teacher. Wear eye protection.

Place a few drops of alcohol on your skin. How does it make your skin feel? Explain. Place a mixture of water and ether in a vacuum bottle. Stir the mixture rapidly. What do you observe? Explain.
— Skin feels cool because alcohol absorbs heat as it evaporates.
— Evaporating ether absorbs enough heat from the water to make it freeze.

Evaporation of a liquid is a cooling process. When ethyl alcohol evaporates, it gains 204 calories of heat per gram. During evaporation, ether takes heat from its surroundings and makes them cooler. A gram of ether takes on 89 calories when it evaporates. Evaporation of ether can cause water to freeze by absorbing heat from the water.

Refrigerators, freezers, and air conditioners operate by evaporation. A gas called a *refrigerant* (rih FRIJ ruhnt) is circulated through pipes in the cooling unit. Ammonia (NH_3) is most often used in large freezers. Freon, an organic compound, is used in home freezers and air conditioners. Carbon dioxide (CO_2) can also be used as a refrigerant.

The ammonia gas in a freezer is compressed by a pump called a compressor. To compress means to squeeze into a smaller space. As the ammonia gas is compressed, a fan blows cool air across the compressor. Compression and cooling cause a change in phase. The

Figure 2-18. Freon gas is compressed and cooled in a compressor. As liquid freon is pumped through the coils, it warms up and returns to the gaseous phase. The freon gas then returns to the compressor and goes through the same process again.

ammonia gas becomes a liquid. Liquid ammonia is pumped through pipes in the freezer. As the liquid ammonia circulates, the pressure on it decreases. The ammonia evaporates. Each gram of liquid ammonia absorbs 320 calories of heat as it changes from a liquid to a gas. The freezer cabinet is cooled as it loses heat to the evaporating ammonia.

How does a freezer work?

2:5 Heat Engines

Engines change heat energy into mechanical energy. The mechanical energy does work. Hero's engine, steam engines, gasoline engines, and diesel engines are examples of engines that do work. Each uses the heat from a burning fuel and the pressure of hot gases. Gasoline and diesel engines are called internal combustion engines. This means the combustion or burning of fuel occurs inside the engine.

How do engines produce power?

The Hero's engine in Figure 2–19 operates by action-reaction forces. An action force is a force exerted on an object. A reaction force is an opposite force that the object exerts. The action force of steam out of the jet causes an equal and opposite reaction force. The reaction force causes the engine to spin around in a circle.

Figure 2-19. Hero's engine operates on the same principle as a jet engine. This illustrates Newton's third law of motion — action-reaction forces.

Most gasoline engines burn gasoline vapor inside cylinders. In most automobile engines there are 4, 6, or 8 cylinders. Each cylinder has a piston that can move up and down. Burning fuel produces an explosion of hot gases inside the cylinder above the piston (Figure 2–20). These gases push against the pistons. The force of the hot gas makes the pistons go up and down. Force and motion result, and work is done.

A gasoline engine has a carburetor. The carburetor supplies the gasoline-air mixture to the cylinder. Gases enter and leave the cylinder through openings called valves. Find the intake and exhaust valve in Figure 2-20. The spark plug produces an electric spark which ignites the fuel.

In a four-cycle engine, the piston inside a cylinder makes four strokes in its cycle:

intake stroke—piston moves downward and a mixture of gas and air comes into the cylinder through the intake valve

compression stroke—piston moves upward and compresses the fuel and air mixture within the cylinder; at the completion of the compression stroke, the spark plug fires and the fuel mixture burns almost instantly

power stroke—pressure of hot gases produced by combustion forces the piston downward; this stroke gives the force that drives the car wheels

exhaust stroke—piston moves upward and expels exhaust gases through the exhaust valve

In a four-cycle engine, the four strokes in a cycle are repeated about 25 times per second. The pistons are connected to a rotating rod called a crankshaft. The crankshaft is connected to a driveshaft. As the pistons move up and down, they rotate the crankshaft which turns the driveshaft. The driveshaft extends underneath the car to the rear wheels. It turns the rear wheels. They, in turn, push against

Figure 2-20. Gasoline engines use burning gas to produce an explosion which moves the pistons up and down.

HEAT ENGINES

the ground and exert the force to move the car. Where would the driveshaft be connected in a front-wheel drive car?

A gasoline engine has a low efficiency. Only 25 percent of the fuel it burns is changed to power. Much of the fuel goes out through the exhaust pipe in the form of unburned hydrocarbons. Also, the engine emits carbon dioxide (CO_2), carbon monoxide (CO), and oxides of nitrogen (NO, NO_2). The wastes from a gasoline engine make it a source of pollution. Wastes from the engine are acted on by sunlight to form *photochemical smog*. Most large cities have polluted air due partly to large amounts of automobile pollutants.

How efficient is a gasoline engine?

PROBLEM

5. What are car manufacturers doing to reduce or eliminate engine fuel wastes? What suggestions do you have? See Teacher's Guide.

A Wankel rotary engine is a gasoline engine that does not use pistons. At the center of the engine there is a triangular rotor. The rotor is a metal part that rotates in a chamber shaped like a figure eight. There is an intake valve, exhaust valve, and two spark plugs. As the rotor rotates, gas is taken in, compressed, burned, and forced out through the exhaust valve. Explosion of the gas produces power as in a piston engine.

A small Wankel engine can produce as much power as a large piston engine. Also, it runs smoother with less vibration. The use of Wankel engines may reduce automobile pollution. Because of its smaller size, the Wankel engine can be equipped with smog control devices and not become too large and heavy for use in automobiles.

Mazda Motors of America

Figure 2-21. Wankel engines can produce as much power as large piston engines.

Figure 2-22. Operation of a rotary engine: (a) fuel and air mixture enters rotary, (b) turning rotary compresses mixture, (c) spark plugs ignite compressed mixture, (d) exhaust gases exit rotary.

Why can a gas turbine be more efficient than a gasoline engine?

Turbine engines may be more efficient but, in airplanes at least, they still produce considerable amounts of pollution.

A gas turbine can be more efficient than a gasoline engine. It has fewer moving parts and less vibration. Fuel and air are compressed in a turbine and burned. The pressure of hot gases against the turbine blades makes the drive shaft rotate (Figure 2–24).

Figure 2-23. Turbines in electric power plants change heat energy (steam) into electric energy.

Rochester Gas and Electric Company

Figure 2-24. In a gas turbine, air and gas are mixed and then ignited.

The Stirling engine is an experimental source of power. Although it was developed many years ago, there is now new interest in it. It is more efficient and produces less pollution than a gasoline engine.

The main part of this engine is a sealed cylinder. This cylinder contains either helium or hydrogen gas. The engine operates by heating, then cooling, the gas. The gas is heated at the beginning of the cycle. A heater is found on the outside of the cylinder. This heater provides extra heat by burning a fuel such as kerosene. The gas is then cooled by another device found outside the main cylinder. The alternate pressure changes cause a power piston to move back and forth inside the cylinder. This action produces the power.

Figure 2-25. Stirling engines operate by heating, then cooling a gas. Pressure changes cause the power piston to move back and forth. This results in the power needed to operate a vehicle.

2:6 Thermal Pollution

Engines, turbines, furnaces, electric lamps, and stoves give off heat. All the energy we use—light, electricity, chemical energy, mechanical energy—ends up as heat. Heat is the end product from the energy we use each day. Much of this heat is wasted. It goes off into the atmosphere.

How can heat be used rather than wasted? Waste heat could be used to desalinate (dee SAL uh nayt) salt water. Desalinate means to take the salt out of salt water. The salt water is distilled by heating it. Through evaporation and condensation, salt is separated from the water. Desalinated water from the ocean can be used for drinking, washing, and farming.

Waste heat from power plants could also be used to heat greenhouses for plant production. Someday the growing season on farms may be lengthened through the use of irrigation water heated by waste heat from power plants. Another idea would be to use waste heat to melt the ice in harbors normally closed in winter.

What other ways can you think of to utilize "waste" heat? Answers will vary.

Electric power plants use heat to make steam and generate electricity. Power plants and many other industries must discharge waste heat. Often this is done by using water to cool machinery. The hot water is then dumped into a nearby river, lake, or ocean. Heat may increase plant growth and may cause the water to become clogged with slimy growths of green algae. The water may become so hot that fish are killed off. Most fish cannot survive drastic changes in water temperature. Brook trout, for example, can live only 30 minutes at 28°C and only 12 hours at an average 25°C.

An increased supply of phosphates from detergents and fertilizers as well as elevated temperatures make conditions favorable for algae blooms.

Dumping heated water into lakes, rivers, and oceans produces **thermal pollution.** Water temperatures in some rivers have been recorded as high as 48°C. More than 200 trillion liters of warm water are discharged from electric power plants in the United States each year.

How do cooling towers reduce thermal pollution? Excess heat in atmosphere may be hazardous, also. Pollution abatement is very much a system of trade-offs. We should try to dump wastes where they cause the least damage at least over a short time. Much more research is necessary to even determine how pollution affects the environment.

Cooling towers are one solution to thermal pollution. Hot water from a power plant or factory is cooled to air temperature as it flows through pipes in the tower. After the water is air cooled, it is discharged into a nearby body of water. Because the water is cooled, it does not have a harmful effect on water life. There is no thermal pollution of the water. The excess heat is released into the air.

U.S. Department of The Interior, Office of Saline Water

Figure 2-26. Salt water is distilled by heating. One source of heat needed for this process could be the waste heat from some industries.

CRYOGENICS

PROBLEM

6. Industry is important to the growth of a country. It also can have some harmful effects. Compare the good and the bad points of industrial growth. See Teacher's Guide.

2:7 Cryogenics

When matter is cooled to very low temperatures, its properties change. For example, metals become better electrical conductors when they are cooled. As a substance is cooled, it loses heat. Molecules in the substance vibrate more slowly and take on a more orderly pattern.

Cryogenics (kry uh JEN iks) is the study of physical and chemical properties at very low temperatures. Cryogenic temperatures are usually indicated on the Kelvin temperature scale. On the Kelvin temperature scale, 0° is absolute zero. *Absolute zero* is the lowest temperature to which a substance can be cooled. In theory, it is the temperature at which all molecular motion stops. Zero degrees Kelvin (0°K) is equivalent to −273°C. Cryogenic temperatures are about 90°K (−183°C) or colder.

One method for producing very low temperatures is to use liquids that are gases at room temperature. Oxygen, nitrogen, and helium are gases that can be compressed and cooled to liquid form. In liquid form, they are used to cool many substances.

Helium can be compressed and cooled to form a liquid at 4°K (−269°C). The liquid helium is kept in insulated containers built like vacuum bottles. Even lower temperatures are reached by allowing the helium to evaporate. Remember, evaporation is a cooling process. In a vacuum, the liquid helium cools to an even lower temperature.

Liquid helium cooled below 2.2°K shows a very unusual property. The thickness (viscosity) of the helium liquid decreases greatly. It flows easily from place to place. The helium will flow up the sides of its container and down the outside. No force is needed to push it. It can flow through cracks not visible to the unaided eye. Helium in this unusual state is called a *superfluid*.

Liquid helium is used in refrigeration. For example, it is used to cool metals to extremely low temperatures. When supercooled, metals can hold an electrical current for unusually long lengths of time. They become *superconductors*. Supercooled metals can be used to make *supermagnets*. A supermagnet can hold its magnetism forever.

Cryogenics is also used in the medical field. Preservation of cells, tissues, and whole organs is a current area of research. Tissues can

Figure 2-27. Zero degrees Kelvin is equal to −273° Celsius.

Define cryogenics.

How are very low temperatures produced?

Figure 2-28. Superconducting magnets have low temperatures. Liquid helium is often used to produce these low temperatures.

Ken Kay

be preserved by freezing, stored, and later thawed for use in research. Whole blood, cooled to the temperature of liquid nitrogen, can be preserved for more than two years. Donated human eye corneas can be stockpiled by freezing. They are later thawed and made available for cornea transplants. Liquid nitrogen is also used in the treatment of skin disorders. It reduces the size of scars, removes warts, and clears up severe acne.

Students might like to report on some low-temperature effects such as superconductivity and superfluidity.

PROBLEM

See Teacher's Guide.

7. What are some of the medical uses of cryogenics?

MAIN IDEAS

2:1 1. The amount of heat lost or gained by a body is equal to mass times change in temperature times specific heat.

2:1 2. Water has a high specific heat (1 cal/g-C°). It can absorb or release more heat than most substances.

2:2 3. Water in a hot water heating system travels by convection.

2:2 4. Steam heating systems usually supply more heat than hot water systems.

2:2 5. The bimetallic strip in a thermostat serves as a switch in an electric circuit. Changes in temperature cause the switch to go on and off.

2:4 6. Evaporation is a cooling process.

HEAT AND ITS USES

2:5 **7.** Engines convert heat energy into mechanical energy. Engines do work.

2:6 **8.** Thermal pollution results from dumping heated water into a lake, river, or ocean. This can be remedied by the use of cooling towers.

2:7 **9.** Properties of a substance change when the substance is cooled to very low temperatures.

2:7 **10.** At very low temperatures, some metals can hold an electrical current for unusual lengths of time. They become superconductors.

VOCABULARY

Write a sentence in which you correctly use each of the following words or terms.

barometer	heat of condensation	superfluid
Boyle's law	heat of fusion	temperature
Charles' law	photochemical smog	thermal pollution
cryogenics	pressure	thermostat
Gay-Lussac's law	specific heat	volume

STUDY QUESTIONS

A. True or False

Have students rewrite false statements to make the statements correct.

Determine whether each of the following sentences is true or false. (Do not write in this book.)

T **1.** Still air is a poor conductor of heat.

F **2.** The specific heat of iron is greater than that of water. *not*

T **3.** Evaporation is a cooling process.

F **4.** A hot water heating system is better than a steam heating system. *not*

F **5.** Cryogenics is the study of very ~~high~~ temperatures. *low*

F **6.** A barometer measures ~~the specific heat of a substance.~~ *air pressure*

F **7.** The most common refrigerant in household refrigerators is liquid ~~ammonia.~~ *freon*

F **8.** A rotary engine has ~~only two~~ pistons. *no*

F **9.** Absolute zero is ~~zero~~ degrees on the Celsius scale. *−273*

T **10.** A thermometer measures the amount of heat a substance contains.

Some questions in Parts B and C may have more than one correct answer. Only one answer is required.

B. Multiple Choice

Choose one word or phrase that correctly completes each of the following sentences. (Do not write in this book.)

1. A vacuum bottle is a good heat *(insulator, conductor, radiator)*.
2. In convection, heat is moved by *(conduction, currents, radiation)*.
3. If 10 g of water are heated from 15°C to 65°C, *(650, 800, 500)* calories are added.
4. Steam gives up *(540, 54, 80)* calories per gram when it condenses.
5. A *(thermostat, vacuum bottle, magnet)* has a bimetallic strip.
6. If a bar of metal is heated, its length *(increases, decreases, remains the same)*.
7. Absolute zero is *(0°C, 273°K, 0°K)*.
8. Evaporation *(cools, warms, does not change the temperature of)* a substance.
9. Cooling in a refrigerator occurs by *(evaporation, freezing, an increase in pressure)*.
10. Your body would experience most pressure *(on a water surface, on a mountaintop, under water)*.

C. Completion

Complete each of the following sentences with a word or phrase that will make the sentence correct. (Do not write in this book.)

reaction 1. A Hero's engine operates by action and _____ forces.
gases 2. Forces are produced in engines by expansion of hot _____ .
low 3. A gasoline engine has _____ efficiency.
exhaust 4. CO_2, CO, NO, NO_2, and unburned hydrocarbons are found in the _____ from gasoline engines.
less 5. A gas turbine creates _____ air pollution than a gasoline engine.
thermal 6. Cooling towers are used to decrease _____ pollution.
evaporation 7. Water may be desalinated by _____ and condensation.
compressed 8. Helium becomes a liquid when it is _____ and cooled.
0 9. A temperature of −273°C is _____ °K.
cryogenics 10. Freezing tissues for later use is a medical use of _____ .

See Teacher's Guide for answers to this section.

D. How and Why

1. How can thermal pollution be prevented?

HEAT AND ITS USES

2. Why does metal heat up faster than water? Give an example.
3. Why are fruit orchards often located near large bodies of water?
4. Compare the operations of a hot water system and a steam heating system.
5. How does a thermostat work?
6. How do the gas laws explain the properties of a gas?
7. Explain how a gasoline engine produces power.
8. How is a Wankel rotary engine different from a piston engine?
9. How can waste heat be used?
10. What happens to substances that are cooled to temperatures near absolute zero?

INVESTIGATIONS

See Teacher's Guide at the front of the book for answers and suggestions.

1. Write a report on the latest types of engines being developed. What fuels do they use? What are the advantages and disadvantages?
2. Obtain information about past ice ages and theories that explain the cyclical warming and cooling of the earth.
3. Visit a local refrigeration repair shop to learn how refrigeration units operate.
4. Look up and report on some recent advances in cryogenics.
5. There are several theories on how we shall heat our homes in the near future. One proposed method is drilling holes deep into the earth and using the earth's heat to generate electricity. Research and report on this method, geothermal power, as well as others.
6. Make a model of a turbine engine.

INTERESTING READING

Corbett, Scott, *What About the Wankel Engine?* New York, Four Winds Press/Scholastic Book Service, 1974.

Dark, Harris E., *The Wankel Rotary Engine: Introduction and Guide*. Bloomington, Ind., Indiana University Press, 1974.

Pierce, John R., "The Fuel Consumption of Automobiles." *Scientific American,* (January, 1975), p. 34.

Urquhart, David I., *The Refrigerator and How It Works*. New York, Henry Z. Walck, Inc., 1972.

Walker, Graham, "The Stirling Engine." *Scientific American,* (August, 1973), p. 80.

Ocean waves break on the shore and return to the ocean in the direction from which they came.   *Craig W. Kramer*

3 Waves

Chapter 3 discusses the transfer of energy by waves. The properties of waves are investigated and the electromagnetic spectrum is introduced.

GOAL: You will gain an understanding of the properties of waves and the electromagnetic spectrum.

Many things can be learned about waves by watching the ocean, a lake, or a stream. Wave frequency can be determined by counting the number of waves which break upon the shore or slap against a rock. What is another way to determine wave frequency?

The patterns produced by a wave give clues about how they are made. Circular waves which spread out forming larger and even larger circles can be formed from a falling stone. How do you think waves in the ocean are formed?

WAVES (45M) 333

3:1 Waves

Have you ever watched waves in an ocean or lake? The waves travel forward as the water moves up and down. When a wave passes a point in the water, the water molecules move up and down. **Waves** are rhythmic disturbances which travel through space or matter such as air, water, and metal.

> Time: 25 minutes.
> ACTIVITY. Take a rope about 4.5 m long and tie one end to a doorknob. Hold the other end of the rope with your hand. Shake it up and down so waves begin to form. Make a diagram of the shape of the waves produced.
> Shake the end of a long "Slinky" coil spring so waves travel the length of the spring. How are these waves different from the waves you made with the rope?
> *compressional waves rather than transverse waves*

Figure 3-1.

A wave consists of a hill and a valley (Figure 3–2). The hill is called the *crest*. The valley is called the *trough* (TRAHF). The distance between the crest of one wave and the crest of the next wave is the *wavelength*. *Amplitude* (AM pluh tood) is the distance a wave rises or falls from its usual rest position.

Define wave crest, trough, amplitude, and wavelength.

Figure 3-2. Amplitude depends on the amount of energy which creates the wave. The greater the wave energy, the larger the amplitude.

Figure 3-3. Ripples or waves represent the kinetic energy of water.

Increase the distance you move the end of the rope when making a wave.

Vibrations produce waves in solids, liquids, and gases.

How is a transverse wave different from a compressional wave?

Amplitude depends on the amount of energy which creates the wave. As the wave energy increases, the amplitude increases. For example, if you drop a large rock instead of a pebble into a pond, a bigger wave results. The amplitude is greater. How can you produce waves of large amplitude with a rope?

Waves formed by water or a rope are transverse waves. In a transverse (tranz VUHRS) wave, matter vibrates at right angles to the direction in which the wave travels. *Vibrate* means to move back and forth rapidly. In a water wave, the water molecules vibrate vertically. The wave travels horizontally. Light, heat, and radio waves are examples of transverse waves.

Waves can be produced in a coil spring by pinching together several coils and then releasing them. Parts of the spring move to and fro in a rhythm. At times, the particles of matter in the wave

Figure 3-4. Areas of rarefaction alternate with areas of compression throughout the spring. This is one characteristic of a sound wave.

Area of rarefaction   Area of compression

334 (46M)

WAVES

are compressed together. At other times, they are moved farther apart. This wave is called a compressional (kuhm PRESH uhn uhl) or longitudinal (lahn juh TOOD nuhl) wave. **In a compressional wave,** matter vibrates in the same direction as the wave travels. Sound waves are one type of compressional wave.

> Time: 10 minutes.
> ACTIVITY. Obtain a "Slinky" toy or a large spring. Place the "Slinky" or spring on a level surface. Squeeze six or seven loops together. Release. Observe what happens. What type of wave results? Repeat. In what direction does the wave move?

In a compressional wave in a coil spring, each area in which the coils are pushed together is an *area of compression.* When the coils are spread apart, the area is an *area of rarefaction* (rar uh FAK shuhn). Each part of the spring is alternately compressed and rarefied as a compressional wave travels through it. The spring vibrates in the same direction as the wave travels.

The blue curve in Figure 3–6 represents a transverse wave. It can also represent a compressional wave. The upward curve represents one complete compression. The downward curve shows one complete rarefaction. The *wavelength* of a compressional wave is the distance from one compression to the next compression.

Courtesy of Kodansha, Ltd.

Figure 3-5. Compressional waves travel from the right along a slinky which is held horizontally. The compressional wave in a spring is similar to a sound wave.

What is an area of rarefaction?

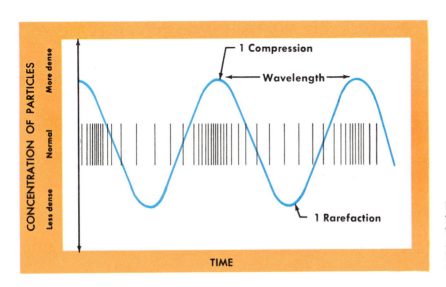

Figure 3-6. Air does not travel forward as a sound wave passes through it. As the wave passes a point, air compresses and expands.

Figure 3-7. What determines the shape of a wave trace made by a tuning fork?

amplitude of vibration and frequency

What is frequency?

3:2 Wave Frequency

All waves have a certain frequency. **Frequency** (FREE kwuhn see) is the number of waves that pass a given point in a given unit of time. Suppose you throw a pebble into a pond. Three wave crests caused by the disturbance go by a stationary rock in 15 seconds. What is the wave frequency? The wave frequency is three waves per 15 seconds, or one wave per 5 seconds $\left(\dfrac{3 \text{ waves}}{15 \text{ sec}} = \dfrac{1 \text{ wave}}{5 \text{ sec}}\right)$. As the number of waves that pass a given point per unit of time increases, the frequency also increases.

Have you ever stood on a pier and watched water waves pass underneath? The number of waves that pass per unit of time is the wave frequency. The longer the wave, the more time it takes to pass a given point. The shorter the wave, the less time it takes to pass a given point.

Figure 3-8.

Time: 20 minutes.
ACTIVITY. Hold one end of a thin strip of metal in your hand. Place the other end in a pan of water. Vibrate the metal strip so waves are produced. How do the waves behave? Count the number of waves that strike the side of the pan in 30 sec. What is the frequency? Obtain a tuning fork and hold it by the stem. Tap it lightly so the prongs vibrate. Dip the vibrating prongs into a pan of water. What happens? Explain your observations. *vibrations set up in water*

You can project the waves produced if you use a flat, clear glass dish set on an overhead projector. The waves will project onto a wall or screen.

Have you ever watched a floating cork or bottle? What happens when a wave passes through the water? The cork moves up and down. The number of up and down movements of the cork in a given unit of time is the wave frequency.

How is wavelength related to frequency?

$\lambda \propto \dfrac{1}{f}$, inverse variation. As wavelength increases frequency decreases.

Figure 3-9. These two waves have the same amplitude but different frequencies. What is the frequency of each?

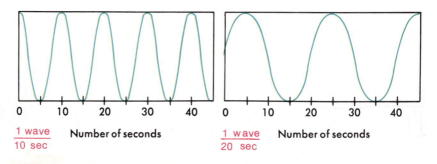

SOUND WAVES

Wavelength and frequency vary inversely. Vary inversely means that as one value increases, the other decreases. If you double the wavelength, the frequency is halved. If you double the frequency, the wavelength is halved. Long waves have a low frequency. Short waves have a high frequency.

Problems

1. A cork floating on water moves up and down 10 times in 30 sec. What is the frequency of the water wave? 0.3 vib/sec
2. A tuning fork produces a sound of musical note middle C. It moves back and forth 256 times each second. What is the frequency of the tuning fork? 256 vib/sec

Figure 3-10. Sound waves produced by vibrations are to-and-fro movements of particles of matter. They may be detected by the ear.

3:3 Sound Waves

When a bell or the prongs of a tuning fork vibrate, they produce sound waves. When a person speaks, vibrations of his vocal cords produce sound waves. **Sound waves are compressional waves produced by vibrations. Sound waves move through air or other matter.** They may be detected by the ear and certain sensitive electrical instruments. For example, a telephone mouthpiece can detect sound waves. The telephone converts sound waves into electrical waves which carry the message over telephone lines.

What are sound waves?

A metal disc or diaphragm inside the telephone mouthpiece vibrates when it is struck by sound waves.

General Dynamics Corporation

Figure 3-11. Microwave radio is used to transmit messages over distances without wires (a). The sound of a musical note is made up of many vibrations of different intensities (b).

Lee Boltin from Time-Life Library of Science © Time Inc.

> Time: 20 minutes.
>
> ACTIVITY. Obtain a glass pop bottle or narrow jar. Fill the glass container halfway with water. Blow across the top. Where is the sound wave produced, in the <u>air</u> or water?
>
> Stand on one side of the wall of your classroom. Place your ear next to the wall. Have another student tap on the wall with a stick while standing on the other side. How could a sound wave pass from one room to another? through the wall/ air space/ wall

> Time: 30 minutes.
>
> ACTIVITY. Mount an electric bell inside a bottle so that the bell can be connected to a dry cell outside. The bottle should be sealed with a one-hole stopper containing a piece of glass tubing. Attach a rubber tube to the glass tubing and connect it to a vacuum pump. Connect the bell so it rings. Then pump the air out of the bottle. Does the loudness of the sound increase, <u>decrease</u>, or remain the same?

Figure 3-13. Tuning forks are often used in the study of sound waves.

Figure 3-12.

Henry Groskinsky, Time-Life Picture Agency © Time Inc.

Sound cannot travel through empty space or a vacuum. The activity above shows this. It must have a substance or medium to go through. Sound waves produced by vibrations are to-and-fro movements of particles of matter. It is easy to transfer vibrations from molecule to molecule if the molecules are close together. The molecules of a solid are packed closely together. Therefore, sound waves move faster through solids than through liquids and gases. Do sound waves move faster through a <u>liquid</u> or a gas? Explain why.

The speed of sound in air at 0°C and one atmosphere pressure is 335 m/sec. For convenience, remember that the **speed of sound in**

The molecules are closer together.

Edward Young

Figure 3-14. Acoustics is the science of sound and its control. It is often used to solve problems of sound in buildings and amphitheaters.

air is about 340 m/sec. Sound travels through warm air faster than through cold air. Explain why. The speed of sound increases about 60 cm/sec for each Celsius degree rise in temperature. At 20°C sound travels through air at 344 m/sec.

Explain why sound cannot travel through a vacuum.
Sound is transmitted by the motion of molecules.

Molecules in warm air move much faster than in cold air. Thus, they bump into each other more often. This causes them to travel a greater distance in less time.

Table 3–1. Speed of Sound Through Various Substances

Air	340 m/sec
Water	1454 m/sec
Wood	3828 m/sec
Iron	5103 m/sec
Stone	5971 m/sec

3:4 Resonance, Wavelength, and Frequency

A tuning fork vibrates in only one frequency. Another tuning fork vibrating in the same frequency can cause the first tuning fork to begin vibrating spontaneously. This is called *sympathetic vibration*. The tuning fork vibrating and the fork which caused it to vibrate are said to be in **resonance** (REZ uhn uhnts). That is, they vibrate at the same frequency.

What is resonance?

Figure 3-15.

Time: 35 minutes.

ACTIVITY. Resonance may be used to find the wavelength of a sound wave. (1) Lower a glass tube (45 cm long, 2.5 cm in diameter) into a jar of water. Hold a vibrating tuning fork over the end of the tube. Meanwhile, change the length of the tube by moving it up and down in the water. When the air in the tube is in resonance with the tuning fork, the sound becomes much louder. Resonance results when the air in the tube vibrates at the same frequency as the tuning fork. (2) At the resonance point, measure the length of the air column in the tube above the water. The wavelength of the sound wave produced by the tuning fork is four times the length of the air column at resonance. Why is the sound louder when resonance occurs? Repeat this activity with a tuning fork of different frequency. Is the resonance column of air longer or shorter? Explain. Waves reflected back through the tube combine with and reinforce waves coming into the tube. Crest adds to crest and trough adds to trough, making the sound louder. Higher pitch sound has a shorter wavelength. Length of wave at resonance is four times the length of the air column.

How can you find the length of a sound wave?

The speed of sound can be used to calculate the wavelength of a sound wave. To find the wavelength, divide speed by frequency. Use the formula

$$\lambda = \frac{v}{f}$$

wavelength equals speed divided by frequency

EXAMPLE

What is the wavelength of sound waves that have a frequency of 43 vib/sec in air at 20°C?

Solution: (a) Write equation: $\lambda = \dfrac{v}{f}$

(b) Substitute 344 m/sec for v and 43 vib/sec for f:

$$\lambda = \frac{344 \text{ m/sec}}{43 \text{ vib/sec}}$$

(c) Divide 344 by 43 to find λ

(d) Answer. $\lambda = 8$ m/vib, or simply 8 m

PROBLEM

3. What is the wavelength of sound waves having a frequency of 256 vib/sec at 20°C? 1.32 m

To find the frequency of a sound wave, divide the speed by the wavelength. Use the equation

$$f = \frac{v}{\lambda}$$

frequency equals speed divided by wavelength

RESONANCE, WAVELENGTH, AND FREQUENCY   (53M)   341

PROBLEM

4. What is the frequency of a sound wave with a wavelength of 1 m at 0°C? 335 vib/sec

Time: 10 minutes.

ACTIVITY. Obtain three tuning forks. Strike each lightly to sound a tone. Why does each fork make a sound when struck? The frequency of vibrations is marked on each fork. Compare the frequency to the tone produced.

The human ear can detect a certain physical order in almost all the sounds considered musical. The frequencies of musical sounds have an arithmetic order and the frequencies of nonmusical sounds have no arithmetic order.

Notes made by a piano show the relationship between frequency and wavelength. Sound waves of different frequencies have different wavelengths. As frequency increases, wavelength decreases. When you strike the extreme right key of a piano, you produce sound waves of high frequency. Their wavelengths are about 7.7 cm long. Strike the extreme left key and you produce waves of low frequency. Their wavelengths are about 12.2 m.

Wave A and wave B have the same amplitude.

Figure 3-16. Wave B has a wavelength one-half that of wave A. The frequency of wave B is twice the frequency of wave A.

Problems

5. What is the frequency of sound waves which have wavelengths of 6 cm when the air temperature is 20°C? *5733 vib/sec*

6. What is the frequency of sound waves which have wavelengths of 12 m when the air temperature is 20°C? *28.7 vib/sec*

7. What is the frequency of sound waves which have wavelengths of 12 m when the air temperature is 25°C? *28.9 vib/sec*

8. At 20°C, sound travels 1.61 km in 5 sec. How far away is a lightning bolt if you hear the thunder 10 sec after you see the flash? *3.22 km*

Figure 3-17. Guitar strings can be made to vibrate rapidly or slowly.

Gary Walker

What determines the pitch of a string?

3:5 Pitch

Sounds produced by irregular vibrations are called *noise*. A musical sound is produced by matter vibrating in a regular fashion. Musical sounds may be made with a stringed instrument. To make music, the strings of the instrument must be made to vibrate. The frequency with which the string vibrates is called *pitch*.

In a guitar, all of the strings are the same length. Thin, tight strings produce high notes. Thick, loose strings produce low notes. The pitch of the sound produced is determined by the frequency of the sound waves. Sounds of high pitch have high frequencies. Sounds of low pitch have low frequencies.

Problem

9. How can a musician change the pitch of the sound made by a guitar string? *tightening or shortening it with fingers on the frets*

Figure 3-18.

Time: 30 minutes.

ACTIVITY. A wind instrument uses the length of an air column to change pitch. Obtain a test tube rack, water, medicine dropper, and 8 test tubes. Put different amounts of water in each test tube. Blow across the top of each tube to sound a musical note. Use the medicine dropper to adjust the level of water in each test tube so you can play the eight notes of a musical scale. Make a drawing of the test tubes showing the amount of water in each test tube.

PEOPLE CAREERS FRONTIERS
FOCUS ON PHYSICAL SCIENCE

Dr. Virginia Trimble
Astronomer

Dr. Virginia Trimble says that she became an astronomer by chance. She was not sure what she wanted to do until she went to college. She looked at an alphabetical list of courses and decided astronomy was what she wanted.

To become an astronomer, Dr. Trimble took many courses in astronomy, mathematics, and physics. She completed a bachelor of arts degree in three years. Later, she completed a Ph.D. degree at the California Institute of Technology in Pasadena. There, she studied the Crab Nebula. This nebula is an enormous cloud of gas that is expanding outward at 1610 km/hr.

Since graduating with a Ph.D. in astronomy, she has studied the life story of stars. Currently, Dr. Trimble is studying and forming theories on the origin and development of binary stars (double stars).

• • • • • • • • • • • • •

Courtesy of the American Association of Physics Teachers.

Dr. Trimble is preparing a paper she has written about the Crab Nebula.

Dr. Diana H. McSherry – Biophysicist

"I've developed a system that lets doctors see inside a person's body without hurting the patient in any way," says Dr. Diana McSherry.

This special system uses ultrasound waves plus computer processing to see inside the body. This is done instead of surgery which can be very painful. Doctors send a beam of ultrasound waves right into the problem area, such as the heart. The beam hits the heart and is reflected back out. The reflected beam forms an image of the heart. The unclear image then undergoes computer processing. This processing focuses the image into a clear picture.

Although Diana has developed a successful system, it did not happen overnight. It took years of experimenting and testing. In addition, many years of study were necessary before she became a biophysicist. Diana majored in physics in college and obtained a bachelor's degree. She also obtained a Ph.D. in nuclear physics.

• • • • • • • • • • • • •

Courtesy of the American Association of Physics Teachers.

Dr. McSherry looks at films resulting from the computer processing.

A musical scale is made up of several different pitches. Therefore, in playing the scale on a musical instrument, a musician changes pitch. The higher the note is on the scale, the higher its frequency. There are many different kinds of musical scales. A musical scale is based on the ratios between sound frequencies.

3:6 Volume

Which properties of a sound wave determine loudness and pitch?
amplitude and frequency

Some sounds are so loud they hurt your ears. The *loudness* of a sound is determined by the amplitude of the sound waves. As the amplitude of the sound waves increases, the loudness of the sound increases. Do you ever shout at a basketball or football game? When you yell you produce sounds with amplitudes larger than those of normal speech.

Two different sound waves may meet and interfere with each other. This **interference** (int uhr FIR uhnts) may be *destructive* or *constructive*. When the crest of one sound wave meets the trough of another sound wave, destructive interference takes place. The sound decreases in loudness and may disappear. When the crest of one sound wave meets the crest of another sound wave, constructive interference takes place. The sound increases in loudness. The same thing happens when two troughs meet.

Figure 3-19.

Time: 30 minutes.
   ACTIVITY. Have a classmate blow two whistles at the same time. How is the sound different from the sound made by one whistle? Obtain two tuning forks of the same frequency. The forks must be fastened to resonator boxes. First, sound the two forks together. Then attach several rubber bands tightly around one prong of one fork to decrease its frequency slightly. Sound the two forks again. The wavering sound is called a beat. Count the number of beats in 15 sec. Repeat the procedure, each time increasing the number of rubber bands. How is the frequency of beats related to the difference in frequency of two sounds? Interference causes alternating reinforcement and destruction of sound waves. When is the sound volume loudest and lowest? The number of beats is equal to the difference in frequencies. Volume is loudest when waves are in phase (crest adds to crest and trough adds to trough) and lowest when out of phase (crest and trough cancel).

What is ultrasonic sound?

There are many sound waves all around you. Some you cannot hear. Most people hear compressional waves if their frequency is between about 20 vib/sec and about 20,000 vib/sec. Sounds above this frequency range are said to be **ultrasonic** (uhl truh SAHN ik).

Figure 3-20. Many dentists use ultrasonic drills.

The development of sonar was spurred by the need to detect icebergs and submarines. One kind of sonar system emits short sound pulses (0.1 sec) with a frequency ranging from 10,000 to 26,000 vib/sec.
Since the velocity of sound in seawater is 2400 km/sec the wavelengths of these sounds are from 5 to 13 centimeters.

William Maddox

Ultrasonic sounds cannot be heard by human beings. Some animals, however, can hear ultrasonic sounds. For example, a dog can hear sounds with frequencies up to 25,000 vib/sec.

At one time it was believed that the oceans were silent. Since the development of under-water sound detecting equipment it has been learned that all sorts of sea animals make grunts, whistles, cracks, rattles, and pops.

PROBLEMS

10. Why can some whistles be heard by dogs and not by people? *Dogs hear the ultrasonic vibrations.*
11. How does a bat use ultrasonic sound echoes to find its way through a dark cave? *Bats emit high frequency sound waves which reflect off objects.*
12. How can sonar sound waves be used in naval navigation? *Sonar waves are sent out from a ship. The echo of the wave from the bottom is timed.*

3:7 Ripple Tank

To study waves, a device known as a ripple tank is often used. A **ripple tank** is a shallow, transparent, waterproof box containing a layer of water one or two centimeters deep (Figure 3–21).

Waves produced in the ripple tank are models of sound, light, and other kinds of energy waves. Vibrations or disturbances in the center of the tank cause water waves to spread out in concentric circles. These ripple tank waves are two-dimensional. Sound waves, light waves, and other energy waves are three-dimensional. Energy waves

How is a ripple tank used to study waves?
Images of water waves in a ripple tank are produced on the screen below the glass bottom of the tank.

These images are produced because the crest of the waves act as converging (convex) lenses and tend to focus light from the lamp. The troughs act as diverging (concave) lenses and tend to spread the light out. The crests appear as light bands and the troughs appear as bright bands.

Figure 3-21. As waves move through the water in a ripple tank, their shadows make a pattern on the screen.

spread away from their source in a spherical pattern. The ripple tank gives us a two-dimensional idea of how a three-dimensional wave may act.

Energy waves appear to straighten out when far away from their source. They move in straight lines parallel to each other. To illustrate, waves in the ocean or on a large lake approach the shore parallel to each other. Because these waves are distant from their source, they no longer appear circular. However, the ripple tank is too small to show this change. A ripple tank does not permit circular waves to travel far enough to become parallel waves. Ripple tank waves and energy waves are not exactly alike. A model is never exactly like the real thing. However, a ripple tank will help in the study of waves.

3:8 Reflection

What is wave reflection?

A ripple tank can be used to investigate the reflection of waves. **Wave reflection** (rih FLEK shuhn) **occurs when a wave strikes an object and is bounced off in a different direction.** The waves that strike an object are called *incident waves*. The waves that bounce off the object are called *reflected waves* (Figure 3–22b). Reflection in a ripple tank can be seen by floating a piece of wood on the water. The wood serves as a barrier to the waves. When a stream of waves is generated, the waves strike the wooden barrier and bounce back in the direction from which they came (Figure 3–23a). The reflecting barrier can be set at an angle to the oncoming waves. Then the waves are reflected off the barrier at an angle.

Think of a wave as a straight line striking a wall at an angle. The angle between the wave and a line drawn normal to the wall is the

Figure 3-22. Vibrations at a point in the water produce circular waves (a). Waves which are reflected from a straight barrier keep a circular pattern (b).

Figure 3-23. When waves strike a barrier head-on, the waves bounce back in the direction from which they came (a). When waves strike a barrier at an angle, the waves are reflected off at the same angle (b). Make certain that students understand "normal" and that angles are measured from it.

angle of incidence (IN suh dents). It is angle *i* in Figure 3–23b. *Normal* to the wall means a line drawn perpendicular to the wall at the point where the wave strikes the wall. The angle between the reflected wave and the normal is the *angle of reflection*. It is labeled angle *r*.

angle of incidence equals angle of reflection

$$i = r$$

Time: 15 minutes.

ACTIVITY. Roll a ball so that it strikes a wall head-on. How was it reflected? [reflected straight back] Roll a ball toward the wall at an angle. How is it reflected? [reflected at the same angle] Repeat. Chalkmark the path of the ball in both cases. Identify the angles of incidence and reflection.

Time: 90 minutes.

ACTIVITY. How are water waves reflected in a ripple tank? (1) Set up a ripple tank as shown in Figure 3–21. Touch the water with your finger and observe the waves on the screen. Release drops of water into the tank from a medicine dropper and observe the wave pattern on the screen. Generate straight wave pulses by rolling a dowel in the water. Practice until you get sharp wave images on the screen. (2) Place a wooden block in the center of the tank; then produce waves with the dowel which strike the block at 0°. Then vary the position of the block so as to reflect waves at different angles. (3) Bend a rubber tube so it forms a curve across one end of the tank (Figure 3–24). Use the tube as a reflector for the waves you generate with the dowel.

How does the angle of incidence of the waves compare with the angle of reflection? How is reflection from the hose different from the wooden block? [Angle of incidence = angle of reflection. Waves reflected off the block are parallel. Waves reflected from the hose are curved and focus at a point in front of the hose. Both the waves in the tank and electromagnetic waves can be reflected and refracted.]

Figure 3-24.

3:9 Refraction

What is refraction?

Refraction (rih FRAK shuhn) is the bending of waves. You can study refraction in a ripple tank.

> Time: 50 minutes.
> ACTIVITY. Set up a ripple tank. Place a flat glass plate (about 12 cm × 18 cm) on some metal washers at one end of the tank. Adjust the plate so that its upper surface is about 1 mm below the water surface. This makes the water above the plate very shallow. The plate should be parallel to waves generated at the opposite end of the tank. Generate waves with a wooden dowel (Figure 3–25). Observe the wave path over the glass plate. Now set the plate so that its edge is at a 45° angle to the waves. Repeat the wave generation and observe the wave path over the glass plate. What change occurs?

Figure 3-25.

As water waves pass into shallow water, their wavelength becomes shorter and their velocity decreases. Why? Remember the equation $v = \lambda f$? Speed equals wavelength times frequency. If the frequency (f) stays the same and the wavelength (λ) becomes smaller, the speed (v) must decrease. This is what happens to water waves as they pass from deep to shallow water. In the activity, you see the wavelength of the waves decrease over the glass plate. Therefore, you can assume the velocity of the waves decreases.

How is refraction studied in a ripple tank?

When waves pass into shallow water at an angle, the waves are bent, or refracted (Figure 3–26). Refraction occurs because one

Figure 3-26. Waves are refracted as they pass at an angle into shallow water.

side of the wave passes from deep to shallow water before the rest of the wave. This side of the wave is slowed down. With one side going slow and one side going fast, the wave curves. It is refracted toward the slow side.

Refraction always occurs toward the area in which the speed of a wave slows down. This principle of refraction may be explained by a comparison. Suppose two small wheels are mounted on an axle. As they roll across a tabletop, one wheel reaches a soft velvet cloth and is slowed down by friction. The other wheel continues at its faster speed. It is pulled toward the slower wheel. The change in speed of the wheel on the cloth causes a change in direction of the wheels and axle. The wheels turn toward the soft cloth, the area in which speed is decreased.

Any type of wave can be refracted. Whenever a wave passes from one substance to another substance, its speed changes. If the wave approaches the boundary between two substances at an angle, it is refracted.

Explain how a wave is refracted.

Figure 3-27. Waves are refracted when their speed decreases.

Figure 3-28. As a high speed racing car approaches, the sound of the motor increases in pitch. As it passes and continues down the track, the pitch of the motor decreases. This is known as the Doppler effect.

PROBLEMS

Sound waves are refracted because they change speed when passing from one medium to another. That portion of the wave front which enters first, changes first and causes the rest of the wave front to refract (turn). Thus, the direction of the wave front changes.

13. Sound waves may be refracted when they pass from a solid into a gas. Why?
14. Sound waves may also be refracted when they pass from warm air into cold air, or from cold air into warm air. Why?

See Teacher's Guide.

3:10 Doppler Effect

Explain the Doppler effect.

Pitch and frequency are related. The pitch of a sound is determined by its frequency. The higher the frequency, the higher the pitch. A change in pitch can be caused by the Doppler (DAHP luhr) effect. **The Doppler effect is a change in wave frequency caused by the motion of the wave source.** For example, sound from the siren of an approaching police car increases in pitch. Why? As the car approaches, its movement crowds the siren sound waves together. This causes a higher wave frequency and higher pitch. As the car passes by and moves away, the pitch of the sound you hear decreases. The sound waves are now farther apart. Both frequency and pitch of the waves decreases.

The Doppler effect may also be produced if the observer moves toward the source of sound. If you ride on a train moving toward a warning bell at a crossing, the sound of the clanging bell rises in pitch. Increasing pitch means that wave frequency is increasing and wavelength is decreasing.

Figure 3-29.

Time: 30 minutes.
ACTIVITY. Set up a ripple tank as described in Section 3:7. Make waves with a vibrating metal strip. Move the metal strip forward slowly while it vibrates. Observe the wavelengths in front and in back of the moving strip.

Figure 3-30. To demonstrate this example of the Doppler effect, swing a toy whistle rapidly around on a string.

The Doppler effect has been used to support the theory that the universe is expanding. Light from distant stars has longer wavelengths than light from nearby stars. This phenomenon is explained by the movement of these stars away from us at tremendous speeds.

By traveling in a small boat, you can witness an effect similar to the Doppler effect. If you travel against the waves, they strike the boat with a relatively high frequency. The ride may be very choppy. If you travel with the waves, they catch up to the boat more slowly. The frequency with which the waves strike the boat is relatively low.

One practical use of the Doppler effect is in radar speed-detecting devices. Radar waves are sent out and reflected back from a moving car to a receiver. Changes in frequency of the radar waves are caused by the car moving toward the receiver. The change in frequency is converted to speed in miles or kilometers per hour by the radar receiver. In this way, it is possible to detect vehicles traveling faster than legal speed limits.

William Maddox

Figure 3-31. Police cars are often equipped with radar devices.

351 (63M)

3:11 Electromagnetic Spectrum

What kinds of waves are in the electromagnetic spectrum?

There are waves all around you. Many are invisible—radio, television, radar, infrared, ultraviolet, X-ray, and gamma-ray waves. Infrared waves are radiant heat. Gamma rays are one kind of nuclear radiation.

How are the waves in the electromagnetic spectrum similar to and different from each other?

Each kind of wave has a different wavelength and frequency. They range from low to high frequency. Arranged in order of their wavelength and frequency, the waves form an **electromagnetic spectrum** (ih lek troh mag NET ik · SPEK truhm). The term electromagnetic comes from the fact that these waves can be produced by electricity or magnetism.

All of the waves which make up the electromagnetic spectrum are transverse waves. These waves can pass through space. All electromagnetic waves travel at the speed of light, 300,000,000 m/sec, in a vacuum.

Figure 3-32. Film, which is sensitive to infrared rays, is often used to study the earth. This photo, taken from a satellite, shows the vegetation (in red) of the New Orleans area.

E.R.O.S. Data Center, U.S. Geological Survey

Figure 3-33. Nerve endings in the eye are sensitive to electromagnetic waves with wavelengths of 4×10^{-5} cm (violet light) to 7×10^{-5} cm (red light). This is known as visible light.

You may wish to introduce angstrom as a unit for measuring wavelength.

Wavelengths range from 10^{12} cm (electric waves) to 10^{-14} cm (cosmic rays). Therefore, frequencies range from very low to very high. The longer the wavelength—the lower the frequency. The shorter the wavelength—the higher the frequency. Waves with the highest frequencies have the greatest amount of wave energy.

MAIN IDEAS

3:1 **1.** Wavelength, frequency, and amplitude are three properties of a wave.

3:1 **2.** There are two kinds of waves—transverse and compressional.

3:1, 3:3 **3.** A sound wave is a kind of compressional wave which travels through matter.

3:4 **4.** Wavelength and frequency vary inversely. Long waves have a low frequency. Short waves have a high frequency.

3:5 **5.** The pitch of a sound depends on wave frequency.

3:7 **6.** Models of energy waves can be produced in a ripple tank and projected on a screen.

3:8 **7.** For a reflected wave, the angle of incidence equals the angle of reflection.

3:9 **8.** Refraction is the bending of waves passing from one substance to another.

3:9 **9.** When a wave passes from one substance to another substance, its velocity changes.

3:10 **10.** The Doppler effect is a change in wave frequency caused by the motion of the wave source.

3:11 **11.** Electromagnetic waves are transverse waves capable of traveling in a vacuum at the speed of light.

3:11 **12.** Different energy waves in the electromagnetic spectrum differ in wavelength and frequency.

VOCABULARY

Write a sentence in which you correctly use each of the following words or terms.

amplitude	interference	transverse wave
compressional wave	noise	ultrasonic
Doppler effect	pitch	vibration
electromagnetic spectrum	reflection	wave
	refraction	wavelength
frequency	resonance	

STUDY QUESTIONS

Have students rewrite false statements to make the statements correct.

A. True or False

Determine whether each of the following sentences is true or false. (Do not write in this book.)

T **1.** Sound travels in compressional waves.

T **2.** The pitch of a sound wave depends on its frequency.

decreases F **3.** When frequency increases, wavelength ~~increases~~.

T **4.** Short waves usually have a relatively high frequency.

cannot F **5.** Sound waves ₍travel ~~easily~~ through a vacuum.

T **6.** Resonance is an example of sympathetic vibration.

Wave amplitude F **7.** ~~Frequency~~ determines the loudness of a sound wave.

above 20,000 F **8.** Sound waves having a frequency ~~below 200~~ vib/sec are called ultrasonic.

not F **9.** Most people can ₍hear sound with frequencies above 20,000 vib/sec.

do not F **10.** All visible light waves ₍have the same wavelength.

WAVES (67M) 355

B. Multiple Choice

Some questions in Parts B and C may have more than one correct answer. Only one answer is required.

Choose one word or phrase that correctly completes each of the following sentences. (Do not write in this book.)

1. Sound waves are *(transverse, compressional, visible)* waves.
2. A light wave is a(n) *(transverse, compressional, invisible)* wave.
3. The number of vibrations/unit time is *(wavelength, frequency, velocity)*.
4. As frequency increases, wavelength *(increases, decreases, remains the same)*.
5. The loudness of a sound is determined by *(amplitude, wavelength, frequency)*.
6. A sound with a frequency of 25,000 vib/sec *(has a long wavelength, cannot be heard by human beings, has a high velocity)*.
7. To produce a wave in a ripple tank, *(turn on a lamp, put water in the tank, make a vibration in the water)*.
8. When a wave is reflected, its wavelength *(increases, decreases, remains the same)*.
9. The law of reflection states that the angle of incidence and the angle of reflection *(are equal, vary inversely, vary directly)*.
10. The amount that a wave is refracted depends upon the *(velocity, change in velocity, frequency)*.

C. Completion

Complete each of the following sentences with a word or phrase that will make the sentence correct. (Do not write in this book.)

1. The Doppler effect is caused by a change in the _____ of a wave source. position or motion
2. The use of radar speed-detecting devices is an application of the _____. Doppler effect
3. All electromagnetic waves have the _____ velocity. same
4. _____ waves have the shortest wavelength in the electromagnetic spectrum. Cosmic
5. _____ waves have the highest frequency in the electromagnetic spectrum. Cosmic
6. Sound waves move faster through _____ than _____. glass, air (answers may vary)
7. To produce refraction in a ripple tank, change the _____ of the water waves. speed

frequency **8.** An increase in the pitch of a sound results from an increase in the _____ of the sound.

Waves **9.** _____ are rhythmic disturbances which travel through matter or space.

same **10.** Matter vibrates in the _____ direction as a compressional travels.

D. How and Why

See Teacher's Guide for diagram. **1.** A wave approaches a flat barrier at an angle of 25°. Draw a diagram to show the angle of incidence and the angle of reflection for the wave.

5 waves/sec **2.** A ripple tank wave generator produces 15 waves in 3 seconds. What is the wave frequency?

speed changes so they are refracted **3.** What happens to water waves traveling from shallow to deep water?

See Teacher's Guide. **4.** How is a transverse wave different from a compressional wave? Name two examples of each kind of wave.

It cannot be done. **5.** How can you attract the attention of a friend standing 90 m away without using energy waves?

See Teacher's Guide for diagram. **6.** Draw a diagram of a wave and label the wavelength and amplitude. Draw a second diagram of a wave with a greater frequency than the first wave.

See Teacher's Guide. **7.** What is the electromagnetic spectrum?

See Teacher's Guide. **8.** How are infrared waves different from red light waves? How are ultraviolet waves different from violet light waves? In what ways are infrared, red, ultraviolet, and violet light waves alike?

Move the rippler. **9.** How can you demonstrate the Doppler effect in a ripple tank?

600 m **10.** What is the wavelength in meters of a radio wave with a frequency of 540,000 vib/sec?

See Teacher's Guide at the front of the book for answers and suggestions.

INVESTIGATIONS

1. When studying the stars, scientists frequently refer to the "red shift." Do library research and report on this topic.

2. Research and report on the history of radar.

3. Obtain an 8-mm motion picture camera and make a short film of waves at the seashore. Picture different kinds of wave motion and the effects of waves. Show the film and make a report to your class.

4. Find photos of waves in old magazines. Set up a display with drawings and pictures that illustrate properties of water waves. Investigate the factors that cause the production of waves most suitable for water surfing.

5. Obtain information on acoustics. Learn how auditoriums and other buildings are designed with sound in mind.

6. Sound travels about 1.6 km in 5 sec. During a thunderstorm, time the interval between the flash of lightning you see and the thunder you hear. Be sure to remain indoors when you make your observations. Calculate the average distance of each lightning bolt. Average your results.

INTERESTING READING

Bamberger, Richard, *Physics Through Experiments*. New York, Sterling Press, 1969.

Bascom, Willard, *Waves and Beaches: The Dynamics of the Ocean Surface*. New York, Doubleday & Company, Inc., 1964.

Stevens, S. S., and Warshofsky, Fred, *Sound and Hearing*. New York, Life Science Library, Time Inc., 1965.

Thomsen, D. E., "Rock Around the Garden." *Science News,* CII (July 15, 1972), pp. 44–45.

Reflection of a lighted city in a river shows many principles of light.   *William Maddox*

Chapter 4 describes the properties of light. Students will use mirrors and lenses to produce images through reflection and refraction. Theories of the nature of light and supporting evidence for the theories will be presented.

 Optics

GOAL: You will gain an understanding of the properties of light and how to use mirrors and lenses to produce images.

Light is given off by the sun, stars, light bulbs, and even lightning bugs. Light is produced in certain chemical changes such as burning. Light is also given off when solids such as steel are heated to very high temperatures. In what other ways can light be produced?

Scientists study light through the use of mirrors and lenses. They use these devices to show how light can be reflected. What else would mirrors and lenses reveal about light?

PLANE MIRRORS   (71M)   359

4:1 *Plane Mirrors*

Optics is the branch of science which deals with the nature and properties of light. One way to study light is through the use of mirrors. A mirror produces an image due to the physical properties of light. Light travels in a straight line.

What is optics?

When a mirror is placed in the path of light, reflection occurs. The smooth surface of a mirror causes nearly all light rays to be reflected in a regular pattern. If you were to measure the angle of incidence of the light ray, it would equal the angle of reflection (Section 3:8).

PROBLEM

1. Name five things in which you can see an image of yourself.

Examples are surface of a still pond and a newly-waxed car fender.

You cannot see an image in a rough surface such as a concrete floor, a grass lawn, or a brick wall. Light is reflected from these surfaces in many directions. When this occurs, light rays are bounced off in a haphazard fashion. The reflected light has no pattern and produces no image.

Figure 4-1. Mirrors with smooth surfaces cause light rays to be reflected in a regular pattern (a). Rough surfaces cause light rays to be reflected in all directions (b).

Figure 4-2. Plane mirrors produce images and demonstrate the law of reflection — angle of reflection equals angle of incidence (a). Light directed at a piece of paper is reflected in a haphazard pattern (b).

Courtesy of Kodansha Ltd.

Figure 4-3.

Time: 20 minutes.

ACTIVITY. Where does an image appear in a plane (flat surfaced) mirror? Set up a small plane mirror perpendicular to a tabletop. Place a candle taller than the mirror 10 cm in front of the mirror. Place a second candle (the same size as the first candle) behind the mirror. Look at the image of the first candle in the mirror. Move the second candle to the point at which its top portion equals (coincides with) the top portion of the image. How far is the candle beyond the mirror? 10 cm

Figure 4-4. A virtual image, produced in a plane mirror, appears to be the same distance behind the mirror as the object is in front of the mirror.

A virtual image in a mirror can be seen although the image has no physical form.

Look at your reflection in a mirror. Your image appears to be behind the mirror. It appears the same distance behind the mirror as you are in front of the mirror. The image produced in a plane mirror is called a *virtual* (VUHRCH wuhl) *image*. Although you can see it, a virtual image does not really exist. It only appears to exist. A virtual image cannot be projected onto a screen.

Figure 4-5. This lighthouse has a parabolic mirror behind the lamp to reflect parallel rays of light.

4:2 Parabolic Mirrors

Curved mirrors are used in amusement parks to produce amusing images.

Special curved mirrors are called **parabolic** (par uh BAHL ik) **mirrors.** They are used as reflectors for searchlights and automobile headlights. A shaving mirror is also a parabolic mirror. A parabolic mirror reflects light rays parallel to an imaginary line drawn straight out from the mirror's center.

The surface of a parabolic mirror curves in the shape of a line called a **parabola** (puh RAB uh luh, Figure 4–6b). A line straight out from the center of the mirror is called the *principal axis*. Light rays striking a parabolic mirror parallel to its principal axis are reflected toward a common point in front of the mirror. This point is called the *principal focus*. The distance from the center of the mirror to the principal focus is the *focal length* of the mirror. Solar ovens

Have the students learn the terms that apply to the parabolic mirror and lens (e.g.: principal axis, principal focus, focal length).

U.S. Coast Guard

have a parabolic mirror. The parabolic shape of the reflecting mirror surface concentrates reflected heat onto a small spot for cooking.

Figure 4-6. Parabolic mirrors in solar ovens concentrate the sun's parallel rays by focusing them onto a single place in the oven (a). Light reflected from a concave parabolic mirror passes through the principal focus. The greater the curvature, the shorter the focal length (b).

Time: 30 minutes.

ACTIVITY. CAUTION: Use care when working with lighted candles.

(a) Use a shaving mirror of the magnifying type to produce a virtual image. Darken the room. Place a lighted candle 10 cm in front of the mirror. You will see a virtual image of the candle in the mirror. Compare the size of the image with the size of the candle itself. Is the image upright or inverted? Does the image appear to be in back of or in front of the mirror? (b) Set the candle 30 cm away from a wall. Hold the mirror 10 cm from the candle, facing the wall. Slowly move the mirror away from the candle until the image of the candle flame appears on the wall. How is this image different from the image produced in the mirror? *smaller, in front of mirror, upside down*

larger

Figure 4-7.

Time: 45 minutes.

ACTIVITY. Place a candle about 2 m in front of a curved mirror. Use a white index card or white sheet of paper to locate the image. Be careful to hold the card slightly off center from the principal axis of the mirror to allow light rays to reach the mirror and be reflected. Is the image upright or <u>inverted</u>? Is it larger or <u>smaller</u> than the candle? Is it a <u>real</u> or a virtual image?

Now move the candle closer to the mirror. Locate the image. How has the size changed? Move the candle toward the mirror until the candle and its real image are at the same point. Compare the size of the candle and its image. Is the image upright or <u>inverted</u>? Continue to move the candle toward the mirror until the image becomes blurred and begins to turn over. This is the focal point of the mirror. What is the focal length of your mirror? Answers will vary.

same size

Figure 4-8.

Real images can be projected onto a screen, virtual images cannot.

What is the difference between a real image and a virtual image?

Figure 4-9. Refraction changes the direction of light rays.

Jim Elliott

A *real image* formed by a parabolic mirror appears somewhere in front of the mirror. A real image can be projected onto a screen. With a real image, light rays strike the screen to form the image. A parabolic mirror can produce both virtual images and real images. Its optical (AHP tih kuhl) effects are similar to a convex lens (Section 4:4).

4:3 Index of Refraction

Suppose you see a coin on the bottom of a swimming pool and want to dive for it. Where do you aim? Not at the coin! The light rays reflected off the coin are bent as they pass through the water to your eye. The bending of light rays as they pass from one material to another is called **refraction** (rih FRAK shuhn). Refraction changes the direction of the light rays. The light rays are refracted at an angle as they pass from the water into the air. This explains why it is hard for you to locate the coin. When you dive in for the coin, aim in front of it.

> Time: 15 minutes.
>
> ACTIVITY. Hold a pencil in a glass of water so that the upper half of the pencil is above the water surface. View the pencil with your eye level to the water's surface. What do you observe? *Pencil appears bent.* Place a coin in a teacup. Place your eye so the coin is just out of sight. Now have someone fill the teacup with water. Can you see the coin? *Yes* Explain. *Light is refracted so image of coin reaches eye.*

Refraction is caused by an increase or decrease in the speed of light. The speed of light changes as it passes from one transparent substance to another. For example, if light passes into glass at an angle, its speed decreases, and it is refracted. Index of refraction is a measure of the amount that light is refracted by a substance. The greater the change in the speed of light, the larger the index of refraction.

Refraction changes the direction of light rays.

Explain the difference between refraction and index of refraction.

To be refracted, light must strike the surface of a transparent material at an angle. If light strikes perpendicular to a surface, the angle of incidence is zero. Then the light is not refracted.

When is light refracted? Why?
Light is refracted when it passes obliquely from one substance into another. It changes speed.

Index of refraction for glass is shown by the equation below:

$$\text{index of refraction (glass)} = \frac{\text{speed of light in vacuum}}{\text{speed of light in glass}}$$

Table 4–1. Index of Refraction and Speed of Light in Various Substances

Substance	Index of Refraction	Speed of Light
Air	1.00	3.00×10^8 m/sec
Water	1.33	2.23×10^8 m/sec
Ethyl alcohol	1.36	2.21×10^8 m/sec
Glycerine	1.47	2.04×10^8 m/sec
Glass	1.50	2.00×10^8 m/sec
Carbon disulfide	1.63	1.71×10^8 m/sec
Diamond	2.42	1.24×10^8 m/sec

The speed of light in air is very close to the speed of light in a vacuum. Therefore, the index of refraction is usually found by comparing speed in a substance and in air, instead of in a vacuum. Measuring the speed of light is complicated. The index of refraction for a material is measured by measuring the angles formed by a refracted light ray passing through a transparent surface.

Figure 4-10. As a light ray enters a liquid, its speed decreases. The ray is refracted. The slower the speed of light in a transparent material, the higher the index of refraction.

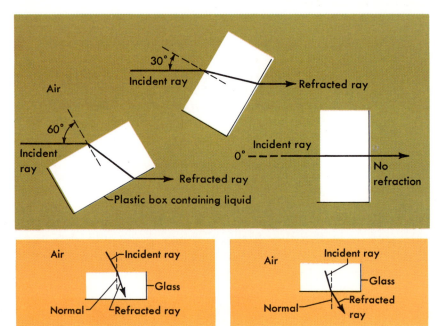

Figure 4-11. Two refractions occur when a light ray passes through a pane of glass. The light is refracted in one direction when it enters the glass and in an opposite direction when it leaves the glass.

What is a normal?

To find the angles formed by a refracted ray, a line is drawn perpendicular to the transparent surface. This is called a *normal*. When light enters a transparent surface at an angle and its velocity is decreased, the light is bent toward the normal. For example, when light passes from air into water or glass, the light is bent toward the normal. When light strikes a transparent surface at an angle and its velocity increases, it is bent away from the normal. For example, when light passes out of glass or water into air, the light is bent away from the normal.

PROBLEM See Teacher's Guide at the front of this book.

2. How is light bent if it passes from glass into water? To find the answer, you must know the speed of light in glass and the speed of light in water (Table 4–1). Make a drawing with a light ray to show the refraction.

4:4 Lenses

A **lens** is a curved transparent object, usually made of glass or clear plastic. It may have one curved and one straight surface or two curved surfaces. There are two kinds of lenses: convex and concave. A **convex lens** is thicker in the middle than at the edges. Magnifying glasses are examples of convex lenses. A **concave lens** is thinner in the middle than at the edges. Each surface is shaped like the inside of an orange peel. Figure 4–13 shows the shape of a convex lens and the shape of a concave lens.

Courtesy of Kodansha Ltd.

Figure 4-12. Convex lenses bring light rays together into a principal focus (a). Concave lenses spread light rays apart (b).

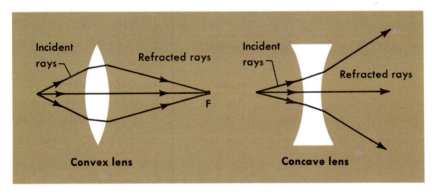

Figure 4-13. Light is refracted when it enters and when it leaves a lens. The greater the lens is curved, the shorter the focal length.

Time: 30 minutes.

ACTIVITY. Place two triangular prisms apex to apex. Pass a narrow beam of light through the prisms. How is the light bent? Repeat the procedure using a concave lens. How is the effect of the lens similar to the two prisms?

Hold the concave lens over this page. Move it toward and away from the page until you can see an image. Is the image real or *virtual*? Why is a concave lens sometimes called a reducing lens? The virtual image is reduced in size.

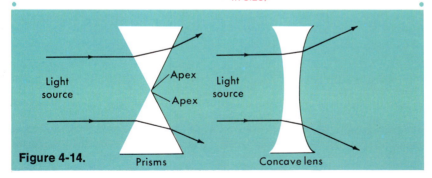

Figure 4-14.

Many terms that apply to mirrors also apply to lenses. A convex lens brings light rays together into a principal focus. For this reason, a convex lens is also called a converging lens. Light is refracted as it

Why is a convex lens called a converging lens?

Figure 4-15. There is less distance from a convex lens to its principal focus when the lens is thick.

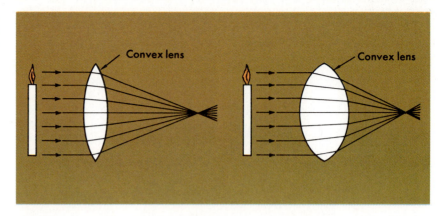

passes in and out of the lens (Figure 4–15). Light is bent as it enters and when it leaves the lens. Rays passing through a thick convex lens are bent more than light rays passing through a thin convex lens. The thicker the center of a convex lens, the shorter the focal length (Figure 4–15).

Time: 30 minutes.

ACTIVITY. You can produce a real image with a convex lens. Place a piece of white cardboard upright on a table. Set a lighted candle about 30 cm away. Move a convex lens back and forth between the candle and the cardboard. Does an image appear on the cardboard? Is the image of the candle <u>upright</u> or inverted? The focal length of the lens is halfway between the lens and the image on the screen. Find the focal length of the lens you are using. Answers will vary.

Figure 4-16.

PEOPLE CAREERS FRONTIERS
FOCUS ON PHYSICAL SCIENCE

Acoustical Engineers Work in Du Pont's 'Noise Room'

Loud industrial noises can reduce the hearing levels of workers. For this reason, efforts are being made to reduce industrial noise at Du Pont.

To help study the problem, a "noise room" was built. The noise room has concrete walls about 30 cm thick. The room is designed to pick up only sounds from within. Sounds from outside this room cannot be detected even with special instruments.

Acoustical engineers use this room to run tests on equipment noise levels. Accurate measurements are made of the noise levels for each piece of equipment tested. If any machine produces sounds above a certain level, engineers try to reduce the noise. Changes in design are often made so that equipment operates at safe sound levels.

Courtesy of *ChemEcology*, December, 1975.

Noise room at Du Pont's Engineering Test Center.

Test specialist Tony Caputo takes a noise frequency reading.

Astronomers

How was the solar system created? What do cosmic rays tell us about the origin of the universe? These are some of the questions considered and answered by astronomers. Astronomers, often called astrophysicists, use principles of physics and mathematics to study the universe.

Astronomers gather information about the sun, stars, moon, and planets. This is used to determine the size, shape, temperature, and chemical make-up of these bodies. Also, astronomers often study the earth and its atmosphere.

Studying these things requires the use of complex equipment. Therefore, astronomers need to know how to use devices such as the spectroscope. This device separates light into its seven colors and is used to identify chemical elements in the universe. Other devices, carried by balloons, rockets, and satellites, are used by astronomers to study radio waves, X rays, gamma rays, and cosmic rays.

Astronomers use specialized equipment like this combination spectrograph and telescope.

Most astronomers specialize in one of these areas—instruments, the sun, the solar system, or stars. More than 85 percent teach or do research.

Young people planning careers in astronomy should have a strong background in physics and mathematics. A bachelor's, master's, and a doctorate degree are usually required for most jobs in astronomy.

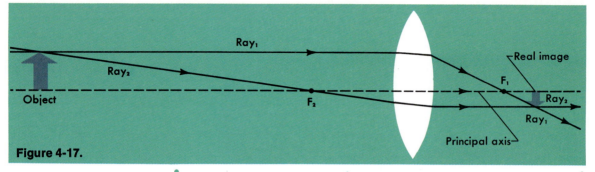

Figure 4-17.

> Time: 50 minutes.
>
> ACTIVITY. You can locate a real image with a diagram. On the left side of a piece of paper, draw an upright 2-cm arrow. The arrow represents the object. Fifteen centimeters to the right of the arrow, draw a side view of a convex lens 5 cm high. With a ruler, draw a dotted line across the paper through the center of the lens to show its axis. Then measure two 5-cm focal lengths: one to the right of the lens and one to the left of the lens. Mark the principal focus to the left as F_2. Mark the principal focus to the right as F_1.
>
> Now draw a line parallel to the axis from the top of the arrow to the lens. This line represents a light ray. Continue the line from the lens to the principal focus F_1. Draw a second line from the top of the arrow through the principal focus F_2. Continue the line until it meets the lens. As the ray leaves the lens on the opposite side, continue the ray parallel to the principal axis. The point at which the two lines cross is the top of the real image (Figure 4-17).

You can use an equation to find the size of the image produced by a convex lens:

$$\frac{H_i}{H_o} = \frac{D_i}{D_o}$$

$$\frac{\text{image height}}{\text{object height}} = \frac{\text{image distance}}{\text{object distance}}$$

To use the equation, you must know three of the values. Then you can calculate the fourth, unknown value.

EXAMPLE

An object 2 cm tall is placed 10 cm from a convex lens. The real image is 24 cm tall. Find the distance of the image from the lens.

LENSES

Solution: (a) Write the equation:
$$\frac{H_i}{H_o} = \frac{D_i}{D_o}$$
(b) Rewrite the equation to solve for D_i:
$$D_i = \frac{H_i D_o}{H_o}$$
(c) Substitute 24 cm for H_i, 10 cm for D_o, and 2 cm for H_o:
$$D_i = \frac{(24 \text{ cm})(10 \text{ cm})}{2 \text{ cm}}$$
(d) Divide and multiply to solve for D_i:
$D_i = 120$ cm
(e) Answer: $D_i = 120$ cm or 1.2 m

Problems

3. A 10-cm tall image of an object 2 cm tall is produced by a convex lens. The image is 24 cm from the lens. Find the distance of the object from the lens. 4.8 cm

4. An image 2.5 cm tall is formed 100 cm from a convex lens. How tall is the object if it is 10 cm from the lens? 0.25 cm

An image produced by a convex lens may be larger than the object. Or it can be the same size or smaller than the object. When the image is larger than the object, the object is said to be *magnified*. Microscopes, telescopes, binoculars, and picture projectors use convex lenses to magnify objects. If the image is twice as long as the

How does a convex lens magnify an object?

This question represents an inquiry or discovery situation. Have students solve the problem on a chalkboard or on paper.

Allan Roberts

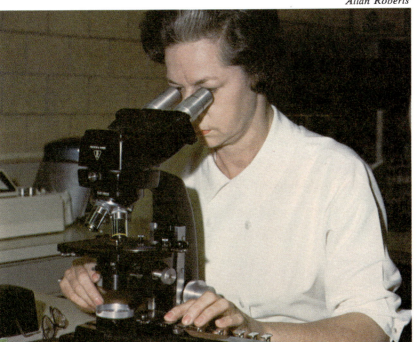

Figure 4-18. Convex lenses are used in microscopes to magnify objects.

Figure 4-19. A convex lens produces a virtual, erect, enlarged image of an object which is less than one focal length from the lens. The image is on the same side of the lens as the object.

object, the magnification produced by the lens is expressed as two power, or $2\times$. *Magnification* (mag nuh fuh KAY shuhn) is the image length divided by the object length. For example, if the image length is 12 cm and the object length is 3 cm, the magnification is four power, or $4\times$.

If an object is placed between a convex lens and its principal focus, the lens produces a virtual image. When you use a magnifying glass to read fine print, you see a virtual image of the print. The virtual image formed by a convex lens is larger than the object and is upright. Remember, a virtual image cannot be projected on a screen. Figure 4–19 shows how a virtual image is produced by a convex lens.

PROBLEM

5. Close-up pictures may be made by using an extension tube between the lens and a camera. This moves the lens toward the object and away from the film. How does the image size change when the lens is extended? image becomes larger

4:5 Lenses and Vision

Lenses may be used to correct vision problems. For example, farsightedness and nearsightedness can be corrected. The convex lens in a human eye is attached to muscles which can either relax or tighten. When the muscles are relaxed, they allow the lens to thicken at the center. However, when the muscles tighten, they pull on the sides of the lens. As a result, the center of the lens becomes thinner. Changing the shape of a lens changes the focus of the lens. If the muscles cannot properly control the shape of the lens in the eye, a person has defective vision. The person may be farsighted or nearsighted.

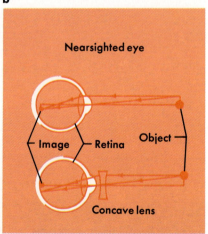

Figure 4-20. Convex lenses are used to correct farsightedness (a). Concave lenses are used to correct nearsightedness (b).

Figure 4-21. Many vision problems can be corrected with the lenses used in glasses and contact lenses.

A farsighted person can see things better at a distance. The image of nearby objects is blurred. The image is being produced beyond the retina. A convex lens brings the light rays together. The proper convex lens will form a sharp image on the retina. A nearsighted person sees things better when they are very close. The focused image is produced in front of the retina. When this occurs, distant objects are not seen clearly. Nearsightedness can be corrected with a concave lens. A concave lens, being thinner in the middle, spreads the light rays entering the eye. Therefore, the lens forms an image farther back inside the eyeball. The proper concave lens will form a clear, sharp image on the retina.

How does a convex lens help correct farsightedness?

How does a concave lens help correct nearsightedness?

4:6 Telescopes

Lenses are used in telescopes to produce enlarged images of distant objects. A simple telescope has two convex lenses: the eyepiece lens and objective lens. The *eyepiece lens* has a short focal length. The *objective lens* has a long focal length. Because its lenses refract light, this type of telescope is called a *refracting telescope* (Figure 4–22).

Describe the convex lenses in a refracting telescope.

Figure 4-22. Two convex lenses combine to form a refracting telescope. One lens has a long focal length and the other has a short focal length.

a *Yerkes Observatory Photo* b California Institute of Technology & Carnegie Institution of Washington

Figure 4-23. Refracting telescopes use two convex lenses to produce enlarged images (a). Reflecting telescopes are capable of much larger magnification through the use of parabolic mirrors (b).

Figure 4-24. Images formed by the mirror are real, inverted, and near the principal focus. Images are magnified by the convex lens in the eyepiece of the reflecting telescope (a). Mirror cells of the Hale telescope (b).

Convex lenses cannot be made much larger than about 100 cm in diameter. When a convex lens is made larger than this, the sheer weight of the lens material causes it to sag. It slowly goes out of shape. How is it possible to make astronomical (as truh NAHM ih kuhl) telescopes with huge magnifications? The very large astronomical telescopes in observatories use parabolic mirrors (Section 4:2). Such telescopes are called reflecting telescopes. The Hale telescope at Mt. Palomar, California, contains a parabolic mirror 5 m in diameter. *Because the earth rotates at 15°/hr, an observatory telescope is mounted so that it rotates in the opposite direction at 15°/hr and thereby continues to be aimed at the same point in the sky as time passes.*

PROBLEM

6. Does a reflecting telescope produce a <u>real</u> or virtual image?
Reflecting telescopes produce real images, otherwise they could not be used to photograph stars.

a b

Courtesy of the Hale Observatories

Figure 4-25. Light rays are refracted in the same direction as they enter and leave a glass prism.

4:7 Prisms

The direction of a light beam changes when it passes through a piece of glass with two faces at an angle to each other. The light is refracted twice: once as it enters and once as it leaves. Both refractions are in the same direction (Figure 4–25). A transparent material with two straight faces at an angle to each other is called a **prism.**

Glass prisms can be obtained from scientific supply companies and from some "surplus" stores.

A spectrum may be projected onto a screen by placing a rectangular, clear plastic box on an overhead projector and then filling the box two-thirds full of water.

What is dispersion?

ACTIVITY. Time: 10 minutes. White light may be separated into a color spectrum. Darken the room and pass a narrow beam of light through a prism. Form a spectrum on a white cardboard or screen. What colors do you see? red, orange, yellow, green, blue, violet

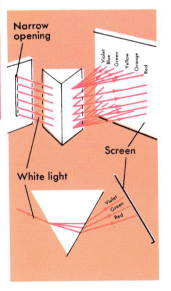

Figure 4-26. Differences in the wavelengths (colors) of light cause differences in the amount of refraction.

When a beam of white light travels through a prism, the light is spread out. The beam leaving the prism is broader than the beam entering the prism. The beam leaving the prism is also separated into the colors of the rainbow. These separated colors always appear in the same order: violet, blue, green, yellow, orange, red. A band of colors produced by a prism is called *visible light spectrum.* **Dispersion** (dis PUHR shuhn) is the separation of light into its component colors.

How does a glass prism disperse light? White light is composed of the different colors of the rainbow. The index of refraction for each color of light in glass is slightly different. The angled faces of a glass prism produce a large refraction of light. The light is refracted twice in the same direction: once as it enters and once as it leaves the prism. The resulting refraction is so large that the various colors of light are separated. Red light is refracted least. Violet light is refracted most.

Figure 4-27. A prism may be used to separate a narrow beam of white light into a spectrum of colors. A transparent colored material, called a filter, absorbs some colors and allows one or more colors to pass through. The color of the filter corresponds to the color of the light it transmits. Differences in the color of light are caused by differences in wavelength. The human eye is believed to have three separate color receptors sensitive to red, blue, and green light. Every color you see is the effect of the joint stimulation of these receptors in some definite proportion. Any color can be produced by mixing together the proper proportions of red, blue, and green light. Red, blue, and green are known as the primary colors of light. Mixed in equal intensities they produce white light.

Eastman Kodak Co.

No filter

Red filter

Green filter

Ask the students to observe the photographs and note the following: the shape of the prism used (equilateral); the angles of incidence and refraction; some of the light is reflected from the surface of the prism rather than refracted; there appears to be a second, faint spectrum produced in the last three photographs, nearly parallel to the reflected light. Have the students explain these observations.

Blue filter

Figure 4-28. When the sun's rays are refracted in raindrops, they are separated into the seven colors of the spectrum.

Allan Roberts

PROBLEMS

7. Which color in the visible light spectrum has the largest index of refraction for glass (Table 4–2)? violet
8. Which color has the smallest index of refraction? red
9. Which color in the visible light spectrum is refracted most by a glass prism? violet
10. Which color is refracted the least? red

Table 4–2. Index of Refraction in Glass for Spectrum Colors

Color	Index of Refraction
violet	1.532
blue	1.528
green	1.519
yellow	1.517
orange	1.514
red	1.513

Spectroscopy is not restricted to visible light. Beyond the violet end of the spectrum the normal eye sees nothing, but photographic plates and fluorescent dyes show the existence of many ultraviolet lines. Invisible infrared light exists beyond the red light end of the visible spectrum.

Figure 4–29 shows how a second glass prism can recombine the colors of a visible light spectrum into white light.

Many light sources do not emit white light. Some sources emit only one color of the spectrum. For example, a sodium vapor lamp

Flame tests use colored light emitted by heated and vaporized elements to identify specific elements.

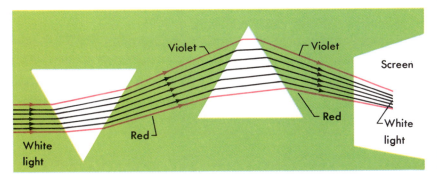

Figure 4-29. Refraction in the two prisms is equal and opposite.

Figure 4-30. Mercury vapor lamps, found in most cities, emit several colors of light.

emits only yellow light. Other sources, such as a mercury vapor lamp, emit several colors of light. An important property of a chemical element is the colors it emits when heated to a high temperature. Each element has its own spectrum. An unknown substance can be identified by heating and vaporizing it. Light from the glowing vapor is then passed through a prism. From the colors in the spectrum, the substance can be identified. Rubidium, cesium, helium, and hafnium were discovered through analysis of their light spectra.

PROBLEM

11. How might a color-blind person identify a color band in a spectrum? The color band can be identified by its position in the spectrum.

4:8 Wavelength and Frequency

How are wavelength and frequency related to color?

Light waves vary in wavelength and frequency. Each color of light has a different wavelength and frequency. Thus, the color of light is somewhat similar to the pitch of sound (Section 3:5). The frequency of a sound wave determines its pitch. The frequency of a light wave determines its color. Frequency is a physical property of a light wave. Color is what you sense with your eyes and your brain.

Each color of the visible spectrum has its own wavelength. Light waves have very short wavelengths. The wavelength of violet light waves is 4×10^{-5} cm (0.00004 cm). The wavelength of red light waves is 7×10^{-5} cm (0.00007 cm). Light waves with shorter wavelengths have higher frequencies.

PROBLEM

12. Which has the higher wave frequency, violet or red?

4:9 Polarization and Interference

Light consists of packets or bundles of radiant wave energy called *photons* (FOH tahnz). This wave property of light is shown by *polarization* (poh luh ruh ZAY shuhn). Polarization is a process that causes light waves to vibrate in a definite pattern.

Time: 15 minutes.
ACTIVITY. Hold two polarizing filters against each other. Look through them toward a lamp or window. Rotate one filter slowly. How does the brightness change?

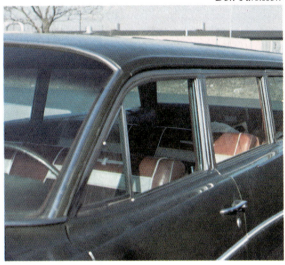

Figure 4-31. Polarizing filters absorb reflections. The picture on the left was taken without a polarizing filter. The picture on the right was taken with one.

Transparent polarizing crystals can be used to demonstrate polarization. Two crystals are held together and one crystal is rotated. The light passing through the polarizing crystals changes from bright to dim and back to bright again. You may notice the same effect while wearing polarizing sunglasses. Look through the windshield of a car and move your head back and forth.

You can understand polarization if you think of light as transverse waves (Section 3:1). A polarizing crystal permits only waves vibrating in the same plane to pass through. In effect, a polarizing crystal has an endless number of parallel "slits." Light waves vibrating in the same plane can pass through these slits. Light not vibrating in the same plane as the "slits" is reflected or absorbed. Light passing through the polarizing crystal is vibrating only in a single plane. It is called *polarized light*.

How can light be polarized?

Analogy: A rope can vibrate in a vertical plane through a picket fence but we cannot make it vibrate in a horizontal plane.
If the pickets are horizontal we can make the rope vibrate in a horizontal plane but not in a vertical plane.

PROBLEM

13. What is the position of the "slits" in the two crystals when the light is bright? When it is dim? perpendicular
parallel

In 1801, Thomas Young (1773–1829), an English physicist, performed an important experiment with light. He showed that two different light beams interfere with each other under certain conditions. In his experiment, Young passed light through a narrow slit in a barrier. The light passing through the slit spread out and passed through two more narrow slits side by side in another barrier. These two slits were the same distance from the first slit. The light again spread out and fell upon a screen. Young observed that the screen showed a series of light and dark bands (Figure 4–32). The light and dark bands are caused by wave **interference.** In the areas of the light bands, the waves were *in phase*. Here the waves reinforced each other. In the areas of the dark bands, the waves were *out of phase*.

Vocabulary: *In phase* means that the crests and troughs of two or more waves coincide and reinforce each other. *Out of phase* means that wave crests are matched with troughs and cancel each other.

How is interference explained?

Figure 4-32. Interference patterns can be varied by changing the distance between the two slits. The light and dark bands are smaller when the distance between the slits is reduced.

Here the waves canceled or destroyed the effect of each other. Thus there were dark bands.

Interference occurs when a diffraction grating is used to produce a color spectrum. A *diffraction grating* is a piece of glass containing as many as 25,000 slits in 2.5 cm. The slits are produced by a machine which makes parallel scratches on the glass with a diamond needle. When white light passes through the slits of the diffraction grating, interference occurs. This causes different wavelengths of light to reinforce or cancel each other. The net result is a spectrum of colors.

Light is stopped where the filters overlap. Polarized light passes out of the filters where they do not overlap.

Figure 4-33. Wave interference causes alternate bright and dark bands (a). Waves are in phase in the areas of the bright bands (b). Waves are out of phase in the areas of the dark bands (c).

Time: 45 minutes.

ACTIVITY. Construct a diffraction grating spectroscope. Use a piece of cardboard tubing or a cardboard box. Cover one end of the tube with aluminum foil containing a slit cut with a knife. Mount a square piece of plastic diffraction grating, measuring 1 cm², in the opposite end. The lines in the grating must be parallel to the slit. Observe white light from a lamp through the spectroscope. Observe light from a fluorescent lamp. What colors are formed? bands of violet and blue

Figure 4-34.

4:10 Photoelectric Effect

When light strikes certain metals, electrons may be released. The light causes electrons to be released from atoms in the metal. The flow of the released electrons can produce an electric current. This photoelectric effect is used in light meters and other light-sensitive devices.

What is the photoelectric effect?

Time: 45 minutes.

ACTIVITY. Obtain a light meter. Open the face of the meter so that the photocell is exposed. Darken the room. Place a light source 10 cm from the opening in the light meter. Record the reading on the meter. Now move the source 20 cm away from the light meter. Record the reading. Keep moving the source away 10 cm at a time until the light meter registers near zero. Note: Other sources of light in the room may affect the reading on the meter. If possible, remove them. Make a graph comparing the reading on the meter to the distance from the light source. How does light intensity (read on the meter) compare to the distance of the source of light? Intensity should vary inversely as the square of the distance.

Figure 4-35.

MAIN IDEAS

4:1 **1.** Mirrors, lenses, and prisms are often used in the study of optics.

4:1 **2.** Light travels in a straight line. In reflection, angle of incidence equals angle of reflection.

4:1 **3.** A plane mirror produces a virtual image by the reflection of light.

4:2 **4.** A parabolic mirror can produce a real or a virtual image.

4:3 **5.** Light is refracted as it passes into or out of a transparent substance at an angle.

4:3 **6.** The index of refraction for a substance depends upon the speed of light in the substance.

4:4 **7.** A convex lens can produce a real and a virtual image.

4:4 **8.** A convex lens brings light rays together. A concave lens spreads light rays out.

4:6 **9.** A refracting telescope contains convex lenses.

4:6 **10.** A reflecting telescope contains a parabolic mirror.

4:7 **11.** A prism or a diffraction grating separates light into its various colors.

4:7 **12.** The index of refraction is slightly different for different colors of light.

4:7, 4:8 **13.** The color of a light is determined by its frequency. Color depends on frequency of light just as pitch depends upon the frequency of a sound wave.

4:9 **14.** Interference and polarization result from the wave property of light.

4:9 **15.** Light is composed of photons of radiant wave energy.

4:10 **16.** The photoelectric effect is used in many light-sensitive devices.

VOCABULARY

Write a sentence in which you correctly use each of the following words or terms.

concave lens	normal	principal focus
convex lens	optics	prism
dispersion	parabolic mirror	real image
focal length	photoelectric effect	virtual image
index of refraction	plane mirror	visible light
magnification	polarized light	spectrum

OPTICS

STUDY QUESTIONS

A. True or False

Determine whether each of the following sentences is true or false. (Do not write in this book.)

F 1. A concave lens makes light rays ~~converge~~. *diverge*

T 2. The angle of reflection of a light ray is always equal to the incident angle of the ray.

F 3. The ~~amplitude~~ of a light wave determines its color. *frequency*

F 4. A parabolic mirror always gives an enlarged image. *does not*

F 5. The image in a plane mirror is ~~always~~ inverted. *never*

T 6. A plane mirror produces a virtual image.

T 7. A parabolic mirror can produce a real image.

T 8. A prism disperses light rays.

T 9. The angle of incidence always equals the angle of reflection.

T 10. The color of light depends on its frequency.

B. Multiple Choice

Choose one word or phrase that correctly completes each of the following sentences. (Do not write in this book.)

Some questions in Parts B and C may have more than one correct answer. Only one answer is required.

1. A *(real, virtual)* image can be projected on a screen.
2. The angle of incidence *(equals, is greater than, is less than)* the angle of reflection.
3. A parabolic mirror *(refracts, disperses, reflects)* light.
4. A parabolic mirror produces *(real, virtual, both real and virtual)* images.
5. Light is refracted when *(it is reflected, it is bent, its frequency decreases)*.
6. If light changes speed, it is *(refracted, reflected, unchanged)*.
7. The optical effects of a convex lens are most like those of a *(concave lens, parabolic mirror, prism)*.
8. As the thickness of a convex lens increases, its focal length *(increases, decreases, remains the same)*.
9. The equation $\frac{H_i}{H_o} = \frac{D_i}{D_o}$ may be used to predict *(focal length, wavelength, distance of an image from a convex lens)*.
10. The enlarged image seen with a magnifying glass is a *(real, dispersed, virtual)* image.

C. Completion

Complete each of the following sentences with a word or phrase that will make the sentence correct. (Do not write in this book.)

reflection 1. When a mirror is placed in the path of light, _____ occurs.

refracting 2. A(n) _____ telescope contains convex lenses.

parabolic 3. The very large astronomical telescopes in observatories contain a(n) _____ mirror.

prism 4. Light is dispersed by a glass _____ .

violet 5. When a beam of white light passes through a prism, _____ light is refracted more than blue light.

prism, diffraction 6. A spectroscope makes use of a glass _____ or a(n) _____ grating.

spectrum 7. A chemical element may be identified by its color _____ .

pitch 8. The color of light is similar to the _____ of sound.

4×10^{-5} cm to 7×10^{-5} cm 9. Visible light has a range of _____ to _____ centimeters.

polarized 10. Light vibrating in a single plane is _____ light.

See Teacher's Guide at the front of this book.

D. How and Why

1. How does polarization show the wave property of light?
2. How can light interference produce a color spectrum?
3. What is the photoelectric effect?
4. How is a light meter used?
5. Why might you see a color spectrum in an aquarium tank?
6. The figure below shows the path of light traveling from air into glass. Is the glass (a) or (b)?

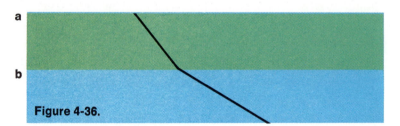

Figure 4-36.

7. Sunlight is refracted as it enters the earth's atmosphere. The sun on the horizon always looks higher in the sky than it really is. How does refraction explain this?
8. Explain why you cannot see an image in a rough surface.

OPTICS

9. What is the difference between real and virtual images? Give an example of each. Draw diagrams to illustrate your answer.
10. How do concave and convex lenses correct vision problems?

INVESTIGATIONS

1. Make a periscope out of a shoebox and two pocket mirrors. Tape the mirrors at 45° angles at opposite ends of the box. Cut a window opposite each mirror and then tape the cover on. Use your periscope to see around corners.
2. Obtain a camera and a light meter. Use the camera to take photographs of the same scene at different times during the day. Measure and record the illumination with a light meter each time you take a picture. Make a poster with your prints. Label each print with the light meter reading you made.

INTERESTING READING

Brinkworth, B. J., *Solar Energy for Man*. New York, Halsted Press, 1973.

Gregg, James R., *Experiments in Visual Science: For Home and School*. New York, Ronald Press Company, 1966.

Lyttle, Richard B., *Paints, Inks, and Dyes: The Story of Colors at Work*. New York, Holiday House, Inc., 1974.

Reid, R. W., *The Spectroscope*. New York, New American Library, Inc., 1966.

Wacker, Charles H., *Lasers: How They Work*. New York, G. P. Putnam's Sons, 1973.

Wilson, John, Jr., *Albert A. Michelson: America's First Nobel Prize Physicist*. New York, Julian Messner Publications, 1958.

See Teacher's Guide at the front of this book.

Unit Six

Electrical and Nuclear Energy

Rich Brommer

This chapter develops the concept of energy with a discussion of electricity and its effects. The objective is for the student to learn the different kinds of electricity and their effects and the relationship between electricity and magnetism.

1 Electricity

GOAL: You will gain an understanding of the different kinds of electricity and of the relationship between electricity and magnetism.

Electricity is used to light lamps, heat buildings, and operate electric motors. Refrigerators, stoves, televisions, and lawn mowers may be powered by electricity. What are other uses?

The effects of electricity appear in many forms. We see these forms daily. One example is lightning. Lightning occurs when electricity is discharged from one cloud to another. Another effect of electricity is the shock received from walking across a wool carpet, then touching a metal object. What are other examples?

ELECTRIC CHARGES (3M) 387

1:1 Electric Charges

Scientists have studied the nature of **electricity** for hundreds of years. They have determined that it is a form of energy. Energy can do work. Tiny, invisible, electrically charged particles are present in atoms, the basic building blocks of all matter. The amount and kind of electric particles determine the properties of an atom.

The word electricity comes from *elektron*, the Greek word for amber. The Greek philosopher Thales is said to have observed electric forces about 25 centuries ago when he rubbed amber and discovered it attracted light objects.
Describe electricity.

Do this activity as an introduction to electricity.

Time: 30 minutes.
ACTIVITY. Run a comb through dry hair several times. Then try to pick up bits of paper with the comb. What happens?
Rub a glass rod with a piece of silk. Hang the rod horizontally with silk threads. Rub a second glass rod in the same way. Hang it by a silk thread and bring it near the first rod. What happens?
Using silk threads, hang two plastic rods separately. Rub the two rods with wool. Bring them close together. Do they repel or attract each other?
Now bring a suspended plastic rod rubbed with wool near a suspended glass rod rubbed with silk.
Does glass repel glass? Does plastic normally repel plastic? Does glass normally attract plastic? Explain what you observe. Friction can produce static electricity.

Figure 1-1.

Some materials when rubbed gain an *electric charge*. The charge can be positive (+) or negative (−). When two rods have the same charge, the rods repel each other. When two rods have different charges, the rods attract each other. For this reason, charged glass and plastic rods attract each other. The charge on the glass rod is opposite to the charge on the plastic rod. Like charges repel each other. Opposite charges attract each other.

Figure 1-2. Lightning is a discharge of electricity from one cloud to another or from a cloud to Earth.

Positively charged spheres

Negatively charged spheres

Figure 1-3. When two objects have the same charge, they repel each other. When the charges are opposite, the objects attract each other.

An atom contains equal numbers of protons and electrons. For example, an oxygen atom has 8 protons and 8 electrons. A *proton* is a positively charged particle in the nucleus of an atom. An *electron* is a negatively charged particle outside the nucleus. Since the number of negative charges in an atom is equal to the number of positive charges, an atom is neutral.

If a body gains electrons, the result will be more electrons than protons. The object is then negatively charged. If an object loses electrons, the result will be more protons than electrons. Then the object is positively **charged.**

Time: 20 minutes.
ACTIVITY. Attach a silk thread to a glass rod. Attach a silk thread to a piece of silk cloth. Rub the rod with the silk. Suspend the rod and silk cloth separately. Bring the silk cloth near the rod. What do you observe?
There is an attraction.

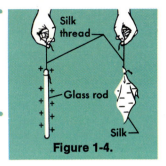

Figure 1-4.

If you rub a glass rod with silk, the glass rod loses electrons to the silk. The rod becomes positively charged. The silk becomes negatively charged. Opposite charges attract, so the rod and silk attract each other.

When you rub a plastic rod with wool, the plastic rod gains electrons from the wool. Thus, the plastic rod becomes negatively charged. The wool becomes positively charged. Will the wool and the plastic rod attract each other? Why?
yes

Will Miles

Figure 1-5. Hair is often "fly-away" because of static electricity.

Charged bodies have **static electricity,** or electricity at rest. There are two kinds of static electricity. *Positive static electricity* results when an object loses electrons. It has a positive charge. *Negative static electricity* results when an object gains electrons. It has a negative charge.

What is static electricity?

Figure 1-6. These balloons were rubbed on a wool sweater. Static electricity causes them to stick to the wall.

William Maddox

You may see examples of static electricity when
(a) charged clouds produce lightning
(b) someone wearing rubber-soled shoes walks over a wool rug
(c) a driver in a wool coat rubs against plastic car seats
(d) a nylon dress comes out of a clothes dryer
(e) a blown-up balloon is rubbed against a wool sweater.

PROBLEMS

1. Why may static electricity be produced in each example given above? In every case, electrons are transferred causing a negative charge on one surface and a positive charge on the other.
2. Name three other examples of static electricity. Answers will vary.
3. When you comb your hair, the comb may gain a negative charge. Where do the added electrons come from? your hair

1:2 Conduction

An *electroscope* (ih LEK truh skohp) is a device which detects an electric charge. A simple electroscope contains two thin leaves of metal hanging from the bottom of a metal rod. The rod is suspended in the neck of a jar (Figure 1–7). The top of the metal rod is connected to a metal knob.

Figure 1-7.

Time: 30 minutes.
ACTIVITY. You can make a simple electroscope. Take a metal curtain rod that has a ball end. Including the ball end, cut off a piece 20 cm long. Obtain a bottle and a cork to fit. Make a hole in the cork and insert the rod through the hole. Flatten 5 cm of the end of the rod and attach two pieces of lightweight metal foil, ½ cm × 2 cm in size. Insert the cork into the bottle so that it fits snugly.

Figure 1-8. Is the charge on the electroscope the same as or opposite to the charge on the rod?
The same. The electroscope is charged by conduction.

An electroscope can be charged positively or negatively. When charged, the leaves spread apart. Like charges in the leaves make them repel each other. When not charged, the leaves hang down.

You can use a negatively charged plastic rod to give an electroscope a static charge of electricity. Touch the metal knob of the electroscope with the charged rod. Electrons from the plastic rod move into the electroscope. This is known as conduction (kuhn DUHK shuhn). The electroscope gains electrons and has a negative charge. The charged leaves will spring apart.

Conduction occurs when electrons are gained or lost through direct contact with a charged object. An object charged by conduction takes the same charge as the original charged object. Objects with a negative charge can produce negative charges on other objects. Objects with a positive charge can produce positive charges on other objects.

How is an electroscope used to detect electric charges?
The electroscope is charged by conduction. When a charge of the same sign is brought near, the leaves diverge; when the opposite charge is brought near, the leaves converge.

Time: 35 minutes.
ACTIVITY. (1) Charge a plastic rod with a wool cloth. Using the charged rod, charge the electroscope by conduction. An electroscope can also be discharged by conduction. Discharge means to lose charge. (2) Touch the knob of a negatively charged electroscope. What happens? (3) Repeat Part 1. To discharge the electroscope this time, use a piece of pencil "lead" (graphite, a form of carbon). (4) Repeat Parts 1 and 2 with a metal wire. (5) Repeat Part 1 with a glass rod. (6) Repeat Parts 1, 2, 3, and 4 using a glass rod and silk cloth instead.

Figure 1-9.

In Part 2 of the activity above, the electroscope became uncharged. It lost electrons which were conducted into your hand. In Parts 3 and 4, the electroscope was also discharged. Electrons

Figure 1-10. Electrical wires are insulated to prevent electric short circuits. Short circuits can cause electrical shocks, damage to equipment, or fire.

traveled through the graphite or through the wire to your body. A material through which electrons can travel is a **conductor.** Graphite and metal are electrical conductors.

Some materials will not discharge an electroscope. Glass, hard rubber, porcelain, and plastic will not. Electrons do not flow well through these substances. Such materials are called insulators (IN suh layt uhrz). An **insulator** is a substance through which electrons will not flow readily.

1:3 Electrostatic Induction

An electroscope can be charged without ever touching a charged body. This is done by **electrostatic induction** (ih lek truh STAT ik in DUHK shuhn). Electrostatic induction occurs because electrons repel each other.

Time: 20 minutes.

ACTIVITY. Charge an electroscope by electrostatic induction. Bring a negatively charged rod close to the knob of an uncharged electroscope. What happens? Touch your finger to the side of the knob away from the charged rod. Then take your finger away and remove the charged rod. Explain what happens.

When a negatively charged plastic rod is brought near the knob of an electroscope, some of the electrons in the knob are repelled. They flow down into the leaves and to the side of the knob opposite the rod. The leaves become negatively charged. When the negative side of the knob is touched with your finger, some of the electrons are conducted out of the knob. When the finger is removed from the knob, the electrons cannot flow back into the electroscope. As a result, the electroscope has fewer electrons than protons.

The charged electroscope can be made neutral and induction repeated with a positively charged glass rod. This time the charged rod attracts electrons from the leaves and from the other side of the knob. Thus, the leaves and opposite side of the knob become positively charged. When you touch the knob, electrons flow from your body into the electroscope. The electroscope gains electrons. It becomes negatively charged. Electrons may flow from one object to another but protons never do. Why? Protons are in the nucleus of an atom.

The charge produced by induction is always opposite to the charge of the charging object. Through induction, positively

Figure 1-11. Electroscopes can be charged by electrostatic induction.

charged objects can produce negative charges on other objects. Negatively charged objects can produce positive charges on other objects.

PROBLEMS

4. Name several electrical insulators used in home appliances. Glass and plastic are insulators.
5. How is a charge produced by induction different from a charge produced by conduction? The charge produced by induction is opposite that of the charging object. The charge produced by conduction is the same as the charging object.
6. How is the rod in an electroscope insulated?

To *ground* means to connect an object to the earth with a conductor. Grounding allows electrons to move freely in and out of the object. Think of the earth as a huge reservoir of electrons. Electrons from the earth can be conducted into an object. Electrons from an object can be conducted into the earth. For example, lightning rods and television antennas are grounded to the earth. This is done by wires sunk into the ground. A gasoline truck may be grounded by a long chain that drags on the road. Why does a lightning rod, a television antenna, or a gasoline truck need to be grounded?

How is a body grounded? Grounding allows electrons to move into or out of the body and the earth. Thus lightning can pass through a lightning rod or TV antenna to the ground without causing damage. If plastic seat covers are grounded they cannot become charged because any excess of electrons they gain will flow into the earth.

Figure 1-12.

Time: 35 minutes.

ACTIVITY. (1) Place two metal rods, supported by two glass beakers, end to end so that they touch. Charge a plastic rod by rubbing it with wool. Bring the charged rod close to one of the metal rods. At the same time, slowly separate the rods by moving one of the beakers. Do not touch the metal rods. (2) Charge the plastic rod again. Use it to charge an electroscope. Bring each of the metal rods, separately, near the electroscope knob. What do you observe? Why are the beakers used? Are the metal rods charged? Explain. Describe a way to tell if a metal rod has a positive or a negative charge.

Yes _____

The beakers are insulators. Charge an electroscope negatively and bring the rod near without touching it. If the knob is negative the leaves will spread farther apart. If the rod is positive the leaves will fall closer together.

1:4 Direct Current

What is direct current?

Direct current (D.C.) is the flow of electrons through a conductor. The flow may vary in rate but it is always in the same direction. When an electroscope is discharged, a tiny direct current is formed for a fraction of a second. The flow of electrons out of the electroscope through a conductor is the current. Similarly, a flash of lightning is a direct current. So is lightning traveling through a lightning rod into the ground. The electrical connection to a car battery carries a direct current.

Figure 1-13. Lightning rods connected to buildings and grounded in the earth carry the electrons from the lightning away from the buildings.

a   *Allan Roberts*   b

394 (10M)

PEOPLE CAREERS FRONTIERS
FOCUS ON PHYSICAL SCIENCE

Engineering Fields

Designers of automobiles, refrigerators, spacecraft, and computers have something in common. They are all engineers. Next to teaching, engineering is the largest professional occupation. There are well over one million engineers working in the United States today.

What do all these men and women do? Some are designing new energy power sources. Others are developing machines that will safely harvest delicate crops. Even our food and clothing are engineered.

Chemical engineers often design industrial plants or improve existing ones.

Engineering is so vast and varied that an engineer usually specializes in one area. There are twenty-five officially recognized engineering specialities. Chemical, electrical, civil, and mechanical engineering are four of these twenty-five. Each speciality is often subdivided. For example, sanitary and highway engineering are two subdivisions of civil engineering.

Although there are many types of engineers, they all have a few things in common. All engineers use scientific principles to solve design and production problems. Their work emphasizes *applying* existing scientific information rather than *discovering* new information. An engineer's concerns range from raw materials and ideas through design and manufacturing. His or her interests may even go beyond the finished product to packaging, distribution, and sales.

Engineers must consider many factors when developing a new product. Does it meet safety standards? Will it cost too much or take too long to produce? Is it really needed? Can it be easily used?

To qualify for an engineering job, a person should have a bachelor's degree in engineering. Some graduates in science or mathematics are also considered for engineering jobs. A master's degree is required for many of the more technical areas. Licensing is also required in some areas of engineering.

Alan White of Bell Laboratories, an electrical engineer, adjusts a miniature helium-neon laser which he developed.

Dr. Rha, an agricultural engineer, conducts research in the area of synthetic foods.

Figure 1-14.

Time: 50 minutes.

ACTIVITY. CAUTION: Do this only under direct supervision of your teacher. Do not get any sulfuric acid on your body or clothing.

Wet cells produce a direct current through chemical changes. To make a wet cell, put two different metals into a salt, basic, or acid solution. Then connect the metals with a wire. *For example, a strip of zinc (Zn) and a strip of copper (Cu) placed in a solution of dilute sulfuric acid (H_2SO_4) form a wet cell (Figure 1-14). A current is produced when the two metals are connected by a wire.* Electricity will flow only when there is a complete circuit.

The metals are in two different solutions.

The wire is not connected.

How does a wet cell generate an electric current?

A wet cell works because of ions in a solution. An ion is a charged particle. It is a charged atom or a charged group of atoms. When acids, bases, or salts dissolve in water, they release ions. Every ion has either a positive or negative charge. In a wet cell, the solution has an equal number of positive and negative ions.

Suppose a wet cell contains a sulfuric acid solution, a strip of zinc, and a strip of copper. The ions in the sulfuric acid solution are hydrogen (H^+)* and sulfate (SO_4^{2-}). The hydrogen ion is positively charged. What is the charge of the sulfate ion? Zinc atoms in the strip of zinc metal dissolve in the acid solution. Each atom loses two electrons. The zinc atoms (Zn) become zinc ions (Zn^{2+}). The following equation shows this change:

$$Zn(s) \rightarrow Zn^{2+}(aq) + 2\,e^-$$
(Zinc atom)   (Zinc ion)

A zinc atom is uncharged. A zinc ion has a charge of $2+$. The symbol e^- represents an electron. The 2 in front of the electron symbol shows that two electrons are released when a zinc atom becomes a zinc ion. Electrons given off by the zinc move through the wire to the copper.

Figure 1-15. Zinc atoms will lose electrons and dissolve in the acid solution when the zinc is connected to a copper rod placed in the same solution.

*In water, hydrogen ions (H^+) react with water (H_2O) to yield hydronium ions (H_3O^+).

Figure 1-16. Wet cells (a) produce direct current because chemical energy in atoms is changed into electrical energy. Dry cells (b) produce direct current like wet cells except the chemicals are in a moist paste form.

The positive charge of the zinc ions repels the positive charge of the hydrogen ions in the solution. The hydrogen ions move to the copper side of the cell. At the same time, electrons come into the copper through the wire from the zinc. The hydrogen ions gain these electrons from the copper and become hydrogen atoms. These atoms form diatomic molecules (molecules with two atoms) of hydrogen gas. This gas bubbles out of the solution (Figure 1–16a). This is the equation for the reaction:

$$2 H^+(aq) + 2 e^- \longrightarrow H_2(g)$$

In a wet cell, such as the one just described, ions move in the solution. Electrons move in the wire. Electrons flow from the zinc to the copper through the wire. This produces a direct current. However, electrons do not gather in a large number in any one spot. There is always an even distribution of electrons. The current can be stopped by opening the circuit. No point in the conductor is charged either negatively or positively. In this way a current differs from static electricity. Static electricity is a gathering or shortage of electrons in one place. A current is a flow of electrons.

Electric current produced by a wet cell results from an energy change. Chemical energy in atoms is changed into electrical energy. A dry cell and a storage battery also produce direct current. They do this by converting chemical energy to electrical energy.

A "dry" cell works in much the same way as a wet cell; however, there are differences. A **dry cell** has chemicals in the form of a moist paste instead of a liquid. A dry cell is composed of a carbon rod set in the middle of a zinc can. The rest of the can is filled with a moist paste. The paste reacts with the zinc and releases electrons. These electrons flow through a conductor to the carbon rod. The flow of electrons is direct current (Figure 1–16b).

An automobile storage battery has wet cells containing lead and lead oxide plates suspended in dilute sulfuric acid.

How does a dry cell generate an electric current?

Figure 1-17. Small dry cell batteries are often used in radios, flashlights, and toys.

> Time: 25 minutes.
> ACTIVITY. Obtain a used dry cell. With a hacksaw carefully cut the cell lengthwise down the middle. CAUTION: Do not touch the inside. The material can cause burns. Study the parts of the cell. Was the inside of the battery <u>moist</u> or dry? Why? If dry, will not produce current.

PROBLEM

7. Why will a dry cell fail to work if it dries out completely?
   The electrons cannot move.

Two or more cells (wet or dry) can be connected together in a single circuit. This is called a **battery.** Electricity in a car is produced by a storage battery. The battery contains lead plates and sulfuric acid solution.

A direct current can also be produced by the **photoelectric effect.** When certain metals are exposed to light, they give off electrons. These electrons can flow in a circuit and form a direct current. Photoelectric cells convert light energy into electrical energy.

Figure 1-18. In a diode, a direct current flows from the filament to the metal cylinder.

1:5 Diode and Thermocouple

A flow of electrons can be produced from heat energy. Heat energy can be changed into electrical energy by a diode. A **diode** (DY ohd) is a thin, glass bulb containing a hollow metal cylinder (Figure 1–18). Inside the metal cylinder is a tungsten wire filament. There is no air inside the tube.

DIODE AND THERMOCOUPLE

When a diode filament is connected to an electric current, its filament becomes hot. Electrons "boil off" and leave the hot metal filament. The electrons travel through the empty space to the metal cylinder. In effect, a direct current flows from filament to cylinder. This produces a direct current in the circuit.

The rate at which electrons are released by a diode depends on the temperature of the filament. The higher the temperature, the faster electrons are released. There must be no air inside the diode. If air were present, the filament would react with the air and be destroyed.

A thermocouple (THUHR muh kuhp uhl) is a device used to produce electric current. It has two different metals bonded or twisted together at two separate points. Copper and iron wire are sometimes used as the two metals. One bonded point is placed in a cold substance. The other point is heated. The metals in the thermocouple produce an electric current. Differences in temperature cause an electric current to flow. The amount of current produced by a thermocouple depends on the temperature difference between the two contact points. The greater the temperature difference, the greater the current.

Why is there a vacuum inside a diode?

See Teacher's Guide for additional information on thermocouples.

Courtesy of Battelle Columbus Laboratories

Figure 1-19. Two metals are twisted together in a thermocouple (a). A thermocouple is used to produce an electric current (b).

Table 1–1. Production of Direct Current (D.C.)

Static Discharge	Chemical	Light	Heat
lightning	wet cell	photoelectric cell	diode
	dry cell		thermocouple
	storage battery		

Figure 1-20. Magnets within a generator produce electric currents. These electric generators can produce a maximum of 150,000 kilowatts of power.

Tennessee Valley Authority

1:6 Magnetism

How is magnetism used to produce electricity?

Magnetism is a property of matter. Magnetism can produce electricity and electricity can produce magnetism. In an electric generator, magnets produce an electric current. In an electromagnet, an electric current produces magnetism.

Figure 1-21. Dry Cell, Wire, Nail, Electromagnet

Time: 50 minutes.

ACTIVITY. Obtain a long piece of copper wire. Wrap it around a large nail as shown in Figure 1–21. Attach the free ends of the wire to the poles of a dry cell. You now have an electromagnet. Try picking up paper clips or small bits of iron with it.

Wrap more wire around the nail. What happens to the strength of the magnet? Add another cell to the magnet. What happens to the strength of the magnet? *In both cases, strength of magnet increases.*

Figure 1-22. Lines of magnetic force are indicated by the pattern of iron filings.

Bell Telephone Laboratories

400 (16M)

Magnets are usually made of *steel, cobalt,* or *nickel*. Each of these metals has the property of being attracted to magnets. They become magnets themselves when surrounded by a coil of wire bearing an electric current. For example, a piece of steel can be magnetized by an electric current (Figure 1–21). The steel retains its magnetism after the current is removed. The magnetized piece of steel is called a *permanent* magnet.

Figure 1-23. To suit different industrial purposes, magnets are made in a variety of shapes, such as bar-type (a) and disc-type (b).

How is electricity used to produce magnetism? Metals become magnets when surrounded by a coil of wire bearing an electric current.

....
: Time: 25 minutes.
:   ACTIVITY.   Obtain a bar magnet. Place it on a desk
: top or table. Cover the magnet with a piece of thin pa-
: per, clear plastic, or glass. Sprinkle iron filings on top
: of the paper where it covers the magnet. Draw the
: pattern formed by the filings. What do the iron filings
: reveal? lines of magnetic force
:..

Bar magnets and horseshoe magnets are permanent magnets. Alnico, an alloy of aluminum, nickel, and cobalt, is also used to make permanent magnets. In time, a permanent magnet slowly loses its magnetism. A permanent magnet can also lose its magnetic properties rapidly. This happens if it is heated or hit over and over with a hard object such as a hammer. Under normal conditions, a permanent magnet retains its magnetism for a long time.

Figure 1-24. Magnetite, also known as lodestone, is a natural magnet.

....
: Time: 15 minutes.
:   ACTIVITY.   Hold two bar magnets, one in each hand.
: Now bring their opposite poles together. What hap-
: pens? What happens when both south poles or both
: north poles of the two magnets are brought together?
:   Why does this happen? There is an attraction. There is no attraction.
: Like poles have like charges. Only opposite charges are attracted to each other.
:..

Courtesy of Kodansha Ltd.

401   (17M)

Figure 1-25. Compasses are used by navigators of ships and planes and by hikers to determine directions.

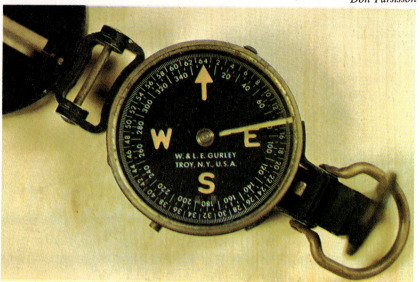

Free-floating magnets always line up with the earth's *magnetic poles*. A compass uses this principle. It is used for detecting direction. The end of the needle that points north is called its north-seeking pole. The opposite end is its south-seeking pole. All compass magnets have a north-seeking pole and a south-seeking pole.

> Time: 15 minutes.
> ACTIVITY. Cut a thin slice of cork and float it on the surface of water in a beaker or tumbler. Stroke a needle on a bar magnet. Place the needle on the cork. Does the needle rotate to a north-south or east-west position? Explain.

A magnet has these properties:

(1) Two unlike poles—north and south. One pole is at each end. If a bar magnet is cut in two, two magnets are formed. Each magnet will have a north and south pole.

(2) Like poles of a magnet repel. Unlike poles of a magnet attract.

(3) Lines of force, forming a magnetic field, surround a magnet. The magnetic field can be revealed by covering the magnet with iron filings (Figure 1–22).

(4) A magnet attracts iron, cobalt, and nickel.

(5) A magnet can magnetize iron, cobalt, and nickel if a piece of one of these metals is stroked with the magnet.

(6) When a magnet is free-floating, the poles of the magnet line up with the earth's north and south magnetic poles.

ALTERNATING CURRENT

(7) A magnet can cause electric currents in conductors. If a bar magnet is moved back and forth inside a coil of wire, an electric current is produced in the wire.

1:7 Alternating Current

Alternating current (A.C.) is the back-and-forth movement of electrons in a circuit. The circuits in your home have alternating current. When the electricity is on, free electrons in the wires vibrate to and fro. For example, in a 60-cycle home circuit, the electrons vibrate 60 times per second.

What is alternating current?

Figure 1-26.

Time: 45 minutes.

ACTIVITY. Induction in a coil of wire. (1) Bend a wire to form a coil with 10 loops, 5 cm in diameter. Connect the ends of the wire to a galvanometer (gal vuh NAHM uht uhr). Hold a bar magnet and thrust it in and out of the coil. Vary the speed at which the magnet moves and observe the reading on the galvanometer. (2) Change the number of coils in the wire and repeat the procedure.

What effect does the speed at which the magnet moves have on a galvanometer reading? How is the reading changed by the number of turns in the coil? What kind of electric current is produced in the coil? — alternating current

Suggestion: Introduce this activity by explaining that induction means that electrons are forced to move by means of a magnetic field. Each electron has an associated magnetic field. The presence of another magnetic field which is in motion will force the electrons to move, causing a current.

Current varies directly with the number of turns and the speed with which the magnet moves.

Alternating current is produced through electromagnetic induction. The simplest way to make an alternating current is to move a wire back and forth in a magnetic field. A weak alternating current is produced in the wire.

An electric generator produces an electric current by induction. A generator contains magnets and a loop or coil of wire. The coil

Figure 1-27. Magnetic lines of force move electrons through the wire coil as it turns. Why is the generated current A.C. and not D.C.?

of wire, called an armature (AHR muh chur), rotates within a magnetic field. As the armature rotates, electric current is produced in the coil. The induced current is conducted by metal slip rings and brushes to an external circuit.

When the armature is rotated, one side of the armature loop moves toward the north pole. The other side moves toward the south pole. Every 180° the two sides of the loop change direction with respect to the magnets. For 180° of turn, the electrons move in one direction. Through the next 180° of turn, the electrons move in the opposite direction. Thus, the electrons vibrate to and fro with each complete turn of the armature. As the armature turns, A.C. is produced. Figure 1-27 shows how the current is produced by a single-loop armature.

PROBLEM

8. What kind of energy change occurs in an electric generator?
kinetic energy to electrical energy

1:8 Electrical Units

A **galvanometer** is a device which can detect weak electric currents. Its operation is based on the rotation of a wire coil set between two permanent magnetic poles. If an electric current is passed through the coil, it becomes magnetized. North and south poles of the magnetized coil are repelled by the nearby permanent magnetic poles. The north pole of the coil moves away from the north pole of the permanent magnet. The south pole of the coil moves away from the south pole of the permanent magnet. How much the coil rotates depends on the strength of the current. The greater the electric

How does a galvanometer detect an electric current?
A galvanometer detects weak currents as changes in magnetic strength.

Caution: Connecting a galvanometer to high voltage will cause the coil to burn out.

Figure 1-28. When a current flows through the coil, the forces on opposite sides of the coil cause it to rotate until it is stopped by the spring.

Figure 1-29. Ammeters measure current in amperes. This ammeter indicates the number of amperes in the electric current produced through the thermoelectric effect.

current, the greater the amount of rotation. As the coil rotates, a needle attached to the coil moves on a scale. The position of the needle indicates the size of the current.

Ampere, volt, ohm, and *watt* are standard electrical units. The ampere expresses the rate of electron flow in a current. One **ampere** (AM pir) (amp) is a current of one coulomb (KOO lohm) per second (1 C/sec). One coulomb equals 6.25×10^{18} electrons. When a current is one ampere, 6.25×10^{18} electrons pass a given point in a circuit every second. An **ammeter** (AM eet uhr) measures current in amperes. Like a galvanometer, the ammeter is based on the rotation of a current-bearing coil in a magnetic field. The charge on one electron is 1.6×10^{-19} coulomb.

An electric current may be compared to running water in a hose. Pressure forces the water through the hose in a stream. Similarly, an *electromotive force* (emf) causes the movement of electrons in a circuit. The **volt** (V) is a unit of electromotive force.

A common dry cell has a voltage of 1½ V. An automobile storage battery operates on 6 V or 12 V. Many home appliances operate on 110–120 V. A television picture tube may operate on more than 20,000 V. Electric transmission lines have thousands of volts of electromotive force. You may wish to expand upon the definition of volt. A volt expresses potential difference between two points in a conductor.

Electric potential refers to electromotive force or voltage.

PROBLEM

9. Which of the following yields the most energy: dry cell, storage battery, house current?

Many substances, such as metals, conduct electricity. Some are better conductors than others. Electricity flows through some materials more easily than through others. This is due to resistance, the

---

The *ampere* expresses rate of electron flow in a current. The *volt* is a unit of electromotive force. The *ohm* expresses electrical resistance.

Define ampere, volt, and ohm.

How are amperes measured?

Relate the use of standard electric units to standard units in the metric and English systems with which the student is familiar. For example:

$1 \frac{\text{volt}}{\text{sec}} = 0.737$ ft-lb

$1 \text{ watt} = 1 \frac{\text{joule}}{\text{sec}}$

The international joule, a unit of electrical energy, is the work expended per second by a current of one ampere flowing through one ohm.

$1 \text{ joule} = \frac{1 \text{ amp} \times 1 \text{ ohm}}{1 \text{ sec}}$

$= \frac{1 \text{ volt}}{1 \text{ sec}}$

$= 2.8 \times 10^{-7}$ kw/hr

$= 0.737$ ft-lb

$= 0.24$ calories

Have students note that copper is used extensively for electric wires because of its low resistance. Silver is too expensive for most circuits. Aluminum is used in some circuits and has the advantage of being less costly than copper.

Table 1–2. A Comparison of Electrical Resistance

Metal

Silver (Ag) — Lowest resistance
Copper (Cu)
Gold (Au)
Aluminum (Al)
Tungsten (W)
Nickel (Ni)
Iron (Fe)
Tin (Sn) — Highest resistance

What is the relationship between resistance and conductivity?
The lower the resistance, the better the conductor.

opposition to the flow of electricity. A good conductor of electricity has low resistance. A poor conductor has high resistance (Table 1–2). Resistance (rih ZIS tuhnts) is measured in ohms. One **ohm** of resistance exists when there is one ampere of current in a one-volt circuit (1 V/amp).

PROBLEMS

silver and copper

10. Which metals listed in Table 1–2 would be best for electrical wiring? Why? They have the lowest resistances.
11. Why is silver not used in household electrical wiring?
Silver is not used because it is too expensive and too soft.

This activity is designed to derive Ohm's law as explained in the paragraph that follows the activity. Caution students to check the polarity of each item as it is placed in the circuit. Voltmeters and ammeters can be ruined by connecting them in the circuit backward. Check the circuit before the cell is added. The center pole of the cell is positive and the outer pole is negative. Always connect ammeters in *series* with the resistance, and always connect voltmeters in *parallel* with the resistance. This is also for the protection of the meters.
watts = volts × amperes

Time: 50 minutes.
ACTIVITY. How are volts, amperes, and ohms related? Connect a variable resistor in series to a dry cell and ammeter. Connect the two poles of the resistor to a voltmeter. Vary the resistance by moving the slide to 3 or 4 different positions. Record in a chart the amperes and volts for each position. Resistance (ohms) increases as the length of the resistor in the circuit increases. How do the ohms of resistance (length of resistor) affect the current and voltage? Write the relationship as an equation.

Figure 1-30.

ELECTRICAL UNITS

George Simon Ohm (1787–1854), a German physicist, discovered the relationship between volts and amperes in a circuit. This relationship is expressed in *Ohm's law:* $I = \dfrac{V}{R}$

amperes of current equals voltage divided by resistance in ohms

EXAMPLE

What is the current in a 3-ohm circuit connected to a 6-V battery?

Solution: (a) Write the equation: $I = \dfrac{V}{R}$

(b) Substitute 6 V for V and 3 ohms for R:
$$I = \dfrac{6 \text{ volts}}{3 \text{ ohms}}$$

(c) Divide to find the current: $I = 2$ amp

(d) Answer: current $= 2$ amp

PROBLEMS

12. What is the current in a 3-ohm circuit connected to a 12-V battery? 4 amp
13. What is the resistance of an electric lamp using 5 amp of current in a 120-V circuit? 24 ohms

Figure 1-31. Electric meters indicate the amount of electric current used.

Explain Ohm's law.
Current varies directly with e.m.f. and varies inversely with resistance.

Table 1-3. *Electrical Energy Used by Some Home Appliances*

Appliance	Wattage	Hourly "on" time	KWH used
Hair dryer, blower	1000	¼ hr	.25
Microwave oven	1450	½ hr	.72
Radio/record player	109	2½ hr	0.25
Range (oven)	2600	1 hr	2.60
Refrigerator/freezer* (15 cu ft)	326	24 hr	7.86
Refrigerator/freezer* (15 cu ft frostless)	615	24 hr	14.76
Slow cooker (low)	75	9 hr	0.675
Television (B & W) (solid state)	55	3¼ hr	0.16
Television (color) (solid state)	200	3¼ hr	0.65
Electric toothbrush	7	5 min	0.0006
100-watt light bulb	100	6 hr	0.60
40-watt fluorescent light bulb	50	1 hr	0.05

*Costs and usage vary due to living styles.

Fuses and circuit breakers are used to protect circuits from overheating due to large currents. Joule's law: The heat developed in a conductor is directly proportional to the resistance of the conductor, the square of the current, and the time the current is maintained.
H (joules) $= I^2Rt$
1 joule $= 0.24$ cal
H $= 0.24\ I^2Rt$ calories

How are watts, watt-hours, and kilowatt-hours calculated?

The power of an electric circuit is measured in watts. One **watt** of power exists in a circuit having a one-ampere current under a pressure of one volt. To calculate watts, multiply volts by amperes:

$$\text{watts} = \text{volts} \times \text{amperes}$$

The watt is the unit of power in the metric system and is used for mechanical power as well as electrical power.

$$\text{Power} = \frac{\text{Work}}{\text{time}}$$

1 watt = 1 volt × 1 ampere = $\frac{1 \text{ joule}}{1 \text{ coulomb}} \cdot \frac{1 \text{ coulomb}}{1 \text{ sec}} = \frac{1 \text{ joule}}{\text{sec}} = \frac{1 \text{ newton-meter}}{\text{sec}}$

Energy in an electric circuit can be measured in *watt-hours*:

$$\text{watt-hours (W-hr)} = \text{watts} \times \text{hours}$$

For example, a 100-watt light bulb burns for 10 hours. It uses 1000 watt-hours of electricity (100 watts × 10 hours = 1000 watt-hours). One *kilowatt-hour* (KWH) is 1000 watt-hours. To change watts to kilowatts, divide by 1000. Electric bills are figured in terms of charge per kilowatt-hour (Table 1–3).

The kw/hr is a unit of energy: $\frac{1 \text{ kw/hr}}{1 \text{ kw}} \cdot \frac{10^3 \text{ watt}}{1 \text{ hr}} \cdot \frac{3600 \text{ sec}}{1 \text{ watt}} \cdot \frac{1 \text{ joule/sec}}{}$

Problems

14. If a 6-V circuit has 30 amp of current, what is the resistance? 0.2 ohm
15. How many kilowatt hours are used by a 500-W heater operated overnight for 10 hr? 5 kw/hr

MAIN IDEAS

1:1 **1.** Objects become electrically charged when they gain or lose electrons.

1:1 **2.** Like charges repel and unlike charges attract.

1:2, 1:3 **3.** A body may be charged by conduction or induction.

1:3 **4.** A body may be grounded by connecting it with a conductor to the earth.

1:4 **5.** Direct current (D.C.) may be produced by static discharge, chemical change, heat, and light.

1:6 **6.** Electricity can produce magnetism. A magnet can induce an alternating current in a conductor.

1:7 **7.** Alternating current (A.C.) may be produced in a conductor by a magnet.

1:7 **8.** The induction of an alternating current changes kinetic energy into electrical energy.

1:8 **9.** The quantity and properties of electricity may be measured in standard units such as ampere, volt, ohm, watt, kilowatt, kilowatt-hour.

1:8 **10.** Many substances conduct electricity. Some materials are better conductors than others.

ELECTRICITY (25M) 409

VOCABULARY

Write a sentence in which you correctly use each of the following words or terms.

alternating current	electricity	ionization
ammeter	electron	magnetism
battery	electroscope	ohm
conductor	electrostatic	thermocouple
diode	galvanometer	volt
direct current	induction	voltmeter
dry cell	insulator	watt
electric generator	ion	wet cell

STUDY QUESTIONS

A. True or False

Determine whether each of the following sentences is true or false. (Do not write in this book.)

Have students rewrite false statements to make the statements correct.

T **1.** A dry cell is a source of electricity.

T **2.** A static charge is an excess of protons or electrons on a body.

T **3.** Hard rubber is a poor conductor of electricity.

T **4.** A charged atom is an ion.

T **5.** An electroscope can be charged by conduction by touching it with a charged rod.

T **6.** A working dry cell battery contains moisture.

F **7.** Photoelectric cells convert ~~electrical~~ energy into ~~light~~ energy. *light, electrical*

T **8.** A magnet will attract cobalt.

T **9.** Glass is a good insulator.

F **10.** All ions have a net charge of zero. *do not*

B. Multiple Choice

Some questions in Parts B and C may have more than one correct answer. Only one answer is required.

Choose one word or phrase that correctly completes each of the following sentences. (Do not write in this book.)

1. A glass rod rubbed with silk has *(a negative charge, <u>a positive charge</u>, no charge).*

2. Electrons are *(uncharged, positively charged, <u>negatively charged</u>)* particles.

3. When the leaves of an electroscope stand apart, the electroscope is *(uncharged, neutral, <u>charged</u>).*

4. Graphite is a(n) *(insulator, natural magnet, conductor)*.
5. Glass and plastic are *(insulators, conductors)*.
6. Two electrons *(repel, attract, neutralize)* each other.
7. A(n) *(voltmeter, ammeter, ohmmeter, electroscope)* gives a reading in amperes.
8. A galvanometer contains a(n) *(electroscope, uncharged rod, magnet and coil)*.
9. When the temperature of a conductor decreases, its resistance *(increases, decreases, remains the same)*.
10. *(Copper, Nickel, Cobalt)* is *not* attracted by a magnet.

C. Completion

Complete each of the following sentences with a word or phrase that will make the sentence correct. *(Do not write in this book.)*

loses   1. A body gains a positive charge when it _____ electrons.

Like   2. _____ charges repel each other.

electroscope   3. The _____ is used to detect static electricity.

insulator   4. Conductor is the opposite of _____ .

direct   5. A wet cell produces _____ current.

generator   6. An electric _____ changes kinetic energy into electrical energy.

induction   7. A.C. is produced by electromagnetic _____ .

watts   8. The power of an electric circuit is measured in _____ .

kilowatt-hours   9. Electric bill charges are figured on the basis of _____ used.

high   10. A poor conductor has _____ resistance.

D. How and Why

friction   1. How is static electricity produced?

kinetic   2. What kind of energy is used to produce static electricity?

See Teacher's Guide.   3. How are chemicals in a wet cell used to produce electricity?

See Teacher's Guide.   4. Compare a diode with a photoelectric cell. How are they alike and different?

See Teacher's Guide.   5. Compare an electric generator with a galvanometer. How are they alike and different?

6 amp   6. A 12-V circuit has a resistance of 2 ohms. Calculate the amperes of current.

Canadian nickel contains nickel and American nickel does not.   7. Why is a Canadian nickel attracted by a magnet and a recently-minted American nickel not attracted?

ELECTRICITY

8. Why is glass used as an insulator by electric companies? What other materials do they use? *inexpensive, others are ceramics and rubber.*
9. Why do some buildings have lightning rods? *to discharge clouds to avoid being struck by lightning*
10. Name four devices used to produce electric current. *wet cell, dry cell, induction coil and magnet, and generator are some examples.*

INVESTIGATIONS

See Teacher's Guide at the front of this book.

1. Visit an electric power plant to learn how electricity is generated.
2. Take an old electric motor apart. Identify the magnets, brushes, and armature. Make a diagram showing the parts.
3. Obtain several magnets of different sizes. Measure the relative strengths of the magnets. Strength may be measured by the number of paper clips or tacks a magnet can raise in a chain.
4. Using an electric bill, calculate the cost of electricity per kilowatt-hour. Divide the amount of the bill by the number of kilowatt-hours used. Make a list of the appliances which probably use the most electricity in your home.

INTERESTING READING

Clifford, Martin, *Basic Electricity and Beginning Electronics*. Blue Ridge Summit, Pa., TAB Books, 1973.

Kennedy, Thomas, Jr., *Fun With Electricity*. New York, Gernsback Library, Inc., 1961.

Noll, Edward M., *Science Projects in Electricity*. New York, Howard Sams & Company, 1963.

The Way Things Work, Volume Two. New York, Simon and Schuster, 1971.

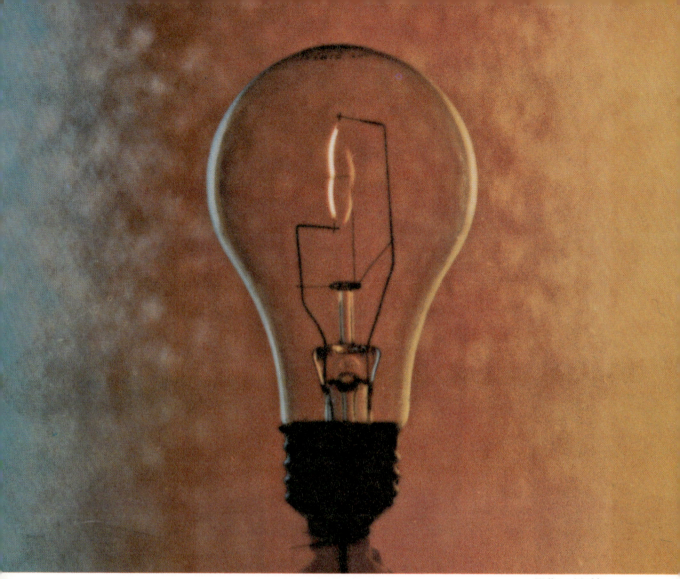

William Maddox

Chapter 2 builds on the study of electricity in Chapter 1 through a discussion of principles involved in electronic devices such as diodes, triodes, rectifiers, transistors, and cathode ray tubes. Computers and other practical applications of electronics are presented and discussed.

 # Electronics

GOAL: You will gain an understanding of the principles involved in electronic devices.

Electronic devices are important for many reasons. Pictures taken on other continents reach their destinations in seconds by means of special satellites. Calculators which were once desk-size are now hand-size. Sewing machines can now be programmed to sew the desired stitch at the touch of a button.

What advances in electronics made these things possible? What other changes in our lives are now possible because of electronics?

CIRCUITS (29M) 413

2:1 Circuits

An electric **circuit** (SUHR kuht) is a pathway through which electric current travels. An electric current is a flow of electrons. The circuit may be connected directly to a power source such as a battery or generator. Also, it may be connected to another circuit. For example, when a television set is plugged into a wall outlet, the television's circuits are connected to the house circuit. A diagram may be made to show the parts of a circuit.

What is a circuit?

Zenith Radio Corp.

Figure 2-1. Electrons flow through the circuits of a television from the household circuits when the set is turned on.

Figure 2-2. Diagram of a circuit.

PROBLEM

1. Using the symbols in Table 2–1, name the parts of the circuit in Figure 2–2. Straight lines represent wires. *See Teacher's Guide.*

a

b
Series circuit
Figure 2-3.

c
Parallel circuit

Time: 50 minutes.

ACTIVITY. **CAUTION:** *If any wires become warm, disconnect battery.* (1) A microlamp is a small electric bulb that can be connected to a circuit. Cut two pieces of bell wire about 30 cm long. Strip 2 cm of insulation from each end of the wires. Use the wires to connect the microlamp to a 6-V battery. Does the lamp light? yes Make a diagram of the circuit. (2) Using pieces of bell wire, connect three microlamps as shown in Figure 2-3b. What happens if you disconnect one of the lamps? none light (3) Connect the three lamps as shown in Figure 2-3c. Disconnect one of the lamps. What do you observe? two light

In a **series** circuit, the same current flows through all parts of the circuit. If one part is disconnected, the current stops. There is no longer a circuit. A **parallel** circuit has branches. If one branch of the circuit is disconnected, current continues in the rest of the circuit. Does your home have series or parallel circuits? What kind of circuit is in a flashlight? series

Time: 30 minutes.

ACTIVITY. **CAUTION:** *If any wires become warm, disconnect battery.* Connect a dry cell, bell, lamp, and switch in an electric circuit. Test your circuit to see if it works. Make a diagram of the circuit, using correct symbols. Did you make a series or parallel circuit? series Draw a diagram of a circuit which would allow the bell and lamp to be operated separately.

Bell   Lamp   Switch   Dry cell

Figure 2-4.

Figure 2-5.

- **Time: 25 minutes.**
  ACTIVITY. Connect an ammeter, lamp, and switch to a 6-V battery. Keep switch open while wiring circuit. Watch ammeter closely as you close the switch. If the needle moves backward, quickly open the switch. Reverse the connections to the ammeter. Did you make a series or parallel circuit? Why? Make a diagram of the circuit.

PROBLEM

2. Draw a diagram of a circuit with an electromagnet, voltmeter, and fuse. See Teacher's Guide at the front of this book.

2:2 Vacuum Tubes
The vacuum tube was invented by Lee DeForest (1873–1961).

Electronics deals with the release, behavior, and effects of electrons. An electron is a tiny particle of negative charge. It has a mass of 9.1×10^{-28} g. Electrons are found in atoms. They can also be found outside atoms under certain conditions.

Radios and televisions contain vacuum tubes. A **vacuum tube** is a gas-tight container. It is usually made of glass. Air has been removed from the tube to form a vacuum. Inside the tube there is an electron source called the *filament*. There is also an electron collector. This is called the *plate*. A vacuum tube is made so that the filament and plate can be connected to an electric circuit. The diode described in Section 1:5 is a vacuum tube.

In a circuit, the part which releases electrons is negatively charged. It is the **cathode** (−). The part of a circuit which gains electrons is positively charged. It is called the **anode** (+). In a vacuum tube, the filament releases electrons and the plate gains electrons. Therefore, the filament is the cathode and the plate is the anode. Electrons travel through a circuit from cathode to anode; that is, from negative to positive.

Vacuum tubes are used in radios, televisions, and stereos. They can be used to **amplify (AM pluh fy) voltage.** Amplify means to increase the **number of volts** in a circuit. When a vacuum tube is used

Explain the operation of a vacuum tube.
Voltage is applied to a cathode which emits electrons. The electrons travel across the vacuum to the plate which is positively charged.

Figure 2-6. A diode is a vacuum tube which has a filament and plate.

Figure 2-7. A triode is a vacuum tube with a filament, plate, and grid (a) Symbols are used to show filament, grid, and plate of a triode. (b).

Most tubes used in radios and TV sets are pentodes, an improvement on the triode which gives greater amplification.

Electrons are released from atoms in a hot filament.

Why do electrons move from the cathode to the anode?
Opposite charges attract. Electrons are negative and are attracted to the positive anode.

as an amplifier, the grid of the tube is connected to a circuit with small voltage. This circuit is called the *input*. The plate of the vacuum tube is connected to a circuit with high voltage. This circuit is called the *output*. The flow of electrons from the hot filament increases the voltage in the output circuit. For example, an amplifier vacuum tube can increase a 1-volt input to a 40-volt output.

Triodes are one type of vacuum tube. They have a filament and plate. In addition, the triode has a *grid* of fine wire between the filament and the plate (Figure 2–7b). The grid controls the flow of electrons between the filament and plate. When the filament is heated by an electric current, electrons "boil off" the filament. An electron "boils off" because heat energy overcomes forces that hold the electrons in the metal. Electrons released from the filament are attracted to the positively charged plate. They pass through the grid in their path from filament (cathode) to plate (anode).

In a triode vacuum tube, the grid is connected to a circuit. This gives it an electric charge. The electric charge in the grid can be increased or decreased. By changing charge, the grid controls the rate at which electrons flow from the filament to the plate. A grid in a triode can be made negative or positive. If the grid is made many times more negative than the filament, it stops the current. The electrons are pushed back toward the filament. Remember, like charges repel each other. As a result, few electrons pass through the grid to the plate. When this happens, the current is about zero. The triode is said to be cut off. As the grid is made less negative, electrons begin to stream through the grid. The flow of electrons makes a current in the plate.

If the grid is made positive, it speeds up the flow of electrons moving from filament to plate. The positive charge on the grid is opposite to the negative charge of the electrons. Since opposite charges attract, more electrons travel from filament to plate. Thus, the output voltage becomes many times greater than the input voltage. The electrons are traveling very fast. They seldom strike the grid. They fly through the openings in the grid and go directly to the plate.

CAPACITORS

The voltage of the output circuit connected to the plate can be increased or decreased. This is done by changing the voltage of the grid. A grid acts like a valve in a water pipe. It controls the flow of electrons and the voltage output. Output voltage can be increased or decreased by changing grid voltage. This causes amplification.

2:3 Capacitors
Condenser is another name for capacitor.

A capacitor (kuh PAS uht uhr) **is a device that stores electricity.** Capacitors have many uses. They are used in electronic photoflash units. The capacitor may be charged from a battery inside the unit. Some photoflash units can also operate on house current. When the capacitor is discharged, its stored electric current flows through the lamp in the unit. The lamp provides the flash of light needed to take the photograph.

A one-tube, battery-operated radio receiver also contains a capacitor (Figure 2–8). Radio waves passing through the air strike the radio antenna. The radio waves cause electrons in the antenna to vibrate. Vibrating electrons form a weak alternating current in the antenna and in the input coil attached to the antenna. Alternating current in the input coil induces an alternating current in the circuit and capacitor. The capacitor in a radio circuit stores electrons for a short time.

Alternating current flows between the capacitor and the grid of the triode vacuum tube. As the charge on the grid changes, the direct current to the speaker is changed. The headphones are operated by electricity from the triode. They produce the sound of the radio. Headphones change electrical energy to sound energy. By using two triodes in a radio circuit, voltage can be amplified again. This makes the radio reception louder.

What is a capacitor?

The behavior of current in a capacitor is similar to the oscillations of a spring from which a weight is suspended. Relate this description of the operation of a simple radio to Figures 2–8 and 2–9.

Figure 2-8. Each part of this radio circuit has a special function. The capacitor stores electricity for a short time.

Figure 2-9. Alternating current flows between the capacitor and the grid of the triode.

Name two uses for a capacitor.
photoflash units, tune radios

Tuning means to adjust the capacitor so that its A.C. frequency is the same as the broadcast radio wave frequency of a station. When tuned the capacitor is in resonance with the radio waves.

A capacitor is used to tune a radio receiver. A tuning capacitor contains two sets of parallel metal plates. The plates of one set fit into the spaces between the plates of the other set. One set of plates is in a fixed position. The other set can be turned by hand. One set is connected to the cathode of a circuit. The other set is connected to the anode. By rotating the movable set of plates, the area of overlap is changed.

When the two sets of plates are in close alignment, the capacitor holds its greatest charge of electricity. The amount of charge decreases as the amount of overlap between the plates decreases. The electrical storing capacity of the capacitor is changed by rotating one set of plates with a knob. Frequency of the alternating current in the circuit is changed by changing the capacity of the capacitor. That is, turning the knob changes the frequency. When the capacitor holds a large charge, the plates are close together. The frequency is low. When the capacitor holds a small charge, the plates overlap very little. The frequency is high.

To tune a radio set, you adjust the capacitor with a knob until you hear the station you want. You set the capacitor plates so that

Figure 2-10. In a capacitor used to tune a radio receiver, there are two sets of parallel metal plates. The plates are moved closer together when changing from a high frequency to a low frequency radio station.

418 (34M)

Figure 2-11. Tuning a television set is similar to tuning a radio. Television waves from the station's antenna are received by the television's antenna. The tuner selects only the signals wanted by the viewer.

Different radio and TV stations broadcast at different broadcast frequencies.

the alternating current frequency is equal to the radio waves sent out by the radio station. For example, station **KDKA** in Pittsburgh has a broadcast frequency of 1020 kilohertz/sec or 1,020,000 vib/sec. A radio receiver tuned to this station has an alternating current of the same frequency in its circuit. Changing a station means a shift to another radio wave frequency. When a shift is made from a high frequency to a low frequency radio station, the plates are moved closer together.

Time: 30 minutes.

ACTIVITY. Electric charge can be stored in a Leyden (LYD uhn) jar. (1) Line and coat a jar with aluminum foil or coat the inside and outside with aluminum paint. Place a clean bare copper wire inside the bottle. Stand the bottle on a piece of bare copper wire. (2) Charge the Leyden jar by connecting the two wires to an electrostatic generator. (3) Disconnect the generator and discharge the jar with a loop of wire attached to a nonconducting handle. Touch the ends of the loop to the two wires connected to the jar. yes

Is a Leyden jar a capacitor? What charge is produced on the inside of the jar? On the outside of the jar? What material used *serves* as an insulator? The Leyden jar has two metal plates separated by an insulator. Opposite charges (− and +) are produced on the two plates. Glass is the insulator.

Figure 2-12.

419 (35M)

Figure 2-13. Battery chargers contain rectifiers which change A.C. to D.C.

William Maddox

2:4 Rectifiers

Most electrical appliances in the home use alternating current supplied by a power station. However, some electrical devices use direct current. One example is a battery charger. To recharge a battery, direct current must be sent backwards through the battery from the cathode to the anode. A battery charger contains a rectifier. The **rectifier** (REK tuh fyr) changes alternating current to direct current.

What is the function of a rectifier?

PROBLEM

3. A battery cannot be recharged by A.C. Why not? *When a battery is recharged current is pumped from cathode to anode. A.C. current would alternate cathode to anode—anode to cathode.*

Many battery chargers contain a gas-filled tube called the "tungar rectifier." The tube of the tungar rectifier contains a filament and a plate. It is filled with a noble gas, such as argon, under low pressure. A *noble gas* does not chemically combine with other substances under ordinary conditions.

The filament of the tungar rectifier is heated by an alternating current. Because the gas is not chemically active, the filament does not burn when heated. Electrons "boil off" the filament and travel toward the positive plate. These electrons knock loose electrons which are normally attached to the gas atoms. The atoms become charged positively. Charged atoms are called ions. The gas in the tube is said to be ionized because it contains many ions. An ionized gas conducts electricity.

Electrons in the tube can flow in only one direction—filament to plate.

The tungar rectifier changes the alternating current in the filament to direct current in the plate. Positive ions go to the negative

Explain the operation of a tungar rectifier.

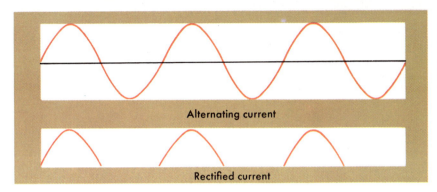

Figure 2-14. In rectified current (D.C.) an electron is forced constantly ahead through the circuit. It does not vibrate back to its original position as it would in A.C. current.

filament (cathode). At the same time, electrons stream away from the filament to the positive plate (anode). From here they go into the output circuit. The current produced in the output circuit attached to the plate is direct current. In a direct current, electrons flow in one direction only.

There are many different kinds of rectifiers. For instance, both diode and triode vacuum tubes act as rectifiers. Since an X-ray tube is a diode, it acts as a rectifier.

PROBLEM

4. Use Figure 2–14 to explain how a diode acts as a rectifier. See Teacher's Guide.

2:5 *Cathode-Ray Tube*

A television picture is produced on the surface of a cathode-ray tube. A **cathode-ray tube** is a special kind of vacuum tube. Radar sets, some computers, and various kinds of electrical testing equipment also contain cathode-ray tubes.

What is a cathode-ray tube?
It is a special kind of vacuum tube with a filament and a screen coated with fluorescent material.

Figure 2-15. Cathode ray tubes produce beams of light on a fluorescent screen.

Figure 2-16. Bright spots, called "pips," are produced on a radar screen.

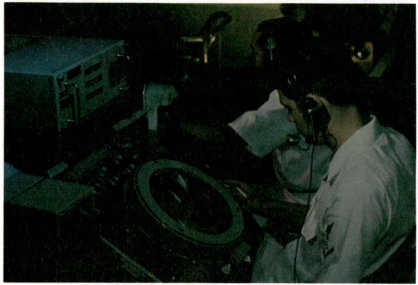

U.S. Naval Photographic Center

A cathode-ray tube contains a filament and a screen coated with fluorescent material. The cathode-ray tube takes its name from rays of electrons. Electrons stream from the negative cathode filament to the screen at the opposite end of the tube. Electrons in the cathode-ray are given off from the heated filament. They form a beam directed at the screen on the face of the tube. Fluorescent material on the screen glows when it is struck by electrons. It gives off visible light at each point where an electron beam strikes the fluorescent material.

The electron beam moves across the screen. In this way it produces a pattern of light which conveys information. In a radar receiver, a bright spot may appear. It is called a "pip." The pip shows the location of a moving airplane. In an electronic computer, numbers showing the solution to a problem may appear on the screen. The computer is designed to "read out" answers with a cathode-ray tube. The picture tube of a television set is a cathode-ray tube. The electron beam moves swiftly back and forth across the fluorescent face of the tube. This movement forms the picture.

Name three uses for a cathode-ray tube.

radar, computers, television

Caution: All of these electron tubes operate on extremely high voltages. You may wish to perform this activity as a teacher demonstration.

Figure 2-17.

Time: 40 minutes.

ACTIVITY. How is a beam of electrons affected by a magnet? (1) Bring the S-pole of a bar magnet near the beam of a Crookes tube or a cathode-ray tube. Repeat with the N-pole of the magnet. (2) Repeat this activity with magnets of different strength. Does the strength of the magnet make a difference? Yes. Beam is deflected more by stronger magnet.

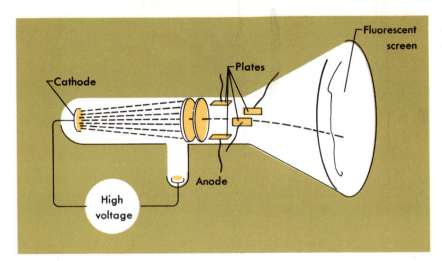

Figure 2-18. Cathode ray tubes are used in oscilloscopes, radar, and television receivers to present information visually.

Either electrostatic charge or magnets control the movement of an electron beam in a cathode-ray tube. When controlled by electrostatic charge, the beam passes through charged plates. The charge on the plates varies. So the beam can be moved both horizontally and vertically as the charge is changed.

Large cathode-ray tubes contain electromagnets. An example is the picture tube in a black and white television set. The cathode ray in the picture tube is deflected or bent from its path by the magnetic fields. By varying the strength of the electromagnets, the cathode ray can be moved both horizontally and vertically. The electron beam scans the screen by moving back and forth and up and down on the screen many times per second.

The electromagnet can force the cathode ray into different positions, depending on the strength of the magnet.

Magnets and charged plates are used to focus electrons in beams much as glass lenses are used to focus light beams.

William Maddox

Figure 2-19. Bright spots, produced by electrons striking the screen, are blended with dark spots by the eye and brain. This results in a picture on the TV screen.

Electromagnets in a television set are controlled by television waves coming to the antenna. Changes in the magnetic fields regulate the path of the electron beam. The magnets regulate the number of electrons that strike the screen at different spots. Each spot hit by electrons glows for a fraction of a second. Your eye and brain blend the bright spots and the dark areas into a picture.

PROBLEM

5. Why can an electromagnet control the position of an electron beam in a cathode-ray tube?

The strength of the electromagnet can be varied. Poles, attracting or repelling a varying amount of negatively charged electrons, can cause the beam to change position.

2:6 *Transistors*

The principle of the transistor was discovered in 1948, a discovery for which W.H. Brattain, John Bardeen, and W.B. Shockley received the Nobel Prize in 1956.

Transistors (tranz IS tuhrz) have replaced vacuum tubes for many uses. They make pocket radios, portable TV sets, and desk-top computers possible. The transistor has unique advantages. It is long-lasting and small. A typical transistor is about 0.5 to 2.0 cm in size (Figure 2–20a). Transistors operate on very low voltage. For example, a transistor radio can operate on low voltage (3-V to 12-V) batteries. Yet, it can produce sound volume equal to a vacuum tube radio connected to a 110-volt house circuit. Transistors often replace vacuum tubes in the circuits of other electronic equipment.

A transistor is a germanium (juhr MAY nee uhm) or silicon (SIL ih kuhn) crystal. It has either an excess or a lack of free electrons. A *free electron* is an electron that can drift through the crystal if a voltage is applied. *Germanium* is a gray-white, brittle, crystalline metal. It is 5.4 times as dense as water. Germanium is obtained from the residues of certain zinc ores. *Silicon* is the second most plentiful element on the earth. It makes up about one fourth of the crust of the earth. It is 2.4 times as dense as water. Silicon is present in quartz

Why have transistors replaced some vacuum tubes?
They are smaller, more reliable, long-lasting, and comparatively costly.

A large electronic computer may contain more than 100,000 transistors.

Impurities in transistor crystals are sometimes called doping agents and their addition to a crystal is called doping.

Figure 2-20. Transistors are smaller than vacuum tubes (a). They are often used in radios, televisions, and calculators (b).

Don Parsisson   *Will Miles*

INTEGRATED CIRCUITS

and many other minerals. Pure silicon is a nonmetallic element with several forms. The crystalline form is used in transistors.

Both germanium and silicon are semiconductors. A *semiconductor* is a substance with a resistance between that of a conductor and an insulator. Pure germanium has a resistance 46,000 times that of copper! Impurities in germanium, however, greatly reduce this resistance. For example, the addition of one-millionth of one percent of arsenic to pure germanium doubles its conductivity at room temperature. Increase the impurities in a germanium crystal, or other semiconductors, and electrical conductivity increases.

Figure 2-21. Integrated circuits are often made in chips of silicon crystals.

2:7 Integrated Circuits

A recent advance in electronics is the development of the integrated circuit. An **integrated circuit** is a very small electronic device capable of doing many complex jobs. Like a transistor, it is long-lasting and reliable. Many are made in chips of silicon crystals.

Integrated circuits are often used instead of wired circuits. Wired circuits are made up of many parts which take up a lot of space. However, integrated circuits are a hundred times smaller and lighter than a wired circuit. Small size and low cost are the main advantages of this device.

Why are integrated circuits used instead of wired circuits?
smaller size, lighter, more reliable

Integrated circuits were first used in spacecraft and other military equipment. Today, they are often found in radios, televisions, and cars. Computers depend upon them for their reliability. Digital watches, hand-held calculators, and electronic sewing machines are now possible because of the integrated circuit.

Edward Young

Figure 2-22. Integrated circuits are often mounted on circuit boards. Shown here is a memory stack of a computer which uses printed circuit boards.

Figure 2-23. Small hand calculators use integrated circuits instead of transistors.

2:8 Computers

Computers are used to solve problems in mathematics, control traffic, navigate ships, forecast weather, and compose music. The uses of computers are almost endless.

Electronic **computers** are very complex machines. They contain electric circuits and electronic devices such as vacuum tubes, transistors, integrated circuits, and electromagnets. A computer can solve difficult equations with only a few numbers. In computing an answer, it follows known mathematical operations. A computer can add, subtract, multiply, and divide in a small fraction of the time it takes a person.

Computers are classified as analog and digital. An *analog* is something which is similar to something else. For example, a basketball is an analog of the earth. Both have a spherical shape and can be made to rotate on an axis. An ordinary mercury thermometer is another example of an analog device. The up-and-down movement of mercury in the thermometer is the analog of temperature change. As the temperature increases, the mercury moves up the thermometer. As the temperature decreases, the mercury moves down. An analog computer works by making a model of real things or mathematical values. The model is made by electric circuits or moving parts, such as rotating wheels.

An electronic analog computer is made with electronic circuits. The equations for the circuits are the same as for the problem the computer is built to solve. For example, an analog computer can be built to calculate the thrust (force) of a rocket. The equation for the thrust of a rocket is thrust = mass × acceleration, or $T = ma$.

Computers can be used not only for solving mathematical problems, but also for comparing data, making predictions from data, recording complex motions, analyzing complex data, and simulating any kind of program that can be programmed. The computer seems to be limited only by the limit of the computer's capabilities and the programmer's imagination.

What is an analog computer?

An analog computer uses electronic circuits to solve problems.

William Maddox

Figure 2-24. Speedometers are analog devices. The right and left movement of the indicator is an analog of speed changes.

Ohm's law (Section 1:8) states that the voltage in a circuit is the product of resistance times current. The equation is voltage = resistance × current, or $V = RI$. This equation for an electric circuit is similar to the equation for finding a rocket's thrust. Ohm's law equation is an analog of the rocket thrust equation.

Figure 2–25 shows a simplified version of an analog circuit built to solve the rocket thrust problem. Voltage (V) is the analog of thrust (T). Resistance (R) is the analog of mass (m). Current (I) is the analog of acceleration (a).

When the current (I) is turned on by closing the switch, it is multiplied by the resistance setting (R). The product RI is the voltage. It can be read on the dial of the voltmeter. The value of the computed voltage is the analog of the rocket's thrust.

The *digital* computer is smaller, faster, and more reliable than an analog computer. This is due to the development of the transistor and the integrated circuit. For this reason, they are more popular than the analog computer. Many companies use digital computers for payroll checks, credit ratings, and billing.

Why are digital computers used more than analog computers?
smaller, faster, more reliable

Figure 2-25. Simplified version of an analog computer circuit.

427 (43M)

Figure 2-26. Digital computers are used in many businesses.

Edward Young

Name the five major units in a digital computer.
input, storage, output, arithmetic, control

The digital computer operates with numbers. It has five major units: input, output, storage, arithmetic, and control. **Input** is information sent into the circuits of a computer. The *input unit* can be operated by keyboard, punched cards, punched paper tape, or magnetic tape. The input unit enters information, numbers, and problem-solving instructions in the form of a *program*. The program enters the *storage unit,* the computer's "memory." Information obtained from a computer's circuits is called **output.** The *output unit* records the results of the computer's computation. In other words, it gives the answer to the problem put into the computer. A computer may give out information in one or more ways. It may punch cards or paper tape, record on magnetic tape, or print words and numbers.

In a digital computer, the *arithmetic unit* performs operations needed to solve the problem. The *control unit* acts on earlier instructions put into the storage unit. It regulates the operation of the computer.

Figure 2-27. Digital computers have five major units.

428 (44M)

Edward Young

Figure 2-28. Computer programs enter a computer by means of a keyboard, punched cards, or magnetic tape.

PROBLEM

6. Classify the following devices as analog or digital:

hourglass a	abacus d	ammeter a
slide rule d	fingers d	voltmeter a
clock a	telephone dial d	odometer a
Geiger counter d	hygrometer a	spring scale a

MAIN IDEAS

2:1   **1.** The pathway through which an electric current flows is an electric circuit.

2:2   **2.** A vacuum tube is an electronic device.

2:2   **3.** Electrons travel from cathode ($-$) to anode ($+$).

2:2   **4.** The filament inside a vacuum tube is a cathode. The plate is an anode.

2:2   **5.** The grid in a triode tube controls the voltage output.

2:3   **6.** A capacitor stores electricity.

2:4   **7.** Rectifiers change alternating current to direct current.

2:5   **8.** A cathode-ray tube contains a controlled beam of electrons.

2:6   **9.** Transistors contain semiconductors and amplify current.

2:6 **10.** Impurities increase the electrical conductivity of semiconductors such as silicon and germanium.

2:7 **11.** Integrated circuits are very small and often take the place of large wired circuits.

2:8 **12.** Electronic computers use electricity to solve mathematical problems.

VOCABULARY

Write a sentence in which you correctly use each of the following words or terms.

alternating current	computer	rectifier
analog	diode	semiconductor
anode	electronics	series circuit
capacitor	input	transistor
cathode	integrated circuit	triode
cathode-ray tube	output	vacuum tube
circuit	parallel circuit	voltmeter

STUDY QUESTIONS

Have students rewrite false statements to make the statements correct.

A. True or False

Determine whether each of the following sentences is true or false. (Do not write in this book.)

cathode, anode   F **1.** Electrons flow through a circuit from ~~anode~~ to ~~cathode~~.

repel   F **2.** Like charges ~~attract~~ each other.

T **3.** A rectifier changes alternating current to direct current.

negative   F **4.** The ~~positive~~ plate of a vacuum tube is called the cathode.

T **5.** An analog is a model of something.

T **6.** A vacuum tube can increase voltage.

negatively   F **7.** An electron is ~~positively~~ charged.

electrons   F **8.** Electricity is the flow of ~~protons~~ through a circuit.

T **9.** A capacitor can store electricity.

T **10.** A charged atom is called an ion.

Some questions in Parts B and C may have more than one correct answer. Only one answer is required.

B. Multiple Choice

Choose one word or phrase that correctly completes each of the following sentences. (Do not write in this book.)

1. The *(filament, plate, grid)* of a triode is a cathode.

2. The voltage output of a triode is controlled by the *(filament, plate, grid).*

3. A *(triode, diode, capacitor, transistor)* is used to store electricity.

4. As the two sets of plates in a capacitor are moved farther apart,

ELECTRONICS (47M) 431

the amount of charge the capacitor can hold *(increases, <u>decreases</u>, remains the same)*.

5. The symbol ─┤│┊│├─ in an electric circuit diagram is a *(<u>battery</u>, switch, bell)*.
6. Germanium and silicon are *(conductors, insulators, <u>semiconductors</u>)*.
7. The electrical conductivity of pure germanium is *(the same as, <u>less than</u>, greater than)* that of impure germanium.
8. Transistors operate on voltages *(more than, <u>less than</u>, the same as)* a vacuum tube.
9. A cathode-ray tube is most like a *(<u>rectifier</u>, triode, transistor)*.
10. Information sent into a computer's circuits is called *(output, storage, <u>input</u>)*.

C. Completion

Complete each of the following sentences with a word or phrase that will make the sentence correct. (Do not write in this book.)

1. The movement of the beam of electrons in a cathode-ray tube is regulated by _____ . charged plates
2. A(n) _____ is an example of an analog device. Answers will vary.
3. The five units of a digital computer are the _____ , _____ , _____ , _____ , and _____ . input, storage, arithmetic, output, control
4. A computer _____ is a set of instructions for computing the answer to a mathematical problem. program
5. A(n) _____ is a gas-tight container. vacuum tube
6. Information from a computer's circuits is called _____ . output
7. The _____ unit of a digital computer performs operations that solve problems. arithmetic
8. _____ is the study of the behavior of electrons. Electronics
9. A(n) _____ circuit only works when all parts are connected. series
10. A(n) _____ is a device that stores electricity. capacitor

D. How and Why

See Teacher's Guide at the front of this book.

1. How is a triode different from a diode vacuum tube?
2. Why must the two sets of plates in a capacitor contain opposite charges when the capacitor is connected to a battery?

3. How is an electric current in an ionized gas similar to an electric current in a solution?
4. How does a rectifier change alternating current to direct current?
5. What are some of the main uses of vacuum tubes?
6. Describe an experiment you could perform to show that a magnet deflects a beam of electrons.
7. Why have transistors replaced vacuum tubes in many electronic devices?
8. Explain why a thermometer, speedometer, tree, and thermostat are analog devices.
9. Why is the development of the integrated circuit important?
10. How do you tune a radio? What is actually happening?

See Teacher's Guide at the front of this book.

INVESTIGATIONS

1. Many stores have vacuum tube testing machines. Obtain several used vacuum tubes and learn how to test them.
2. Arrange to visit a TV repair shop. Find out what kinds of electronic equipment are used to test and repair television sets.
3. Learn how a color television set works. A library book on television is a good starting point.
4. Build a crystal radio. An encyclopedia or book about radio will tell you how.
5. Write a report on various uses of the integrated circuit in industry.

INTERESTING READING

Asimov, Isaac, "Happy Birthday, Transistor." *Saturday Review,* LV (October 23, 1972), pp. 45–51.

Bender, Alfred, *Let's Explore with the Electron.* New York, Sentinel Book Publishers, Inc., 1960.

Berger, Melvin, *Computers* (Science Is What & Why Book Series). New York, Coward, McCann & Geoghegan, Inc., 1972.

Cahn, William and Rhoda, *The Story of Writing: Communication From Cave Art to Computer.* Irving-on-Hudson, New York, Harvey House, Inc., Publishers, 1963.

Carroll, John M., *Secrets of Electronic Espionage*. New York, E. P. Dutton & Company, Inc., 1966.

Goldman, H. L., "Nikola Tesla's Bold Adventure." *American West,* VIII (March, 1971), pp. 4–9.

Halacy, D. S., Jr., *Computers: The Machines We Think With*. New York, Dell Publishing Company, Inc., 1962.

Morgan, Alfred, *First Electrical Book for Boys*. New York, Charles Scribner's Sons, 1962.

Morgan, Alfred, *The Boy's Third Book of Radio and Electronics*. New York, Charles Scribner's Sons, 1962.

Rowland, John, *The Television Man: The Story of John L. Baird*. New York, Roy Publishers, Inc., 1966.

U.S. Energy Research and Development Administration

Chapter 3 discusses radiation, its detection, and measurement. The students will become acquainted with the concepts of natural radioactivity, artificial radioactivity, and half-life. Some aspects are studied within the framework of the historical development of the science of nuclear physics.

3 Radiation

GOAL: You will gain an understanding of radiation and the methods for the detection and measurement of radiation.

Uranium, because of its radioactivity, can "take its own picture." A sheet of color negative film is placed directly on the uranium in the dark. The film is exposed to radiation for 18 hours. After the film is processed normally, the features of the uranium can be seen on the photograph. Why can radiation produce images on film in the dark? What are other characteristics of radiation?

3:1 X rays

An important discovery was made in 1895 by the German physicist, W. K. Roentgen (RENT guhn, 1845–1923). Roentgen passed an electric current through a discharge tube. A fluorescent (flur ES uhnt) screen placed nearby took on a greenish glow. A *fluorescent material* glows when exposed to radiation. **Radiation** is the energy given off when atoms and molecules change internally. Roentgen reasoned that an unknown kind of radiation was given off by the electric discharge tube. He called the radiation **X rays.** X stood for unknown. Other experiments showed that a beam of electrons produces X rays when the electrons strike a solid such as glass. The beam of electrons is called a cathode ray. We now know that X rays are a form of electromagnetic radiation. X rays have a wavelength of about 1×10^{-9} to 5×10^{-6} cm.

Mercury vapor inside the fluorescent lamp produces radiation when an electric current is passing through it. Radiation strikes the fluorescent coating to emit light.

What are X rays?

Figure 3-1. X rays have wavelengths about 1000 times smaller than those of visible light waves.

Ultra-Violet Products, Inc.

Figure 3-2. These two photos show the same fluorescent rock under normal light (a) and ultraviolet light (b).

Figure 3-3. X rays are sometimes used to control insect populations. Here, a biology technician uses radiation to sterilize insects.

The wavelengths of visible light are longer than those of X rays; the wavelengths of radio waves are longer than those of visible light.

How are X rays produced?

The anode in an X-ray tube must be cooled or the heat produced will cause it to deteriorate. The wavelengths of X rays are about 1000 times smaller than those of visible light waves.

PROBLEM

1. How does the wavelength of X rays compare with the wavelength of visible blue light? of radio waves (Figure 3–1)?

X rays can be produced in an X-ray tube. An X-ray tube is a high voltage cathode-ray tube. It contains a metal target and a metal filament. Voltages as high as 100,000 volts are common for an X-ray tube. The target is a dense metal, such as tungsten, set into a copper electrode. The filament in the X-ray tube is heated by the electric current in the high-voltage circuit (Section 2:1). Electrons "boil off" the hot filament. The target has a positive charge so the electrons rush toward it because opposite charges attract. The electrons stream from the negative filament to the positive target (Figure 3–4). When the electrons strike the metal target, X rays are emitted (released) by the metal.

Why do electrons produce X rays when they strike a tungsten target? A moving electron has kinetic energy. When a high-speed electron penetrates the tungsten, it collides with a tungsten atom. Often, the electron must collide with several atoms before it is stopped. Some of the kinetic energy, lost by the electron when it is stopped, changes into X rays. Actually, one percent or less of the kinetic energy is changed to X-ray radiation. The rest becomes heat energy of the target.

X rays travel at the speed of light, about 3×10^8 m/sec. They are emitted by an X-ray tube in tiny "bundles" of energy which are

Figure 3-4. Varying the temperature of the filament in an X-ray tube varies the number of electrons striking the target which emits X rays.

called **photons** (FOH tahnz). The energy of one photon of X rays varies directly with the wave frequency. X rays range in frequency from 3×10^{11} to 6×10^{17} vibrations per second. The higher the frequency, the greater the energy in one photon.

What is a photon?

Time: 40 minutes.
ACTIVITY. Can a cathode-ray tube discharge an electroscope? Charge an electroscope with a charged plastic or hard rubber rod. Aim the beam of an operating Crookes tube or cathode-ray tube at the electroscope knob. Measure the time it takes for the electroscope leaves to fall. Why do the electroscope leaves fall? How are charged particles produced by the cathode-ray tube? Would the leaves fall less rapidly if the cathode-ray tube were covered with a lead sheet? Explain your answer.

X rays produced by the tube ionize (remove electrons from) air molecules which are attracted to the electroscope where they neutralize its charge. Lead sheet shields the electroscope from radiation.

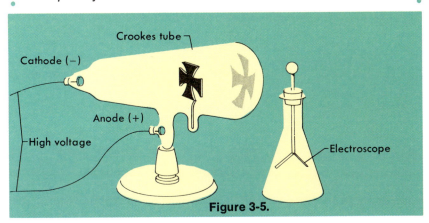

Figure 3-5.

All substances, including gases, absorb X rays to some degree. The amount of absorption depends upon the density of the material. For example, bone absorbs more X rays than flesh. Lead absorbs

437 (53M)

Figure 3-6. X-ray photographs of teeth and internal bone structure are helpful in dental treatment.

Name the main properties of X rays.

X-ray diffraction photographs are also used to probe the structure of molecules. For example, the structure of DNA, deoxyribonucleic acid (Watson-Crick model), was determined from X-ray diffraction studies. DNA is the genetic material in living cell nuclei through which hereditary traits are passed from one generation to another.

more than aluminum. You may have had X rays taken by a doctor or dentist. Why can X rays be used to make pictures of internal body parts? X rays may be displayed by taping them to glass windows.

Properties of X rays
(1) travel in a straight line at the speed of light, 3×10^8 m/sec
(2) make a fluorescent screen glow
(3) pass through many solid substances, such as flesh
(4) are greatly absorbed by dense substances, such as bone, iron, and lead
(5) cast shadows of dense objects on a fluorescent screen
(6) expose a photographic film
(7) produce ions in a gas
(8) are not deflected by electric charges or magnetic fields
(9) burn flesh that is exposed to them too long

X rays are used to detect the order and spacing of atoms in substances. If a narrow beam of X rays is passed through a crystal, the X rays are *diffracted* by the atoms in the crystal.

Figure 3–7 shows a diffraction pattern. These patterns are produced because rows of atoms in a crystal affect X rays. The X rays change direction when they strike an atom. This is similar to the way a diffraction grating affects light. Light rays, passing through the slits, reinforce or cancel each other.

Figure 3-7. X-ray diffraction patterns show the atom arrangement in a crystal (a). The big spot in the center of the diffraction pattern corresponds to the main unscattered beam. Other spots represent a scattering of the original beam through various angles (b).

Spots form in an X-ray diffraction pattern when the waves are reinforced. Spots do not form where the waves are not in phase. The waves cancel each other, or destructive interference occurs. X-ray diffraction patterns help to show the arrangement of atoms in a crystal.

3:2 The Roentgen

X rays and other high-energy radiation can be harmful. Too much can cause burns, illness, and death. The standard unit used to measure radiation is the **roentgen.** This unit is based on the number of ions produced in a gas. One roentgen is the amount of radiation that will produce 2.08×10^9 pairs of negative and positive ions in 1 cm^3 of air at standard conditions. Standard conditions are 0°C and 760 mm of air pressure. A chest X ray uses about 0.5 roentgen.

The amount and time of exposure to radiation determine its harmful effects. Large doses in a short time or small doses over a long period can be fatal. Exposure of up to 0.3 roentgen per week for the entire body is considered fairly safe. Lead absorbs most X rays. Thus, it is used to shield X-ray equipment. X-ray technicians also wear lead-coated aprons.

Figure 3-8. Lead-coated aprons protect patients from X rays.

What is a roentgen?
A roentgen is a standard unit of radiation.

How are people protected from X rays?
Lead can be used to shield people from X rays.

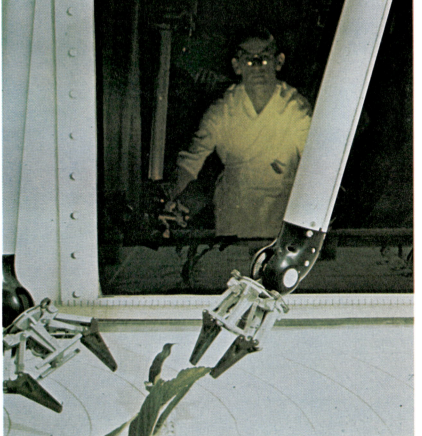

U.S.D.A.

Figure 3-9. Radioactive materials must be handled with care. Mechanical arms are used to handle materials exposed to radiation. The arms are controlled from the other side of a specially-shielded window.

RADIATION

3:3 Radioactivity

Certain atoms emit invisible high-energy radiation from their nuclei. These atoms are **radioactive.** As the radiation is released, the element decays and becomes a different element. Decay means to lose nuclear particles.

Radioactivity was discovered by a French physicist, Henri Becquerel (bek uh REL, 1852–1908), in 1896. He accidently left some uranium salt lying on a photographic plate in a dark desk drawer. When he developed the plate, Becquerel was surprised to find a silhouette of the uranium salt. Experimenting further, he proved that uranium releases radiant energy.

In 1898, Marie (1867–1934) and Pierre (1859–1906) Curie discovered two new radioactive elements. These elements were named polonium and radium. The Curies extracted them from pitchblende, a uranium ore. The radioactivity of one gram of polonium or radium is greater than the radioactivity of one gram of uranium.

Radioactivity usually occurs naturally in atoms heavier than lead. Such atoms have an atomic mass number greater than 206. However, many natural isotopes of lighter elements are radioactive. Remember, isotopes are atoms of the same element with different numbers of neutrons. For example, potassium, rubidium, and carbon each have radioactive isotopes.

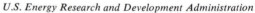
U.S. Energy Research and Development Administration

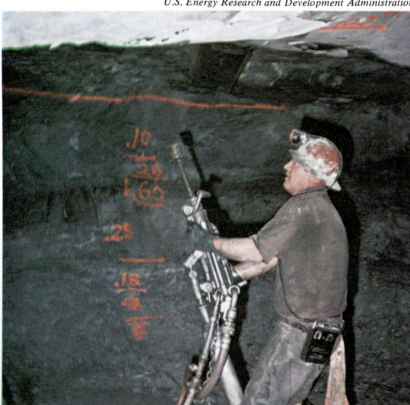

Figure 3-10. Uranium ore is extracted from rocks much like other ores.

Sidenotes:

Distinguish between X rays produced by energy changes in atomic electrons and radioactivity produced by energy changes in the nucleus.

What is radioactivity?
Radioactivity is an invisible high-energy radiation emitted spontaneously from the nuclei of certain atoms.

Radioactivity is a physical property and not a chemical property.

Name three radioactive elements.
Three examples of radioactive elements are U 230, Po 210, and Ra 226.

What elements are naturally radioactive?

PEOPLE CAREERS FRONTIERS
FOCUS ON PHYSICAL SCIENCE

Dr. Llewellya Hillis-Colinvaus

Dr. Hillis-Colinvaus is studying marine life in a controlled environment room.

Dr. Llewellya Hillis-Colinvaus is a marine biologist. She is currently studying the effects of radiation. She became interested in the effects of radiation as a result of a dive to the bottom of an atomic bomb crater in the Pacific Ocean. This crater was created from the testing of atomic devices in the 1950's.

Dr. Hillis-Colinvaus was interested in the plant life in this area of nuclear testing. The study of sea plants is her specialty. She collected some of the plants from this Pacific area. Upon analysis, she found that the plants contained more radiation than plants in surrounding waters.

She plans to continue research in this area. Her goal is to find out how long it takes radiation to clear from plants and animals which have been exposed to radiation.

Courtesy of *The Columbus Dispatch*.

Dr. Chien Shiung Wu

Dr. Wu is a nuclear physicist. She is often called a "modern Madam Curie" because of her many brilliant achievements. One of her experiments conducted in the late 1950's disproved what was thought to be a basic law in physics. She has been recognized for this work around the world.

Dr. Wu has been a professor of physics at Columbia University in New York City for more than thirty years. She is also active in nuclear physics research.

Currently, Dr. Wu is using nuclear physics to study sickle cell anemia. She is also engaged in nuclear research at the bottom of a salt mine near Cleveland, Ohio.

Dr. Wu is well qualified for her work. She attended the National Central University in China and received a bachelor's degree in physics. At the age of twenty-two she came to the United States. She completed a Ph.D. in nuclear physics at the University of California, Berkeley.

Courtesy of the American Association of Physics Teachers.

Dr. Wu is involved in many nuclear physics experiments.

American Association of Physics Teachers

3:4 Radioactive Isotopes

How are radioactive isotopes produced?

The radioactive isotopes of some elements occur in nature. In addition, radioactive isotopes may be produced in the laboratory. These are made by bombarding elements with high-speed neutrons or charged particles. Some natural and artificially made radioactive elements are listed in Table 3-1.

Table 3-1. Radioactive Elements

Element	At. Number (protons)	At. Mass Number (protons + neutrons)
Natural		
Polonium (Po)	84	210
Astatine (At)	85	210
Radon (Rn)	86	222
Francium (Fr)	87	223
Radium (Ra)	88	226
Actinium (Ac)	89	227
Thorium (Th)	90	232
Protactinium (Pa)	91	231
Uranium (U)	92	238
Artificial		
Neptunium (Np)	93	237
Plutonium (Pu)	94	242
Americium (Am)	95	243
Curium (Cm)	96	245
Berkelium (Bk)	97	245
Californium (Cf)	98	249
Einsteinium (E)	99	254
Fermium (Fm)	100	252
Mendelevium (Md)	101	256
Nobelium (No)	102	251
Lawrencium (Lw)	103	257

The proton-neutron ratio in the nucleus of an atom determines nuclear stability.

Figure 3-11. Stable (non-radioactive) nuclei form an area of stability on this graph. When the ratio of protons to neutrons is about 1:1, the nucleus is stable.

Why are certain isotopes radioactive? This depends upon the number of protons and neutrons a nucleus contains. When the ratio of protons to neutrons in an atom is about 1:1, the nucleus of the atom is stable. **Stable** means that the nucleus is not radioactive. Carbon 12 is an example of a stable atom. It has six protons and six neutrons. The ratio of protons to neutrons in carbon 12 is 1:1.

When there are more neutrons than protons in an atom, that element or its isotope may be radioactive. Carbon 14 has six protons and eight neutrons and is radioactive. Many of the common elements have radioactive isotopes (Table 3-2).

Table 3-2. Radioactive Isotopes of Some Common Elements

Isotope	Protons	Neutrons
Tritium (hydrogen 3)	1	2
Helium 5	2	3
Lithium 8	3	5
Carbon 14	6	8
Nitrogen 16	7	9
Potassium 40	19	21

Most radioactive elements have more neutrons than protons. Uranium 238, for example, has 92 protons and 146 neutrons.

PROBLEM

2. What is the ratio of protons to neutrons in elements with $Z = 92$ and $Z = 103$? Are these elements radioactive? See Teacher's Guide.

Note: Radiation can also kill healthy cells.

Artificially-made radioactive isotopes have many practical uses. Radiation from radioactive isotopes such as cobalt 60 is used to treat cancer. High-energy radiation kills cancer cells. Radioactive isotopes are also used to trace the movement of an element in a plant or animal. For example, phosphorus 32 placed in the soil around a plant will be absorbed into the plant. The movement of the phosphorus 32 through the plant can be followed with a Geiger counter. Since a radioactive isotope can be traced, it is called a "tagged atom." Its radiation is a tag which allows it to be detected.

Name two uses for radioactive isotopes.
Treatment of cancer, tracers in plants and animals, and detection of tumors are examples.

Radioactive isotopes are also used to detect tumors and other diseases in organs. A small amount can be injected into the blood which carries it to the organ. Detailed X rays can then be taken of that organ.

William Maddox

Figure 3-12. Radioactive isotopes can be used to detect the areas of blockage in a coronary artery. In this X ray, the blockages shown were the cause of a major heart attack.

Figure 3-13. Alpha particles are helium nuclei, beta particles are electrons, and gamma rays are energy waves.

Define transmutation.

In transmutation, the number of protons in the nucleus of an atom is changed. Thus, an atom of a different element is formed.

How are gamma rays different from X rays?

3:5 Alpha, Beta, and Gamma Rays

A radioactive element can change from one element to another. This process is called *transmutation* (tranz myoo TAY shuhn) (Section 4:3). During transmutation, radioactive materials may emit three types of radiation: alpha (α), beta (β), and gamma (γ) rays.

Alpha rays are high-speed particles shot out from atomic nuclei. The particles are **alpha particles.** Each alpha particle is a helium nucleus with two protons and two neutrons. It has a positive charge. The particle travels at a speed of 16,000 to 32,000 km/sec. However, it does not have much penetrating power. An alpha particle can be stopped by a thin sheet of paper. Most alpha particles are absorbed after traveling through only a few centimeters of air.

Beta rays are streams of fast moving electrons shot out from a radioactive atom. These particles are **beta particles.** They are negatively charged. Beta particles travel faster and farther than alpha particles. The penetrating power of beta particles is about 100 times that of alpha particles. However, beta rays can be stopped by a sheet of aluminum one centimeter thick.

Every beta ray is a potential producer of X rays. X rays can be produced by slowing down beta particles. The kinetic energy lost by an electron as it slows down becomes X-ray radiation and heat energy. When the moving negative charge is slowed, radiation is emitted.

Gamma rays are energy waves of short wavelength and high frequency. Their wavelengths are about 10^{-10} centimeter. Gamma wavelengths are shorter than X-ray wavelengths. Most important, gamma rays are not charged particles. Gamma rays contain photons, or "bundles" of energy. They travel at the speed of light. Gamma rays are more penetrating than either alpha or beta rays. It takes several centimeters of lead or several meters of concrete to stop gamma rays.

PROBLEMS

3. Compare the penetrating power of gamma rays, alpha particles, and beta particles.   alpha particles—stopped by thin piece of paper, beta particles—stopped by 1 cm thick sheet of aluminum, gamma rays—stopped by lead or thick concrete

4. Which has the shorter wavelength, cosmic rays or gamma rays (Figure 3–14)?

Figure 3-14. Gamma rays have short wavelengths and high frequencies.

3:6 Half-Life

Nuclear changes which produce radiation are completely different from chemical and physical changes. Factors in the environ-

HALF-LIFE

ment, such as temperature and pressure, affect chemical and physical changes. However, the rate of nuclear change is not affected by any environmental change.

Radioactive elements have a unique property called half-life. **Half-life is the time it takes for half of the atoms in a radioactive material to decay.** For one isotope, half-life may be a fraction of a second. For another isotope, it may be thousands of years or more. In each succeeding half-life time interval, half the atoms left of a given radioactive element will decay. For example, barium 139 has a half-life of 86 minutes. Suppose you had 10 g of pure barium 139 in a lead container. After 86 minutes, one half of the atoms would have decayed. You would have only 5 g of radioactive barium 139. After another 86 minutes, one half of the remaining barium 139 atoms would have decayed. You would then have 2.5 g.

Define half-life.

It is impossible to determine when a given radioactive nucleus will decay.

PROBLEMS

5. You have a 10-g sample of barium 139. How much would be left after 4 hr and 18 min? *1.25 grams*

6. How long would it take for all the barium 139 in Problem 6 to decay? *theoretically, an infinitely long period of time*

The shorter the half-life, the more radioactive the isotope. For example, radon 222 is more radioactive than radium. It is a radioactive gas produced in the decay of uranium. Its half-life is 3.82 days. The half-life of radium is 1620 years. Radon 222 is less radioactive than polonium 214. The half-life of polonium 214 is 0.0001 second. The half-life of uranium is 4.5 billion years. In 4.5 billion years, 1 g of uranium 238 decays to 0.5 g.

PROBLEM

7. Is uranium 238 more or <u>less</u> radioactive than radon 222 or polonium 214?

Figure 3-15. Radon, the heaviest gas known, is more radioactive than radium.

Figure 3-16.

Time: 45 minutes.

ACTIVITY. *This is one model for radioactive decay. Obtain a square or rectangular box. Mark an X on one side of the box. Place exactly 100 kernels of corn in the box. (1) Put the lid on the box and shake. Remove the lid. Pick out all the kernels that point toward the marked side of the box. Assume that these have "decayed." Count these kernels and set them aside. How many "undecayed" kernels are still in the box? Record the number of "decayed" and "undecayed" kernels. (2) Repeat Part 1 until all kernels are removed.*

What is the principle behind carbon dating?

Radioactive isotopes have many practical uses. For example, carbon 14, with a half-life of 5600 years, is used to determine the age of ancient objects. This is done by measuring the amount of undecayed, natural carbon 14 in fossils and ancient remains. Carbon-14 dating is so exact that some materials can be dated to within a few decades.

3:7 Radiation Detection

Alpha, beta, and gamma rays cannot be seen, heard, tasted, smelled, or touched. However, it is possible to detect their presence. They can produce three changes:

(1) ions
(2) scintillations (sint uhl AY shuhnz) or flashes of light
(3) tracks in photographic film

Figure 3-17. In carbon dating, a small sample of an object is used. Age is estimated by determining the amount of carbon 14 in an object. This is done by counting the beta rays given off.

University of Houston

CLOUD CHAMBERS AND BUBBLE CHAMBERS   (63M)   447

The easiest way to detect radioactivity is with an electroscope (Section 1:2). A charged electroscope loses its charge more rapidly when ionizing radiation is present than when it is absent. This loss of charge is due to the formation of ions by the radiation. Ions form in the air around the electroscope and are attracted to the knob of the electroscope.

A positively charged electroscope attracts negative ions. A negatively charged electroscope attracts positive ions. The electroscope, depending on its charge, either gains or loses electrons and becomes neutral. As the charge is lost, the leaves of the electroscope drop down. The rate of charge loss depends upon the number of ions formed per second by the radiation. The greater the radiation, the more ions formed per second. Thus, the rate at which the leaves drop is a measure of the strength of a radioactive material.

Figure 3-18. Charged particles cause an electroscope to lose its charge and become neutral. The leaves of the electroscope will drop as it discharges.

PROBLEM

8. How could you use an electroscope to detect radiation? See Teacher's Guide.

3:8 *Cloud Chambers and Bubble Chambers*

Radioactivity can be detected with a cloud chamber. **A cloud chamber detects nuclear particles which leave tracks in the form of clouds. A cloud track is a line of condensed water vapor formed along a particle's path.** It is very similar to the vapor trail of a high flying jet.

How does a cloud chamber operate?

Courtesy of Kodansha Ltd.

Figure 3-19. Tracks of alpha particles are shown by a Wilson's Cloud Chamber.

Figure 3-20. Diffusion cloud chambers are easily made by suspending a jar on a piece of dry ice.

One kind of cloud chamber contains air supersaturated with water vapor. Supersaturated means the air holds more moisture than normal. As the particle passes through the water vapor, the water condenses. The tiny condensed water drops produce the cloud track. A beta particle forms a long thin cloud track. The track of an alpha particle is shorter and thicker.

The **diffusion cloud chamber** requires little equipment. One kind of diffusion cloud chamber is a glass jar containing a liquid. Alcohol is often used because it vaporizes easily. The jar is set on a piece of dry ice. A bright beam of light is passed through it. The dry ice cools the bottom of the jar. Warmer vapor in the upper portion of the jar descends, cools, and becomes supersaturated. Cloud tracks produced by radiation are visible in the lighted supersaturated vapor (Figure 3–20).

Explain the operation of a bubble chamber.

Another device used to detect nuclear particles is the **bubble chamber.** It is based on the formation of bubbles within a superheated liquid. A **superheated liquid** is produced by heating the liquid under pressure and then suddenly releasing the pressure. An ionizing nuclear particle passing through a superheated liquid leaves behind a track of bubbles in its wake. Liquid is much denser than vapor. Therefore, high-energy rays which pass unnoticed through the gas of a cloud chamber show up in the denser liquid of a bubble chamber.

Figure 3-21. Silver bromide is reduced to silver, forming a black streak along the path of a radioactive particle.

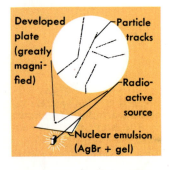

3:9 Nuclear Emulsions

Charged particles, such as alpha and beta particles and gamma rays, can be detected in a nuclear emulsion (ih MUHL shuhn). A **nuclear emulsion** is a thick layer of photographic emulsion. Photo-

448 (64M)

graphic emulsion contains grains of silver bromide (AgBr) in a gelatinlike solid. It is the shiny coating on photographic film and some prints. The thick layer forming a nuclear emulsion sometimes is called a "frozen cloud chamber." This is because the emulsion is a solid rather than a gas or a liquid.

The charged particles "expose" the grains of silver bromide in the emulsion. When placed in chemical developer, the "exposed" silver bromide is reduced to silver. In the developed emulsion, the path of the nuclear particle appears as a dark track. The principle is the same as the exposure and development of photographic film. Nuclear particles travel relatively short distances. Because the emulsion is very dense, nuclear tracks are a few millimeters or less in length. Because they are short, the tracks are studied with a microscope.

Why is a nuclear emulsion called a "frozen cloud chamber"?
The emulsion which detects nuclear radiation is a solid, rather than a gas or liquid.

PROBLEM

9. How are photographic plates used in tracking nuclear particles?

Nuclear particles expose photographic plates and thus leave a permanent record of their paths.

3:10 *Radiation Counters*

A **Geiger counter** detects radiation through the formation of an electric current. The current is formed in a metal cylinder called a Geiger-Müller tube. The *Geiger-Müller tube* contains a gas, such as argon or helium, under reduced pressure. A thin sheet of mica in the tube forms a "window." Fine tungsten wire is stretched along the axis of the tube. The wire and the metal cylinder are connected to an electric circuit (Figure 3–22).

Explain how a Geiger counter detects nuclear radiation.
Geiger counter is named after its designer, Hans Geiger (1882–1945), a German physicist.

A pulse of current flows between the tungsten wire and copper cylinder when ions are formed in the tube.

Figure 3-22. When a radioactive particle enters the gas inside the tube, ionization occurs. This causes a small, brief current in the circuit.

When radiation passes through the gas in the cylinder, ions are produced. The ions generate an electric current in the circuit connected to the tube. For example, when an alpha particle enters through the mica window, it frees a few electrons from the gas atoms. The gas atoms become positively charged ions. These positive ions are attracted to the negative wall of the tube (cathode). The free electrons are attracted to the positive wire in the center of the tube (anode). The flow of electrons to the wire produces a flash of current in the external circuit. This current is amplified and fed into recording or counting devices.

A small lamp or loudspeaker is used as a counting device in a Geiger counter. A flash of the lamp or a click in the loudspeaker occurs when a radioactive particle enters the Geiger-Müller tube. The number of clicks or flashes a Geiger counter makes per unit of time indicates the strength of the radiation.

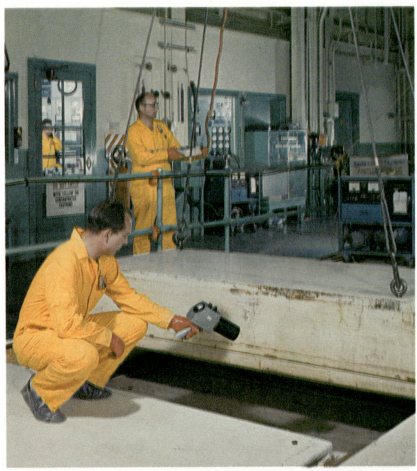

Figure 3-23. Geiger counters are used to detect radiation levels.

U.S. Energy Research and Development Administration

Time: 60 minutes.

ACTIVITY. A Geiger counter may be used to detect many types of radiation. (1) Turn on a Geiger counter. Count the number of clicks for 3 minutes and compute the average clicks per minute (clicks ÷ 3). (2) Bring a watch with a radium dial near the counter. Find the average clicks per minute. (3) Place a 2 mm-thick piece of aluminum between the Geiger tube and the watch. Again count the average clicks per minute. What do you observe? Explain. What would you observe if you put a lead plate between the watch and the Geiger counter? (4) Measure at four different distances from the radioactive source. Record distances and average number of clicks per minute. How does distance from a radioactive source affect radiation?
—Aluminum absorbs radiation and shields the Geiger counter. Lead plate shields the Geiger counter. There would only be "background" clicks.

Watches with radium dials are no longer manufactured because of the hazards to people working with radioactive paint. Radioactive sources may be purchased from a laboratory supply house. You may wish to try using the mantle from a gas camp lantern. These mantles are made from cloth dipped in thorium and cerium salts.

Radiation varies inversely with the square of the distance; similar to light-distance and sound-distance relationships.

Figure 3-24.

MAIN IDEAS

3:1 **1.** X rays are a form of electromagnetic radiation.

3:1 **2.** X rays are produced by cathode rays striking a metal target inside an X-ray tube.

3:1 **3.** High frequency waves have more energy per photon than low energy waves.

3:2 **4.** The roentgen is a unit of radiation.

3:2 **5.** One large dose of radiation, or small doses over a period of time, are harmful and can cause death.

3:3 **6.** Radioactivity results from the decay of unstable atomic nuclei.

3:4 **7.** As the number of neutrons in the nucleus of an element increases, the stability of the element generally decreases.

3:4 **8.** Some radioactive isotopes occur in nature. Some are made artificially.

452 (68M)

- 3:5 **9.** An alpha particle is a helium nucleus containing two protons and two neutrons. It has a positive charge.
- 3:5 **10.** A beta particle is a high-speed electron emitted from a radioactive atom. It has a negative charge.
- 3:5 **11.** Gamma radiation is a form of electromagnetic radiation with wavelengths shorter than X-ray wavelengths.
- 3:6 **12.** Half-life is a measure of the radioactivity of an element.
- 3:7, 3:8, 3:9, 3:10 **13.** Radiation can be detected with an electroscope, Geiger counter, cloud chamber, bubble chamber, or nuclear emulsion.

VOCABULARY

Write a sentence in which you correctly use each of the following words or terms.

alpha particle	Geiger counter	radioactive isotope
beta particle	half-life	radioactivity
bubble chamber	nuclear emulsion	roentgen
cloud chamber	photon	X rays
gamma ray	radiation	

STUDY QUESTIONS

Have students rewrite false statements to make the statements correct.

A. True or False

Determine whether each of the following sentences is true or false. (Do not write in this book.)

- an electron F **1.** A beta particle is actually a hydrogen nucleus.
- T **2.** A beta ray has a negative charge.
- a positive F **3.** An alpha particle has no charge.
- T **4.** Radiation can be detected with an electroscope.
- T **5.** X rays travel at the speed of light.
- T **6.** X-ray machines use small doses of X rays over a short time.
- Becquerel F **7.** Radioactivity was discovered by Marie and Pierre Curie.
- T **8.** A Geiger counter cannot detect X rays.
- less F **9.** Uranium 238 is more radioactive than radium 226.
- shorter F **10.** The longer the half-life, the more radioactive the isotope.

RADIATION (69M) 453

B. Multiple Choice

Choose one word or phrase that correctly completes each of the following sentences. (Do not write in this book.)

Some questions in Parts B and C may have more than one correct answer. Only one answer is required.

1. The wavelengths of X rays are smaller than *(radio waves, gamma rays, cosmic rays)*.
2. The speed of X rays is *(less than the speed of light, greater than the speed of light, 3×10^8 m/sec)*.
3. The energy of an X-ray photon depends on the photon's *(speed, frequency, size)*.
4. As the proton-neutron ratio approaches one, the stability of a nucleus *(increases, decreases, remains the same)*.
5. *(Lead, Aluminum, Copper)* is the best shield against radiation.
6. The standard unit used to measure radiation is *(wavelength, roentgen, photon)*.
7. A fluorescent screen glows when it is exposed to *(heat, light, radiation)*.
8. A particle containing two protons and two neutrons is a(n) *(alpha, beta, gamma)* particle.
9. A helium nucleus is a(n) *(alpha particle, beta particle, gamma ray)*.
10. X rays can pass most easily through *(aluminum, flesh, lead)*.

C. Completion

Complete each of the following sentences with a word or phrase that will make the sentence correct. (Do not write in this book.)

1. A beta particle has a(n) _____ charge. negative
2. When the speed of a beta particle is decreased, its _____ energy becomes X rays and heat. lost kinetic
3. The half-life of a radioactive element is the amount of _____ it takes for _____ of the atoms in a sample to decay. time / half
4. A charged electroscope can detect radioactivity because radioactivity _____ atoms in air. ionizes
5. The cloud tracks in a cloud chamber are produced in a(n) _____ mixture of liquid vapor in air. supersaturated
6. Silver bromide is a chemical in the _____ emulsion used to detect radioactivity. photographic
7. A(n) _____ is a radiation detector in which an electric current is produced by alpha and beta particles. Geiger counter

gamma **8.** The most penetrating rays are _____ rays.

C 14 **9.** _____ is a radioactive carbon isotope.

photon **10.** A(n) _____ is a bundle of energy.

See Teacher's Guide at the front of the book.

D. How and Why

1. How are X rays produced in an X-ray tube?
2. How do X rays detect the order and spacing of atoms in a crystal?
3. Why do X rays and radioactivity discharge a charged electroscope?
4. Why are alpha and beta particles deflected in opposite directions by a magnetic field?
5. How are a cloud chamber, bubble chamber, and nuclear emulsion used to detect radioactivity?
6. Why does a Geiger counter click when it is near radioactive material?
7. What are the properties of alpha rays, beta rays, and gamma radiation?
8. What are some common uses of radioactive isotopes?
9. What are some harmful effects of overexposure to radiation?
10. How can you tell if an element is stable or radioactive?

See Teacher's Guide at the front of the book for answers and suggestions.

INVESTIGATIONS

1. Find out how radiation is used to treat diseases. Make a report to your class.
2. Obtain X-ray photographs from a hospital or physician. Label the parts shown in each. Tape on classroom windows for display.
3. Read a biography of Marie Curie which describes her discovery of radium.
4. Write a report on how the carbon-14 dating method is used to determine the age of a fossil.

INTERESTING READING

Asimov, Isaac, *Inside the Atom.* New York, Abelard-Schuman, Ltd., 1961.

Hatcher, Charles, *The Atom*. London, Macmillan & Co., Ltd., 1963.

Lefort, Marc, *Nuclear Radiations*. New York, Walker and Co., 1963.

Stepp, Ann, *The Story of Radioactivity*. Irvington-on-Hudson, N. Y., Harvey House, 1971.

Preparing a nuclear reactor for operation requires the work of many skilled technicians.

U.S. Energy Research and Development Administration

Chapter 4 describes the relationship between nuclear science and technology. It discusses the structure of the nucleus and three kinds of nuclear reactions: transmutation, fission, and fusion. Transmutation reactions of radioactive isotopes are explained and the practical uses of the isotopes are studied. The operation of nuclear accelerators and nuclear reactors is explained. Production and control of thermonuclear power is presented as a scientific frontier of research and future discovery.

Nuclear Reactors and Reactions

GOAL: You will gain an understanding of the structure of the atomic nucleus, the types of nuclear change, and the relationship between nuclear science and technology.

From early times, people have failed in their attempts to change metal such as iron into gold. However, with the aid of atom smashing machines, scientists today can change one element into another.

Research in nuclear physics has led to the production of new elements. It has also led to many practical uses of nuclear energy. It can be used to light entire cities. It enables ships and submarines to travel the oceans. What are some other uses of nuclear energy?

THE CYCLOTRON

4:1 The Cyclotron

E.O. Lawrence (1901–1958), an American physicist, invented the cyclotron in 1931.

A **cyclotron** (SY kluh trahn) is a kind of atom smasher. It has been used to split the atoms of most elements. It is a machine which produces high-speed beams of atomic particles. The beams contain protons, heavy hydrogen nuclei, or alpha particles. By firing high-speed particles into an atom's nucleus, scientists cause the nucleus to split in two. The high-speed particles are called *atomic "bullets."* Through nuclear reactions of this kind, much has been learned about the nucleus and its structure.

How does a cyclotron work? The main parts of a cyclotron are an electromagnet, a vacuum chamber, and two hollow, semicircular metal electrodes. The electrodes are called *dees*. Each electrode has a D shape. The dees are placed inside the vacuum chamber with their straight edges parallel and slightly separated. They look like a pillbox (Figure 4–1). The whole assembly sits between the poles of a large electromagnet. Thus, a magnetic field runs through the dees.

The dees of the cyclotron are connected to a high-voltage alternating current. The alternating current produces an electric field along the slit between the dees. One dee is charged negatively. The other dee is charged positively. Since alternating current is used, the electric field and the charges on the dees keep changing. First, a dee is negative. Then it is positive. The change in charge on each dee occurs many times per second.

Atomic "bullets" are injected at the center of the chamber between the dees. These "bullets" are charged particles or "ions" traveling at very high speeds. One method of producing atomic "bullets" is through use of a heated wire and a gas. The hot wire inside the chamber knocks electrons from the atoms of the gas. Positively charged atomic nuclei are formed from the atoms. If the

How does a cyclotron split an atom?
Electric and magnetic forces produced by the cyclotron accelerate nuclear particles.

Name the parts of a cyclotron.

What kinds of "bullets" are used in a cyclotron?
helium nuclei or alpha particles

Figure 4-1. Cyclotrons produce high-speed beams of atomic particles. These charged particles take a spiral course, traveling faster each revolution. This is caused by the magnetic field and the alternating current.

458 (74M) NUCLEAR REACTORS AND REACTIONS

gas is hydrogen, protons are produced. Heavy hydrogen gas produces deuterons (DOOT uh rahnz). A deuteron is a heavy hydrogen nucleus. Helium gas produces alpha particles. These particles become the "bullets."

What happens when atomic "bullets" are injected into the cyclotron? The particles used as "bullets" are acted on by two powerful forces. The two forces are the magnetic field and alternating electric current. Positive particles are attracted to the negative electric charge. They are deflected from a straight path into a curved path by the magnetic field. The positive particles are first drawn to the negative dee. Then the magnetic field pulls the particles in a semicircular path back to the space between the dees. At the same time, the electrical charge on the dees is reversed. The positive particles are now attracted to the negative charge of the opposite dee. Again the magnetic field pulls the particles back between the dees. And again the electric charge on the dees is reversed.

The rapid changing of the charge on the dees gives a constant acceleration to the particles. The particles soon reach a very high speed. They gain speed and kinetic energy as they whirl around through the dees. The particles travel in an ever-widening circle until they are near the outer edge of the dees. Here they exit through a thin window as a beam of high-energy particles. These alpha rays have 4.5 times more energy than the natural alpha particles released from a radioactive element.

The first cyclotron was only 10 cm in diameter and accelerated protons to an energy of about 13 Kev. The first cyclotron to produce an artificial nuclear disintegration (1932) was a 28–cm model which produced 1.2 Mev protons.

The time for a complete circle is always the same. Therefore the velocity of a particle is greater in the large circles.

Figure 4-2. Cyclotrons are used to split the atoms of elements.

U.S. Energy Research and Development Administration

U.S. Energy Research and Development Administration

Figure 4-3. Linear accelerators use alternating positive and negative charges to speed particles.

4:2 Atomic Nucleus

The basic particles of an atom are the proton, neutron, and electron. One model of an atom pictures a dense, positively charged nucleus. A cloud of negative electricity surrounds it. The cloud is produced by electrons orbiting around the nucleus. The nucleus contains neutrons and positively charged protons.

A nucleus is only a tiny fraction of an atom. Yet, it contains almost the total mass of an atom. The mass of an electron is almost nothing compared to the mass of a proton or a neutron. The mass of one proton or one neutron equals the mass of 1837 electrons.

Atoms are assigned a mass number based on a scale of atomic mass units. Atomic mass unit is abbreviated as a.m.u. For example, a helium nucleus has a mass of 4 a.m.u. Sodium has a mass of 23

Why does the nucleus contain most of an atom's mass?

Most of the volume of an atom is space and the mass of its electrons is almost zero.

a

Electron cloud model

b

Bohr model

Figure 4-4. Electrons orbiting the nucleus may look like a cloud of negative electricity (a). Most of the mass of an atom is in the nucleus (b).

Figure 4-5. Forces hold the entire universe together. The Trifid nebula is held together by forces.

Courtesy of the Hale Observatories

a.m.u. Sulfur has a mass of 32 a.m.u. The mass is about equal to the sum of the atom's protons and neutrons.

Name four kinds of forces in the universe.

The entire universe is held together by forces. The force of gravity holds the parts of the solar system together. Atoms and molecules are held together by the ionic and magnetic forces of charged particles. Nuclear forces hold the parts of an atomic nucleus together.

Nuclear forces hold protons and neutrons together in a nucleus. However, they are not like the force of gravity or the forces between charged electrical particles. **Nuclear forces** exist only in distances shorter than the size of an atomic nucleus (10^{-12} cm or less). Thus, at distances of 10^{-12} cm or less, protons are held together by nuclear forces. At larger distances, the positive charges of the protons cause them to repel each other. Nuclear forces also cause protons and neutrons to bind together within a nucleus.

Remind students that 10^{-12}cm = 0.000000000001 cm.

PROBLEM

1. Draw a diagram of a sodium atom (11 protons, 11 electrons, 12 neutrons). Name three ways in which your diagram is different from an actual atom. *See Teacher's Guide.*

4:3 *Transmutation*

Name three kinds of nuclear change.

An atomic nucleus can undergo three kinds of nuclear change. These nuclear changes are transmutation, fission (Section 4:4), and

TRANSMUTATION

fusion (Section 4:6). In a **transmutation,** the nuclei of a radioactive element decay at a fixed rate. They do this by emitting nuclear particles. In this process, one element is changed into a different element.

Radioactive elements which can undergo nuclear change are found in Table 3–1. Nine of these elements are naturally radioactive. Those with atomic numbers greater than uranium ($Z=92$) are artificially-made. For example, radioactive radium transmutes into radon, a radioactive gas.

Figure 4-6. Mass and charge of the radium atom is equal to the combined mass and charge of the radon atom and alpha particle.

A nuclear change may be represented by a *nuclear equation.* The nuclear equation for the transmutation of radium is

$$^{226}_{88}Ra \longrightarrow {}^{222}_{86}Rn + {}^{4}_{2}He$$

The word equation for this reaction is

one atom of radium 226 yields one atom of radon plus one alpha particle

Nuclear equations show in simple form the changes which occur in nuclear reactions. To aid the student's learning, a word equation is given for each nuclear reaction.

In a nuclear equation, the symbols for the elements are the same as in a chemical equation. In addition, the atomic mass number of each element is written to the top left of the symbol. The atomic number is written to the bottom left of the symbol.

How is a nuclear equation different from a chemical equation?

U.S. Energy Research and Development Administration

The U. S. Energy Research and Development Agency is the largest supplier of radioactive isotopes. They are produced in its nuclear reactor at Oak Ridge, Tennessee.

Figure 4-7. Located in Tennessee, the Oak Ridge Uranium Enrichment Facilities produce enriched uranium for nuclear plants around the world.

You may wish to go over the meaning of the Greek symbols used in the Table.

Table 4–1. Uranium 238 Decay Series

Symbol	Element	Half-Life	Emitted Ray
$^{238}_{92}U$	uranium	4.5×10^9 yr	α
$^{234}_{90}Th$	thorium	24 days	$\beta\ (\gamma)$*
$^{234}_{91}Pa$	protactinium	1.14 min	$\beta\ (\gamma)$
$^{234}_{92}U$	uranium	3×10^5 yr	α
$^{230}_{90}Th$	thorium	83,000 yr	$\alpha\ (\gamma)$
$^{226}_{88}Ra$	radium	1600 yr	$\alpha\ (\gamma)$
$^{222}_{86}Rn$	radon	3.8 days	α
$^{218}_{84}Po$	polonium	3.05 min	α
$^{214}_{82}Pb$	lead	26.8 min	$\beta\ (\gamma)$
$^{214}_{83}Bi$	bismuth	19.7 min	$\beta\ (\gamma)$
$^{214}_{84}Po$	polonium	10^{-5} sec	$\alpha\ (\gamma)$
$^{210}_{82}Pb$	lead	22 yr	β
$^{210}_{83}Bi$	bismuth	5 days	$\beta\ (\gamma)$
$^{210}_{84}Po$	polonium	140 days	α
$^{206}_{82}Pb$	lead	stable	

Key: α —alpha ray, β —beta ray

*(γ)—gamma radiation may also be emitted

Note that lead is the final element in the U 238 decay series.

A nuclear equation must be balanced. It must follow the laws of conservation of mass and conservation of charge. The sum of the atomic mass numbers to the left of the arrow must equal the sum of the atomic mass numbers to the right of the arrow. This shows conservation of mass. Also, the sum of the atomic numbers (protons) on the left must equal the sum of the atomic numbers on the right. This shows conservation of charge.

In the radium nuclear decay reaction, the total atomic mass to the left of the arrow is 226. This number equals the sum of the atomic mass numbers to the right of the arrow ($222 + 4 = 226$). The atomic number to the left of the arrow is 88. This represents the sum of the atomic numbers to the right of the arrow ($86 + 2 = 88$).

PROBLEM

The symbol ^4_2He is the alpha particle because an alpha particle is a helium nucleus. The helium nucleus contains 2 protons and 2 neutrons for an atomic mass of 4 a.m.u.

How is a nuclear equation different from a chemical equation?

2. What symbol in the equation on the previous page is an alpha particle? Why is an alpha particle part of the reaction?

A nuclear change is completely different from a chemical or physical change. In a chemical change, atoms are rearranged. New compounds are formed or elements are separated from compounds. In a physical change, such as freezing or boiling, a substance changes its physical form. No new elements or compounds are

NUCLEAR FISSION

"Radioactive" and "radiation" both come from the Latin word *radius* meaning ray.

produced. In a **nuclear change,** one element is changed into a different element. There is a change in the number of protons in the atoms.

Uranium 238 is a radioactive element. It decays through a series of nuclear reactions to form lead. Lead 206 is a stable isotope. It is not radioactive. The nuclear reactions through which uranium becomes lead are known as a **nuclear decay series.** In each reaction of the uranium decay series, a different radioactive element is formed.

PROBLEMS

3. Which of the radioactive isotopes in the uranium decay series are alpha emitters? U 238, U 234, Th 230, Ra 226, Rn 222, Po 218, Po 214, Po 210
4. Which of the radioactive isotopes in the uranium decay series are beta emitters? Th 234, Pa 234, Pb 214, Bi 214, Pb 210, Bi 210

Figure 4-8. This sample of uranium ore is uraninite, a type of pitchblende.

4:4 *Nuclear Fission*

Atoms have a tremendous amount of energy locked within their nuclei. This nuclear energy can be released and used in many ways. Nuclear fission is one way in which nuclear energy may be released.

U. S. Energy Research and Development Administration

Figure 4-9. Much has been learned about nuclear fission and fusion through testing. Carefully controlled bomb explosions reveal much information about these processes.

NUCLEAR REACTORS AND REACTIONS

Fission means to divide. In **nuclear fission**, a nucleus divides into two nuclei. Nuclear fission is a nuclear change. When a uranium-235 atom is bombarded with neutrons, it may split into two nuclei. The nuclei are about equal in size. For example, a uranium-235 nucleus may gain a neutron. It divides to form barium 144 and krypton 90. In this nuclear fission, two neutrons are released:

$$^{235}_{92}U + ^{1}_{0}n \longrightarrow ^{144}_{56}Ba + ^{90}_{36}Kr + 2\, ^{1}_{0}n$$

one atom of uranium 235 plus one neutron yields one atom of barium 144 plus one atom of krypton 90 plus two neutrons

PROBLEM

5. Why is nuclear fission a nuclear change?

Nuclear fission is a nuclear change since elements are changed into different elements when they are split.

Uranium fission may result in a chain reaction. A *nuclear chain reaction* is a series of rapid nuclear fissions. First, one uranium-235 nucleus is split by a neutron. This releases two neutrons. The two neutrons released in the fission are captured by two more uranium nuclei. This causes them to split. These two nuclei each emit two neutrons. They are captured by four more nuclei, causing them to split. The fission of nuclei and emission of neutrons continue through the uranium sample.

Figure 4-10. Nuclear fission rates are constant and not affected by changes in temperature or pressure.

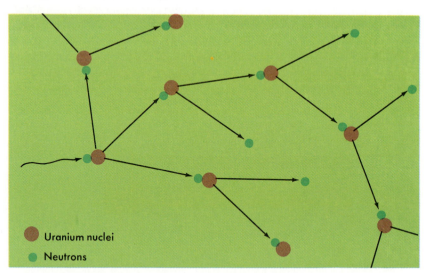

Figure 4-11. Nuclear chain reactions begin with the splitting of a uranium nucleus by a neutron.

Time: 20 minutes.
ACTIVITY. Arrange and nail a series of mousetraps onto a wooden board to demonstrate a chain reaction. They should be linked together with string so that release of the first trap is followed in rapid order by the release of two traps, four traps, and so on.

PEOPLE CAREERS FRONTIERS
FOCUS ON PHYSICAL SCIENCE

The Future of Energy
Power Tower

The use of the sun to produce energy is not a new idea. However, new methods for using the sun are being developed.

One idea is that of a "power tower." This tower would generate electricity from steam. Steam would be produced by using water heated by solar energy. Mirrors, at the base of the tower, would be controlled by a computer. The computer constantly keeps track of the movement of the earth in relation to the sun. In this way, the mirror can always be pointed in the right direction. The mirrors would focus the sun's rays on pipes containing water. These pipes would be located in a cylinder at the top of the tower. The water is heated to produce steam. This steam then drives a generator located at the base of the tower.

A "power tower" has at least one problem to be solved. This is the development of a means of storing heat for cloudy days.

Adapted from "Picturing The Future of Energy," *Science News*, July 26, 1975.

A "Power Tower" may be a future source of electricity.

Wind Power

The world's largest wind turbine is now turning at NASA's Plum Brook Station in Sandusky, Ohio. Wind power is an alternative method of producing energy. The wind turbine will be studied over the next few years. Data collected from these studies will be used as a basis for a wind energy program. This program will be run by NASA for ERDA, the Energy Research and Development Administration.

The Plum Brook wind machine is 30 m tall. Its two aluminum blades measure about 38 m across. Each blade has a mass of about 900 kg. Wind from Lake Erie drives the blades. A 12 km/hr wind is needed to start the blades turning. The blades reach a maximum output in a 29 km/hr wind. The turbine can produce as much as 100 kilowatts of electricity. This is enough to meet the needs of 25 to 30 one-family homes.

If this wind turbine is found to be practical, it will be used as a model in designing larger machines.

Courtesy of *The Columbus Dispatch*.

A large wind turbine can generate the electricity required by 25 to 30 homes.

What is needed before a nuclear chain reaction will occur?

What is critical mass?

What quantity is represented by each letter in $E=mc^2$?

Potential difference may need to be explained at this point. It is equal to the amount of work done in moving a relatively small charge from one point to another.

A chain reaction occurs if enough uranium is present. Otherwise, the neutrons escape from the uranium without striking nuclei. Then there are no fissions and a chain reaction does not begin. A neutron must travel at least 10 cm before it slows down enough to be captured by a uranium nucleus. If it escapes before it has gone this distance, the neutron will not cause an atom to split. The smallest amount of an element needed for a chain reaction is called the element's **critical mass.** The critical mass of uranium 235 is about 24 kg.

During fission, mass is converted to energy. The energy is given off as gamma radiation. The total mass of the two nuclei and two neutrons produced in fission is less than the mass of the original uranium-235 nucleus. The energy released by nuclear fission can be calculated by the equation:

$$E = mc^2$$

energy equals mass times the speed of light squared

The energy released through the fission of a single uranium-235 nucleus is about 200 million electron volts. An *electron volt* is the energy required to move an electron between two points with a potential difference of one volt. For comparison, the energy in a photon of visible light is about 2.5 electron volts. The electrons hitting the screen of a television set have an energy of about 20,000 electron volts. Fantastic amounts of energy are released in nuclear fission! Energy equal to about 25 million kilowatt-hours is released through the fission of only one gram of uranium. A piece of uranium no heavier than a loaf of bread and smaller than a golf ball can provide the energy of 1000 metric tons of coal.

Figure 4-12. Nuclear power plants use a nuclear reactor to generate energy.

U.S. Energy Research and Development Administration

NUCLEAR REACTORS

4:5 Nuclear Reactors

Nuclear fission produces tremendous amounts of energy. For example, the heat produced by the fission of 28 g of uranium is equal to the heat produced by burning 60 metric tons of coal! A **nuclear reactor** is a device for producing heat from a nuclear fuel. A nuclear reactor is sometimes called a "pile." The parts of a nuclear reactor are

(1) fuel
(2) moderator
(3) control rods
(4) coolant
(5) heat exchanger
(6) safety shields

Locate each of these parts in Figure 4–13.

The *fuel* in a nuclear reactor is uranium 235 or plutonium 239. It is enclosed in rod-shaped cans made of a magnesium alloy. Through a nuclear fission chain reaction within the fuel element, nuclear energy is released as heat. The cans holding the fuel have fins like those on the cylinder of motorcycle and lawnmower engines. These fins aid the transfer of heat out of the fuel by conduction.

The *moderator* is a material which slows down neutrons released through nuclear fission. To keep a fission chain reaction going, the speed of the released neutrons must be reduced. Neutrons are able to split atomic nuclei when they are moving relatively slowly.

Pure graphite, a crystalline form of carbon, is the most common type of moderator. It is placed in the reactor as blocks. The blocks surround the cans containing the uranium rods. Great care and precision go into the design and placing of graphite blocks in the

Figure 4-13. In a nuclear reactor, the coolant is about 315°C as it carries heat to the heat exchanger. Heat from the reactor converts water to steam which drives a steam turbine.

468 (84M)   NUCLEAR REACTORS AND REACTIONS

pile. A reactor may have 2500 metric tons of graphite moderator arranged in 100,000 or more blocks.

Ordinary water, heavy water, and beryllium can also be used as moderators. These substances are able to slow down speeding neutrons. Heavy water is water which contains deuterium rather than ordinary hydrogen. A deuterium atom has a neutron as well as a proton in the nucleus. Heavy water and beryllium are expensive. Graphite has the advantage of being relatively cheap.

Control rods regulate the rate of fission in the fuel element of a reactor. They absorb any excess neutrons not required to keep the chain reaction going. Control rods are made of boron or cadmium alloyed with aluminum or steel. These materials absorb neutrons.

By inserting or withdrawing the control rods, the fission rate of a reactor is regulated. The farther the rods are pushed into the reactor, the more neutrons are absorbed and the slower the nuclear fission. Inserting the rods all the way stops the fission completely. In some reactors, the rods are raised and lowered with a steel cable operated by an electric motor.

The *coolant* removes heat energy from the reactor. Several substances have general use as nuclear reactor coolants. These substances include gases, such as helium, nitrogen, and carbon dioxide. Water, heavy water, organic liquid, and liquid metals are also used as coolants. Many reactors use carbon dioxide gas under pressure as a coolant because it is inexpensive and does not burn.

U.S. Energy Research and Development Administration

Figure 4-14. Preparing a nuclear reactor requires careful planning. Here, a 40-ton covering is lowered over the control rod drive shafts.

Explain how moderators and control rods are used in reactors.
See p.467 (83M).

Figure 4-15. Nuclear reactions permit controlled fission of nuclear material.

U.S. Energy Research and Development Administration

Figure 4-16. Heat produced by nuclear fission inside the reactor is carried away by a coolant pumped out to the heat exchanger.

The coolant is pumped through spaces in the reactor. As it contacts the cans of fuel, it absorbs heat released from fission. The coolant carries the heat to the heat exchanger.

In the *heat exchanger,* the reactor coolant is allowed to flow around pipes containing circulating water. The heat from the coolant converts the water to steam. Steam carries the heat away from the reactor to a turbine.

What is the function of a nuclear reactor coolant and heat exchanger?

Safety shields are necessary to protect people from the nuclear radiation produced by a reactor. Nuclear radiation can produce burns, cancer, loss of hair, vomiting, and destruction of blood cells. An overdose of radiation can cause death. Lead and concrete are used as shields for reactors. Concrete walls 2 m thick or more are needed to protect people from the harmful radiation given off by a reactor (Figure 4–17).

Brookhaven National Laboratory

Figure 4-17. Many safety precautions are taken in a nuclear power plant. Geiger counters are used to check radiation levels.

Figure 4-18. A nuclear reactor provides the energy necessary to propel this submarine.
The first nuclear submarine *(U.S.S. Nautilus)* uses pressurized water as a coolant, while the second nuclear powered submarine *(U.S.S. Seawolf)* uses a liquid sodium coolant.

General Dynamics Corp.

PROBLEM

Refer to Figure 4–13.

6. Draw a diagram of a nuclear reactor showing its main parts.

Steam produced by a nuclear reactor is used to do work. Steam is carried from the heat exchangers to turbines. A steam turbine is a machine with a central shaft connected to large blades. Steam under pressure passes over the blades causing the shaft to rotate. Nuclear energy is converted to heat energy in a reactor. Heat is converted to kinetic energy in a turbine. The rotating shaft of a turbine can produce power to move a ship or a submarine. Steam turbines are also used to turn electrical generators which produce electricity. A reactor generating one million watts of electric power per year uses about one gram of uranium per day.

Nuclear reactors are used to produce radioactive isotopes. Also, nuclear reactors can produce nuclear fuels such as plutonium.

What are some uses for nuclear reactors?

Figure 4-19. Deuterium and tritium are two raw materials used for nuclear fusion.

Deuterium

PROBLEM

7. A nuclear reactor is equipped with a device which can automatically drop all of the control rods into the reactor. Why?

See Teacher's Guide.

4:6 Nuclear Fusion

Nuclear fusion is the opposite of nuclear fission. To fuse means to join together. In **nuclear fusion,** two or more atomic nuclei unite to form a single, heavier nucleus. Elements with small masses combine to form elements with greater masses.

Tritium

470 (86M)

NUCLEAR FUSION

Ordinary hydrogen, deuterium, and tritium are raw materials used for nuclear fusion. Deuterium is an isotope of hydrogen with one proton and one neutron in its nucleus. Tritium is an isotope of hydrogen with one proton and two neutrons in its nucleus. Tritium is expensive and scarce. However, almost an unlimited supply of deuterium can be obtained from water.

For nuclear fusion to occur, temperatures in the millions of degrees must be reached. *Thermo* means heat. Thus, nuclear fusion is called a *thermonuclear reaction*. Why? At the tremendous temperatures of thermonuclear reactions, atoms as such no longer exist. The atoms lose their electrons. This phase of matter is known as the **plasma phase.** It consists of nuclei and free electrons. The plasma phase is different from the liquid, solid, and gas phases.

At nuclear fusion temperatures, matter becomes plasma. Atoms are stripped of their electrons. Charged nuclei are formed. The nuclei have enough energy to overcome the large forces of repulsion between them. It is now possible for the nuclei to be squeezed together and fused.

Conditions for nuclear fusion exist in the sun and other stars. The sun has an internal temperature of about 20 million °C. In the sun, hydrogen nuclei fuse to form a helium nucleus. Through a complex series of nuclear changes, four hydrogen nuclei are fused into one helium nucleus.

The sun is constantly losing hydrogen and gaining helium. This occurs through nuclear fusion. About 25 million electron volts of energy are freed in the fusion of four hydrogen atoms. Energy comes from mass which is converted to energy. The helium atom has a mass almost one percent less than the mass of the original four hydrogen atoms.

How is nuclear fusion different from nuclear fission?

What is a thermonuclear reaction?

Describe the plasma phase of matter.

Point out that the fusion occurs in a series of steps rather than all at once.

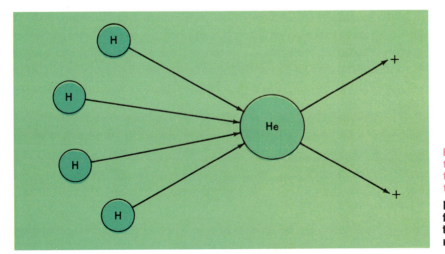

Every minute, about 4×10^{10} tons of hydrogen atoms are fused in thermonuclear reactions occurring in the sun.

Figure 4-20. In the sun, four hydrogen nuclei fuse together into one helium nucleus.

a   NASA   b   Gary Ladd

Figure 4-21. Nuclear fusion is constantly going on in the sun and other stars (a). Only a fraction of the light and heat produced by the sun reaches the earth (b).

The hydrogen bomb is a thermonuclear weapon. Production and control of thermonuclear energy is a scientific and engineering frontier.

Light and heat from nuclear fusion travel 150 million kilometers from the sun to the earth. However, the total energy which reaches the earth is only about 1/2,000,000,000 of the total energy released by the sun into space.

Nuclear fusion occurs in the explosion of a hydrogen bomb. The reactions in a hydrogen bomb are similar to the reactions in the sun. The temperature inside an exploding hydrogen bomb is believed to be about 10 million °C. To produce the high temperature required to start nuclear fusion, an atomic bomb is used as a fuse for a hydrogen bomb.

4:7 Thermonuclear Power

The development of controlled nuclear fusion is being investigated by scientists and engineers in many countries. Fusion requires a temperature of millions of degrees. The problem is how such a high temperature can be produced long enough for nuclear fusion to occur. In other words, how can a controlled, tiny sun be made in the laboratory?

How are magnetic "bottles" used in nuclear fusion experiments?

Experiments with nuclear fusion aim toward fusion of heavy hydrogen nuclei in magnetic "bottles." Heavy hydrogen gas is enclosed in an aluminum tube shaped like the inner tube of an automobile tire. High-voltage alternating current is fed to the gas. The current heats the gas to a few million degrees for less than a second. Anything in contact with the hot gas would vaporize. So, the gas must be kept away from the walls of the container. This is accom-

Figure 4-22. At nuclear fusion temperatures, matter becomes plasma. The left photograph shows pinched but still stable plasma. The right photograph, taken a few millionths of a second later, shows the broken up, unstable plasma (a). Magnetic bottles are used in experiments with nuclear fusion. Magnetic pinching keeps the nuclei away from the walls to prevent vaporization (b).

plished by a magnetic field from an electromagnet wound around the tube. The magnetic fields "pinch" the nuclei together inside the tube. Magnetic pinching keeps the nuclei away from the walls.

To make a controlled thermonuclear reaction, scientists must discover how to produce a temperature of several million degrees for several seconds. Further, they must learn how to convert the heat energy produced through fusion into electricity. The solution of these problems is a challenge to science and technology. The possible rewards certainly are worth the effort. Fusion of the nuclei in one gram of heavy hydrogen would produce the power generated by burning eight metric tons of coal!

PROBLEM

8. How could thermonuclear power help solve the world's energy shortage? See Teacher's Guide.

4:8 *Nuclear Energy and the Environment*

Nuclear energy has some advantages over fossil fuels such as coal and oil. The burning of coal and oil can cause air pollution. Nuclear reactors are clean in that they do not add impurities to the air. Also, greater amounts of energy can be produced from small amounts of nuclear fuels.

Nuclear power plants do require huge amounts of water to cool their reactors. If this hot water is dumped into rivers or oceans, thermal pollution may result. The heat can have a harmful effect on fish. To protect the environment, the water must be cooled before it is released. **Large** cooling towers are built for this purpose.

U.S. Energy Research and Development Administration

Figure 4-23. Cooling towers are built to cool the water used in a nuclear power plant.

Figure 4-24. Spent nuclear fuel, contained in a 23-ton cask, is unloaded under water for reprocessing (a). Spent nuclear fuel is shipped in special casks (b).

Nuclear reactors produce radioactive wastes. These wastes must be stored safely for thousands of years until the radiation decreases. Strong safety measures are taken in this underground storage. Accidental escape of radioactive wastes could kill plant and animal life.

a

b

U.S. Energy Research and Development Administration

NUCLEAR REACTORS AND REACTIONS

This is a major environmental problem in the use of nuclear energy. Overheating of the core containing the nuclear fuel could result in the release of wastes into the air. However, many mechanical safeguards are used to prevent overheating. Successful operation of nuclear reactors requires that many safeguards be in constant operation.

Some scientists believe nuclear fusion may be the best solution to the world's energy problems. Controlled nuclear fusion would provide an unlimited source of energy. There would be no radioactive wastes to store. Also, the hydrogen used in fusion does not produce radioactive wastes that could pollute the atmosphere.

What types of safety measures are needed for nuclear reactors?
cooling towers, safety devices for storing wastes underground, backup systems for electrical supply, etc.

Many scientists believe the use of solar energy is a long term solution to the future energy requirements and favor research in this area.

PROBLEMS

9. Why is nuclear energy sometimes called "clean energy"? See Teacher's Guide.
10. Why do some people object to the building and operation of nuclear power plants? See Teacher's Guide.
11. What solutions do you see to the world's energy problems? Answers may vary: nuclear fusion and coal gassification are two examples.

MAIN IDEAS

4:1 1. Cyclotrons are machines which accelerate atomic particles to high speeds and fire them into atomic nuclei. They have been used to study the nucleus and its structure.

4:2 2. An atomic nucleus contains protons and neutrons bonded together by nuclear forces. Energy must be added to a nucleus to separate its nuclear particles.

4:3 3. An element transmutes to form another element through the loss or gain of nuclear particles. The emission of nuclear particles is radioactivity.

4:3 4. In a chemical change, atoms are rearranged to form different compounds. In a physical change, a compound or element is changed from one phase to another. However, in a nuclear change, an element is usually changed into another element.

4:4 5. A chain reaction is a series of continuous, automatic, rapid nuclear fissions.

4:4, 4:5 6. Uranium is a major fuel used in nuclear reactors.

4:6 7. In a thermonuclear reaction, light elements such as hydrogen are fused to form heavier elements. The fusion occurs at millions of degrees Celsius.

476 (92M) NUCLEAR REACTORS AND REACTIONS

4:6, 4:7 **8.** Plasma is a phase of matter different from liquid, solid, and gas. At temperatures of several thousands of degrees, matter enters the plasma phase. In the plasma phase, electrons are set free from atoms.

4:8 **9.** Scientists hope to produce a controlled thermonuclear fusion reaction. Energy from nuclear fusion may be a solution to the world's energy problems.

VOCABULARY

Write a sentence in which you correctly use each of the following words or terms.

atomic "bullets"	nuclear decay	nuclear reactor
chain reaction	series	plasma phase
critical mass	nuclear fission	thermonuclear
cyclotron	nuclear forces	reaction
nuclear change	nuclear fusion	transmutation

STUDY QUESTIONS

Have students rewrite false statements to make the statements correct.

A. True or False

Determine whether each of the following sentences is true or false. (Do not write in this book.)

fewer, than   F **1.** A uranium atom has ~~an equal number of~~ protons ~~and~~ neutrons in its nucleus.

Alpha particles   F **2.** ~~X rays~~ are used as atomic "bullets."

a proton   F **3.** A neutron has the same mass as ~~an electron~~.

transmutation   F **4.** The changing of uranium to lead is an example of ~~atomic fusion~~.

T **5.** Nuclear equations represent nuclear reactions.

T **6.** In a nuclear change, a new element is usually formed.

less than   F **7.** The mass of a helium nucleus is ~~the same as~~ the total mass of two protons plus two neutrons.

12   F **8.** Carbon ~~14~~ has a stable nucleus.

T **9.** Fission is the splitting apart of the nucleus of an atom.

T **10.** Since graphite is inexpensive, it is commonly used as a moderator in a nuclear reactor.

NUCLEAR REACTORS AND REACTIONS   (93M)   477

Some questions in Parts B and C may have more than one correct answer. Only one answer is required.

B. Multiple Choice

Choose one word or phrase that correctly completes each of the following sentences. (Do not write in this book.)

1. The mass of a nucleus is *(greater than, less than, the same as)* the sum of the masses of the particles in the nucleus.
2. During nuclear fission the mass of uranium *(increases, decreases, remains the same)*.
3. The cyclotron produces a beam of high-speed *(protons, neutrons, electrons)*.
4. An element found in the uranium decay series is *(hydrogen, oxygen, carbon, lead)*.
5. Uranium 235 is a *(fuel, moderator, control, coolant)* in a reactor.
6. The *(moderator, control rod, coolant)* regulates the fission rate of a reactor.
7. Hydrogen and its isotopes are raw materials for *(nuclear fission, transmutation, nuclear fusion)*.
8. Two or more nuclei *(split, unite, decay)* in nuclear fusion.
9. The particles in a nucleus are held together by *(charge, gravity, nuclear forces)*.
10. Lead 206 is a(n) *(stable, unstable)* isotope.

C. Completion

Complete each of the following sentences with a word or phrase that will make the sentence correct. (Do not write in this book.)

1. The smallest amount of an element needed for a chain reaction is called its _____. critical mass
2. A nuclear chain reaction is produced when a uranium-235 nucleus is split by a(n) _____. neutron
3. _____ change heat energy into kinetic energy. Turbines
4. One element is changed into a different element in _____. transmutation
5. Nuclear _____ occurs in a thermonuclear reaction. fusion
6. Matter exists in the _____ phase at millions of °C. plasma
7. A(n) _____ is a series of rapid nuclear fissions. chain reaction
8. The _____ in a nuclear reactor slows down neutrons. moderator
9. Uranium finally becomes _____ in the nuclear decay series. lead
10. An element can be made radioactive by bombarding it with _____. nuclear particles

D. How and Why

1. How does a cyclotron work?
2. Why must energy be added to a nucleus to separate its protons and neutrons?
3. Why is a nuclear reactor called a "pile"?
4. Why are the fuel cans in a nuclear reactor made of a substance which is a poor neutron absorber?
5. Why must a nuclear fuel can have a high melting point?
6. How can nuclear energy be converted into kinetic energy?
7. Explain how nuclear fission is different from nuclear fusion. Where does the released energy come from in both fission and fusion?
8. Describe an experiment designed to produce a controlled thermonuclear reaction.
9. What are the advantages of using nuclear power plants to produce energy?
10. How could a nuclear power plant harm the environment?

INVESTIGATIONS

1. Make models of the three isotopes of hydrogen. Use colored clay or styrofoam balls painted with latex paint. Parts of the models can be held together with toothpicks.
2. Look up information about recent research on the plasma phase of matter. Make a report to your class.
3. Obtain information on a career in the nuclear energy field. Find out the educational background needed and where you can prepare for this field.
4. Make a model of a cyclotron or a nuclear power plant.
5. Plan a field trip to a nuclear power plant to learn about its operation. Investigate the advantages and disadvantages of nuclear power plants.

INTERESTING READING

Anderson, William R., and Pizer, Vernon, *The Useful Atom*. New York, World Publishing Co., 1966.

Bethe, H.A., "The Necessity of Fission Power." *Scientific American*, (January, 1976) Volume 234, Number 1, pp. 21–31.

Frisch, O. R., *Working With Atoms*. New York, Basic Books, Inc., 1966.

Fuchs, Erich, translated by Edite, Kroll, *What Makes a Nuclear Power Plant Work?* New York, Delacorte Press, 1972.

Kelman, Peter, and Stone, A. Harry, *Ernest Rutherford: Architect of the Atom*. New York, Prentice-Hall, 1967.

Woodburn, John H., *Radioisotopes*. New York, J. B. Lippincott Co., 1962.

Appendices

Appendix A
Metric System

The metric system is a convenient, widely-used system of measurement which has the advantage of units based on ten and multiples of ten. It was developed by using the mass of pure water in the shape of a cube. The "cube of water" was a cubic centimeter—a cube one centimeter long on each edge. The mass of the cubic centimeter of water was measured at an exact temperature of 3.98°C and was called one gram (g).

The unit of length in the metric system is the meter (m). It is equal to 39.37 inches (in.). The unit of volume in the metric system is the liter (ℓ). A liter is the volume of a kilogram (1000 g) of pure water measured at an exact temperature of 3.98°C.

TABLE A-1. Metric Unit Prefixes and Their Definitions

kilo—	1000	$= 10^3$
hecto—	100	$= 10^2$
deka—	10	$= 10$
deci—	0.1	$= 10^{-1}$
centi—	0.01	$= 10^{-2}$
milli—	0.001	$= 10^{-3}$
micro—	0.000001	$= 10^{-6}$

TABLE A-2. Frequently Used Metric Units

LENGTH
1 centimeter (cm) = 10 millimeters (mm)
1 meter (m) = 100 centimeters (cm)
1 kilometer (km) = 1000 meters (m)

VOLUME
1 liter (ℓ) = 1000 milliliters (ml)

MASS
1 gram (g) = 1000 milligrams (mg)
1 kilogram (kg) = 1000 grams (g)

TABLE A-3. Metric-English Equivalents

LENGTH
1 in. = 2.54 cm   1 cm = 0.3937 in.
1 ft = 0.3048 m   1 m = 39.37 in. = 3.2808 ft
1 mi = 1.609 km   1 km = 39,370 in. = 3280 ft
                                                                = 0.62137 mi

VOLUME
1 in.^{3} = 16.387 cm^3 1 cm^3 = 0.0610 in.^{3}
1 ft^3 = 0.02832 m^3 1 m^3 = 35.315 ft^3
1 mi^3 = 4.1681 km^3 1 km^3 = 0.2399 mi^3
1 qt = 0.946 ℓ 1 ℓ = 1.06 qt

MASS
1 slug* = 1.46 × 10^4 g   1 g = 6.9 × 10^{-5} slugs

---

*The *slug* is the unit of mass in the English system. The *pound* is an English unit used for expressing a force such as the pull of gravity (weight). At sea level, a mass of 1 slug has a weight of 32.170 pounds.

Appendix B
Temperature Scales

The scale of degrees devised by G. D. Fahrenheit is the one used on thermometers for homes. It is called the *Fahrenheit temperature scale*. It is abbreviated as F. The freezing point of pure water at one atmosphere of pressure is assigned a value of thirty-two degrees (32°). The boiling point of pure water at one atmosphere of pressure is assigned a value of two hundred and twelve degrees (212°).

The *Celsius scale* (centigrade), devised by the Swedish astronomer A. Celsius, is used by scientists throughout the world. It is abbreviated as C. The value of zero degrees (0°) is assigned to the freezing point of pure water at one atmosphere of pressure. The boiling point of pure water at one atmosphere of pressure is assigned the value of one hundred degrees (100°) on the Celsius scale.

The Fahrenheit scale has exactly 180 equal divisions or degrees between the freezing point and boiling point of pure water at one atmosphere of pressure. The Celsius scale has exactly 100 equal divisions or degrees between the freezing point and boiling point of pure water at one atmosphere of pressure. Thus, a Fahrenheit degree is 5/9 of a Celsius degree ($\frac{100}{180}=5/9$). A Celsius degree is 9/5 of a Fahrenheit degree ($\frac{180}{100}=9/5$).

To change temperatures from one scale to another, these formulas can be used:

$$°F = (9/5 \times °C) + 32 \qquad °C = (°F - 32°) \times 5/9$$

Temperatures of interest to astronomers range from about $-270°C$ to $50,000,000°C$. Negative numbers, or temperatures expressed in degrees below zero, can be avoided by using the *Kelvin temperature scale*. This is one of many reasons that astronomical publications commonly refer to temperatures in °K. The symbol K is a tribute to Lord Kelvin, an English physicist who made many contributions to the theory and meaning of absolute zero. The Kelvin, or absolute, temperature scale is a Celsius scale with zero equal to $-273°C$. Changing scales from Celsius to Kelvin is a matter of simple addition, as $°K = °C + 273°$.

TABLE B-1. Comparison of Temperature Scales

At one atmosphere of pressure	F	C	K
Freezing point of pure water	32°	0°	273°
Common point	−40°	−40°	233°
Boiling point of pure water	212°	100°	373°

Appendix C
International Atomic Masses

Element	Symbol	Atomic number	Atomic mass	Element	Symbol	Atomic number	Atomic mass
Actinium	Ac	89	227*	Mercury	Hg	80	200.59
Aluminum	Al	13	26.98154	Molybdenum	Mo	42	95.94
Americium	Am	95	243*	Neodymium	Nd	60	144.24
Antimony	Sb	51	121.75	Neon	Ne	10	20.179
Argon	Ar	18	39.948	Neptunium	Np	93	237.0482*
Arsenic	As	33	74.9216	Nickel	Ni	28	58.70
Astatine	At	85	210*	Niobium	Nb	41	92.9064
Barium	Ba	56	137.34	Nitrogen	N	7	14.0067
Berkelium	Bk	97	247*	Nobelium	No	102	255*
Beryllium	Be	4	9.01218	Osmium	Os	76	190.2
Bismuth	Bi	83	208.9804	Oxygen	O	8	15.9994
Boron	B	5	10.81	Palladium	Pd	46	106.4
Bromine	Br	35	79.904	Phosphorus	P	15	30.97376
Cadmium	Cd	48	112.40	Platinum	Pt	78	195.09
Calcium	Ca	20	40.08	Plutonium	Pu	94	244*
Californium	Cf	98	251*	Polonium	Po	84	209*
Carbon	C	6	12.011	Potassium	K	19	39.098
Cerium	Ce	58	140.12	Praseodymium	Pr	59	140.9077
Cesium	Cs	55	132.9054	Promethium	Pm	61	145*
Chlorine	Cl	17	35.453	Protactinium	Pa	91	231.0359*
Chromium	Cr	24	51.996	Radium	Ra	88	226.0254
Cobalt	Co	27	58.9332	Radon	Rn	86	222*
Copper	Cu	29	63.546	Rhenium	Re	75	186.207
Curium	Cm	96	247*	Rhodium	Rh	45	102.9055
Dysprosium	Dy	66	162.50	Rubidium	Rb	37	85.4678
Einsteinium	Es	99	254*	Ruthenium	Ru	44	101.07
Erbium	Er	68	167.26	Samarium	Sm	62	150.4
Europium	Eu	63	151.96	Scandium	Sc	21	44.9559
Fermium	Fm	100	257*	Selenium	Se	34	78.96
Fluorine	F	9	18.99840	Silicon	Si	14	28.086
Francium	Fr	87	223*	Silver	Ag	47	107.868
Gadolinium	Gd	64	157.25	Sodium	Na	11	22.98977
Gallium	Ga	31	69.72	Strontium	Sr	38	87.62
Germanium	Ge	32	72.59	Sulfur	S	16	32.06
Gold	Au	79	196.9665	Tantalum	Ta	73	180.9479
Hafnium	Hf	72	178.49	Technetium	Tc	43	98.9062*
Helium	He	2	4.00260	Tellurium	Te	52	127.60
Holmium	Ho	67	164.9304	Terbium	Tb	65	158.9254
Hydrogen	H	1	1.0079	Thallium	Tl	81	204.37
Indium	In	49	114.82	Thorium	Th	90	232.0381
Iodine	I	53	126.9045	Thulium	Tm	69	168.9342
Iridium	Ir	77	192.22	Tin	Sn	50	118.69
Iron	Fe	26	55.847	Titanium	Ti	22	47.90
Krypton	Kr	36	83.80	Tungsten	W	74	183.85
Lanthanum	La	57	138.9055	Uranium	U	92	238.029
Lawrencium	Lr	103	256*	Vanadium	V	23	50.9414
Lead	Pb	82	207.2	Xenon	Xe	54	131.30
Lithium	Li	3	6.941	Ytterbium	Yb	70	173.04
Lutetium	Lu	71	174.97	Yttrium	Y	39	88.9059
Magnesium	Mg	12	24.305	Zinc	Zn	30	65.38
Manganese	Mn	25	54.9380	Zirconium	Zr	40	91.22
Mendelevium	Md	101	258*	Element 104†		104	257*
				Element 105†		105	260*

*The mass number of the isotope with the longest known half-life.

†Names for elements 104 and 105 have not yet been approved by the IUPAC. The USSR has proposed Kurchatovium (Ku) for element 104 and Bohrium (Bh) for element 105. The United States has proposed Rutherfordium (Rf) for element 104 and Hahnium (Ha) for element 105.

Appendix D
Valences

Positive Valences	Negative Valences
1+	**1−**
Ammonium, NH_4^+	Acetate, $C_2H_3O_2^-$
Copper (I), Cu^+	Bromide, Br^-
Hydrogen, H^+	Chlorate, ClO_3^-
Lithium, Li^+	Chloride, Cl^-
Potassium, K^+	Chlorite, ClO_2^-
Silver, Ag^+	Fluoride, F^-
Sodium, Na^+	Hydroxide, OH^-
	Hypochlorite, ClO^-
	Iodide, I^-
2+	Nitrite, NO_2^-
Barium, Ba^{2+}	Nitrate, NO_3^-
Cadmium, Cd^{2+}	Perchlorate, ClO_4^-
Calcium, Ca^{2+}	Permanganate, MnO_4^-
Chromium, (II), Cr^{2+}	
Cobalt (II), Co^{2+}	**2−**
Copper (II), Cu^{2+}	Carbonate, CO_3^{2-}
Iron (II), Fe^{2+}	Chromate, CrO_4^{2-}
Lead, Pb^{2+}	Dichromate, $Cr_2O_7^{2-}$
Magnesium, Mg^{2+}	Oxalate, $C_2O_4^{2-}$
Manganese (II), Mn^{2+}	Oxide, O^{2-}
Mercury (I), Hg_2^{2+}	Peroxide, O_2^{2-}
Mercury (II), Hg^{2+}	Sulfate, SO_4^{2-}
Tin (II), Sn^{2+}	Sulfide, S^{2-}
Zinc, Zn^{2+}	Sulfite, SO_3^{2-}
	Thiosulfate, $S_2O_3^{2-}$
3+	
Aluminum, Al^{3+}	**3−**
Antimony (III), Sb^{3+}	Phosphate, PO_4^{3-}
Chromium (III), Cr^{3+}	
Iron (III), Fe^{3+}	
4+	
Tin (IV), Sn^{4+}	
5+	
Antimony (V), Sb^{5+}	

Appendix E
The Periodic Table

Appendix F
Physical Laws

GAS LAWS

Boyle's law At constant temperatures, pressure varies directly with volume. As pressure increases, volume decreases and as pressure decreases, volume increases.
$$P \propto V \quad \text{or} \quad P_1 V_1 = P_2 V_2$$

Charles' law The volume of a gas increases as its temperature increases, if the pressure is not changed.
$$V \propto \frac{1}{T} \quad \text{or} \quad \frac{V_1}{T_1} = \frac{V_2}{T_2}$$

Gay-Lussac's law The pressure of a gas increases as the temperature increases, if the volume is not changed.
$$P \propto \frac{1}{T} \quad \text{or} \quad \frac{P_1}{T_1} = \frac{P_2}{T_2}$$

LAWS OF MOTION

Newton's first law of motion A body continues in a state of rest unless a force causes it to move, and a body continues in motion along a straight line unless a force stops it or causes the body to change direction.

Newton's second law of motion The acceleration of a body is directly proportional to the size of the force producing the acceleration and inversely proportional to the mass of the body.

Newton's third law of motion For every force there is an equal and opposite force.

OTHER PHYSICAL LAWS

Law of conservation of mass Mass is neither gained nor lost in a chemical change.

Newton's law of gravitation The gravitational attraction between two bodies is proportional to the product of their masses divided by the square of the distance between them.

Ohm's law The ratio of the potential difference applied to a closed circuit and the current in the circuit is a constant.
$$I = V/R$$

Pascal's law If pressure is applied to a liquid in a closed container, the pressure is transmitted unchanged to all surfaces of the container.

Glossary

Glossary

Pronunciation Key

ay	bake
ah	father, soft
a	back
ee	easy
eh or e + con	less
y or i	life
ih or i + con	trip
oo	food
oh	flow
yoo	cube
uh	cup
u + con	put
th	thin, then
ch	church
zh	measure
sh	ship
j	judge
g	go
s	cents
k	cake
oy	oil
or	orbit

absolute zero: in theory, the lowest temperature to which a substance can be cooled

acceleration (ak sel uh RAY shuhn): rate of increase in speed

acid: a substance which is sour in taste and will turn blue litmus red; a substance which increases the hydronium ion concentration when added to water

acid anhydride (an HY dryd): nonmetallic oxide which produces an acid when added to water

action force: a force exerted on an object

actual mechanical advantage (A.M.A.): the actual amount by which the applied force is multiplied by a machine

alcohol: a substituted hydrocarbon in which a hydrogen atom has been replaced by an −OH group

alkane (AL kayn) **series:** (methane series) group of saturated hydrocarbons having the general formula C_nH_{2n+2}

alkene (AL keen) **series:** group of unsaturated hydrocarbons with one double bond, having the general formula C_nH_{2n}

alkyne (AL kyn) **series:** group of unsaturated hydrocarbons with one triple bond, having the general formula C_nH_{2n-2}

allotropes (AL uh trohps): different molecular forms of the same element

alloy: a mixture of two or more metals

alpha (AL fuh) **particle** (α): a positively charged helium nucleus with two protons and two neutrons

alpha ray: high speed alpha particles (helium nuclei) shot out from radioactive atomic nuclei

alternating current (A.C.): a continuous back and forth movement of electrons in a circuit

ammeter (AM eet uhr): instrument used to measure the amount of electric current in a circuit in amperes

amorphous (uh MOR fuhs) **solid:** material such as glass or plastic which has no regular crystalline shape

ampere (AM pir): the rate of electron flow in a circuit

amplitude (AM pluh tood): the distance a wave rises or falls as it travels

analog (AN uhl ahg): something which is similar to something else

analog computer: a device which solves problems by representing real things or mathematical values with electric circuits or moving parts, such as rotating wheels

angle of incidence: angle made between a wave striking a barrier and the normal to the surface

angle of reflection: angle between a reflected wave and the normal to the barrier from which it is reflected

anhydride (an HY dryd): a compound formed from another by the removal of water; meaning "without water"

anode (+): positive electrode in an electrical circuit; gains electrons in a circuit

aqueous (AK wee uhs): pertaining to water

armature (AHR muh chuhr): an electromagnet that is the rotating part of a motor or generator

atom: smallest piece of an element which retains the properties of that element

atomic "bullets": high speed particles used to split nuclei

atomic mass: mass of an atom compared to a standard mass, the carbon-12 atom

atomic mass number (A): average atomic mass rounded to the nearest whole number

atomic mass unit (a.m.u.): 1/12 the mass of the carbon-12 atom

atomic number (Z): number of protons in the nucleus of an atom

average atomic mass: average of the atomic masses of the naturally occurring isotopes which make up an element

barometer (buh RAHM uht uhr): instrument used to measure air pressure

GLOSSARY

base: a substance which is bitter in taste, feels slippery, and will turn red litmus blue; a substance which increases the hydroxide ion concentration when added to water

basic anhydride: metallic oxide which produces a base when added to water

battery: two or more cells (wet or dry) connected together in a single circuit

beta (BAYT uh) particle (β): electron from a radioactive atom; negatively charged

beta ray: stream of fast moving electrons shot out from a radioactive atom

binary (BY nuh ree) compound: compound composed of only two elements

Bohr model: model of an atom which resembles the solar system; model showing the nucleus of the atom with its protons and neutrons and the arrangement of electrons orbiting the nucleus

boiling point (BP): the temperature at which a substance changes rapidly from a liquid to a gaseous phase; BP of water equals 100°C at 760 mm pressure

Boyle's law: the volume of a gas decreases as the pressure on it increases if the temperature remains constant

British thermal unit (BTU): amount of heat required to raise the temperature of 1 lb of water 1 F°

bubble chamber: device which detects nuclear particles through the formation of bubbles within a superheated liquid

calorie (KAL uh ree): the amount of heat required to raise the temperature of 1 g of water 1 C°

calorimeter (kal uh RIM uht uhr): instrument used to measure heat energy

capacitor (kuh PAS uht uhr): device that stores electricity; combination of conducting plates, each plate separated by an insulator

catalyst (KAT uhl uhst): substance which increases or decreases the rate of a chemical reaction

cathode (−): negative electrode in an electric circuit; releases electrons in a circuit

cathode-ray tube: a kind of vacuum tube which emits a beam of electrons from the cathode to a screen at the opposite end of the tube

Celsius temperature scale: internationally used temperature scale; equivalent to (°F − 32°) × 5/9

centimeter (cm): metric unit of length; 1/100 of a meter

centrifugal (sen TRIF ih guhl) force: the apparent pull away from the center around which a body travels in a circular path

centripetal (sen TRIP uht uhl) force: a force acting toward the center around which a body travels in a circular path

Charles' law: the volume of a gas increases as its temperature increases if the pressure remains constant

chemical activity: ease with which an element reacts with other elements

chemical change: change in which a substance becomes a different substance having different chemical properties

chemical equation: shorthand description of a chemical reaction containing symbols and formulas

chemical property: characteristic of a material which depends on the material's reaction with other materials

chemistry (KEM uh stree): study of what matter is made of and the changes in matter

chromatography (kroh muh TAHG ruh fee): method of separating closely related compounds using paper and solvent

circuit (SUHR kuht): closed-loop path of conduction through which an electric current flows

cleavage (KLEE vij): tendency of a crystal to come apart or split between planes of atoms when hit with a sharp blow

cleavage plane: an area along which a crystal separates

cloud chamber: device which detects nuclear particles through the formation of cloud tracks

coefficient (koh uh FISH uhnt): number placed in front of a formula to show the number of atoms needed for the reaction to take place; used in balancing chemical equations

compound: a substance containing two or more elements chemically combined

compound machine: two or more simple machines working together

compression (kuhm PRESH uhn): most dense concentration of wave particles in a compressional wave

compressional (kuhm PRESH uhn uhl) wave: wave in which matter vibrates in the same direction as the wave moves

computer: complex electronic device used to solve problems through mathematical operations

concave (kahn KAYV) lens: a lens which is thinner in the middle than at the edges; used to correct nearsightedness

Pronunciation Key

ay . . . . bake
ah . . . father, soft
a . . . . back
ee . . . . . easy
eh or
e + con . . less
y or i . . . . life
ih or
i + con . . trip
oo . . . . . food
oh . . . . flow
yoo . . . . cube
uh . . . . . cup
u + con . . put
th . . . . . thin, then
ch . . . . church
zh . . . measure
sh . . . . . ship
j . . . . . judge
g . . . . go
s . . . . . cents
k . . . . cake
oy . . . . . . oil
or . . . . . orbit

concentration (kahn suhn TRAY shuhn): amount of solute per unit volume of solvent

conclusion (kuhn KLOO zhuhn): a judgment or decision based on observation

condensation (kahn duhn SAY shuhn): change from the gaseous phase to the liquid phase

conduction (kuhn DUHK shuhn): movement of heat or electricity through a substance; gain or loss of electrons through direct contact with a charged object

conductor (kuhn DUHK tuhr): a substance through which heat or electricity can flow readily

conservation of momentum: principle which states that momentum cannot be created or destroyed

control: group or activity that serves as a standard of comparison for change in an experiment

convection (kuhn VEK shuhn): transfer of heat energy by the actual movement of the heated matter, occurs in liquids and gases

convex (kahn VEKS) **lens:** a lens which is thicker in the middle than at the edges; used to correct farsightedness

cosmic (KAHZ mik) **rays:** very high energy nuclear rays from outer space

covalent (koh VAY luhnt) **bond:** bond between atoms produced by the sharing of electrons

covalent bonding: type of bonding in which electrons are shared

crest: high point of a wave

critical mass: smallest amount of an element needed to undergo a nuclear chain reaction

cryogenics (kry uh JEN iks): scientific study of physical and chemical properties at very low temperatures

crystal (KRIS tuhl): solid material having a regular, geometric form characteristic of a given compound or element

crystallization (kris tuh luh ZAY shuhn): process by which crystals are formed

cyclotron (SY kluh trahn): a machine which produces high-speed beams of atomic particles; a type of atom smasher

deceleration (dee sel uh RAY shuhn): rate of decrease in speed; negative acceleration

decomposition (dee kahm puh ZISH uhn) **reaction:** chemical change in which a compound breaks down or decomposes into other compounds and/or elements

deliquescent (del ih KWES uhnt): capable of attracting and absorbing moisture from air

density (DEN suht ee): mass of a substance per unit of volume; expressed in g/cm³

deuterium (doo TIR ee uhm): hydrogen isotope with one proton and one neutron in its nucleus

diatomic (dy uh TAHM ik): a molecule composed of two atoms

diffraction (dif RAK shuhn) **grating:** piece of transparent or reflecting material, contains many thousands of parallel lines per centimeter; used to produce a light spectrum by interference

diffusion cloud chamber: device used to detect nuclear particles from the formation of cloud tracks in a supersaturated vapor

digital (DIJ uht uhl) **computer:** a device using numbers to solve mathematical problems; specifically, an electronic machine which uses stored instructions and information to perform complex computations at rapid speed

diode (DY ohd): electrical vacuum tube containing a filament and a plate

dipole-dipole attraction: small attractive force between dipole molecules in which a positively charged end of one molecule is attracted to the negatively charged end of the other molecule

direct current (D.C.): flow of electrons in one direction through a conductor

discharge: loss of negative or positive electrical charge

dispersion (dis PUHR zhuhn): the separation of white light into its component wavelengths (colors)

dissociation (dis oh see AY shuhn): process in which an ionic compound forms ions when dissolved in water

distillation (dis tuh LAY shuhn): physical separation of the parts of a mixture through evaporation and condensation

Doppler effect: change in wavelength caused by the motion of the wave source

double replacement reaction: chemical change in which two ions in two different compounds replace each other, forming a precipitate, gas, or water

dry cell: device for producing a current with moist chemicals

efficiency (ih FISH uhn see): the ratio of the work output of a machine to its work input

efflorescent (ef luh RES uhnt): substance which changes to a powder from the loss of water of hydration

effort arm: the distance from the fulcrum to the effort force in a lever

electricity: a form of energy which can do work

electrolysis (ih lek TRAHL uh suhs): the decomposition of a compound into simpler

---

Pronunciation Key

ay . . . . bake
ah . . . father, soft
a . . . . back
ee . . . . easy
eh or
e + con . . less
y or i . . . . life
ih or
i + con . . trip
oo . . . . food
oh . . . . flow
yoo . . . . cube
uh . . . . cup
u + con . . put
th . . . . thin, then
ch . . . . church
zh . . . measure
sh . . . . ship
j . . . . judge
g . . . . . . go
s . . . . cents
k . . . . cake
oy . . . . . oil
or . . . . . orbit

GLOSSARY

substances by passing an electric current through the compound

electrolyte (ih LEK truh lyt): a substance which is capable of conducting electricity when dissolved in water

electromagnet: soft iron core surrounded by a coil of wire through which an electric current is passed, thus magnetizing the core

electromagnetic spectrum (ih lek troh mag NET ik • SPEK truhm): invisible, transverse energy waves, ranging from low frequency to very high frequency, which can travel at the speed of light in a vacuum

electron (ih LEK trahn): negatively charged particle in an atom

electron cloud model: model of an atom showing a cloud of negative charge surrounding the nucleus

electronics (ih lek TRAHN iks): study of the release, behavior, and effects of electrons

electron volt (eV): the energy required to move an electron between two points that have a potential difference of one volt

electroscope (ih LEK truh skohp): instrument used for detecting positive and negative electrical charges

electrostatic induction (ih lek truh STAT ik • in DUHK shuhn): charging a body with another charged body, without the two bodies touching each other

element: a substance which cannot be broken down into simpler substances by ordinary means

endothermic (en duh THUHR mik) **reaction**: a chemical change in which energy is taken on during the reaction

end reaction: a reaction which does not attain equilibrium; a reaction which goes to completion by forming a gas, a precipitate, or water

energy: ability to produce motion or change

energy level: space where electrons orbit the nucleus in an atom; shell

equilibrium (ee kwuh LIB ree uhm): the state of balance between equal opposing forces

evaporation (ih vap uh RAY shuhn): change from the liquid to the gaseous phase

exothermic (ek soh THUHR mik) **reaction**: a chemical change in which the energy released is greater than the energy required to start the reaction

experiment: a process designed to yield observations under carefully controlled conditions

face: surface of a crystal

flame test: procedure for identifying an element by heating it in a flame and observing the color given off

fluid: material which takes shape of its container

fluorescent (flur ES uhnt): emitting light only when exposed to radiation such as cathode rays, X rays, and ultraviolet rays

focal length: distance between the principal focus of a lens or mirror and its optical center

force: any push or pull

formula: group of symbols used to represent a compound

formula mass: sum of mass numbers of the atoms present in a formula of an ionic compound

fractionation (frak shuh NAY shuhn): a type of distillation in which compounds in petroleum are separated

frequency (FREE kwuhn see): number of waves that pass a given point in a given unit of time

friction (FRIK shuhn): a force that opposes motion

fulcrum (FUL kruhm): the point on which a lever rotates

galvanometer (gal vuh NAHM uht uhr): a device consisting of a coil of wire rotating between the poles of a magnet; used to detect small electric currents

gamma ray (γ): high energy wave of high frequency and with a wavelength shorter than X rays

gas: phase of matter which lacks definite shape or volume

Gay-Lussac's (gay luh SAKS) **law**: as the temperature of a gas increases the pressure of the gas increases if volume remains constant

Geiger counter: instrument used to detect radioactivity through the formation of an electric current

generator: a machine which changes mechanical energy into electrical energy

gram (g): metric unit of mass

graphic formula: a formula which shows the number and kinds of atoms and the structure of the molecule

gravity: mutual force of attraction which exists between all bodies in the universe

ground: connection of an object to the earth by an electrical conductor to allow electrons to move freely into and out of the object

half-life: time required for one half of the atoms in a radioactive material to decay

heat: a form of kinetic energy of molecules

Pronunciation Key

ay .... bake
ah ... father, soft
a ..... back
ee ..... easy
eh or
e + con .. less
y or i .... life
ih or
i + con .. trip
oo ..... food
oh ..... flow
yoo .... cube
uh ..... cup
u + con .. put
th ..... thin, then
ch .... church
zh ... measure
sh ..... ship
j ..... judge
g .... go
s ..... cents
k ..... cake
oy ...... oil
or ..... orbit

heat of condensation: number of calories per gram given up when a vapor changes to a liquid without a change in temperature

heat of fusion: amount of heat required to melt 1 g of a solid

heat of vaporization: amount of heat required to change 1 g of a liquid to a gas

horsepower (hp): English unit of power defined as 550 ft-lb of work done in 1 sec

hydrate: compound formed by the union of water with some other substance

hydrocarbon (hy druh KAHR buhn): compound containing only carbon and hydrogen

hydronium (hy DROH nee uhm) **ion:** H_3O^+; a positive ion containing a proton (hydrogen ion) bonded to a water molecule

hydroxide (hy DRAHK syd) **ion:** OH^-; a negative ion containing one oxygen atom and one hydrogen atom

hypothesis (hy PAHTH uh suhs): proposed answer to a question or tentative solution to a problem

ideal mechanical advantage (I.M.A.): the ideal amount by which the applied force is multiplied by a machine neglecting friction

image: reproduction of an object formed with lenses or mirrors

impulse: product of force multiplied by the time the force acts on a body

inclined plane: a slanted surface used to raise objects; a simple machine

index of refraction: amount that light is refracted when it enters a substance; ratio of speed of light in a vacuum to its speed in a given substance

indicator (IN duh kayt uhr): chemical used to tell, by a color change, whether a solution is an acid or a base

inertia (in UHR shuh): tendency of matter to remain at rest or in uniform motion unless acted on by a force

input: information sent into the circuits of a computer

insulator (IN suh layt uhr): a substance through which heat or electricity cannot flow readily

integrated circuit: small electronic device which has replaced larger transistors and vacuum tubes in electronic equipment

interference (int uhr FIR uhnts): the mutual effect of two waves resulting in a loss of energy in certain areas and reinforcement of energy in other areas

ion (I ahn): a charged particle in which an atom or bonded atoms have gained or lost one or more electrons

ionic (i AHN ik) **bond:** electrostatic bond between atoms produced through gain of electrons by one atom or group of atoms and loss by the other

ionic bonding: a type of bonding in which ions are held together by the strong attraction of their opposite charges

ionization (i uh nuh ZAY shuhn): process in which a molecular compound dissolves in water to form ions

isomers (I suh muhrz): compounds having the same number and kind of atoms, but different structures; compounds having the same molecular formula, but different structural formulas

isotopes (I suh tohps): atoms of the same element with different numbers of neutrons

kilometer (km): metric unit of length; 1000 m

kilowatt-hour (KWH): unit used to measure electrical energy; equal to 1000 watt-hours

kinetic energy: energy of motion

law of conservation of mass: mass is neither gained nor lost in a chemical change

law of multiple proportions: the same two (or more) elements may unite in different ratios to form different compounds

law of reflection: angle of incidence equals the angle of reflection

lens: curved, transparent object; usually made of glass or clear plastic

lever: a bar free to rotate around a point; a simple machine

liquid: phase of matter having a constant volume but no definite shape

litmus paper: an indicator used to test for an acid or base

liter (l): metric unit of volume; volume of 1 kg (1000 g)

luminous (LOO muh nuhs): able to glow in the dark

machine: a device which makes work easier by changing the speed, direction, or amount of a force

magnetism: a property of matter in which there is an attraction due to unlike poles

magnification (mag nuh fuh KAY shuhn): image length divided by object length

magnitude (MAG nuh tood): amount of a force

mass: quantity of matter in a body

matter: anything that has mass and takes up space

Pronunciation Key

ay	bake
ah	father, soft
a	back
ee	easy
eh or e + con	less
y or i, ih or i + con	life, trip
oo	food
oh	flow
yoo	cube
uh	cup
u + con	put
th	thin, then
ch	church
zh	measure
sh	ship
j	judge
g	go
s	cents
k	cake
oy	oil
or	orbit

GLOSSARY

mechanical advantage (M.A.): the amount by which the applied force is multiplied by a machine

melting: change from solid phase to liquid phase

melting point (MP): the temperature at which a substance changes from a solid to a liquid

metal: a substance that has a specific luster, is a good conductor of heat and electricity, and can be pounded or drawn into various shapes; usually has one, two, or three electrons in the outer shell

metallic bonding: type of bonding typical of metals; outer electrons of atoms move throughout the crystal and are shared equally by all ions

metalloid: element, such as boron, having properties of both metals and nonmetals

meter (m): standard unit of length in the metric system

metric system: decimal system of measurement based on the mass of a cubic centimeter of pure water at 3.98°C

millimeter (mm): metric unit of length; 1/1000 of a meter

mixture: two or more elements or compounds which are mingled without combining chemically

model: a representation of an idea in order to make it more understandable

molecular formula: formula showing the number of atoms of each element in a molecule of a compound

molecular kinetic energy: energy of a molecule that results from its vibrating motion

molecular mass: sum of the atomic mass numbers for the atoms in a molecule

molecular potential energy: energy of a molecule that may be released through physical or chemical change; energy of position

molecule (MAHL ih kyool): smallest particle of an element or a compound; particle containing two or more atoms chemically combined

moment: the force on a lever multiplied by the distance from the pivot point (fulcrum); force times lever arm length

momentum (moh MENT uhm); quantity of motion; mass of a body multiplied by its velocity

neutralization (noo truh luh ZAY shuhn): chemical reaction in which hydronium ions (base) and hydroxide ions (acid) combine to form water

neutron (NOO trahn): neutral particle found in the atomic nucleus which has a mass about equal to a proton

newton (nt): metric unit of force; force required to accelerate a 1-kg mass at 1 m/sec^2

Newton's first law of motion: a body remains in a state of rest unless a force causes it to move, and a body continues in motion along a straight line unless a force stops it or causes the body to change direction

Newton's law of gravitation: the gravitational attraction between two bodies is proportional to the product of their masses divided by the square of the distance between them

Newton's second law of motion: the acceleration of a body is directly proportional to the size of the force producing the acceleration and inversely proportional to the mass of the body

Newton's third law of motion: for every force there is an equal and opposite force

noble gas: member of Group VIIIA; a stable gas that does not combine chemically under ordinary conditions; helium, argon, xenon, krypton, neon, radon

noise: sounds produced by irregular vibrations

nonelectrolyte: a substance which does not conduct an electric current when dissolved in water

nonmetal: element with more than four electrons in the outer shell; lacks the typical properties of a metal

normal: a line drawn perpendicular to a line or plane

nuclear chain reaction: series of continuous rapid nuclear fissions, beginning with the splitting of an atom

nuclear decay series: the nuclear reactions through which uranium becomes lead; in each reaction, a different radioactive element is formed

nuclear emulsion (ih MUHL shuhn): a thick layer of photographic emulsion, contains silver bromide dissolved in a gelatinlike solid, used to detect nuclear particles

nuclear fission: nuclear change in which a nucleus is divided into two nuclei

nuclear force: force which holds together the particles in an atomic nucleus

nuclear fusion: nuclear change in which two or more atomic nuclei unite to form a single heavier nucleus

nuclear reactor: device for producing energy from a nuclear fuel, such as uranium or plutonium, through a controlled chain reaction

nucleus (NOO klee uhs): the central portion of an atom that contains almost all of an atom's mass; contains neutrons and protons

Pronunciation Key	
ay	bake
ah	father, soft
a	back
ee	easy
eh or e + con	less
y or i	life
ih or i + con	trip
oo	food
oh	flow
yoo	cube
uh	cup
u + con	put
th	thin, then
ch	church
zh	measure
sh	ship
j	judge
g	go
s	cents
k	cake
oy	oil
or	orbit

Pronunciation Key

ay	bake
ah	father, soft
a	back
ee	easy
eh or e + con	less
y or i or ih or i + con	life, trip
oo	food
oh	flow
yoo	cube
uh	cup
u + con	put
th	thin, then
ch	church
zh	measure
sh	ship
j	judge
g	go
s	cents
k	cake
oy	oil
or	orbit

observation (ahb suhr VAY shuhn): act of taking notice and gathering data; scientific method basic to the process of science

ohm: unit for measuring electrical resistance

Ohm's law: the relationship between volts and amperes in a circuit; $I = V/R$

optics (AHP tiks): science dealing with the nature and properties of light

orbital (OR buht uhl): electron path within an energy level or shell of an atom

organic (or GAN ik): related to, or derived from, living organisms

organic chemistry: study of carbon and its compounds

output: information obtained from a computer's circuits

parabola (puh RAB uh luh): a curved line representing the path of a projectile; the shape of the surface of a parabolic mirror

parabolic (par uh BAHL ik) **mirror:** mirror curved in the shape of a parabola; concentrates light rays into a common point

parallel circuit: a circuit in which two or more conductors are connected across two common points in the circuit to provide separate conducting paths for the current

Pascal's (pas KALZ) **law:** if pressure is applied to a liquid in a closed container, the pressure is transmitted unchanged to all surfaces of the container

periodic law: when elements are arranged in order of increasing atomic number, there is a periodic repetition of similar properties

periodic table: an arrangement of the chemical elements, according to their atomic numbers, in vertical columns having similar properties and horizontal rows showing shifts in properties

permanent magnet: substance that remains magnetized for a long time after the magnetizing force has been removed

perpendicular (puhr puhn DIK yuh luhr): at right angles to

pH: measure of hydronium ion concentration in a solution

phenolphthalein (feen uhl THAYL een): an indicator which is colorless in an acid solution and pink in a basic solution

photochemical smog: substance that forms in the atmosphere as a result of the action of sunlight on airborne pollutants

photoconductor: a metal whose electrical conductivity is controlled by light

photoelectric cell (photocell): a device containing a photoelectric metal which produces an electrical current when struck by light

photoelectric effect: electrons released from the atoms of certain metals when struck by light

photon (FOH tahn): a packet or bundle of radiant wave energy (light)

physical change: change in size, shape, or form without a change in composition

physical property: characteristic of a substance which may be observed without changing the chemical composition of the substance

physical science: the study of matter and energy

physics: the study of how matter and energy are related

pitch: tone of a sound wave, determined by the frequency of the wave; the greater the frequency, the higher the pitch

plane mirror: mirror with a flat surface

plasma (PLAZ muh): phase of matter in which atoms lose their electrons

plastic: material that can be shaped by molding it when it is soft and allowing it to harden

polar: having regions of positive and negative charge

polarized light: light in which all waves are vibrating in a single plane

polyatomic (pahl ee uh TAHM ik) **ion:** ion containing two or more elements chemically combined; a group of atoms which act together as one ion or charged atom

polymer (PAHL uh muhr): large molecule formed from the combination of molecules of many compounds

polymerization (pahl uh muh ruh ZAY shuhn): process in which a large molecule is formed from the combination of smaller units or molecules

potential difference: the difference between the potentials of two points in an electric field

potential energy: energy of rest or position

power: amount of work done per unit of time

precipitate (prih SIP uh tayt): a solid that separates from a solution by a chemical or physical change

pressure: force applied per unit of area

principal axis: a line straight out from the center of a mirror or lens through the focus

principal focus: common point to which rays parallel to the principal axis converge, or from which they diverge, after reflection or refraction

GLOSSARY

prism: transparent material with two straight faces at an angle to each other

product: substance formed as a result of a chemical change; substance to the right of a yield sign (→) in an equation

program: set of instructions which enters a computer

projectile (pruh JEK tuhl): object such as a stone, ball, bullet, or rocket, which is thrown or shot

protium (PROHT ee uhm): hydrogen isotope with one proton in its nucleus; the most common isotope of hydrogen

proton (PROH tahn): positively charged particle in the nucleus of an atom

pulley: a form of a lever; a simple machine

pyrometer (py RAHM uht uhr): a thermometer, containing a thermocouple, used to measure very high temperatures

radiation (rayd ee AY shuhn): process of emission and transmission of radiant heat from areas of high temperature to areas of low temperature; energy released from atoms and molecules as they undergo internal nuclear change

radioactive isotope: form of an element which emits high energy radiation from the nucleus

radioactivity (rayd ee oh ak TIV uht ee): the emitting of high energy radiation from nuclei of radioactive atoms

rarefaction (rar uh FAK shuhn): least dense concentration of wave particles in a compressional wave

rate: relationship between two quantities

reactant: substance which undergoes a chemical change; substance to the left of a yield sign (→) in an equation

reaction force: a force equal to an action force but exerted in the opposite direction

real image: an image which can be projected onto a screen; formed by a parabolic mirror

rectifier (REK tuh fyr): device for changing alternating current to direct current

reflecting telescope: a telescope in which magnification is produced by a parabolic mirror

reflection (rih FLEK shuhn): bouncing of a wave or ray off a surface

refracting telescope: a telescope in which magnification is produced by convex lenses

refraction (rih FRAK shuhn): bending of a wave or ray, caused by a decrease in speed as it passes from one substance into another

resistance (rih ZIS tuhnts): any opposition which slows down or prevents motion; opposition to the flow of electricity

resistance arm: the distance from the fulcrum to the resistance force in a lever

resonance (REZ uhn uhnts): vibrations of two or more waves at the same frequency, induced by a vibrating source having the same or a simply related frequency

resultant (rih ZUHLT uhnt): the net effect of several forces

rhombic (RAHM bik): shape characteristic of a sulfur allotrope in which eight atoms are joined in a ring

ring compound: organic compound in which carbon atoms are joined in the shape of a ring,

ripple tank: shallow, transparent, waterproof box containing a layer of water about 1 cm deep; used to study waves

roentgen (RENT guhn): standard unit used to measure radiation; amount of radiation that will produce 2.08×10^9 pairs of negative and positive ions

salt: solid substance produced if the water is evaporated after a neutralization reaction; compound containing a positive ion from a base and a negative ion from an acid

saturated (SACH uh rayt uhd): solution in which the solvent has dissolved the maximum amount of solute at a given temperature

saturated hydrocarbon: hydrocarbon in which each carbon atom is bonded to four other atoms by single bonds

scale: relative dimensions of a drawing or model; instrument used to measure weight

scientific law: accepted statement of fact based on scientific evidence

scintillation (sint uhl AY shuhn) **counter:** instrument used to detect radioactivity through the production of flashes of light (scintillations) in a material

screw: a modified inclined plane; a simple machine

semiconductor: material with a resistance between that of a conductor and an insulator

series circuit: electric circuit in which the parts are connected so that the same current flows through all parts of the circuit

shell: space where electrons orbit the nucleus in an atom; energy level

Pronunciation Key

ay . . . . bake
ah . . . father, soft
a . . . . . back
ee . . . . . easy
eh or
e + con . . less
y or i . . . . life
ih or
i + con . . trip
oo . . . . . food
oh . . . . . flow
yoo . . . . cube
uh . . . . . cup
u + con . . put
th . . . . thin, then
ch . . . . church
zh . . . measure
sh . . . . . ship
j . . . . . judge
g . . . . . . go
s . . . . . cents
k . . . . . cake
oy . . . . . . oil
or . . . . . orbit

GLOSSARY

simple machine: an elementary device which makes work easier by changing the speed, direction, or amount of a force

single replacement reaction: chemical change in which an uncombined or free element replaces an element which is combined in a compound

solid: phase of matter having a definite volume and shape

solubility (sahl yuh BIL uht ee): the amount of a substance (solute) that will dissolve in a specific amount of another substance (solvent)

solute (SAHL yoot): substance being dissolved in a solvent

solution (suh LOO shuhn): mixture in which a substance (solute) is dissolved in another substance (solvent)

solvent (SAHL vuhnt): substance in which a solute is dissolved

sound wave: compressional wave produced by vibrations

specific heat: the amount of heat needed to raise the temperature of 1 g of a substance 1 C°; cal/g-C°

speed: distance traveled per unit time

stable: term given to a nucleus which is not radioactive; ratio of protons to neutrons is about 1:1

static electricity: electricity produced by charged bodies

structural formula: a simple formula showing the symbols of atoms in a molecule of a compound and how they are bonded

sublimation (suhb luh MAY shuhn): the direct change of phase from a solid to a gas

subscript: small number to the right and slightly lower than a symbol; gives the ratio in which elements are combined in a compound

substituted hydrocarbon: organic compound in which one or more hydrogen atoms in a hydrocarbon have been replaced with another kind of atom

superconductor: supercooled metal which holds electrical current for an unusually long length of time

superfluid: a gas which is compressed and cooled to form an easily flowing liquid

supermagnet: supercooled metal which holds its magnetism indefinitely

supersaturated solution: a solution containing more solute than the amount it would normally take to saturate it at a given temperature

symmetry (SIM uh tree): similarity of form or arrangement on either side of a dividing line, plane, or point

synthesis (SIN thuh suhs) **reaction:** chemical change in which two or more elements or compounds unite to form one compound

technology (tek NAHL uh jee): application of science for practical purposes

temperature: the amount of hotness or coldness of a body, as measured by a thermometer

tetrahedron (teh truh HEE druhn): four-sided shape of the molecule formed when a carbon atom shares electrons with four other atoms

theory (THEE uh ree): an explanation based on available facts

thermal pollution: release of heated water into lakes, streams, and oceans

thermocouple (THUHR muh kuhp uhl): device with two different metals twisted or bonded together, used to produce an electric current

thermonuclear (thuhr moh NOO klee uhr) **reaction:** nuclear fusion reaction occurring at a temperature of millions of degrees

thermostat: device which regulates cooling and heating systems

transistor: semiconductor used as a replacement for vacuum tubes in electronic equipment

transition metals: elements located in the B columns of the periodic table; have two electrons located in the outer shell

transmutation (trans myoo TAY shuhn): natural or artificial process in which one element changes into another element by changing its number of protons

transverse (tranz VUHRS) **wave:** wave in which matter vibrates at right angles to the direction in which the wave travels

triatomic (try uh TAHM ik): molecules composed of three atoms

triode: electric vacuum tube containing a filament, a plate, and a grid

tritium (TRIT ee uhm): hydrogen isotope with two neutrons and one proton in its nucleus

trough (TRAHF): valley of a wave

ultrasonic (uhl truh SAHN ik): sound waves with frequencies above 20,000 vib/sec

unsaturated hydrocarbon: hydrocarbon in which two or more carbon atoms are joined by double or triple bonds

unsaturated solution: solution containing less solute than the amount it would take to saturate it at a given temperature

---

Pronunciation Key

ay . . . . bake
ah . . . father, soft
a . . . . . back
ee . . . . . easy
eh or
e + con . . less
y or i . . . . life
ih or
i + con . . trip
oo . . . . . food
oh . . . . flow
yoo . . . . cube
uh . . . . . cup
u + con . . put
th . . . . . thin, then
ch . . . . church
zh . . . measure
sh . . . . . ship
j . . . . . judge
g . . . . . . go
s . . . . . cents
k . . . . . cake
oy . . . . . oil
or . . . . . orbit

GLOSSARY

vacuum tube: a gas-tight container, usually of glass, from which air is removed to form a vacuum; used in radios, televisions, and stereos

valence (VAY luhntz): combining ability of an element or an ion in forming a compound

van der Waals forces: small attractive forces between atoms caused by the attraction of the positively charged nucleus in one atom to the negatively charged electron cloud in another atom

vaporization (vay puh ruh ZAY shuhn): change from liquid phase to gaseous phase

vector (VEK tuhr): ray used to represent the quantity and direction of force

velocity (vuh LAHS uht ee): speed and direction of a moving body

vibration: rapid back and forth movement

virtual (VUHRCH wuhl) **image:** an image which cannot be projected onto a surface

visible light spectrum: band of colors produced by a prism when white light is passed through it

volt (V): unit of electromotive force

voltmeter: an instrument used to measure the potential difference between two points in an electric circuit

volume: the amount of space matter occupies

watt (w): metric unit of power; 1 watt equals 1/746 horsepower

watt-hour: unit used to measure electric power in a unit of time

wave: rhythmic disturbance which travels through space or matter

wavelength: distance from the crest of one wave to the crest of the next wave

wedge: a simple machine composed of two inclined planes put together

weight: the force with which a body is attracted toward the earth; measurement of gravity force

wet cell: device for producing electric current from two metals in a chemical solution

wheel and axle: a simple machine which is a variation of the lever

work: product of the force exerted on an object multiplied by the distance the object moved

work input: the effort force multiplied by the effort distance

work output: the resistance force multiplied by the resistance distance

X rays: invisible electromagnetic radiation of great penetrating power

Pronunciation Key

ay . . . . bake
ah . . . father, soft
a . . . . . back
ee . . . . easy
eh or e + con . . less
y or i . . . . life
ih or i + con . . trip
oo . . . . . food
oh . . . . flow
yoo . . . . cube
uh . . . . . cup
u + con . . put
th . . . . . thin, then
ch . . . . church
zh . . . measure
sh . . . . . ship
j . . . . . judge
g . . . . . . go
s . . . . . cents
k . . . . . cake
oy . . . . . . oil
or . . . . . orbit

Index

Index

Absolute zero, 327
Acceleration, 54, 55; of gravity, 82; of subatomic particle, 457, 458
Acetic acid, 271, 274
Acetylene, 216, 217; *act.,* 217
Acid, 271-275, 278; pH of, 280, 281; *act.,* 272; 274; 275; 276; 277; 280; 282; *illus.,* 273; *table,* 275; 280; 281
Acid anhydride, 283, 284
Action force, 78, 321
Actual mechanical advantage, 25, 29, 31
Air, convection currents in, 314, 315; distillation of, 187, 201; ionization of, 447, 448; kinetic energy in, 301; nitrogen from, 191, 193; speed of light in, 363; speed of sound in, 338, 339; *exp.,* 8
Air pressure, 316
Alchemist, *illus.,* 3
Alcohol, 219, 220, 448; *table,* 219
Alkali, 275
Alkali metal, 195-198; *act.,* 198; *illus.,* 197; *table,* 196
Alkaline earth metal, 198-201; *table,* 198
Alkane, 211, 214
Alkene, 216
Alkyne, 216
Allotrope, 185, 186, 188, 193, 195
Alloy, 195, 227, 228, 401; magnesium, 467; *table,* 228
Alnico, 401
Alpha particle, 444, 448
Alpha ray, 444
Alternating current, 403-408; amplification of, 417; and nuclear fusion, 472; and particle acceleration, 457, 458; rectification of, 420; *act.,* 403; 406; *table,* 406; 407
Aluminum, 294, 295, 401; density of, 104
Aluminum sulfate, 124
Ammonia, 193, 275, 320, 321; *act.,* 339
Ammonium chloride, 229; *act.,* 229
Ammonium phosphate, 194
Ammonium sulfate, 130
Ampere, 405
Amplifier, 415-417
Amplitude, 333, 334, 344
Amorphous solid, 144

Analog, 426; *illus.,* 427
Angle of incidence, 347
Angle of reflection, 347
Anhydride, 283, 284
Anode, 415, 416, 420, 421, 450
Antacid, 275, 281
Antenna, 417, 424
Antifreeze, 243, 244
Antimony, 195
Aqueous compound, 252
Area of compression, 325
Area of rarefaction, 325
Argon, 201, 420, 449
Aristotle, 80
Armature, 404
Arsenic, 195
Astatine, 185
Atom, 119-122, 168, 207; diffraction by, 438; forces in, 460; ionization of, 125, 396, 397; mass of, 163; radioactive, 440; spectrum of, 196; and static charge, 387, 388, 415; tagged, 443; valence of, 126; *table,* valence, 127
Atomic bullet, 457, 458
Atomic mass, 163-165, 168, 170; average, 169, 170; of isotopes, 168; *act.,* 163; *table,* 164
Atomic mass number, 170, 462
Atomic mass unit, 163, 459
Atomic model, 120, 121
Atomic nucleus, 120, 122, 388, 442, 459-472
Atomic number, 165, 168, 170
Atomic theory, 119-131
Autoclave, 320
Axis of symmetry, 139

Baking soda, 281
Barium, 200, 445
Barium sulfate, 200
Bar magnet, 401
Barometer, 316; *exp.,* 317; *illus.,* 316
Base, 275-277, 278; pH of, 280, 281; *act.,* 276; 277; 280; 282; *table,* 275; 280; 281
Basic anhydride, 283, 284
Battery, 398, 405; *illus.,* 398
Battery charger, 420
Becquerel, Henri, 440
Benzene, 219, 233
Beryllium, 199, 468
Beta particle, 436, 444, 448

Beta ray, 444
Bimetallic strip, 315; *act.,* 315
Binary compound, 128
Bismuth, 195
Blood, 328
Bohr, Niels, 120
Bohr model, 120; *illus.,* 459
Boiling point, 106, 155, 187, 214; of solutions, 244; *act.,* 244
Bond angle, 207, 208, 210, 213
Bonding, 124-127, 140-142, 181, 182; carbon, 207, 208, 213; covalent, 125, 141, 142; ionic, 125, 140, 141; nonstick, 218; in solutions, 229, 230, 232, 233, 234; *illus.,* 230
Boron, 468
Bottled gas, 212
Boyle's law, 317, 318
Branched chain compound, 210
Brass, 227
British thermal unit, 299, 300
Bromide, 184
Bromine, 184
Bronze, 227
Bubble chamber, 448
Butane, 210, 212; *illus.,* 210
Butene, 216
Buttermilk, 271
Butyne, 216

Cadmium, 468
Calcium, 199, 200
Calcium family, 199
Calcium oxide, 199, 283
Calcium phosphate, 194
Calcium sulfate, 200
Calorie, 297, 311, 320; *act.,* 297
Calorimeter, 298, 299, 304; *act.,* 298; 305
Cancer, 443
Capacitor, 417-419; variable, 418; *act.,* 419; *illus.,* 418
Carbon, 207-220, 227, 265, 397, 446, 467
Carbon compound, 207-220; *act.,* 211; 212; 214; 218; *illus.,* 207; 208; 209; 210; 211; 212; 213; 214; 216; 217; 218; 219; 220; *table,* 213; 219
Carbon dioxide, 123, 232, 259, 263, 265, 283, 320
Carbon monoxide, 263
Carbon tetrachloride, 220, 232, 233
Carbon 12, 163

INDEX

Carbon-14 dating, 446
Carburetor, 321
Cathode, 415, 416, 418, 420, 421, 422, 450
Cathode ray, 435
Cathode-ray tube, 421-424, 436; *act.*, 422; 437; *illus.*, 421; 423
Cavendish, Henry, 51
Cell, dry, 397, 398, 405; wet, 396-398
Celsius temperature scale, 106
Centimeter, 11
Centrifugal force, 89
Centrifuge, 89
Centripetal force, 87, 88; *act.*, 88
Cesium, 174, 196
Chain reaction, 464, 466, 467; *act.*, 464; *illus.*, 464
Change of phase, 110, 151-156, 300-305, 320
Change of pitch, 350, 351
Charles' law, 318
Chemical activity, 174, 175
Chemical change, 110-114, 122, 251, 252, 253, 261, 262, 462; *act.*, 111; 112; 113; 114; 131; *table*, 110
Chemical energy, 397
Chemical equation, *See* Equation
Chemical property, 107, 108, 122, 164, 165, 170; *illus.*, 107
Chemical reaction, 281
Chemistry, 9
Chloric acid, 275
Chlorine, 181, 183, 220
Chloroform, 220
Chloropropane, *illus.*, 209
Chromatography, *act.*, 214
Chromium, 227
Circuit, electrical, 413-425; integrated, 425; parallel, 414; series, 414; *act.*, 414; 415; *table*, 413
Citric acid, 271
Cleavage plane, 140
Cloud chamber, 447, 448; *illus.*, 448
Cobalt, 401
Coefficient, 254
Collision, of gas particles, 147; of liquid particles, 155; of molecules, 317, 318; of solid particles, 153
Compass, 402; *act.*, 402; *illus.*, 402
Compound, 101, 102, 123, 124, 125, 126, 181, 193, 210, 252; acid, 271-275; aqueous, 252; base, 275-277; binary, 128; branched chain, 210; carbon, 207-220; crystalline, 137-144; decomposition of, 111; deliquescent, 243; efflorescent, 243; noble gas, 201; ring, 218, 219; salt, 281-283; *act.*, 111; 112; 113; 114; 131; 137; 138; 139; 140; 141; 143; 144; 211; 212; 218; 272; 274; 276; 277; 280; 282; *illus.*, 207; 208; 209; 210; 211; 212; 214; 216; 217; 218; 219; 220; *table*, 102; 218; 219; 275; 280; 281; solubility, 238
Compound machine, 23; *illus.*, 24
Compressional wave, 325
Compression stroke, 322
Computer, 426-428
Concave lens, 364, 371; *act.*, 365; *illus.*, 371
Concentration, 239-242
Conclusion, 6
Condensation, 155, 304, 326; *act.*, 305
Conduction, electrical, 390-393, 394, 397, 405, 406; of heat, 295, 296, 467; *act.*, 293; 294; 295; 391
Conductor, electrical, 236, 237, 420, 421, 425; of heat, 296; *act.*, 236
Conservation of charge, 462
Conservation of mass, 251, 264, 265, 462; *exp.*, 251
Conservation of momentum, 92
Constructive interference, 344, 376-378
Control, 8
Control rod, 468
Convection, 296, 312; *act.*, 293; 294; 296
Convex lens, 365-372; *act.*, 365; 366; 368; *illus.*, 364; 365; 366; 368; 369; 370; 372
Coolant, 468, 469
Cooling tower, 326, 473; *illus.*, 326; 474
Copper, 227, 397, 399, 436
Copper (II) sulfate, 242; *act.*, 231; 255
Cornea, 328
Coulomb, 405
Covalent bond, 182, 185, 192, 201, 208, 234
Covalent bonding, 125, 141, 142
Crankshaft, 322
Crest, 333
Critical mass, 466
Cryogenics, 327, 328
Crystal, 137-144, 231, 233, 237, 245; cleavage of, 139, 140; hydrated, 242, 243; polarizing, 377; seed, 154; X-ray diffracting, 438; *act.*, 137; 138; 139; 140; 141; 143; 144; 154
Crystallization, 142-144, 154; *act.*, 141; 143; 144; 154
Curie, Marie, 190, 440
Curie, Pierre, 440
Curved motion, 87-89
Cyclohexane, 219
Cyclotron, 457, 458; *illus.*, 457; 458
Cylinder, 321, 322

Dalton, John, 119
Decay, radioactive, 445, 446; *act.*, 446
Deceleration, 56, 57
Decomposition reaction, 258
Dees, 457, 458

Dehydrating agent, 271
Deliquescent compound, 243; *act.*, 243
Density, 104, 105, 296; of water, 13, 104; *act.*, 105; *table*, 104
Desalination, 326
Destructive interference, 438
Detergent, 194
Deuterium, 168, 468, 471
Diamond, 141; *illus.*, 142
Diatomic molecule, 182, 185, 192, 259, 262, 397
Diffraction, 438; *illus.*, 438
Diffraction grating, 378, 379; *act.*, 379
Diffusion cloud chamber, 448; *illus.*, 448
Digital computer, 426, 427, 428; *illus.*, 428
Dimethyl ether, *illus.*, 209
Diode, 398, 399
Direct current, 392-399, 420; and magnetism, 400-403; measurement of, 408, 409; *act.*, 396; 406; *table*, 399
Dispersion, 373
Dissociation, 233
Distillation, of air, 187-192, 201; of ants, 274; of petroleum, 214
Doppler effect, 350, 351; *act.*, 350
Double bond, 216
Double replacement reaction, 253
Driveshaft, 322
Dry cell, 397, 405; *act.*, 398
Dry ice, *illus.*, 153

Earth, gravity on, 49
Efficiency, 35-38, 323
Efflorescent compound, 243; *act.*, 243
Effort arm, 27
Electrical energy, 387, 397, 398; measurement of, 408; storage of, 417-419; *table*, 407
Electrical unit, 404-408
Electric charge, 387
Electric circuit, 413-425; integrated, 425; parallel, 414; series, 414; *act.*, 414; 415; *table*, 413
Electric current, 450; alternating, 403-408, 417, 420, 457, 458, 472; direct, 394-399, 400-403, 408, 409, 420; *act.*, 396; 403; 406; *table*, 399; 406; 407
Electricity, 235, 260, 352, 387; alternating current, 403-408, 417; direct current, 394-399; and magnetism, 400-403; measurement of, 404-408; static, 387-393, 397; *act.*, 396; 403; 406; *table*, 399; 406; 407
Electrolysis, 183, 188, 260, 262; *act.*, 261
Electrolyte, 236
Electromagnet, 423, 424, 457
Electromagnetic induction, 403
Electromagnetic spectrum, 352, 353, 373, 378; *illus.*, 353; 435

Electromotive force, 405
Electron, 119-122; as beta rays, 436, 444, 448; and conductors, 190, 192, 236, 392, 393, 397, 403, 404, 405, 417; and electrostatic charge, 388, 389; energy of, 196, 466; free, 142, 424; mass of, 459; photoelectric, 379; in shells, 165, 170, 172, 174, 207; thermocouple, 398, 399, 415, 416, 420, 424, 436; *table,* 121; 122
Electron cloud model, 120, 121; *illus.,* 459
Electronics, 415
Electron pair, 208, 234
Electron volt, 466
Electroscope, 390-393, 447; *act.,* 390; 391; 392; 394; *illus.,* 391; 393
Electrostatic charge, 423
Electrostatic induction, 392, 393
Element, 123, 124, 128; chemical activity of, 174, 175, 207; families of, 170, 172, 175, 181-201; isotopes of, 121, 168, 169; mass of, 163-165; radioactive, 440-446, 461, 463; spectrum of, 376; symbol of, 100, 128; valence of, 126; *act.,* 164; 175; *table,* 100; 442; 443; mass number, 263; periodic, 166, 167; valence, 127
Endothermic reaction, 261, 262
Energy, 196, 259, 260; chemical, 397; and chemical change, 261, 262; electrical, 387, 397, 398, 408; heat, 293-306, 311-328, 398, 399, 416, 436, 444, 467, 468, 469, 470, 473; kinetic, 291-293, 300-305, 317, 318, 436, 446, 458, 470; light, 359-379; nuclear, 463, 466, 467, 471; potential, 291-293, 302, 304; radiant, 400-451; and solutions, 229-232, 240, 241; sound, 417; of waves, 334, 346, 353; *exp.,* 292; 293; 305; *table,* 407
Energy level, 122
Energy wave, 345, 346, 444
Engine, 321-325; four-cycle, 322; gasoline, 321-323; Hero's, 321; rotary, 323; Stirling, 325; turbine, 324; Wankel, 323; *illus.,* 322
Environment, 473, 474, 475
Epsom salt, 199
Equation, 252-262; balanced, 256; chemical, 252, 253, 264, 265; decomposition, 258-260; double replacement, 253-256; nuclear, 461-463; Ohm's law, 427; synthesis, 260, 261; word, 252
Equilibrium, 63
Equator, gravity at, 49
Ester, 218
Ethanol, 220
Ether, 320
Ethyl alcohol, 220, 233, 237, 320
Ethyl amine, *illus.,* 209
Ethylene, 218

Ethyne, 216; *illus.,* 209
Evaporation, 155, 320, 326, 327
Exhaust stroke, 322
Exothermic reaction, 261, 262
Expansion, 300, 301, 315; *act.,* 301
Experiment, 7

Face, 138, 139
Falling bodies, 80, 81; *act.,* 81
Family, 170, 181-201
Farsightedness, 370, 371
Fermentation, 274
Fertilizer, 194
Filament, 398, 399, 415, 416, 420, 421, 422, 436
Fission, nuclear, 463-466, 467
Flame test, 196; *act.,* 198; *illus.,* 197
Fluid, 296
Fluorescent material, 435
Fluoride, 183
Fluorine, 174, 183, 218
Focal length, 360, 366
Food, 298
Force, 21, 149, 321; action, 78, 321; centrifugal, 89; centripetal, 87, 88; electromotive, 405; gravitational, 47-51, 460; nuclear, 460; reaction, 78; resultant, 63; unit of, 12, 21; *act.,* 47; 48; 56; 78; 80; 88; 89
Force diagram, 63
Formic acid, 274
Formula, 101, 123, 252, 254, 256; graphic, 209, 210; molecular, 209, 210; structural, 208, 209
Formula mass, 263, 264
Four-cycle engine, 322
Fractionation, 214; *illus.,* 214
Francium, 196
Frasch process, 188
Free electron, 142, 424
Freezing point, 106, 154, 245; *act.,* 106
Freon, 320
Frequency, 336-344, 352, 376, 418, 419, 437; change of, 350, 351; of wave, 336, 337, 340, 341, 342, 344; *act.,* 341; 342
Friction, 21
Fuel, 467
Fulcrum, 25
Furnace, 312, 314, 315
Fusion, nuclear, 470-472

Galileo, 80, 81, 82
Galvanometer, 404; *illus.,* 404
Gamma radiation, 466
Gamma ray, 444
Gas, 253; bottled, 212; and Boyle's law, 317, 318; and Charles' law, 318; convection currents in, 296; and Gay-Lussac's law, 320, 321; laughing, 193; and Pascal's law, 149-151; phase change in, 153-156, 300, 301, 304; physical properties of, 147-149, 232;

radioactive, 445; in solutions, 227, 232, 237
Gaseous solution, 227, 232, 237
Gas law, 315-320; Boyle's, 317, 318; Charles', 318; Gay-Lussac's, 320, 321; Pascal's, 149-151
Gasoline engine, 321, 323
Gas turbine, 324
Gay-Lussac's law, 320, 321
Geiger counter, 449-451; *act.,* 451; *illus.,* 449; 450
Geiger-Müller tube, 449
Generator, 403; *illus.,* 404
Germanium, 424, 425
Gold, density of, 104
Graduated cylinder, 13; *illus.,* 13
Gram, 12
Graphic formula, 209, 210
Graphite, 142, 392, 467, 468; *illus.,* 142
Gravity, 47-51, 86; acceleration of, 82; force of, 47-51, 460; law of, 50, 51; *act.,* 47; 48
Gray arsenic, 195
Grease, 232, 233
Grid, 416, 417
Ground, 393

Half-life, 183, 444-446
Halogen family, 181-185, 220; *table,* 181
Heat energy, and decomposition, 250, 262; equivalent of, 299-306; measurement of, 297-299; and phase change, 148, 151, 153, 155; from radioactive elements, 444, 467, 468, 469, 470, 473; and solution rate, 230, 231, 232; and solutions, 229-232, 240, 241, 244, 245; specific, 311, 312; and thermionic effect, 416, 436; and thermocouple, 398, 399; transfer of, 293-297; waste, 326; *act.,* 8; 292; 293; 294; 295; 297; 298; 301; 303; 305; 311; 312; *table,* 311
Heat engine, 321-325
Heat exchanger, 469
Heating system, 312-315
Heat of condensation, 313
Heat of fusion, 302, 320
Heat of vaporization, 304
Heavy hydrogen, 472
Heavy water, 468
Helium, 201, 327, 449, 458, 471
Hero's engine, 321
Horsepower, 39, 41
Horseshoe magnet, 401
Hydrate, 242
Hydrated crystal, 242, 243
Hydraulic lift, 150; *illus.,* 151
Hydrocarbon, 211-220; saturated, 211-215; substituted, 220; unsaturated, 216-218
Hydrochloric acid, 271, 273, 274; *act.,* 274; *illus.,* 273
Hydrogen, in acids, 274, 396, 397; combining ratio of, 265; from

INDEX

decomposition, 262; heavy, 472; isotopes of, 168, 471
Hydrogen bomb, 472
Hydrogen chloride, 234, 273
Hydrogen ion, 277
Hydrogen peroxide, 186, 271
Hydronium ion, 234, 277, 278, 280, 281, 284
Hydroxide ion, 277, 278, 280, 281
Hypochlorous acid, 271
Hypothesis, 80

Ice, 302, 320
Ideal mechanical advantage, 25, 29, 31, 32, 33, 34
Image, 360, 362, 370, 371
Incident wave, 346
Inclined plane, 33
Index of refraction, 362-364; *table,* 363; 375; *illus.,* 364
Indicator, 276, 277; *act.,* 277; *illus.,* litmus paper, 276
Induction, electromagnetic, 403; electrostatic, 392, 393; *act.,* 392
Inertia, 73, 84, 87, 89; *act.,* 73
Infrared wave, 352
Inorganic acid, 275
Input, 428
Input circuit, 416
Insulator, 296; electrical, 392
Intake stroke, 322
Integrated circuit, 425; *illus.,* 425
Interference, 344, 376-378; constructive, 344, 376-378; destructive, 438; *act.,* 344; *illus.,* 378
Internal combustion engine, 321
Iodine, 184; reactivity of, 174; solubility of, 237; sublimation of, 152, 153, 184; *act.,* 184
Iodoform, 220
Ion, in crystals, 140, 141; polyatomic, 130; from radiation, 439, 447, 450; in solution, 233, 234, 236, 252, 253, 396, 397; and thermionic effect, 420; *table,* 130; solubility, 238
Ionic bonding, 125; by alkali metals, 196; by alkaline metals, 199; in crystals, 140, 141; dissociation of, 233; by halogen family, 181
Ionic compound, 263, 264
Ionization, of hydrogen chloride, 234; by radiation, 439, 447, 450; in rectifier, 42; of water, 277-281
Iron, 227, 311, 399; density of, 104
Iron oxide, 186
Isobutane, 210; *illus.,* 210
Isomer, 210, 211; *illus.,* 210; 211
Isoprene, 217
Isotope, 121, 440, 471; mass of, 168, 169; radioactive, 442-446; *table,* 443

Joule, James, 299

Joule's experiment, 299, 300; *illus.,* 299

Kelvin temperature scale, 327
Kilometer, 12
Kilowatt-hour, 408
Kinetic energy, 291-293, 470; of electrons, 436, 444; of molecules, 300-305, 317, 318; of subatomic particles, 458; *exp.,* 292; 293; 300
Kinetic theory, 151-156
Krypton, 201
Krypton lamp, *illus.,* 11

Lactic acid, 271
Laughing gas, 193
Law, Boyle's, 317, 318; Charles', 318; conservation of mass, 251; Gay-Lussac's, 320, 321; of gravitation, 50, 51; multiple proportions, 193; Ohm's, 407; Pascal's, 149-151; periodic, 164, 165
Lead, absorbing radiation, 439, 440; density of, 104; from decay series, 463; in storage battery, 398
Length, measurement of, 10-12
Lens, concave, 364, 371; convex, 365-372; eyepiece, 371; objective, 371; *act.,* 365; 366; 368; *illus.,* 364; 365; 366; 368; 370; 371; 372
Lever, mechanical advantage of, 29; *act.,* 25; 27; 28; *illus.,* 26; 27; 28
Leydon jar, *act.,* 419
Light energy, 260, 359-379; dispersion of, 373; interference of, 376-378; polarization of, 376, 377; reflection of, 359-362; speed of, 352, 363; wavelength of, 376; *act.,* 360; 361; 362; 365; 366; 368; *illus.,* 359; 360; 361; 364; 365; 366; 368; 369; 370; 371; 372; *table,* 363; 375
Light intensity, 190
Lightning rod, *illus.,* 394
Lime, 199
Linear accelerator, *illus.,* 459
Liquid, convection current in, 296; phase change in, 155, 156, 245, 302, 304; properties of, 146, 147, 300; speed of sound in, 338; supercooled, 154; superheated, 448; *act.,* 146; 147
Liquid solution, 227
Liter, 13
Lithium, 174, 196
Litmus paper, 276, 277, 283; *illus.,* 274
Longitudinal wave, 325
Loudness, 344
Lye, 275

Machine, compound, 23; efficiency of, 35-38; mechanical advantage of, 24, 25, 29, 30, 32, 33, 34; simple, 25-35; *act.,* 25; 27; 28; 31; *illus.,* 24; 26; 27; 28; 30; 31
Magnesium, 199, 262, 283
Magnesium alloy, 467
Magnesium oxide, 283
Magnet, 327, 401, 423
Magnetic bottle, 472
Magnetic field, 404, 423, 424, 457, 458, 473
Magnetic pole, 402
Magnetism, 352, 400-403, 404, 405; *act.,* 400; 401; 402; *illus.,* 400; 401; 402
Magnification, 370
Mass, 12, 47-51, 193, 297, 459, 460; atomic, 163-165; average, 169, 170; conservation of, 251, 264, 265, 462; critical, 466; of electrons, 415; formula, 263, 264; of isotopes, 168; measurement of, 12; molecular, 263, 264, 265; of subatomic particles, 119; unit of, 12; *act.,* 47; 48; 163; *illus.,* 13
Mass number, 170, 263; *table,* 263
Mass spectrometer, *illus.,* 128
Matter, 47, 99, 300; chemical change in, 110-114, 122, 252-265; chemical properties of, 107, 108, 122; magnetic, 400-403; phases of, 108, 137, 151-156, 300-305; physical changes in, 108, 110; physical properties of, 104-106, 122; plasma phase of, 471; *act.,* 99; 102; 103; 105; 111; 112; 113; 114; 137; 138; 139
Measurement, 9-15; of heat energy, 297-299; indirect, 14, 15; of length, 1-12; mass of, 12; of radiation, 439; of volume, 13; of weight, 12; *act.,* 10; 11; 15
Mechanical advantage, 24, 25, 29, 31, 32, 33, 34; actual, 25, 29, 31; ideal, 25, 29, 31, 32, 33, 34
Mechanical equivalent of heat, 300
Melt, 140
Melting, 302
Melting point, 195
Memory, 428
Mendeleev, 164, 165
Mercury, 316; density of, 104
Mercury barometer, 316
Mercury vapor lamp, 376
Metal, 172, 175, 192; alkali, 195-198; alkaline, 198-201; alloyed, 195, 227, 228, 401, 467; crystallization of, 142; electrical conduction in, 390-393, 405; expansion of, 315; magnetic, 401; and photoelectric effect, 190, 379; reactivity of, 174, 181, 256, 274, 396; specific heat of, 311; supercooled, 327; and thermionic effect, 398, 399, 415, 416, 420, 422, 424, 436; transition, 173; *exp.,* 198; *table,* 196; 198; 228

505

INDEX

Metallic bonding, 142
Metallic oxide, 283
Metalloid, 172, 192
Meter, 10
Meter-newton, 27
Meter stick, *illus.,* 11
Methane, 212; *act.,* 212
Methane series, 211-215; *table,* 213
Methanol, 220
Methyl alcohol, 220
Methyl methanone, *illus.,* 209
Metric system, 10
Mica, 449
Milk of magnesia, 275
Millimeter, 11
Mirror, parabola, 360-362, 372; plane, 359, 360; *act.,* 360; 361; 362; *illus.,* 359; 360; 361
Mixture, 102, 103; *act.,* 102; 103
Moderator, 467, 468
Molecular formula, 209, 210
Molecular kinetic theory, 300
Molecular mass, 263, 264, 265
Molecule, 123, 124, 259, 263, 265, 460; diatomic, 182, 185, 192, 259, 262, 397; kinetic energy of, 300-305, 317, 318, 327; polar, 233, 234; in solution, 229-232; and sound, 338; tetrahedral, 207; triatomic, 186; *exp.,* 123; *illus.,* 208
Moment, 27, 28
Momentum, 90-92; conservation of, 92
Moon, gravity on, 49
Moseley, Henry, 165
Motion, curved, 87-89; of falling bodies, 80-84; laws of, 73-80; relative, 84-87; *act.,* 85; 86
Multiple proportions, law of, 193
Musical scale, 344
Musical tone, 342; *illus.,* 337

Nearsightedness, 370, 371
Neon, 201
Neoprene, 217
Neutralization, 281, 282; *act.,* 282
Neutral solution, 280, 281
Neutron, 119-121, 168; and isotopes, 440, 442; mass of, 164, 459, 460; moderated, 467, 468; and nuclear fission, 464, 466; *table,* 121
Newton, 12, 21
Newton, Sir Isaac, 50
Newton-meter, 22
Newton's law of gravitation, 50, 51
Nickel, 401
Nitrate, 194, 273
Nitric acid, 272; *illus.,* 273
Nitrogen, 328; distillation from air, 191, 193
Nitrogen family, 192-195; *act.,* 193; *table,* 192, 193
Noble gas, 172, 420; *table,* 201
Noise, 342
Nonelectrolyte, 237
Nonmetal, 172, 174, 175, 183, 190, 192, 195, 256

Nonmetallic oxide, 283
Normal, 347, 364
North Pole, gravity at, 49
Nuclear chain reaction, 464, 466, 467; *illus.,* 464
Nuclear change, 463, 464
Nuclear decay series, 463
Nuclear emulsion, 448, 449; *illus.,* 448
Nuclear energy, 463, 466, 467, 471, 475
Nuclear equation, 461, 462
Nuclear fission, 463-466, 467
Nuclear force, 460
Nuclear fusion, 470-472, 475
Nuclear power plant, 473
Nuclear reactor, 467-470; *illus.,* 466; 467; 468; 469
Nucleus, 120, 122, 388, 442, 459-472
Nylon, 218

Observation, 4
Ohm, 406
Ohm, George Simon, 407
Ohm's law, 406
One-tube radio, 417; *illus.,* 417
Optic, 359
Organic acid, 274
Organic chemistry, 207-220
Organic solvent, 233, 236
Orlon, 218
Output, 428
Output circuit, 416
Oxide, 194, 283
Oxygen, and anhydrides, 283; combining ratio of, 265; from decomposition of, 188, 259, 262; diatomic, 123; properties of, 186-188; triatomic, 186; *act.,* 187
Oxygen family, 185-190; *table,* 185
Ozone, 186

Parabola, 86, 360
Parabolic mirror, 360-362, 372; *act.,* 361; 362; *illus.,* 361
Parallel circuit, 414; *act.,* 414, 415
Parallelogram, 64
Pascal, Blaise, 150
Pascal's law, 149-151; *act.,* 150
Pentene, 216
Periodic law, 164, 165; *act.,* 164
Periodic table, 164-167, 170, 172-175; *table,* 166, 167
Permanent magnet, 401
Petroleum, 214
pH, 280, 281; *illus.,* 280; *table,* 281
Phase, change of, 110, 151-156, 300-305, 320; of matter, 108, 137, 151-156, 471
Phenolphthalein, 277, 283; *act.,* 282; *illus.,* 277
Phosphate, 194
Phosphoric acid, 275
Phosphorus, 193, 194
Photocell, 190, 196
Photochemical smog, 323
Photoconductor, 190
Photoelectric cell, 196

Photoelectric effect, 379, 398; *act.,* 379
Photoflash, 417
Photon, 376, 437, 444; energy of, 466
Physical change, 108, 110, 462; *table,* 110
Physical property, 104-106, 122, 164, 165, 170; of alloys, 228; of solutions, 243-245; *illus.,* 107
Physical science, 9
Physics, 9
Picture tube, 423
Pile, 467
Pip, 422; *illus.,* 422
Piston, 321, 322
Pitch, 342, 344, 378; change of, 350, 351; *act.,* 342
Pitchblende, 440
Plane mirror, 359, 360; *act.,* 360; *illus.,* 359; 360; 361
Plasma phase, 471
Plastic, 218
Plate, 415, 418, 420, 421, 423
Plutonium, 467
Polarization, 376, 377; *act.,* 376; *illus.,* 377
Polarized light, 377
Polar molecule, 233, 234
Pollution, 323, 473; thermal, 325-327
Polonium, 190, 440, 445
Polyatomic ion, 130; *table,* 130; 131
Polyester, 218
Polyethylene, 218
Polymer, 217, 218
Polymerization, 217, 218
Polyvinyl chloride, 218
Potassium, 196
Potassium bromide, 236
Potassium chlorate, 259
Potassium chloride, 259
Potassium nitrate, 240
Potential energy, 291-293, 302, 304
Power, 38-41, 408; *act.,* 40
Power stroke, 322
Precipitate, 252, 253
Pressure, 147-150, 153, 155, 156, 315-318, 320, 321; air, 316; and phase change, 110; vapor, 155; *act.,* 150
Principal axis, 360
Principal focus, 360, 370
Prism, 373-376; *act.,* 373; *illus.,* 375
Process of science, 3, 4, 6
Product, 252, 265
Product of science, 3
Program, 428
Projectile, 86
Propane, 156, 212
Propanoic acid, 274
Propene, 216
Propyne, 216
Protium, 168
Proton, 119-122, 165, 168; as a bullet, 458; and electrostatic charge, 388, 392; mass of, 164,

INDEX

458, 459, 460; and stability, 442; and transmutation, 463; *table*, 121
Pulley, 30, 31; *act.*, 31; *illus.*, 30; 31

Radar, 422; *illus.*, 422
Radar wave, 351
Radiant energy, 294, 295, 313, 353, 440-451
Radiation, 435-439, 444, 446, 469; detection of, 446-451; of heat, 294, 295, 313, 352, 353; measurement of, 439; *exp.*, 293; 294
Radiation counter, 449-451; *act.*, 451; *illus.*, 449; 450
Radiator, 312, 313
Radio, 417, 418, 419; *illus.*, one-tube, 417
Radioactive element, 185, 193, 440-446, 461, 463; half-life, 445, 446; *table*, 442; 443
Radioactive gas, 445
Radioactive isotope, 442-446; half-life of, 445, 446; *table*, 443
Radioactive waste, 474, 475
Radioactivity, 440-451
Radio wave, 417
Radium, 200, 440, 445, 461
Radon, 201, 445, 461
Reactant, 252, 265
Reaction force, 78, 321
Real image, 362; *act.*, 366; 368
Rectifier, 420, 421
Red phosphorus, 193, 194
Reflected wave, 346
Reflecting telescope, 372
Reflection, 346, 347, 359-362
Refracting telescope, 371
Refraction, 348, 349, 362-376; index of, 362-364; *act.*, 363; 365; 366; 368; 373; *table*, 363; 375
Refrigerant, 320
Refrigeration, 320, 321, 327
Relative motion, 84-87
Replacement reaction, 256
Resistance, 21; electrical, 405, 406; *act.*, 406; *table*, 406
Resistance arm, 27
Resonance, 339; *act.*, 340
Resultant force, 63
Rhombic sulfur, 188
Ring compound, 218, 219
Ripple tank, 345; *act.*, 347; 348; 350; *illus.*, 345; 346; 347; 348; 349
Roentgen, 439
Roentgen, W. K., 435
Rotary engine, 323
Rubber, 217
Rubidium, 196

Safety shield, 469
Salt, 140, 181, 233, 237, 240, 252, 264, 273, 281, 284, 326; *act.*, 282
Salvarsan, 195

Saturated solution, 241
Screw, 34, 35; *illus.*, 34
Seeding, 154
Selenium, 189, 190
Semiconductor, 425
Series circuit, 414; *act.*, 414, 415
Sextant, 14
Shell, 122, 165, 170, 172
Silicon, 424, 425
Silicon carbide, 142
Silicon dioxide, 186
Silver, 295
Silver bromide, 449
Silver chloride, 252
Silver nitrate, 252; *act.*, 256
Simple machine, 25-35; efficiency of, 35-38; mechanical advantage of, 24, 25, 29, 31, 32, 33, 34; *illus.*, 24
Smog, photochemical, 323
Soap, 194
Sodium, 196
Sodium bicarbonate, 124
Sodium chloride, 140, 181, 233, 240, 252, 264, 273
Sodium hydroxide, 275, 278
Sodium nitrate, 253, 272
Sodium sulfate, 130
Solar heating, 314; *illus.*, 314
Solid, 137-148, 252, 258, 300, 302; amorphous, 144; speed of sound in, 338
Solid solution, 227
Solubility, 237-239; *table*, 238
Solute, 227, 244, 245
Solution, 227-245, 252, 276; acidic, 271-277; basic, 275-277; boiling point of, 244, 245; concentration of, 239-242; conducting, 236, 237; formation of, 229, 230; freezing point of, 245; neutral, 276, 280; pH of, 280, 281; rate of, 230-232; *act.*, 227; 228; 229; 231; 233; 238; 239; 241; 242; 243; 244; 245; *table*, 228; 238
Solvent, 227, 232, 233, 244
Sound energy, 417
Sound wave, 337-351; speed of, 338, 339, 340, 348; *table*, 339
Specific heat, 311, 312; *act.*, 311; 312; *table*, 311
Spectrum, electromagnetic, 352, 353, 373, 378, 435; visible light, 373; *illus.*, 353; 435
Speed, of alpha particle, 444; of gas molecule, 147, 148; of light, 352, 363; of molecules, 301; of sound, 338, 339, 340, 348; of X ray, 436; *act.*, 54
Stable, 442
Standard mass, *illus.*, 13
Static electricity, 387-393, 397; negative, 388, 389, 391, 392; positive, 388, 389, 391, 392; *act.*, 387; 389; 390; 391; 394; *illus.*, 388; 389; 390; 391; 393; 394
Steam, 304, 313, 470; heat of vaporization, 304; *act.*, 305
Steel, 227, 401

Stirling engine, 325
Storage battery, 271, 398, 405
Storage unit, 428
Straight chain compound, 210
Strip, 396
Strong bond, 141
Strontium, 200
Structural formula, 208, 209
Subatomic particle, 388, 415, 444, 448, 457-472; acceleration of, 457, 458
Sublimation, 153, 184, 188
Subscript, 101, 254
Sugar, 229, 230, 237, 240, 334; density of, 104; *act.*, 272
Sulfate, 396
Sulfide, 189
Sulfur, 188, 189, 283
Sulfur dioxide, 271, 283, 284
Sulfuric acid, 271, 272, 273, 396, 398; *act.*, 272
Sun, 471
Superconductor, 327
Supercooled liquid, 154
Superfluid, 327
Superheated liquid, 448
Supermagnet, 327
Supersaturated solution, 241, 448; *act.*, 241
Symbol, 168, 170, 252
Symmetry, 139; *illus.*, 139
Sympathetic vibration, 339
Synthesis reaction, 260
Synthetic fiber, 218
Synthetic rubber, 217

Tagged atom, 443
Target, 436
Technology, 3
Telescope, 371, 372; *illus.*, 372
Television, 421, 422, 424
Tellurium, 190
Temperature, cryogenic, 327; effecting volume and pressure, 146, 153, 155, 156, 317, 318, 320; of fusion, 471, 472; and heat content, 297, 311; and kinetic energy, 301, 306; and phase change, 110; and potential energy, 304; and thermionic effect, 399
Temperature scale, 106
Terminal velocity, 82; *illus.*, 83
Tetrafluoroethylene, 218
Theory, 8, 9; atomic, 119-131; kinetic, 151-156; molecular kinetic, 300-305
Thermal pollution, 325-327, 473
Thermionic effect, 398, 399, 415, 416, 420, 422, 424, 436
Thermocouple, 399; *illus.*, 399
Thermonuclear power, 472
Thermonuclear reaction, 471, 473
Thermostat, 315
Three-dimensional strong bond, 141, 142
Tin, 227
Tone, 342
Transistor, 424, 425; *illus.*, 424
Transition metal, 173

Transmutation, 444, 460-463
Transverse wave, 334, 352; *act.,* 333
Triangulation, 14
Triatomic molecule, 186
Triode, 416, 417; *illus.,* 416
Triple bond, 216
Tritium, 168, 471
Trough, 333
Tungar rectifier, 420
Tungsten, 398, 436
Turbine, 470
Two-dimensional strong bond, 142

Ultrasonic sound, 345
Unsaturated solution, 241
Uranium, 440, 445, 463, 464, 467; energy in, 466; *table,* 462

Vacuum bottle, 293, 294, 295; *exp.,* 294
Vacuum tube, 415-417, 420, 421-429; cathode ray, 421-424, 435; diode, 398, 399; triode, 416, 417; tungar rectifier, 420; X ray, 435-438; *illus.,* 416
Valence, 126; *table,* 127
Valve, 322
Vapor pressure, 155
Vaporization, 304
Variable capacitor, 417-419; *illus.,* 418
Vector, 62-64; *act.,* 66; *illus.,* 62; 63
Vector scale, *illus.,* 63
Velocity, 67; terminal, 82; *ilus.,* 83
Vinegar, 271, 274
Virtual image, 360, 362, 370

Visible light spectrum, 353, 373; *illus.,* 353
Vision, 371, 372
Volt, 405; amplification of, 415-417
Volume, 146, 153, 155, 156, 317, 318, 320; measurement of, 13; unit of, 13

Wankel rotary engine, 323; *illus.,* 323
Waste, 194, 323, 474, 475
Water, 186, 188, 320, 447, 448, 471; boiling point of, 155; as a conductor, 236; convection currents in, 296, 297, 312, 313; and crystal formation, 242; density of, 13, 104; electrolysis of, 262; formation of, 265, 281, 282; and Gay-Lussac's law, 320; heat of fusion of, 302, 320; heat of vaporization of, 304, 313; heavy, 468; hydronium ion in, 234; ionization, 277-281; pH of, 280; and reactivity, 252, 253; as a solvent, 227, 229, 232, 233, 237, 240, 271, 273; specific heat of, 311; wave motion in, 345-349, 351; *act.,* 305; *table,* solubility, 238
Water of hydration, 242, 243
Water pollution, 194, 325-327, 473
Watt, 41, 408
Watt, James, 39, 41
Wave, 333-353, 438; amplitude of, 333, 334, 344; compressional, 335; energy in, 334, 345, 346, 353; infrared, 352; light, 359-379; radar, 351; radio, 417; sound, 337-351; speed of, 338, 339, 340, 348, 349, 352, 363; transverse, 334, 352; *act.,* 333; 335; 336; 338; 340; 341; 342; 344; 347; 348; 350; *illus.,* 333; 334; 335; 336; 337; 338; 339; 341; 345; 346; 347; 349; 350; 351; 353; *table,* 339
Wave energy, 334, 346, 353
Wave frequency, 336-344, 350, 351, 352, 353, 376, 418, 419, 437; change of, 350, 351
Wavelength, 325, 337, 340, 341, 352, 376, 444
Wave reflection, 346, 347, 359, 360
Wave refraction, 348, 349, 362-376; index, 362-364; *act.,* 363; 365; 366; 368; 373; *table,* 363; 375
Wedge, 33, 34
Weight, 47-51; measurement of, 12; *act.,* 47; 48
Wet cell, *act.,* 392; *illus.,* 396; 397
Wheel and axle, 32
White phosphorus, 193, 194
Work, 21-23, 300, 321; unit of, 22
Work input, 35
Work output, 35

Xenon, 201
X ray, 435-439, 444; absorption of, 437, 438; diffraction of, 438; *exp.,* 437
X-ray tube, 436

Young, Thomas, 377

Zinc, 227, 396, 397